PART I

Statics

MECHANICS

By J. L. Meriam

MECHANICS—Second Edition

Part I · Statics

Part II · Dynamics

PART

I

Statics

MECHANICS

Second Edition

J. L. MERIAM

PROFESSOR OF ENGINEERING MECHANICS

UNIVERSITY OF CALIFORNIA

NEW YORK · JOHN WILEY & SONS, INC.

London

FOURTH PRINTING, SEPTEMBER, 1961

Library of Congress Catalog Card Number: 59-5877

Printed in the United States of America

PREFACE

To the Student

Engineering analysis depends heavily on the principles of mechanics, and for this reason it is essential that the student of engineering be well grounded in this basic subject. The emphasis in this book is on engineering or applied mechanics, and it has been designed as a text for the basic mechanics courses in the normal engineering curriculum.

The representation of real situations by mathematical and graphical symbols constitutes an ideal descriptive model which approximates but never quite equals the actual situation. A useful understanding of mechanics requires a dual process of repeated transition of thought between the physical situation and its symbolic representation. The development of ability to make this transition of thought freely is one of the major aims of this book.

Mechanics is based on surprisingly few fundamental principles. Particular emphasis is placed on these principles and their application, and much secondary detail has been reduced or eliminated. Care has been taken not to sacrifice the rigor of the development, and attempt has been made to present the principles in clear and concise terms. The student will find that firm progress can be made only by an understanding of the physical and mathematical principles jointly and not by mere memorization of formulas with mechanical substitution of values therein.

Success in analysis depends to a surprisingly large degree on a well-disciplined method of attack from hypothesis to conclusion where a straight path of rigorous application of principles has been followed. The student is urged to develop ability to represent his work in a clear, logical, and neat manner. The basic training in mechanics is a most excellent place for early development of this disciplined approach which is so necessary in most engineering work which follows.

As in all subjects the student learns more when his interest is stimulated. The author hopes that the reader will find interest and stimulation in many of the real and practical situations included in the problems. Arrangement of problems is generally in the order of increasing difficulty, and the most difficult ones are starred.

J. L. Meriam

January, 1959

PREFACE

To the Instructor

The natural learning process begins with simple situations and progresses to more complicated ones. Thus in mechanics most students are best initiated by exposure to simplified problems where irrelevant factors have been minimized. Problems presented in this way are already partially analyzed. A full and useful appreciation of mechanics does not come, however, until the analysis of real situations and actual working conditions is made. Here the student must be taught to define the problem by first isolating the pertinent factors and discarding the irrelevant ones. Principles are then applied and conclusions drawn. It is only when the principles of mechanics are applied to *practical* problems involving real situations that the full significance of mechanics can be seen. There has been a trend in the treatment of mechanics to avoid real problems of a practical and interesting nature in favor of the ideal symbolic problems which are stripped of reality, practical value, and interest. Such presentation places in jeopardy one of the most fundamental objectives of instruction in mechanics, namely, to develop ability in *problem formulation* where the connection between actuality and symbolic representation is required. The most difficult and at the same time the most interesting phase of engineering design lies in the formulation of problems. It is true that many practical problems involve too many complicating factors for early exposure to the student. However, there is a wealth of problems which describe real, practical, and interesting situations that are not overly complex and which can enrich the experience and develop the ability of the student of mechanics far more than is possible with the overly idealized problems.

It is the purpose of this book to present a large selection of problems which illustrate wide application to the various fields of engineering and which will lead the student from the idealized and symbolic representation to the more practical, real, and interesting engineering situation. The author feels strongly that reality brought into the illustrations is of great help to the student in making the transfer of thought from the physical to the mathematical description. Consequently the book has been profusely illustrated, and effort has been made to produce reality and clarity. The problems in each set represent a considerable range of difficulty and are presented generally in order of increasing difficulty. Those problems which are considered the most difficult are starred. All problems have been worked and checked and are believed to be free of error. Computations have been made with the slide rule so that some disagreement in the third figures may be expected. Answers to approximately two thirds of the problems are given.

The wide response accorded the first edition of *Mechanics* by its users has given convincing support to the advantages of teaching mechanics through the use of problems which emphasize practical and interesting engineering situations. The many helpful comments received from both teachers and students have been studied carefully and have influenced a number of the changes made in the second edition. Those problems which proved to be particularly instructive in the first edition have been retained in the second, while many new ones have been added. As in the first edition the problems in the second edition are almost entirely original. The author has, however, obtained ideas for problems from many published sources.

Full use of graphic procedures is made whenever they are of advantage. The graphic methods have not been isolated from the remainder of the treatment since it is felt that graphical representation is an invaluable aid to the interpretation of physical problems and should be an integral part of the development.

Chapter 1 presents a summary of the foundations of mechanics. An overall introduction to both statics and dynamics is quite appropriate at the outset and can be understood by the average student who has had an introduction to mechanics in his physics course.

Chapters 2 and 3 present the development of the resultants of force systems and the equilibrium of force systems with a minimum of attention to the many separate categories and special cases which many texts in mechanics differentiate so elaborately. Emphasis on the properties common to all cases is the best way to focus attention on the relatively few fundamental ideas involved. Furthermore this approach is made without excessive generality for the average student.

In the second edition the equilibrium of statically determinate beams is included as a topic in Chapter 4 on structures and in Chapter 5 on distributed forces. In Chapter 5 the section on fluid forces has been rewritten to help clarify this topic.

Chapter 7 covers the principles of virtual work and shows the type of problem for which this method is superior to the equilibrium method based on force and moment summation. In this chapter further advantage is taken of the opportunity to illustrate the use of the calculus.

In the second edition a new section on review problems is added as Appendix A. The problems cover a wide range of topics but are arranged without regard for topic or method of solution. A new section on vector algebra is added in Appendix B in which an introduction to the dot and cross product notation is outlined. This notation may be used as an alternative to that used in the text if desired. Moments of inertia of areas and mass are treated in Appendix C and may be included in either the statics or dynamics part of the course as desired.

Special acknowledgment is given to Dr. A. L. Hale not only for his contribution during the preparation of the first edition but also for his critical review of all new problems which are included in the second edition. The valuable suggestions of Dr. K. E. Barnhart have also proved helpful in preparing the second edition as well as the first edition and are duly acknowledged along with those of other colleagues. The author is also deeply grateful for the large number of helpful comments and suggestions received from many users of the book.

J. L. Meriam

Berkeley, California
January, 1959

CONTENTS

APPENDIX D. USEFUL TABLES

MECHANICS

CHAPTER
1

PRINCIPLES OF STATICS

1. Mechanics. Mechanics is that physical science which deals with the state of rest or motion of bodies under the action of forces. There is no one subject which plays a greater role in engineering analysis than does mechanics. The early history of this subject is synonymous with the very beginnings of engineering. Modern research and development in the fields of vibrations, stability, strength of structures and machines, engine performance, fluid flow, electrical machines and apparatus, and molecular, atomic, and subatomic behavior are highly dependent upon the basic principles of mechanics. A thorough understanding of this subject is an absolute prerequisite for work in these and many other fields.

Mechanics is the oldest of the physical sciences. The earliest recorded writings in this field are those of Archimedes (287–212 B.C.) which concern the principle of the lever and the principle of buoyancy. Substantial progress awaited the formulation of the laws of vector combination of forces by Stevinus (1548–1620), who also formulated most of the principles of statics. The first investigation of a dynamic problem is credited to Galileo (1564–1642) in connection with his experiments with falling stones. The accurate formulation of the laws of motion including the law of gravitation was made by Newton (1642–1727), who also conceived the idea of the infinitesimal in mathematical analysis. Substantial contributions to the development of mechanics were also made by da Vinci, Varignon, D'Alembert, Lagrange, Laplace, and others.

The subject of mechanics is logically divided into two parts, *statics*, which concerns the equilibrium of bodies under the action of forces, and *dynamics*, which concerns the motion of bodies. Dynamics in turn includes *kinematics*, which is the study of the motion of bodies without reference to the forces which cause the motion, and *kinetics*, which relates the forces and the resulting motions. *Theoretical mechanics* is primarily the concern of the physicist, while *applied* or *engineering mechanics* is of concern mainly to the engineer. There is no distinct separation between the two, however, since the question is one of emphasis.

2. Basic Concepts. There are certain definitions and concepts which are basic to the study of mechanics, and they should be understood at the outset.

Space is a region extending in all directions. Position in space is determined relative to some reference system by linear and angular measurements.

Time is a measure of the succession of events. The unit of time is the second, which is a convenient fraction of the period of the earth's rotation.

Force is the action of one body on another. A force tends to move a body in the direction of its action upon it. Considerably more will be said about force in Chapter 2.

Matter is substance which occupies space.

Inertia is the property of matter causing a resistance to change in motion.

Mass is the quantitative measure of inertia.

A *body* is matter bounded by a closed surface.

A *particle* is a body of negligible dimensions. In some cases a body of finite size may be treated as a particle, or at other times the particle may be a differential element.

A *rigid body* is one which exhibits no relative deformation between its parts. This is an ideal hypothesis since all real bodies will change shape to a certain extent when subjected to forces. When such changes are small, the body may be termed rigid without appreciable error. With the exception of deformable springs this book is a treatment of the mechanics of rigid bodies only. A body is considered *deformable* when the relations between the applied forces and the resulting deformations are investigated. This problem is taken up in the studies of strength of materials and the theories of elasticity and plasticity.

3. Scalars and Vectors. The quantities dealt with in mechanics are of two kinds. *Scalar* quantities are those with which a magnitude only is associated. Examples of scalars are time, volume, density, speed, energy, and mass. Quantities with which direction as well as magnitude is associated are called *vectors*. Examples of vectors are displacement, velocity, acceleration, force, moment, and momentum. Scalars may be combined according to the ordinary laws of algebra, whereas combination of vectors requires a particular form of algebra to account for both magnitude and direction.

A vector quantity V is represented by a straight line, Fig. 1, having the direction of the vector and having an arrowhead to indicate the sense. The length of the directed line segment represents to some convenient scale the magnitude of V, and the direction of the vector is specified by the angle θ measured from some convenient reference line. The negative of V is a vector $-V$ directed in the opposite sense to V as shown. There are three kinds of vectors, *free*, *sliding*, and *fixed*. A free vector is one which may be represented by a vector arrow anywhere in space as long as the magnitude and direction remain fixed. If a body moves in a straight line without rotation, then the movement of any point in the body may be taken as a vector, and this vector will describe equally well the motion of every point in the body. Thus the displacement of such a body may be represented by a free vector. Velocity and acceleration are examples also of free vectors.

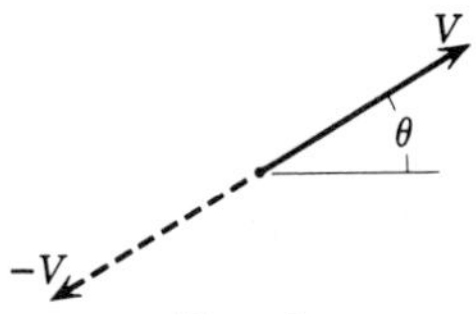

FIG. 1

A sliding vector is one for which a unique line in space must be maintained along which the quantity acts. When dealing with the action of a force on a rigid body, the force may be applied at any point along its line of action without changing its effect on the body as a whole * and thus may be considered a sliding vector.

A fixed vector is one for which a unique point of application is specified, and therefore the vector occupies a fixed position in space. The action of a force on a nonrigid body must be specified by a fixed vector at the point of application of the force. In this problem the forces and movements internal to the body will be a function of the point of application of the force as well as its line of action.

Vectors may be added and subtracted according to the triangle and parallelogram laws. The two free vectors V_1 and V_2 in Fig. 2*a* may be added head-to-tail to obtain their sum as shown in the *b*-part of the figure for the triangle law. The order of their combination does not affect their sum. The identical result in magnitude and direction is obtained

* This is the so-called principle of transmissibility which is discussed in Art. 10, Chapter 2.

by completing the parallelogram as shown in the c-part of the figure. In each case this vector addition is expressed symbolically by the equation

$$V = V_1 \mathrel{+\!\!\!\rightarrow} V_2,$$

where the symbol $\mathrel{+\!\!\!\rightarrow}$ is used to denote *vector addition* in contrast to the + sign used for scalar addition.

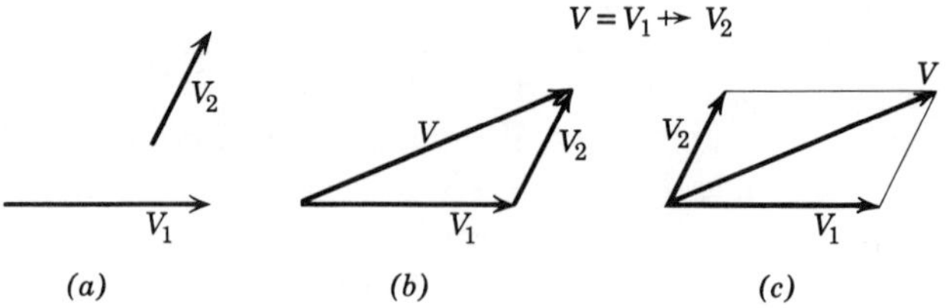

FIG. 2

The difference V' between the vectors V_1 and V_2 may be obtained by either the triangle or the parallelogram procedure as shown in Fig. 3. It is necessary only to add the negative of V_2 to V_1 in order to obtain the vector difference. This difference is indicated symbolically by the equation

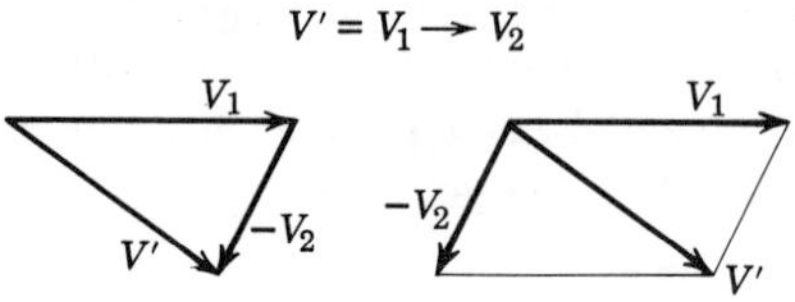

FIG. 3

$$V' = V_1 \rightarrow V_2,$$

where the symbol $\rightarrow$ is used to denote *vector subtraction* as distinguished from the − sign used for scalar subtraction.

Any two or more vectors whose sum equals a certain vector V are said to be the *components* of that vector. Thus the vectors V_1 and V_2 in Fig. 4a are the components of V in the directions 1 and 2, respectively. It is usually more convenient to deal with vector components which are mutually perpendicular, and these are called *rectangular com-*

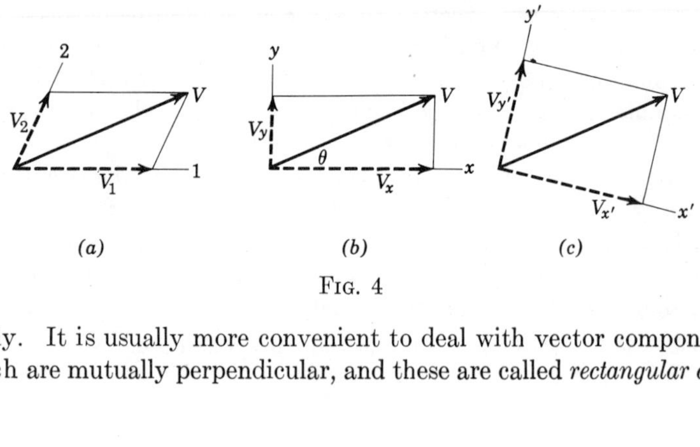

FIG. 4

ponents. The vectors V_x and V_y in Fig. 4*b* are the x- and y-components, respectively, of V. Likewise, in Fig. 4*c*, $V_{x'}$ and $V_{y'}$ are the x'- and y'-components of V. When expressed in rectangular components, the direction of the vector with respect to, say, the x-axis is clearly specified by

$$\theta = \tan^{-1} \frac{V_y}{V_x}.$$

4. Newton's Laws. Sir Isaac Newton was the first to state correctly the basic laws governing the motion of a particle and to demonstrate their validity.* Slightly reworded, these laws are as follows:

Law I. A particle remains at rest or continues to move in a straight line with a uniform velocity if there is no unbalanced force acting on it.

Law II. The acceleration of a particle is proportional to the resultant force acting on it and is in the direction of this force.†

Law III. The forces of action and reaction between contacting bodies are equal in magnitude, opposite in direction, and collinear.

The correctness of these laws has been verified by innumerable accurate physical measurements. Newton's second law forms the basis for most of the analysis in dynamics. As applied to a particle of mass m it may be stated as

$$F = ma, \tag{1}$$

where F is the resultant force acting on the particle and a is the resulting acceleration. This equation is a *vector* equation since the direction of F must be equal to the direction of a in addition to the equality in magnitudes of F and ma. Newton's first law contains the principle of the equilibrium of forces which is the main topic of concern in statics. Actually this law is a consequence of the second law since there is no acceleration when the force is zero, and the particle either is at rest or moves with a constant velocity. The first law adds nothing new to the description of motion but is included since it was a part of Newton's classical statements.

The third law is basic to our understanding of force. It states that forces always occur in pairs of equal and opposite forces. Thus the

* Newton's original formulations may be found in the translation of his *Principia* (1687) revised by F. Cajori, University of California Press, 1934.

† To some it is preferable to interpret Newton's second law as meaning that the resultant force acting on a particle is proportional to the time rate of change of momentum of the particle and that this rate of change is in the direction of the force. Both formulations are equally correct.

downward force exerted on the desk by the pencil is accompanied by an upward force of equal magnitude exerted on the pencil by the desk. This principle holds for all forces, variable or constant, regardless of their source and holds at every instant of time during which the forces are applied. Lack of careful attention to this basic law is the cause of frequent error by the beginner. In analyzing bodies under the action of forces it is absolutely necessary to be clear as to which of the pair of forces is being considered. It is first of all necessary to *isolate* the body under consideration and then to consider only the one force of the pair which acts *on* the body in question.

In addition to formulating the laws of motion for a particle Newton was also responsible for stating the law which governs the mutual attraction between bodies. This *law of gravitation* is expressed by the equation

$$F = \gamma \frac{m_1 m_2}{r^2}, \tag{2}$$

where F = the mutual force of attraction between two particles,
γ = a universal constant known as the constant of gravitation,
m_1, m_2 = the masses of the two particles,
r = the distance between the centers of the particles.

The mutual forces F obey the law of action and reaction since they are equal and opposite and are directed along the line joining the centers of the particles. Experiment yields the value of $\gamma = 6.67 \times 10^{-8}$ cm.^{3}/(gm. sec.^{2}) for the gravitational constant. Gravitational forces exist between every pair of bodies. On the surface of the earth the only gravitational force of appreciable magnitude is the force due to the earth's attraction. Thus each of two iron spheres 4 in. in diameter is attracted to the earth with a force of 8.90 lb. which is called its *weight*. On the other hand the force of mutual attraction between them if they are just touching is 0.0000000234 lb. This force is clearly negligible compared with the earth's attraction of 8.90 lb., and consequently the gravitational attraction of the earth is the only gravitational force of any magnitude which need be considered for experiments conducted on the earth's surface.

The weight of a body is the force of attraction of the body to the earth and depends on the position of the body relative to the earth. An object weighing 10 lb. at the earth's surface will weigh 9.99500 lb. at an altitude of 1 mi., 9.803 lb. at an altitude of 40 mi., and 2.50 lb. at an altitude of 4000 mi. or a height approximately equal to the radius of the earth. It is at once apparent that the variation in the weight of high-altitude rockets must be accounted for.

Every object which is allowed to fall in a vacuum at a given location on the earth's surface will have the same acceleration g as can be seen by combining Eqs. 1 and 2 and cancelling the term representing the mass of the falling object. This combination gives

$$g = \frac{\gamma m_0}{r^2},$$

where m_0 is the mass of the earth and r is the radius of the earth.* The mass m_0 and mean radius r of the earth have been found by experiment to be 5.98×10^{27} gm. and 6.38×10^8 cm., respectively. These values together with the value for γ already cited when substituted into the expression for g give

$$g = 980 \text{ cm./sec.}^2 \qquad \text{or} \qquad g = 32.2 \text{ ft./sec.}^2$$

An accurate determination of the acceleration of gravity measured relative to the earth must account for the fact that the earth is essentially a rotating oblate spheroid with flattening at the poles. The value of g relative to the earth's surface has been found equal to 32.09 ft./sec.^{2} at the equator, 32.17 ft./sec.^{2} at a latitude of 45 deg., and 32.26 ft./sec.^{2} at the poles. The proximity of large land masses will also influence the local value of g to a small but detectable amount. It is sufficiently accurate in almost all engineering calculations to use the value of 32.2 ft./sec.^{2} for g.

The mass m of a body may be calculated from the results of the simple gravitational experiment. If the gravitational force or *weight* is W, then, since the body falls with an acceleration g, Eq. 1 gives

$$W = mg \qquad \text{or} \qquad m = \frac{W}{g}. \tag{3}$$

5. Units. There are a number of systems of units used in relating force, mass, and acceleration. Four of these systems are defined in the table on the following page.

Engineers use a gravitational system in which length, force, and time are considered fundamental quantities and the units of mass are derived. Physicists use an absolute system in which length, mass, and time are considered fundamental and the units of force are derived. Either system, of course, may be used with the same results. The engineer prefers to use force as a fundamental quantity because most of his experiments involve direct measurement of force. The British or FPS

* It can be proved that, for this purpose, the earth may be considered a particle with its entire mass concentrated at its center.

Systems of Units

Type of System (fundamental quantities)	Gravitational (length, force, time)		Absolute (length, mass, time)	
Name of System	British or FPS	MKS	British or FPS	CGS
length L	foot (ft.)	meter (m.)	foot (ft.)	centimeter (cm.)
force F	pound (lb.)	kilogram (kg.)	poundal (pdl.)	dyne
time T	second (sec.)	second (sec.)	second (sec.)	second (sec.)
mass M	lb. ft.$^{-1}$ sec.^{2}	kg. m.$^{-1}$ sec.^{2}	pound (lb.)	gram (gr.)
System in use by	Engineers in English-speaking countries	Engineers in non-English-speaking countries	Physicists (occasionally)	Physicists everywhere

gravitational system is the one used in this book. The engineer has not adopted a unit for mass which is universally used although *slug* and less often *g-pound* are seen occasionally in the literature. One slug (or g-pound) is the mass of a body which weighs 32.2 lb. at the earth's surface.

It is frequently necessary to convert a quantity from one set of units to another. During the process of conversion it is essential that the dimensions of the quantity remain unchanged. In order to convert a velocity of 30 mi./hr., for example, to the equivalent number of centimeters per second it is first necessary to know that

5280 ft. are contained in 1 mi.,
30.48 cm. " " " 1 ft.,
3600 sec. " " " 1 hr.

The conversion is then

$$\left(30\,\frac{\text{mi.}}{\text{hr.}}\right)\left(5280\,\frac{\text{ft.}}{\text{mi.}}\right)\left(30.48\,\frac{\text{cm.}}{\text{ft.}}\right)\left(\frac{1}{3600}\,\frac{\text{hr.}}{\text{sec.}}\right) = 1340\,\frac{\text{cm.}}{\text{sec.}}\cdot$$

The units mi., hr., and ft. cancel, leaving cm./sec.

It is quite customary to write expressions stating equivalents in units such as

$$5280 \text{ ft.} = 1 \text{ mi.},$$

or

$$30 \text{ mi./hr.} = 1340 \text{ cm./sec.}$$

The meaning of these equivalents is clear, but it is important to note that these expressions are *not* algebraic equations. Here the equal sign does not mean mathematical equality since $5280 \neq 1$ and ft. $\neq$ mi. The equal sign when used in this way actually means "are contained in."

6. Description of Physical Problems. The science of mechanics is based on certain physical laws and utilizes mathematics freely in the description of the physical situation. Mathematics establishes the relationships between the various quantities involved and enables the prediction of effects to be made from these relations. The student must recognize that a dual thought process is necessary. He must think in terms of the physical situation, and he must also think in terms of the corresponding mathematical description. Analysis of every problem will require the repeated transition of thought between the physical and the mathematical. Without question one of the greatest difficulties that students have with mechanics is the inability to make this transition freely by interconnecting these two thought processes. The student should make a strong effort to connect each physical thought with its corresponding mathematical expression. He should recognize that the mathematical formulation of a physical problem represents an ideal limiting description or model which is approximated but never quite reached by the actual physical situation.

In the course of constructing the idealized mathematical model for any given engineering problem certain approximations will always be involved. Some of these approximations may be mathematical, whereas others will be physical. For instance, it is often necessary to neglect small distances, angles, or forces compared with large distances, angles, or forces. A force which is actually distributed over a small area of the body upon which it acts may be considered as a concentrated force if the dimensions of the area involved are small compared with other pertinent dimensions. The weight of a steel cable per foot of its length may be neglected if the tension in the cable is many times greater than its total weight, whereas the cable weight may not be neglected if the problem calls for a determination of the deflection or sag of a suspended cable due to its weight. Thus the degree of assumption involved depends upon what information is desired and the accuracy required. The student should be constantly aware of the various assumptions called for in the formulation of real problems in terms of a mathematical model. The ability to understand and make use of the appropriate assumptions in the course of the formulation and solution of engineering problems is certainly one of the most important characteristics of a successful engineer. One of the major aims of this book is to provide a maximum of opportunity to develop this ability through the portrayal of many practical problems.

Graphics is also an important means of description in mechanics and serves in three capacities. First, it enables the representation of a physical system to be made on paper by means of a sketch or diagram. Geometrical representation is vital to physical interpretation and aids greatly in visualizing the three-dimensional aspects of many problems. Second, graphics often affords a means of solving physical relations without the use of an algebraic solution. Graphical solutions not only provide practical means for obtaining results, but they also aid greatly in making the transition of thought between the physical situation and the mathematical expression because both are represented simultaneously. A third use of graphics is in the display of results on charts or graphs which become an invaluable aid to interpretation.

7. Accuracy. The number of significant figures shown in an answer should be no greater than that which corresponds to the least number of significant figures in the given data. Thus the cross-sectional area of a shaft whose diameter, 0.25 in., say, was measured to the nearest hundredth of an inch should be written as 0.049 in.^{2} and not 0.0491 in.^{2} as would be indicated when the numbers were multiplied out.

When calculations involve small differences in large quantities, greater accuracy must be achieved. Thus it is necessary to know the numbers 4.2503 and 4.2391 to an accuracy of five significant figures in order that their difference 0.0112 be expressed to three-figure accuracy. It is often difficult in somewhat lengthy computations to know at the outset the number of significant figures needed in the original data to insure a certain accuracy in the answer.

Slide-rule accuracy, usually three significant figures, is considered satisfactory for the majority of engineering calculations. The decimal point should be located by a rough longhand approximation which also serves as a check against large slide-rule error.

8. Mathematical Limits and Approximations. The essential purpose of applied mechanics is the mathematical description of engineering situations, and as such it is extremely necessary to understand and be able to apply certain limiting and approximating mathematical relations.

The *order* of differential quantities is the subject of frequent misunderstanding by students who are making application of the calculus for the first time. Higher-order differentials may always be neglected compared with lower-order differentials. As an example the element of volume ΔV of a right circular cone of altitude h and base radius r may be taken to be a circular slice a distance x from the vertex and of thickness Δx. It can be verified that the complete expression for the volume of the element may be written as

$$\Delta V = \frac{\pi r^2}{h^2} [x^2 \, \Delta x + x \, (\Delta x)^2 + \tfrac{1}{3} \, (\Delta x)^3] \cdot$$

It should be recognized that, when passing to the limit in going from ΔV to dV and from Δx to dx, the terms in $(\Delta x)^2$ and $(\Delta x)^3$ drop out, leaving merely

$$dV = \frac{\pi r^2}{h^2} x^2 \, dx,$$

which is an exact expression.

In using trigonometric functions of differential quantities it is well to call attention to the following relations which are true in the mathematical limit:

$$\sin d\theta = \tan d\theta = d\theta,$$

$$\cos d\theta = 1.$$

The angle $d\theta$ is, of course, expressed in radian measure. When dealing with small but finite angles it is often convenient to replace the sine by the tangent or either function by the angle itself. These approximations, $\sin \theta = \theta$ and $\tan \theta = \theta$, amount to retaining only the first term in the series expansions for the sine and tangent. If a closer approximation is desired, the first two terms may be retained which give $\sin \theta = \theta - \theta^3/6$ and $\tan \theta = \theta + \theta^3/3$. As an example of the first approximation, for an angle of 1 deg.,

$$\sin 1^\circ = 0.0174524 \qquad \text{and} \qquad 1^\circ \text{ is } 0.0174533 \text{ radian.}$$

The error in replacing the sine by the angle for 1 deg. is only 0.005 per cent. For 5 deg. the error is 0.13 per cent, and for 10 deg. the error is still only 0.51 per cent. Similarly, for small angles the cosine may be approximated by the first two terms in its series expansion which gives $\cos \theta = 1 - \theta^2/2$.

A few of the mathematical relations which are useful in mechanics are listed in Table D3, Appendix D.

9. Method of Problem Solution. An understanding of the method of attack on engineering problems is an essential aspect of their solution. This method involves a logical sequence of steps from hypothesis to conclusion and should include the following:

(*a*) given data,
(*b*) statement of results desired,
(*c*) necessary diagrams,
(*d*) statement of principles and basic equations which apply,
(*e*) application of principles and equations,
(*f*) answers or conclusions.

Presentation of information in this order represents a logical sequence, and all problem work should follow this general pattern. It is also important that the arrangement of work be neat and orderly. Careless solutions which cannot be easily read by others are of little or no value. It will be found that the discipline involved in adherence to good form will in itself be an invaluable aid to the development of the powers of analysis. Many problems which at first may seem difficult and complicated become clear and simple once they are begun with a logical and disciplined method of attack.

The science of mechanics is based on a surprisingly few fundamental concepts and involves mainly the application of these basic relations to a variety of situations. In this application the *method* of analysis is all-important. In solving a problem it is essential that the laws which apply be carefully fixed in mind and that these principles be applied literally and exactly. In applying the principles which define the requirements for forces acting on a body it is essential that the body in question be *isolated* from all other bodies so that complete and accurate account of all forces which act on this body may be taken. This *isolation* should exist mentally as well as be represented on paper. The drawing of such an isolated body with the representation of *all* external forces acting on it is called a *free-body diagram*. It has long been established that the *free-body diagram method* is the key to the understanding of mechanics. This is so because the *isolation* of a body is the tool by which *cause* and *effect* are clearly separated and by which attention on the literal application of a principle is accurately focused. The technique of drawing free-body diagrams will be covered in Chapter 3 where they are first used.

In applying physical laws to the solution of a problem numerical values of the quantities may be used directly in proceeding toward the solution. On the other hand algebraic symbols may be used to represent the quantities involved, and the answer left as a formula. In the first scheme the magnitude of all quantities expressed in their particular units is evident at each stage of the calculation. This is often an advantage when the practical significance of the magnitude of the terms is appraised. The second method, or symbolic solution, has several advantages over the numerical solution. In the first place the abbreviation achieved by the use of symbols aids in focusing attention on the interconnection between the physical situation and its related mathematical description. Secondly, a symbolic solution permits a dimensional check to be made at every step, whereas dimensional homogeneity may not be checked when numerical values are used. Furthermore a symbolic solution may be used repeatedly for obtaining answers to the same problem when different sets and sizes of units may be involved. Facility with both methods of solution is essential, and ample practice with each should be sought in the problem work.

CHAPTER 2

FORCE SYSTEMS

10. Force. Before dealing with a group or *system* of forces it is necessary to examine the properties of a single force in some detail. A force has been defined as the action of one body on another. It is evident that force is a vector quantity since its effect depends on the direction of the action as well as on the magnitude. Furthermore it is necessary to know where it acts. The action of the cable tension P on the bracket in Fig. 5*a* is represented in Fig. 5*b* by the force vector P. The effect of

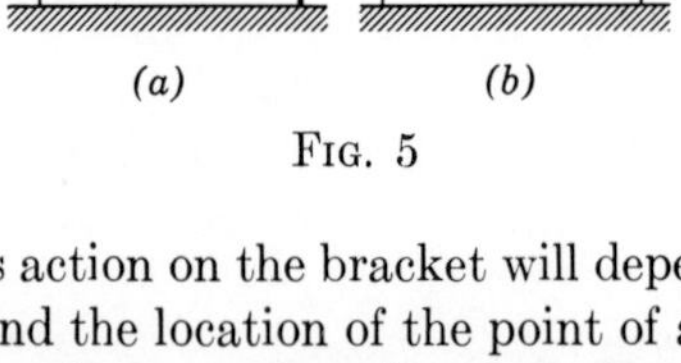

(*a*) (*b*)

FIG. 5

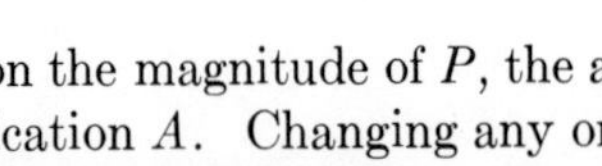

(*a*) (*b*) (*c*)

FIG. 6

this action on the bracket will depend on the magnitude of P, the angle θ, and the location of the point of application A. Changing any one of these three specifications will alter the effect on the bracket. The sense of a force along its line of action is a fourth specification which may be added to distinguish between two forces having identical lines of action but opposite sense, such as with the forces P_1 and P_2 of Fig. 6*a*. The need for the fourth specification disappears if the obtuse angle θ_2 is used as in Fig. 6*b*. Since directions of lines are most frequently measured and represented by acute angles, the specification of an obtuse angle is often inconvenient. The question is most easily resolved if the direction of the force is indicated by an acute angle such as θ in Fig. 6*c*. As long as the force and angle are clearly represented on a sketch or are adequately described, there is need for only the three specifications of force: *magnitude, direction,* and *point of application.*

Force is applied either by direct mechanical contact or by remote action. Gravitational and electrical forces are the two examples of force applied by remote action. All other actual forces are applied through direct physical contact.

The action of a force on a body can be separated into two effects, *external* and *internal.* For the bracket of Fig. 5 the effects of P external to the bracket are the reactions or forces exerted on the bracket by the foundation and bolts in consequence of the action of P. Forces external to a body are then of two kinds, applied or *active* forces and resulting or *reactive* forces. The effects of P internal to the bracket are the resulting internal movements and forces distributed throughout the material of the bracket. The relation between internal forces and internal movements involves the material properties of the body and is studied in the subjects of strength of materials, elasticity, and plasticity.

In dealing with the mechanics of rigid bodies where concern is given only to the net *external* effects of forces, experience shows that it is not necessary to restrict the action of an applied force to a given point. Thus the force P acting on the rigid bracket in Fig. 7 may be applied at A or at B or at any other point on its action line, and the net external effect of P on the bracket will not change. This situation is described by the *principle of transmissibility,* which states that a force may be applied at any point on its given line of action without altering the resultant effects of the force *external* to the rigid body on which it acts. When the resultant external effects only of a force are to be investigated, the force may be treated as a *sliding* vector, and it is necessary and sufficient to specify the *magnitude, direction,* and *line of action* of the force. Since this book deals essentially with the mechanics of rigid bodies, almost all forces will be treated as sliding vectors.

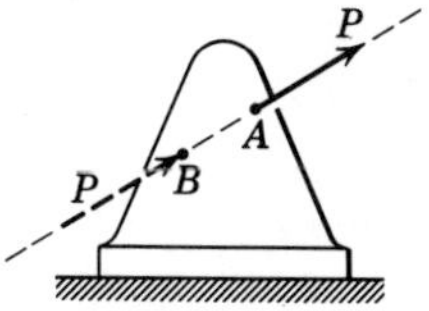

FIG. 7

Forces may be either concentrated or distributed. Actually every contact force is applied over a finite area and is therefore distributed. When the dimensions of the area are negligible compared with the other dimensions of the body, the force may be considered as concentrated at a point. Force may be distributed over an area, as in the case of mechanical contact, or it may be distributed over a volume when gravity or magnetic force is acting. The "weight" of a body is the force of gravity distributed over its volume and may be taken as a concentrated force acting through the center of gravity. The position of the center of gravity is usually obvious from considerations of symmetry. If the position is not clear, then a separate calculation, explained in Chapter 5, will be necessary to locate the center of gravity.

A force may be measured either by comparison with other known forces, using a mechanical balance, or by the calibrated movement of an elastic spring. All such comparisons or calibrations have as their basis a primary standard. The standard pound for the United States is legally defined as 0.4535924277 times the international kilogram and is that force required to support this portion of the standard kilogram in a vacuum and under the standard conditions of sea level and a latitude of 45 deg.*

The characteristic of a force expressed by Newton's third law must be carefully observed. The action of a force is always accompanied by an equal and opposite reaction. It is essential to fix clearly in mind which force of the pair is involved. The answer is always clear when the body in question is *isolated* and the force exerted *on* that body (not *by* the body) is represented. It is very easy to make a careless mistake and consider the wrong force of the pair unless careful distinction between every action and reaction is made.

11. Addition. Two concurrent forces F_1 and F_2 may be added by the parallelogram law to obtain their sum or *resultant* R as shown in Fig. 8*a*. If the two forces lie in the same plane but are applied at two different points as in Fig. 8*b*, they may be moved along their lines of action and their vector sum R completed at the point of concurrency. The resultant R may replace F_1 and F_2 without altering the external effects on the body. The triangle law may also be used to obtain R, but it will require moving the line of action of one of the forces as shown in Fig. 8*c*. In Fig. 8*d* the same two forces are added, and although the correct magnitude and direction of R are preserved, the correct line of action is lost. This type of combination should be avoided. Mathematically the sum of the two forces may be written by the vector equation

$$F_1 \nrightarrow F_2 = R.$$

* More precisely the "standard conditions" refer to any location at which the acceleration of gravity is 32.1740 ft./sec.^{2}

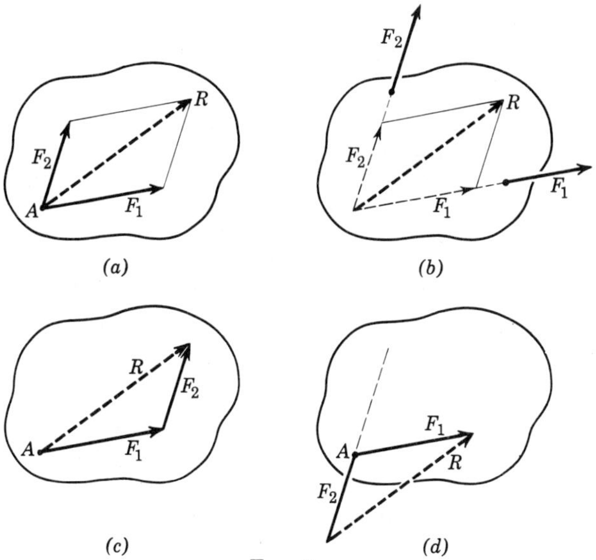

FIG. 8

A special case of addition is presented when the two forces F_1 and F_2 are parallel, Fig. 9. Graphically they may be combined by first adding two equal, opposite, and collinear forces F of convenient magnitude which together produce no external effect on the body. Adding F_1 and F and combining with the sum of F_2 and F yield the resultant R correct in magnitude, direction, and line of action. The procedure here is also useful in obtaining a graphical combination of two forces which are almost parallel and hence may have a remote point of concurrency.

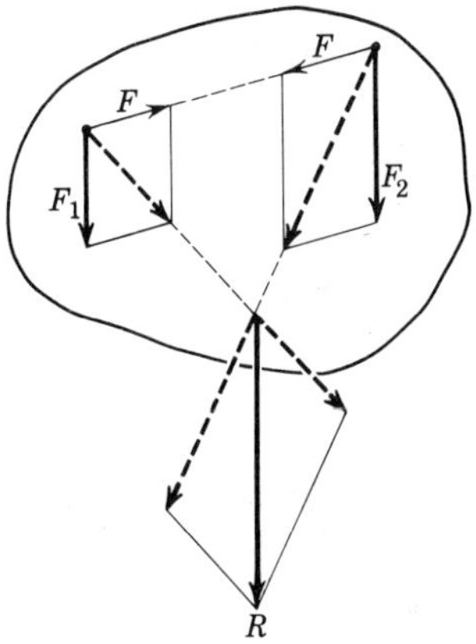

FIG. 9

12. Resolution. The force R of Fig. 10a is said to have the *components* F_1 and F_2 or to be *resolved* in the directions O–1 and O–2, respectively. When the directions of resolution are mutually perpendicular, the force R is said to have *rectangular* components R_x and R_y as in Fig. 10b. It is at once evident from the figure that

$$R_x = R\cos\theta, \qquad R_y = R\sin\theta,$$

$$R = \sqrt{R_x^{\,2} + R_y^{\,2}}, \qquad \theta = \tan^{-1}\frac{R_y}{R_x}. \tag{4}$$

The orientation of axes is arbitrary, and a selection as in Fig. 10*c* could be made. The action of a force and its components at the point of application may also be represented as in Fig. 10*d*.

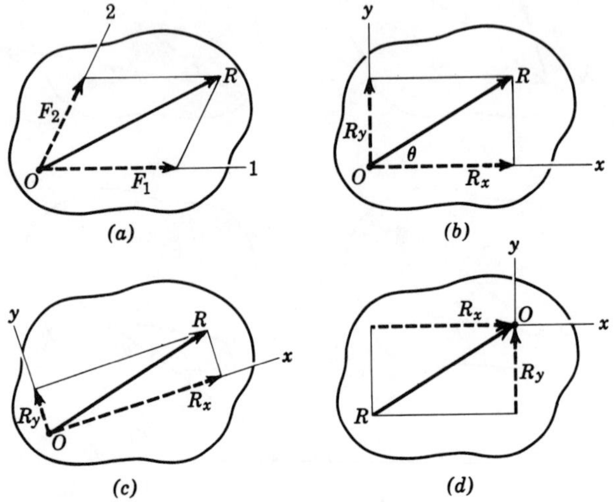

FIG. 10

In order to eliminate ambiguity between the representation of a force and its components it is desirable to show the components in dotted lines and the resultant in a full line, as in Fig. 10, or else to show the components in full lines and their resultant in a dotted line, as in Fig. 8. With this understanding it will always be apparent that a force and its components are represented and not three separate forces.

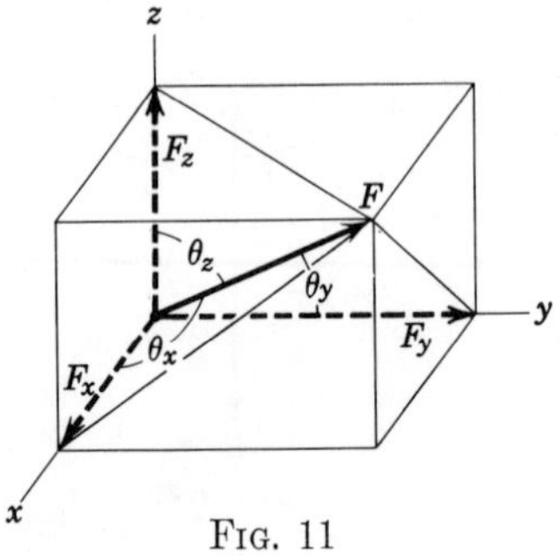

FIG. 11

Many problems are three dimensional, and it becomes necessary to consider the three mutually perpendicular components of a force. In Fig. 11 force F is resolved into its rectangular components F_x, F_y, F_z by forming the edges of the rectangular parallelepiped of which F is a diagonal. When the angles made by F with the x-, y-, and z-axes are designated by θ_x, θ_y, and θ_z, respectively, it is evident from the right triangles involved that

$$\left.\begin{aligned} F_x &= F\cos\theta_x \\ F_y &= F\cos\theta_y \\ F_z &= F\cos\theta_z \end{aligned}\right\} \quad \text{and} \quad F = \sqrt{F_x^{\,2} + F_y^{\,2} + F_z^{\,2}}. \qquad (5)$$

The direction cosines of F are $\cos\theta_x$, $\cos\theta_y$, and $\cos\theta_z$. The choice of the orientation of the axes is quite arbitrary, and considerations of convenience usually determine this selection.

SAMPLE PROBLEMS

1. The 100 lb. force is applied to the bracket as shown in the a-part of the figure accompanying this problem. Determine the rectangular components of

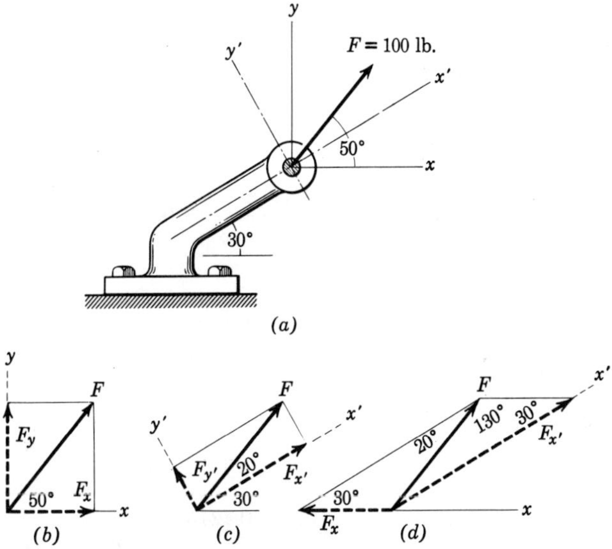

PROB. 1

F in (1) the x- and y-directions and (2) the x'- and y'-directions. Also (3) find the components of F in the x- and x'-directions.

Solution. Part (1). The x- and y-components of F are shown in the b-part of the figure and are

$$F_x = F\cos\theta_x = 100\cos 50^\circ = 64.3 \text{ lb.},$$

$$F_y = F\sin\theta_x = 100\sin 50^\circ = 76.6 \text{ lb.} \qquad \textit{Ans.}$$

Part (2). The x'- and y'-components of F are shown in the c-part of the figure and are

$$F_{x'} = F \cos \theta_{x'} = 100 \cos 20^\circ = 94.0 \text{ lb.},$$

$$F_{y'} = F \sin \theta_{x'} = 100 \sin 20^\circ = 34.2 \text{ lb.} \qquad \textit{Ans.}$$

Part (3). The components of F in the x- and x'-directions are obtained by completing the parallelogram as indicated in the d-part of the figure. F_x and $F_{x'}$ in the directions indicated are obtained from the law of sines. Thus

$$\frac{F_x}{\sin 20^\circ} = \frac{F}{\sin 30^\circ}; \qquad F_x = \frac{0.342}{0.500} \times 100 = 68.4 \text{ lb.};$$

$$\frac{F_{x'}}{\sin 130^\circ} = \frac{F}{\sin 30^\circ}; \qquad F_{x'} = \frac{0.766}{0.500} \times 100 = 153 \text{ lb.} \qquad \textit{Ans.}$$

2. If the force F in Fig. 11 is 100 lb. and passes through a point whose x-, y-, and z-coordinates are 4, 5, and 3, respectively, determine the rectangular components of F. Also find the component of F in the x–y plane.

Solution. The direction cosines are

$$\cos \theta_x = \frac{4}{\sqrt{4^2 + 5^2 + 3^2}} = 0.566,$$

$$\cos \theta_y = \frac{5}{\sqrt{4^2 + 5^2 + 3^2}} = 0.707,$$

$$\cos \theta_z = \frac{3}{\sqrt{4^2 + 5^2 + 3^2}} = 0.424.$$

The components of F are then

$$F_x = F \cos \theta_x = 100 \times 0.566 = 56.6 \text{ lb.},$$

$$F_y = F \cos \theta_y = 100 \times 0.707 = 70.7 \text{ lb.},$$

$$F_z = F \cos \theta_z = 100 \times 0.424 = 42.4 \text{ lb.} \qquad \textit{Ans.}$$

The cosine of the angle θ_{xy} made by F with the x–y plane is

$$\cos \theta_{xy} = \frac{\sqrt{4^2 + 5^2}}{\sqrt{4^2 + 5^2 + 3^2}} = 0.906,$$

and the component of F in the x–y plane is

$$F_{xy} = F \cos \theta_{xy} = 100 \times 0.906 = 90.6 \text{ lb.} \qquad \textit{Ans.}$$

PROBLEMS

3. The cable exerts a pull of $P = 1000$ lb. on the mast band. How much of this force is exerted on the fitting in the x- and y-directions?

Ans. $P_x = 574$ lb., $P_y = 819$ lb.

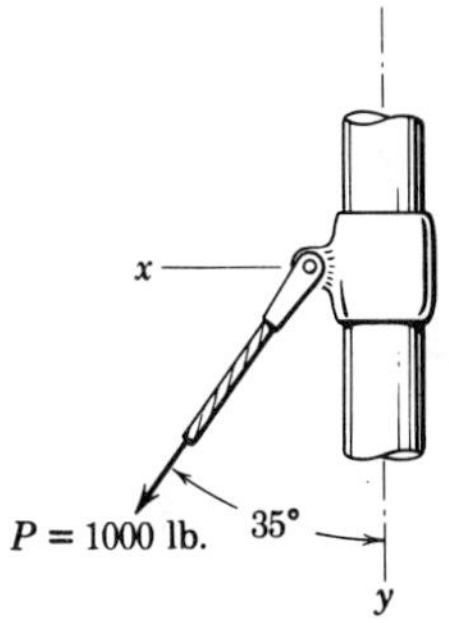

PROB. 3

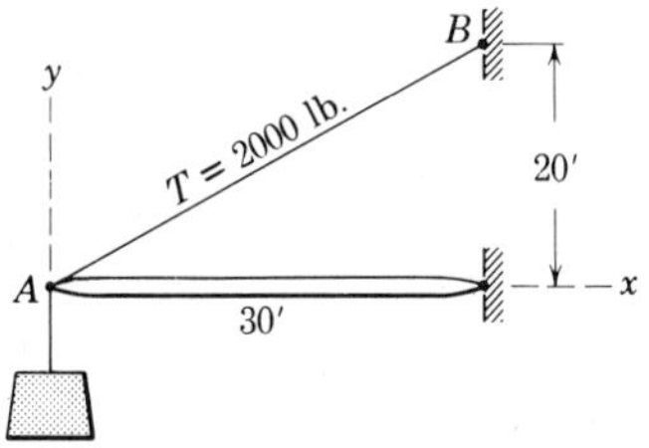

PROB. 4

4. Determine the x- and y-components of the force exerted on the pin at A by the 2000 lb. cable tension T. *Ans.* $T_x = 1660$ lb., $T_y = 1110$ lb.

5. Find the x- and y- components of the force F.

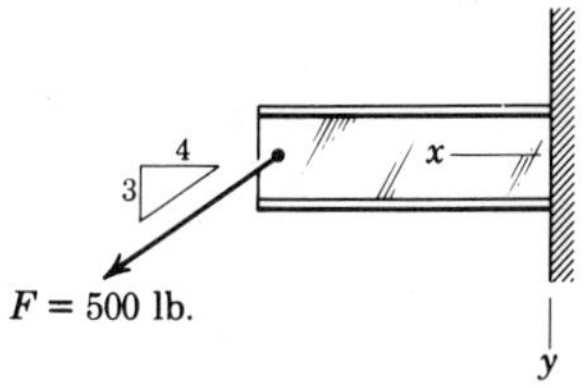

PROB. 5

6. A force F which acts in the x–y plane has a magnitude of 200 lb. and a direction $\theta_x = 130$ deg. Find the x- and y-components of F.

Ans. $F_x = -128$ lb., $F_y = 153$ lb.

7. The force F between the cam A and the follower B is normal to their surfaces of contact and equals 150 lb. for the position shown. Determine the component of F along a–a in the direction of the cam bearing.

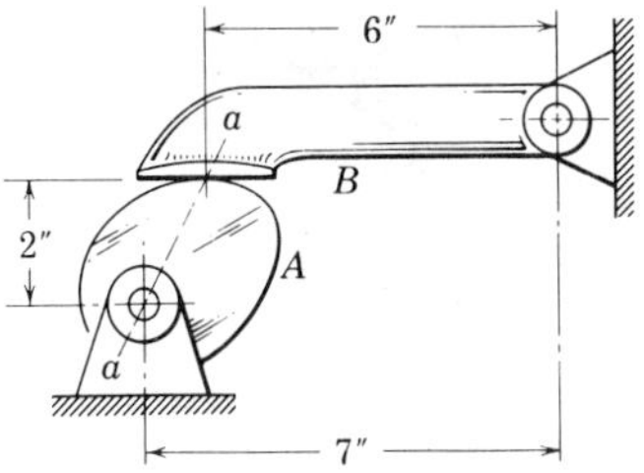

PROB. 7

8. The structural member A is under a tensile load of 3 kips (1 kip = 1000 lb.). Determine the amount of force F transmitted by this member to the gusset plate B in the direction of the I-beam C. *Ans.* $F = 1.03$ kips

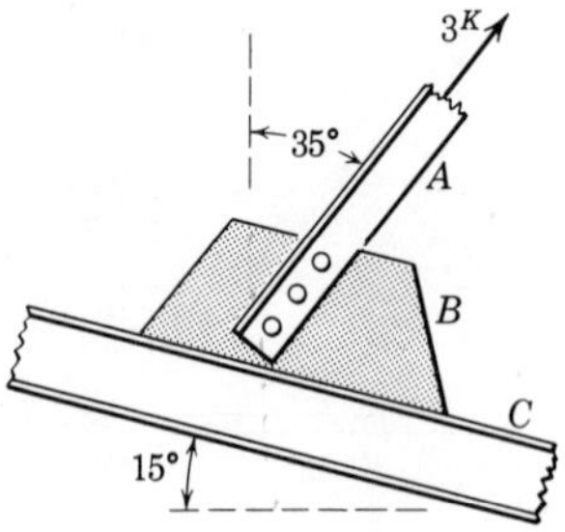

PROB. 8

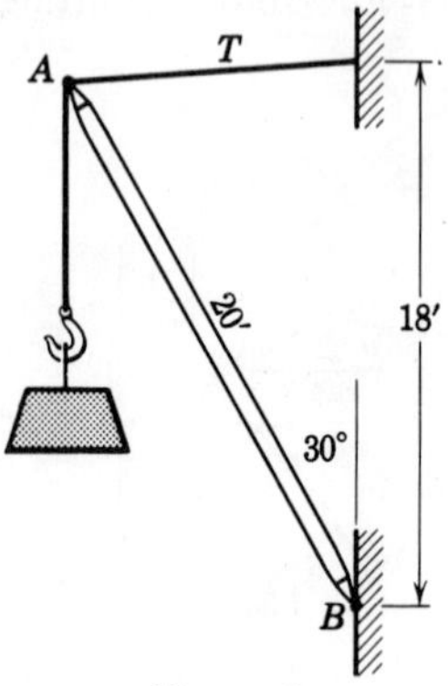

PROB. 9

9. The tension T in the supporting cable of the 20 ft. boom is 2000 lb. Resolve T into two forces applied at A: one, F_n, normal to the boom and the other, F_t, along the boom.

10. The two forces shown are to be replaced by an equivalent force R applied at the point P. Locate P by finding its distance x from AB, and specify the magnitude of R and the angle θ it makes with the horizontal.

Ans. $x = 5.49$ in., $R = 1323$ lb., $\theta = 10° 54'$

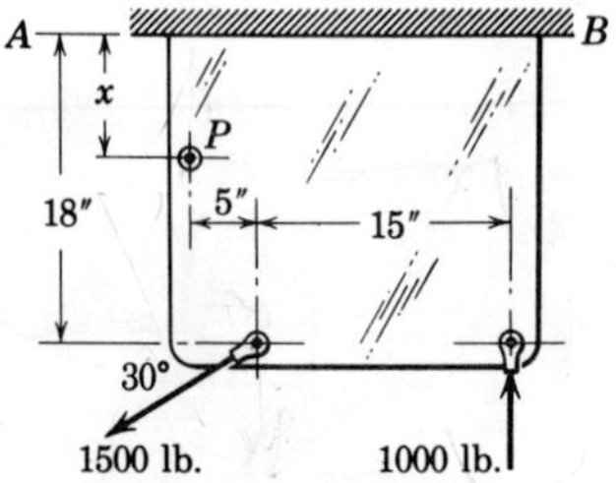

PROB. 10

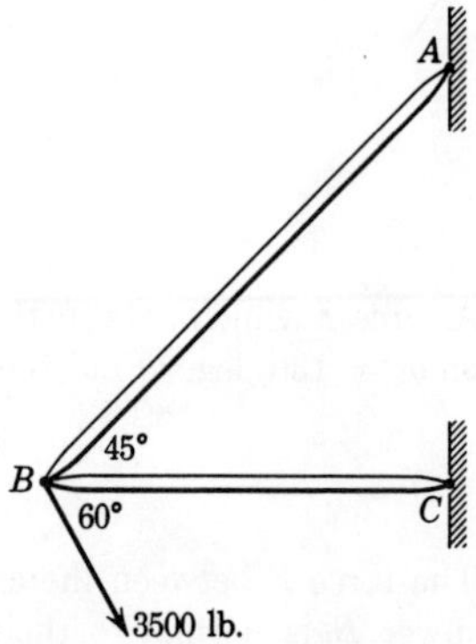

PROB. 11

11. In finding the forces exerted on the pin connections at A and C the 3500 lb. force is resolved into two forces, one along the line AB and the other along BC. Find these components.

12. At what angle θ must F_1 be applied in order that the resultant R of F_1 and F_2 be equal to 100 lb.? For this condition what will be the angle β between R and the horizontal?

Ans. $\theta = 51° 19'$, $\beta = 18° 12'$

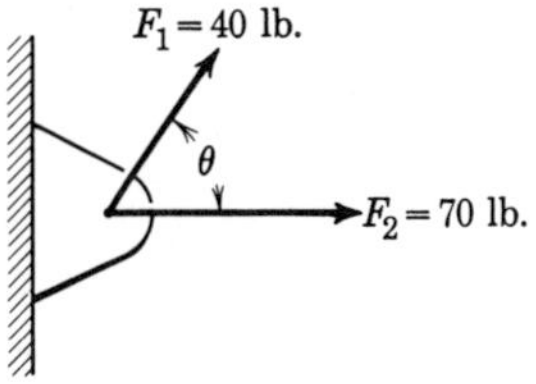

PROB. 12

13. A 100 lb. force which makes an angle of 45 deg. with the horizontal x-axis is to be replaced by two forces, a horizontal force F and a second force of 75 lb. magnitude. Find F.

Ans. $F = 95.7$ lb. or $F = 45.7$ lb.

14. The force R has components F_1 and F_2 acting through O as indicated. Show graphically that R may also be represented by two components through O having the same magnitudes as F_1 and F_2 but differing in direction.

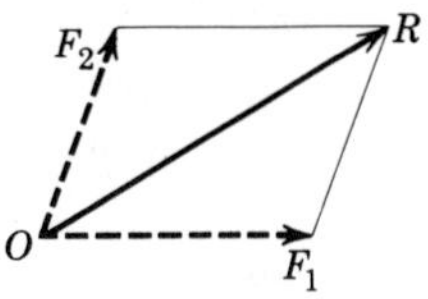

PROB. 14

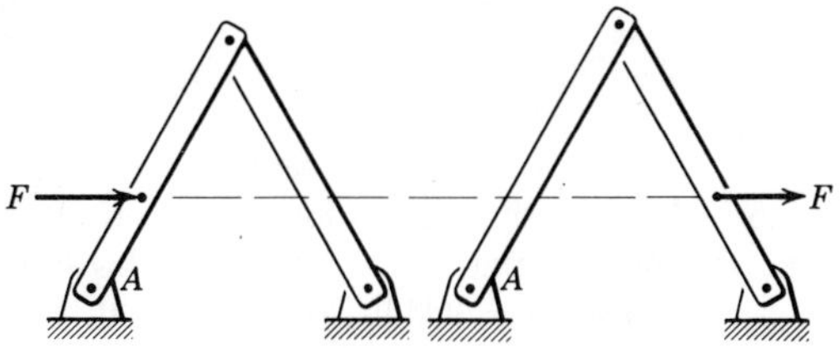

PROB. 15

15. Can it be concluded from the principle of transmissibility that the pin reactions at A are the same for the two identical frames shown? Explain.

16. If the weight of the truss is neglected, the pin force acting on the truss at A is equal and opposite to the resultant of the 10 ton load and the corresponding cable tension T acting on the truss. If the 10 ton load is removed and a force P is applied as indicated by the dotted line, determine the magnitude of P and the corresponding increase ΔT in cable tension so that the reaction on the pin A will remain unchanged. *Ans.* $P = 11.55$ tons, $\Delta T = 5.77$ tons

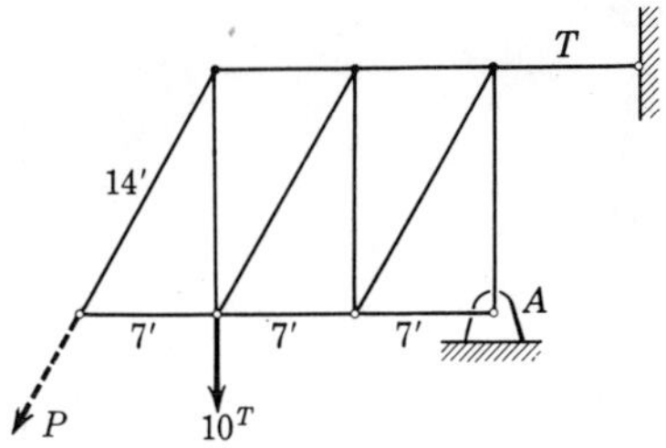

PROB. 16

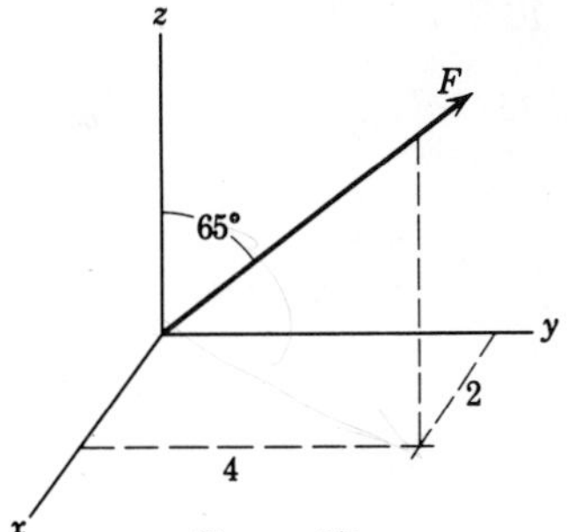

PROB. 17

17. If the x-component of the force F is 300 lb., find F. *Ans.* $F = 740$ lb.

18. Determine the direction cosines of the force F of Prob. 17.

19. The tension T in one of the two supporting cables for the boom is 500 lb. Resolve the force exerted by this cable on the boom into its x-, y-, and z-components. *Ans.* $T_x = -411$ lb., $T_y = 264$ lb., $T_z = 106$ lb.

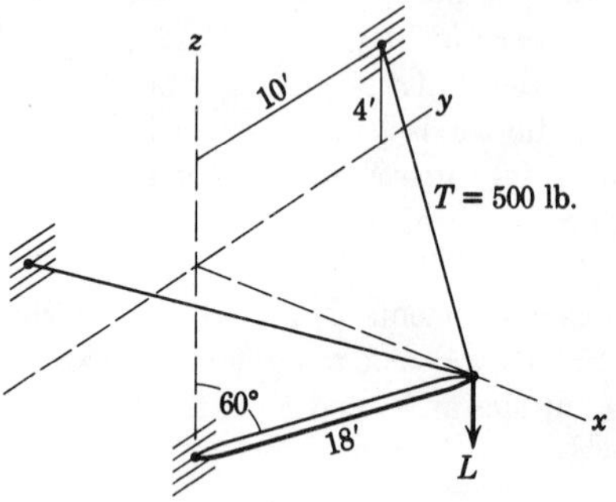

PROB. 19

20. The fixed eyebolt is subjected to the three forces shown. If a single force is to replace the three given forces without altering the effect on the eyebolt, find the correct value of the force F and its direction cosines.

Ans. $F = 906$ lb., $\cos\theta_x = 0.501$, $\cos\theta_y = 0.444$, $\cos\theta_z = -0.743$

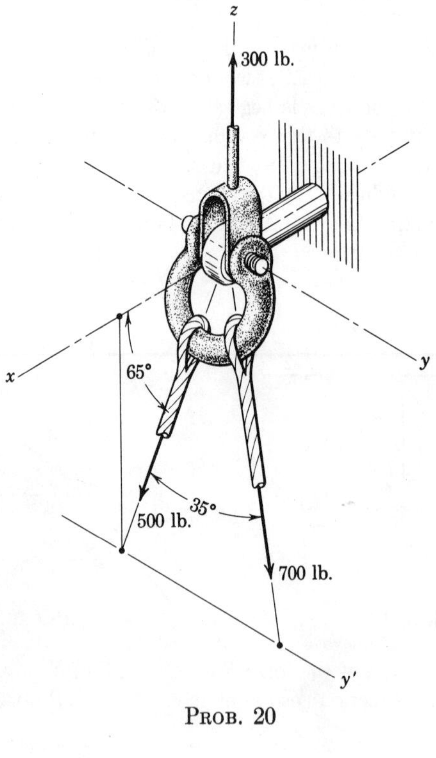

PROB. 20

* **21.** The access door shown is secured in the open position by the chain AB which exerts a tension force $T = 20$ lb. on the door at B and in the direction from B to A. Resolve this force into components T_x, T_y, T_z along the edges of the door and normal to the plane of the door.

Ans. $T_x = 16$ lb., $T_y = -6$ lb., $T_z = 10.4$ lb.

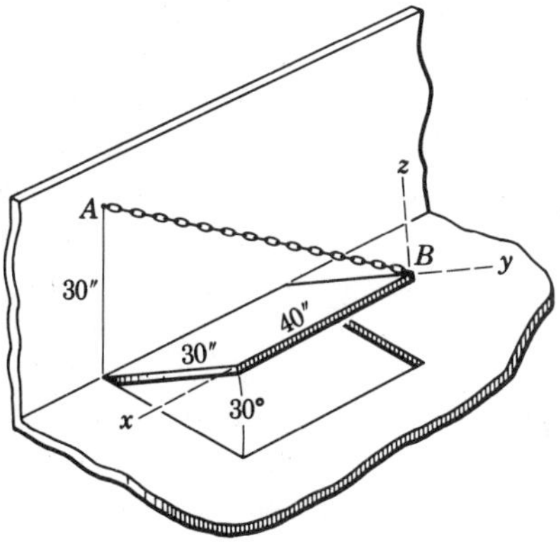

PROB. 21

13. Moment. The tendency of a force to rotate the body upon which it acts about a certain axis is known as the *moment* of the force about that axis. In Fig. 12a consider the moment M about the axis

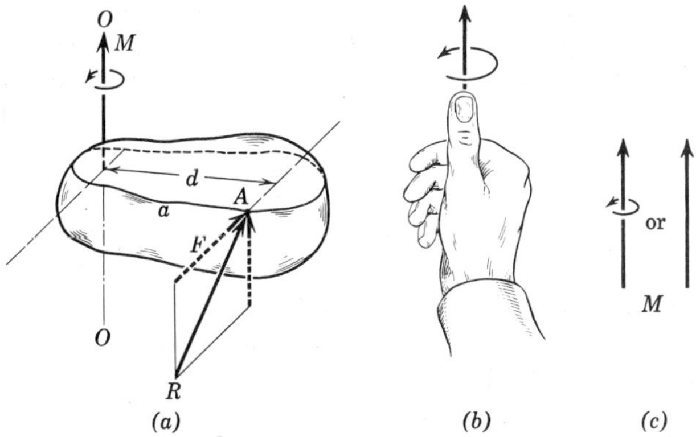

FIG. 12

O–O of a force R applied at any point A on the body as shown. This moment is due entirely to the component of R in a plane normal to the axis and equals this component F multiplied by the perpendicular distance or moment arm d from the line of action of F to the axis O–O. Thus

$$M = Fd. \tag{6}$$

The component of R normal to F is parallel to O–O and hence exerts no tendency to rotate the body about this axis.

Moment is a vector quantity. The vector direction is along the axis about which the moment is taken, and the sense of the vector is specified by the arbitrary but universally used *right-hand rule.* To represent the direction of the moment of R about O–O in Fig. 12*a* the fingers of the right hand are curled in the direction of the tendency to rotate as shown in the *b*-part of the figure. The thumb then points in the direction of the vector M. This vector may be represented in either of the two ways shown in Fig. 12*c*. The small curl is sometimes used to distinguish a moment vector from a force vector. A moment vector obeys all the rules of vector combination and may be considered to be a sliding vector with a line of action coinciding with the moment axis.

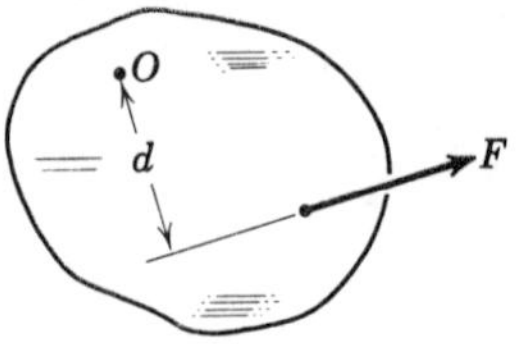

FIG. 13

When dealing with forces all of which act in a given plane it is customary to speak of the moment about a point. Actually the moment with respect to an axis normal to the plane and passing through the point is implied. Thus the moment of force F about point O in Fig. 13 is $M_O = Fd$ and is counterclockwise. Vector representation of moments for coplanar forces is not convenient since the vectors are either out from the paper (counterclockwise) or into the paper (clockwise). Since the addition of parallel free vectors may be accomplished with *scalar* algebra, the moment directions may be accounted for by using a plus sign (+) for counterclockwise moments and a minus sign (−) for clockwise moments, or vice versa. It is necessary only to be consistent within a given problem in using either sign convention.

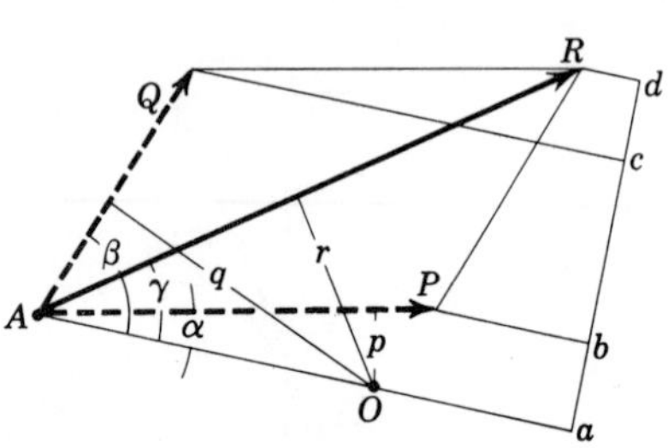

FIG. 14

One of the most important principles of mechanics is *Varignon's theorem,* or the *principle of moments,* which states that the moment of a force about any point is equal to the sum of the moments of its components about the same point. To prove this statement consider a force R and two components P and Q acting at point A, Fig. 14. Point O is selected arbitrarily as the moment center. Construct the line AO and project the three vectors onto the normal to this line. Also construct the moment arms p, q, r of the three forces to point O and designate the angles of the vectors to the line AO by α,

β, γ as shown in the figure. Since the parallelogram whose sides are P and Q requires that $\overline{ac} = \overline{bd}$, it is evident that

$$\overline{ad} = \overline{ab} + \overline{bd} = \overline{ab} + \overline{ac},$$

or

$$R \sin \gamma = P \sin \alpha + Q \sin \beta.$$

Multiplying by the distance $\overline{AO}$ and substituting the values of p, q, r give

$$Rr = Pp + Qq,$$

which proves that the moment of a force about any point equals the sum of the moments of its two components about the same point. Varignon's theorem need not be restricted to the case of only two components but applies equally well to three or more since it is always possible by direct combination to reduce the number of components to two for which the theorem was proved. The theorem may also be applied to the moments of other fixed or sliding vectors.

SAMPLE PROBLEM

22. A force $F = 100$ lb. is applied to the arm shown, which is attached to the rigid shaft. Determine the moment M of F about the shaft axis.

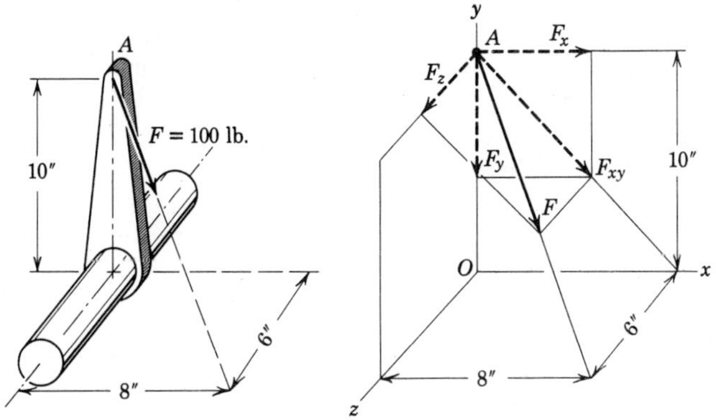

PROB. 22

Solution. In the right-hand part of the figure the force F is shown resolved into components F_{xy} in the x–y plane which is normal to the shaft axis and the component F_z. The moment M of F about the shaft or z-axis is

$$M = F_{xy}d,$$

where d is the perpendicular distance from F_{xy} to O. The cosine of the angle between F and F_{xy} is $\sqrt{8^2 + 10^2}/\sqrt{8^2 + 6^2 + 10^2} = 0.906$, and therefore

$$F_{xy} = 100 \times 0.906 = 90.6 \text{ lb.}$$

The moment arm d equals OA multiplied by the sine of the angle between F_{xy} and OA, or

$$d = 10 \times \frac{8}{\sqrt{8^2 + 10^2}} = 6.25 \text{ in.}$$

Hence the moment of F about the z-axis is

$$M = 90.6 \times 6.25 = 566 \text{ lb. in.} \qquad \textit{Ans.}$$

Calculation of the moment is somewhat simplified by resolving F_{xy} into F_x and F_y. It is clear that F_y exerts no moment about the z-axis so that F_x only need be considered. The direction cosine of F with respect to the x-axis is $8/\sqrt{8^2 + 6^2 + 10^2} = 0.566$ so that $F_x = 100 \times 0.566 = 56.6$ lb. Thus

$$M = 56.6 \times 10 = 566 \text{ lb. in.}$$

Expressed as a vector, M would be in the negative z-direction.

PROBLEMS

23. Prove that the moment of a force about a point equals twice the area of the triangle defined by that point and the two extremities of the force vector.

24. A force F is applied at a point whose coordinates are x, y, z. Show that the moment of F about the x-axis is $M_x = F_z y - F_y z$ and write the expressions for the moments M_y and M_z about the y- and z-axes, respectively.

25. Determine the moment M of the 50 lb. force about the point A.
Ans. $M = 1160$ lb. in.

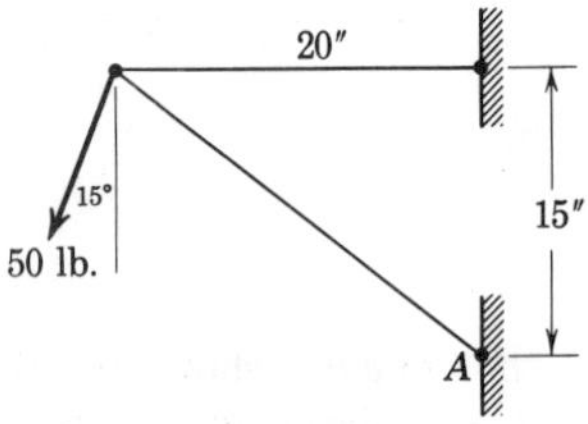

PROB. 25

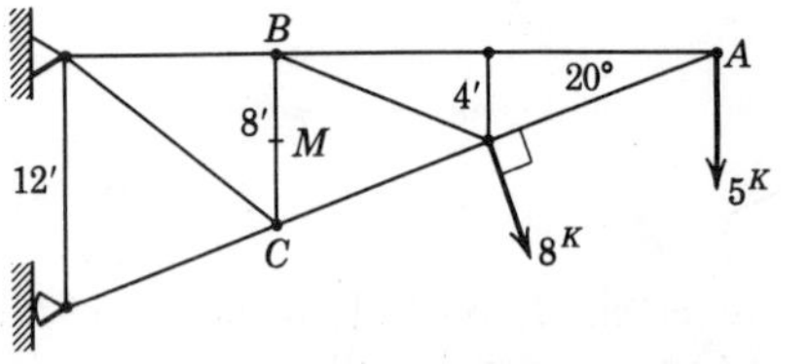

PROB. 26

26. Determine the moment M of the 5 kip force about point M for the overhanging truss. *Ans.* $M = 109,900$ lb. ft.

27. The force F of contact between the teeth of the gears is normal to their contact surfaces. If the smaller gear transmits a torque (moment) of 200 lb. in. about its shaft O and the pressure angle is 20 deg. as shown, find F.

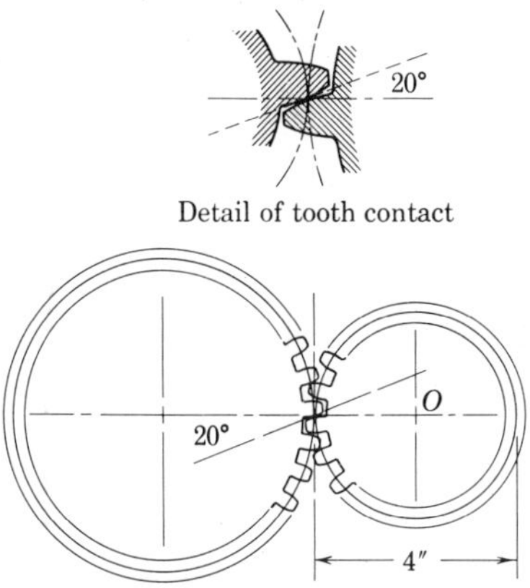

Prob. 27

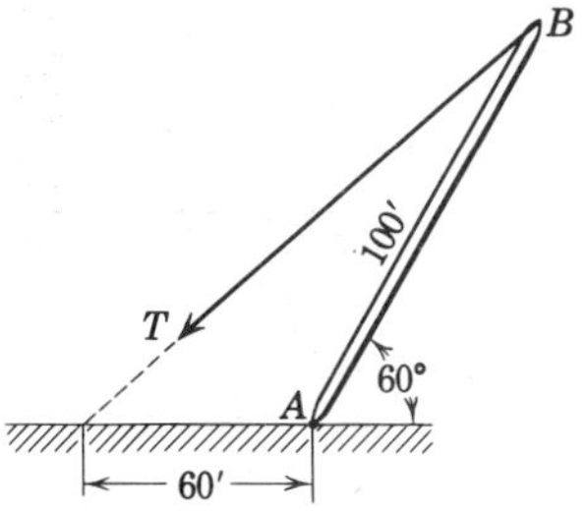

Prob. 28

28. In raising the mast AB from the position shown the tension T in the cable must supply a moment about A of 45,000 lb. ft. Find T. *Ans.* $T = 1212$ lb.

29. A force of 40 lb. is applied to the end of the wrench to tighten a flange bolt which holds the wheel to the axle. Determine the moment M produced by this force about the center O of the wheel for the position of the wrench shown.

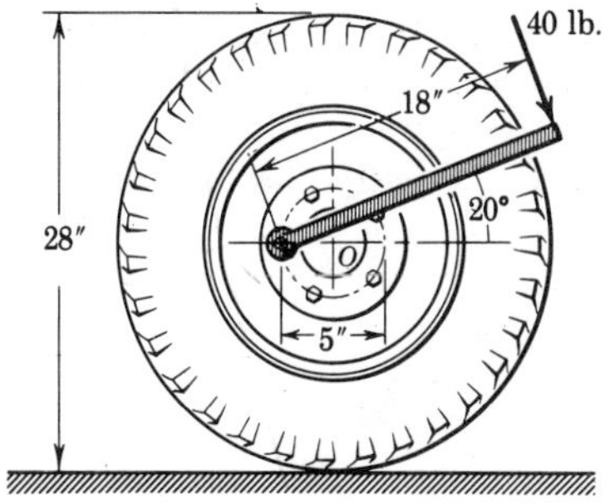

Prob. 29

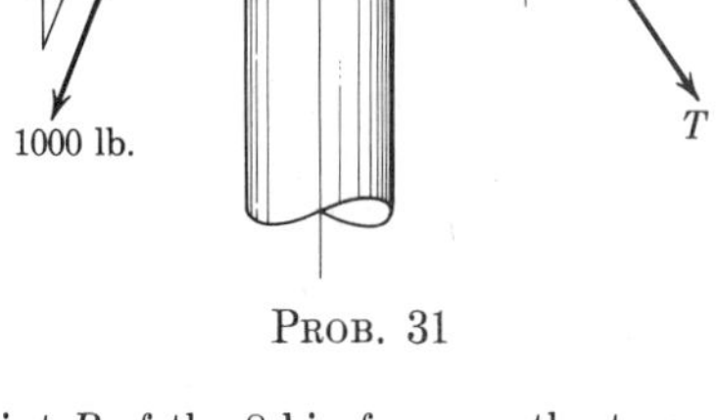

Prob. 31

30. Determine the moment M about point B of the 8 kip force on the truss in Prob. 26. *Ans.* $M = 71{,}700$ lb. ft.

31. The top of the mast is supported by the two cables attached to the mast fitting as shown. In order to prevent bending of the mast at the fitting there must be no resulting moment about point O on the center line of the mast. Determine the necessary value of T. (Will this value of T eliminate bending of the mast at points below O?)

32. The single-cylinder gasoline engine represented in the figure has a stroke of 8 in., and the connecting rod is 14 in. between bearing centers. In the position shown the rod is under a compression (in the direction of the rod) of 4500 lb. Determine the moment M of this force about the crankshaft axis.

Ans. $M = 17{,}330$ lb. in.

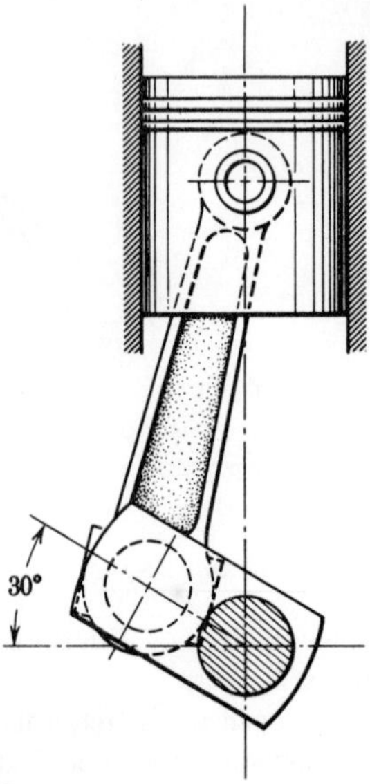

Prob. 32

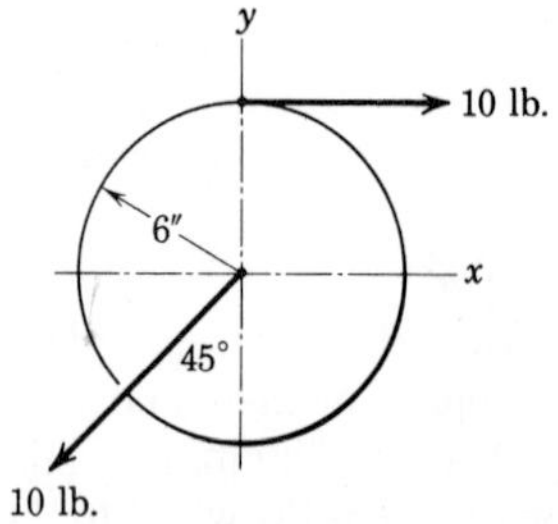

Prob. 33

33. A wheel is subjected to two forces as shown in the figure. Determine graphically the coordinates of the point on the rim of the wheel about which the combined moment M of the two forces is a maximum. Find M for this point. *Ans.* $x = -5.5$ in., $y = -2.3$ in., $M = 106$ lb. in.

34. Determine the moment M_x about the shaft axis of the 500 lb. force applied to the bracket shown.

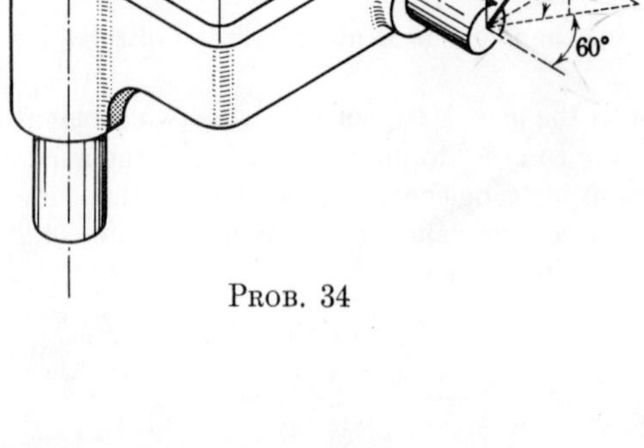

Prob. 34

* **35.** The steel bracket is fastened to the surface *A* by a bolt *B* whose axis is normal to this surface. Determine the moment *M* of the 80 lb. force about the bolt axis. *Ans.* $M = 992$ lb. in.

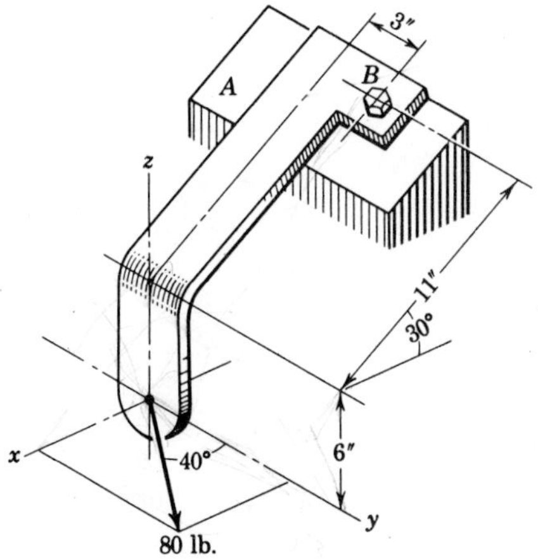

Prob. 35

* **36.** Contact between the two bevel gears shown, which have a speed ratio of 2:1, may be assumed to occur at a point 4.17 in. from the axis of the larger gear. If the contact force is normal to the tooth surfaces shown in the auxiliary view and is 100 lb., determine the magnitude of its moment *M* about each gear axis. *Ans.* $M_x = 404$ lb. in., $M_y = 202$ lb. in.

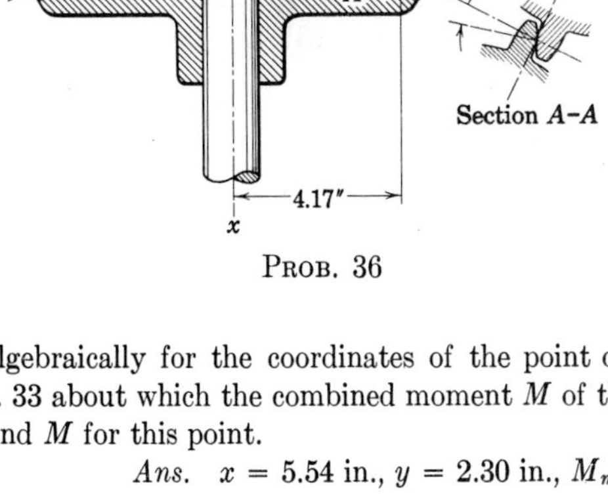

Prob. 36

* **37.** Solve algebraically for the coordinates of the point on the rim of the wheel of Prob. 33 about which the combined moment *M* of the two forces is a minimum. Find *M* for this point.

Ans. $x = 5.54$ in., $y = 2.30$ in., $M_{min.} = 14.1$ lb. in.

14. Couple. Two parallel forces which are equal in magnitude, opposite in direction, and not collinear constitute a *couple*. Consider the action of two such forces as shown in Fig. 15*a*. These two forces

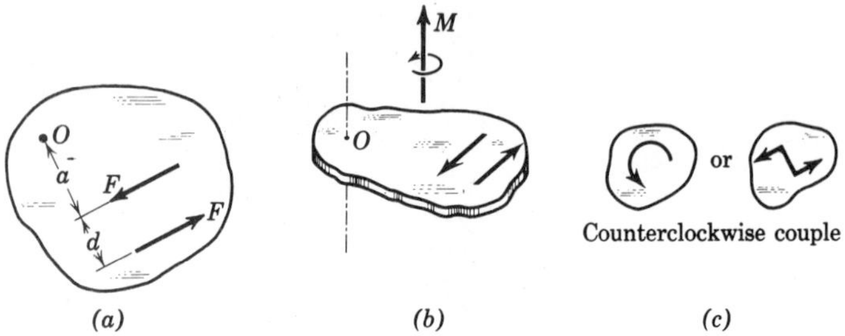

FIG. 15

cannot be combined into a single force since their sum in every direction is zero. Their effect is entirely one of producing a tendency of rotation. The combined moment of the two forces about an axis normal to their plane and passing through any point such as O is

$$M = F(a + d) - Fa,$$

or

$$M = Fd,$$

in a counterclockwise direction. This expression is the value of the couple and does not contain any reference to the dimension a which locates the forces with respect to the moment center O. It follows that the value of a couple is the same for *all* moment centers.

A couple may be represented by the *free* vector M, as shown in Fig. 15*b*, where the direction of M is normal to the plane of the couple and the sense of the vector is established by the right-hand convention. A couple is unchanged as long as the magnitude and direction of its vector remain constant. A given couple will not be altered by changing the

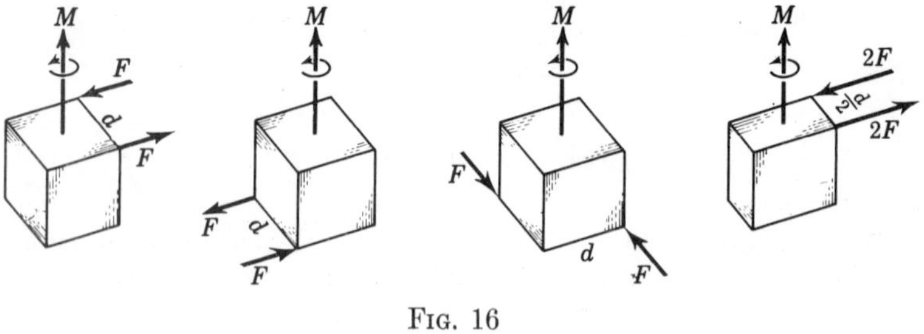

FIG. 16

values of F and d as long as their product remains the same. Likewise a couple is not affected by allowing the forces to act in any one of parallel planes. In Fig. 16 are shown four different configurations of the same couple $M = Fd$. When dealing with couples due to forces all of which act in the same or parallel planes, the couple vectors will be perpendicular to the plane or planes. In this case it is more convenient to represent such a couple by either of the conventions shown in Fig. 15*c*, where the counterclockwise couple may be taken as positive and a clockwise couple negative or vice versa.

Couples which act in nonparallel planes may be added by the ordinary rules of vector combination. Thus the two couples M_1 and M_2 in Fig. 17*a* due to forces which act in the two planes indicated may be

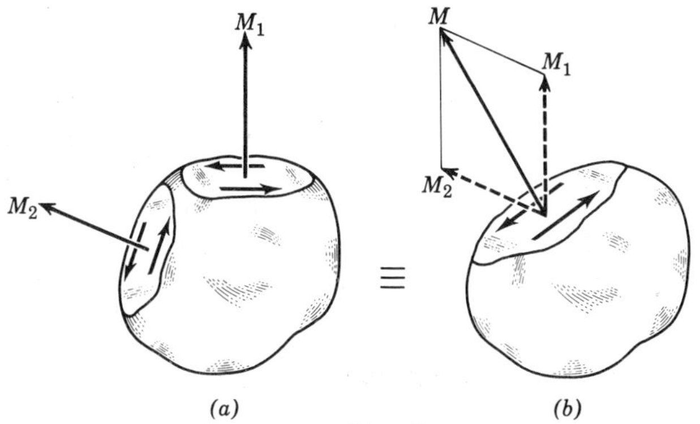

FIG. 17

replaced by their vector sum M shown in Fig. 17*b*, which represents a couple due to forces in a plane normal to M.

15. Resolution of a Force into a Force and a Couple. The effect of a force on a body is, in general, twofold. It tends to push or pull the body in the direction of the force, and it tends to rotate the body about any axis not intersecting its line of action or parallel to it. Analysis of this dual effect is often facilitated by replacing the force by an equal force applied along a different but parallel line of action and by a corresponding couple to compensate for the change in the moment of the force due to moving it to the new position. Consider a body with a force F acting at point A as shown in Fig. 18*a*. At any other point B two equal and opposite forces F may be applied as in Fig. 18*b* with no external effect on the body. If these forces are parallel to the original force F, then a couple $M = Fd$ is formed by the original F and the force F in the opposite direction at B. In representing the couple by the curled arrow in Fig. 18*c*, it becomes evident that the original force F has been replaced by or resolved into a force of the same magnitude and direction as F, but having a different line of action, and a couple. The magnitude of the couple equals the value of the force multiplied by the distance through which its line of action has been shifted. The direction of the couple is the same as the direction

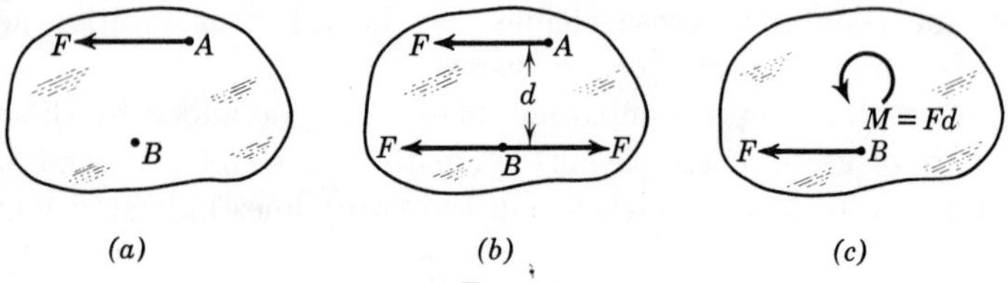

FIG. 18

of the moment of the original force about a point on its new line of action. A force may always be replaced by an equal force having any parallel line of action and the corresponding couple. It follows that a given couple and a given force which lies in the plane of the couple may be combined to yield a single equal force having a unique line of action. The representation of a force by a force and couple has many useful applications.

SAMPLE PROBLEMS

38. Determine the magnitude and direction of the vector M which represents the resultant of the two given couples. Find the two forces F applied in the two faces of the cube parallel to the x–y plane which may replace the four forces shown.

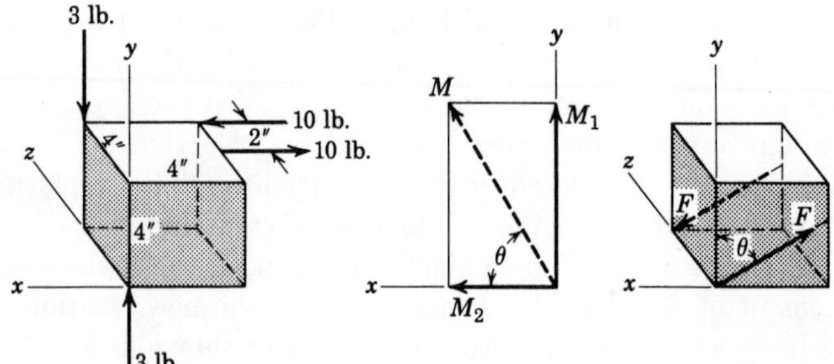

PROB. 38

Solution. The couple due to the 10 lb. forces is $M_1 = 10 \times 2 = 20$ lb. in., and the vector is in the y-direction by the right-hand convention. The couple due to the 3 lb. forces is $M_2 = 3 \times 4 = 12$ lb. in., and the vector is in the x-direction. The vector sum is

$$M = \sqrt{M_1^2 + M_2^2} = \sqrt{(20)^2 + (12)^2} = 23.3 \text{ lb. in.,} \qquad \textit{Ans.}$$

and the direction of M with the x-axis is given by

$$\theta = \tan^{-1}\frac{M_1}{M_2} = \tan^{-1}\frac{20}{12} = 59° \, 2'. \qquad \textit{Ans.}$$

The forces F lie in a plane normal to M and hence make an angle of $\theta = 59° \, 2'$ with the y-direction. The magnitude of the forces is

$$F = \frac{M}{d} = \frac{23.3}{4} = 5.83 \text{ lb.} \qquad \textit{Ans.}$$

39. A force of 100 lb. is applied to a lever which is attached to a fixed shaft as shown. In determining the effect of the force on the shaft at a section such as A it is convenient to replace the force by a force at A and a couple M. Find the magnitude and direction of M.

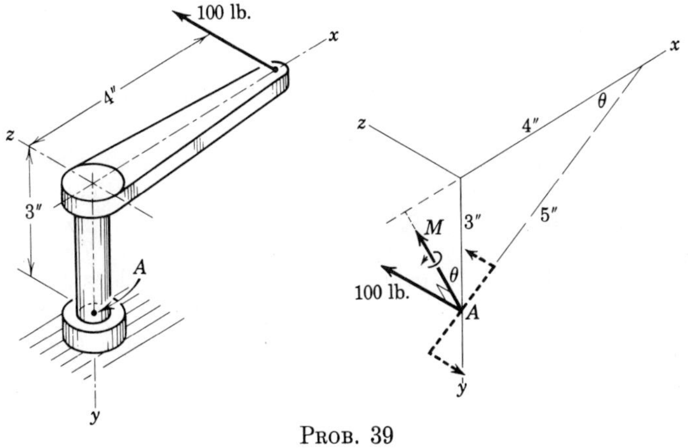

PROB. 39

Solution. Shifting the force a distance of $\sqrt{3^2 + 4^2} = 5$ in. to a parallel position at A requires the addition of a couple of magnitude

$$M = 100 \times 5 = 500 \text{ lb. in.} \qquad \textit{Ans.}$$

The vector M representing the couple is in the x–y plane normal to the force vector and makes an angle with the y-axis of

$$\theta = \cos^{-1}\tfrac{4}{5} = 36° \, 52'. \qquad \textit{Ans.}$$

PROBLEMS

40. The action of the 2000 lb. load on the column may be analyzed by considering it to produce a compression along the center line and a couple. If this couple is 6000 lb. in., find d.

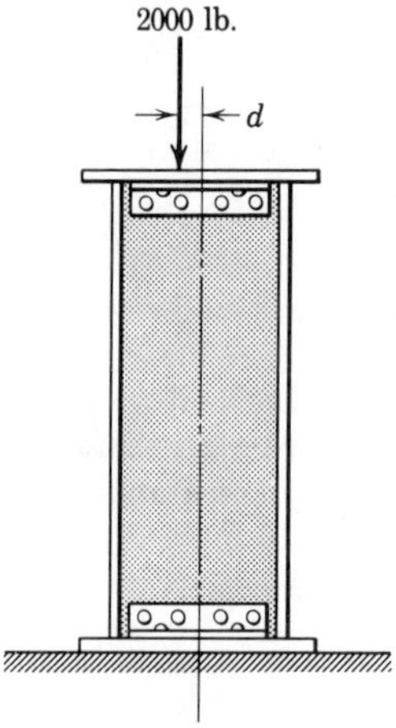

PROB. 40

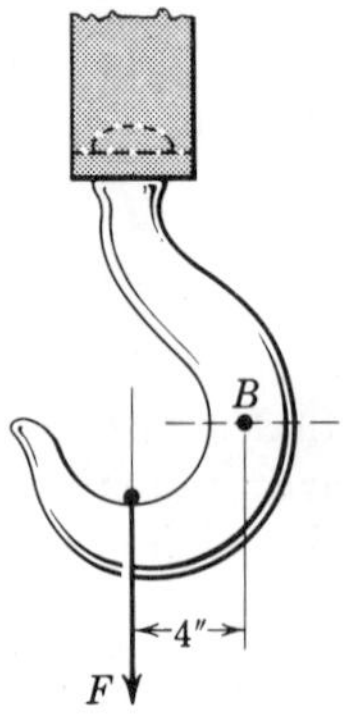

PROB. 41

41. In designing the lifting hook the forces acting on a horizontal section through B may be determined by replacing F by an equivalent force at B and a couple. If the couple is 3 ton ft., determine F.

Ans. $F = 18{,}000$ lb.

42. Each propeller of the twin-screw ship shown develops a full-speed thrust of 80,000 lb. In maneuvering the ship one propeller is turning full speed ahead and the other full speed in reverse. What force F must each tug exert on the ship to counteract the turning effect of the ship's propellers?

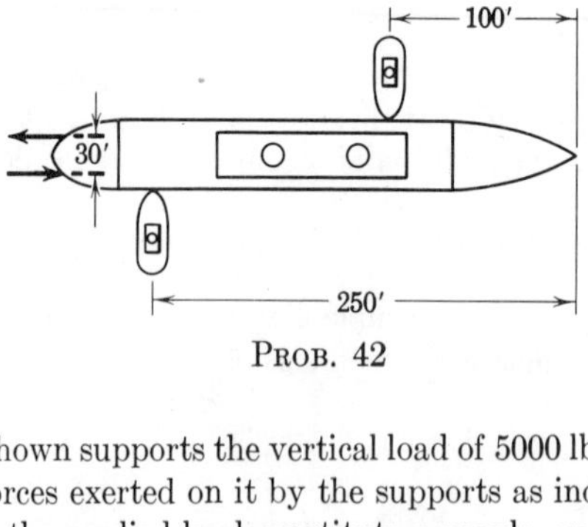

PROB. 42

43. The truss shown supports the vertical load of 5000 lb. and is held in place by the reactive forces exerted on it by the supports as indicated in the figure. The force A_y and the applied load constitute a couple, and the remaining two forces constitute an equal and opposite couple. Find the reaction component B_x and the total force A on the supporting pin connection.

Ans. $B_x = 5710$ lb., $A = 7590$ lb.

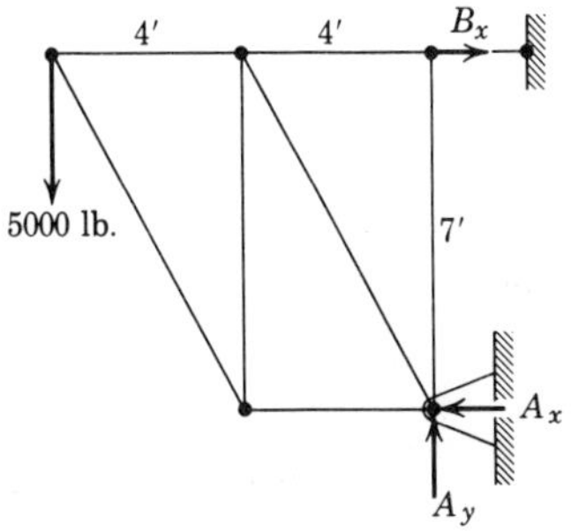

PROB. 43

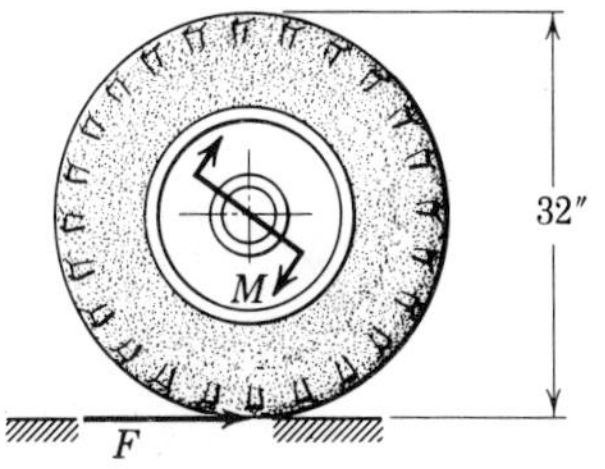

PROB. 44

44. The friction force F and driving couple M which act on the wheel of an accelerating truck may be replaced by a single equivalent force which acts through a point which is 0.4 in. above the center of the wheel. If F equals 500 lb., determine the driving couple M supplied to the wheel through its drive shaft.

45. The control lever is subjected to a clockwise couple of 50 lb. ft. exerted by its shaft at A and is to be designed to operate with a 30 lb. pull as shown. If the resultant of the couple and the force passes through A, determine the proper dimension x of the lever.

Ans. $x = 12.8$ in.

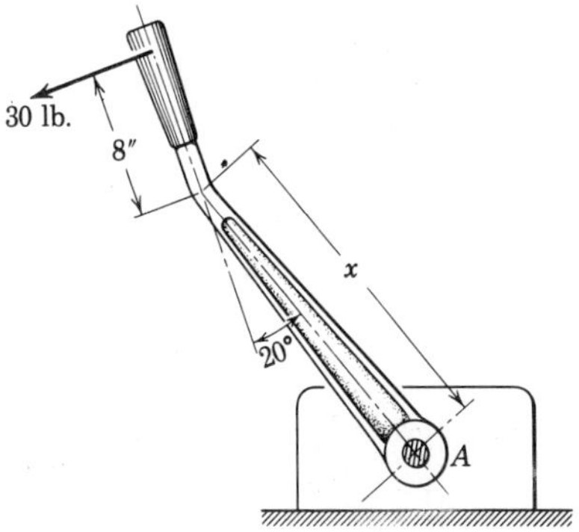

PROB. 45

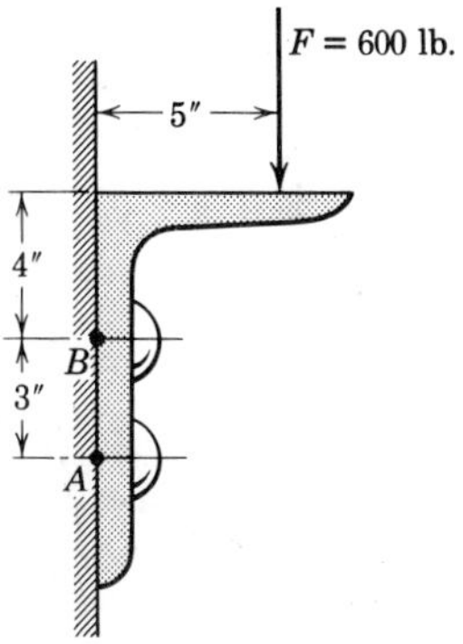

PROB. 46

46. The riveted angle bracket is held in equilibrium by the action of forces which are the equivalent of a force equal and opposite to and collinear with F. Represent these equivalent forces by a vertical force acting on the bracket at A and two horizontal forces P acting on the bracket, one at A and the other at B.

47. The 1000 lb. load is applied to the bracket attached to the free end of a fixed cantilever I-beam. In evaluating the strength of the beam to withstand the applied eccentric load, the load may be replaced by its x- and y-components acting at A on the beam center line and a couple M. Determine M.

Ans. $M = 2100$ lb. in.

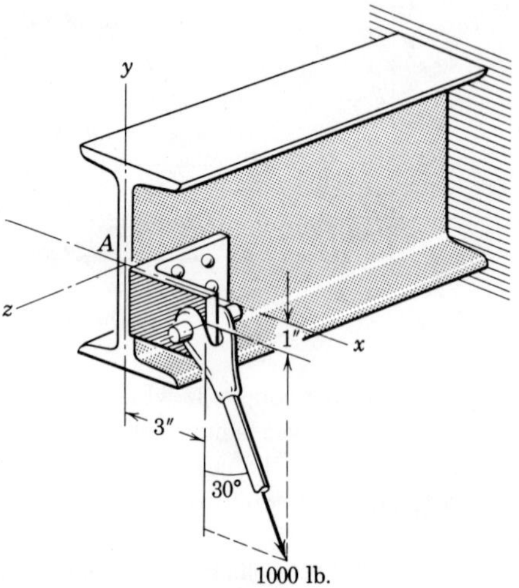

Prob. 47

48. Replace the couple and force shown by a single force F applied at a point D. Locate D by determining the distance b.

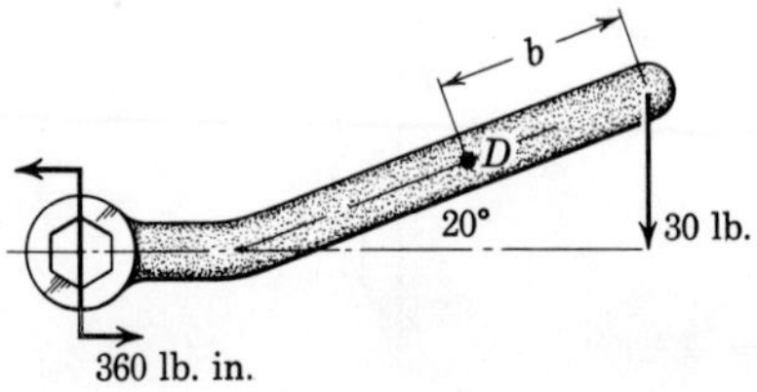

Prob. 48

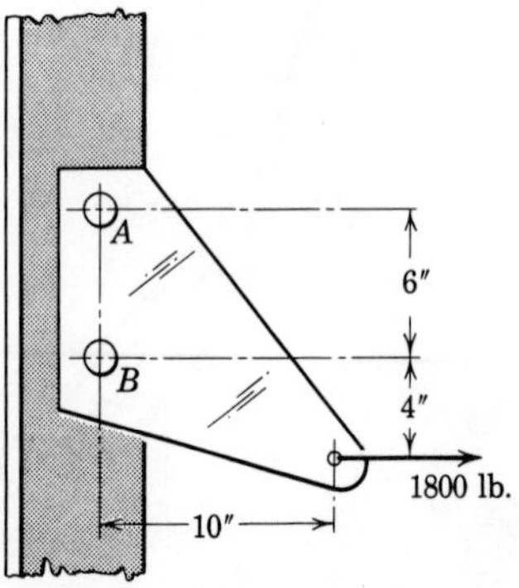

Prob. 49

49. The bracket is fastened to the girder by means of the two rivets A and B. For equilibrium of the bracket the resultant of the forces exerted by the rivets on the bracket must be equal and opposite to and collinear with the 1800 lb. applied force. Find the force supported by each rivet by replacing the applied load by a force along a horizontal center line midway between the rivets and a couple and then by distributing this resulting system appropriately to the rivets. *Ans.* $A = 1200$ lb., $B = 3000$ lb.

50. Combine the force and the couple shown into a single force F, and find the perpendicular distance d from A to F.

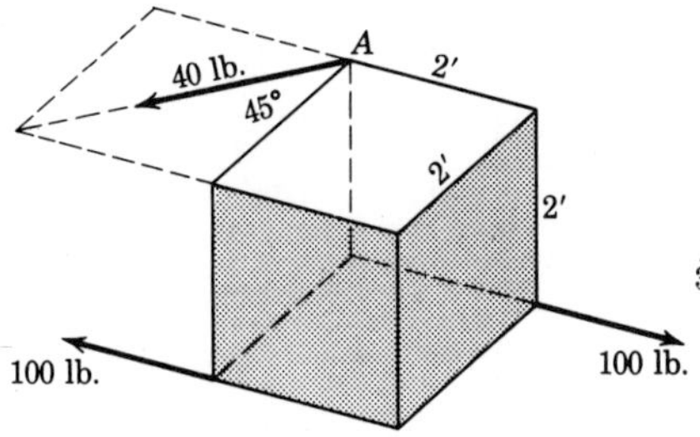

PROB. 50

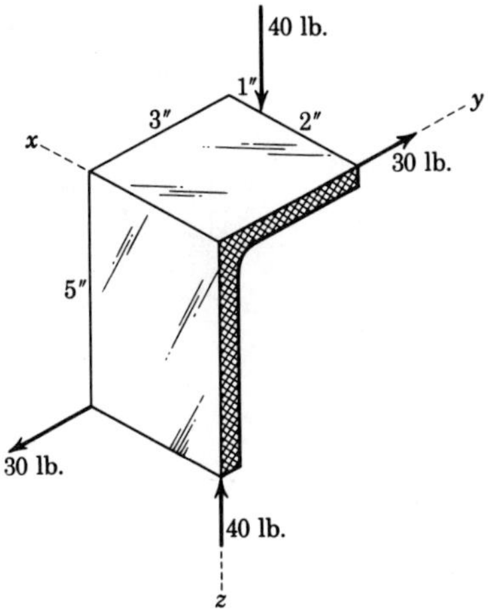

PROB. 51

51. Determine the x-, y-, and z-components of the single couple vector M which is equivalent to the two couples shown.

Ans. $M_x = 270$ lb. in., $M_y = -80$ lb. in., $M_z = -90$ lb. in.

* **52.** Using the principle of transformation of a couple replace the two forces shown acting on the pipe wrenches by a single force F acting at a point P in the x–y plane. Find the coordinates of P.

Ans. $F = 10$ lb., $x = 24$ in., $y = 84$ in.

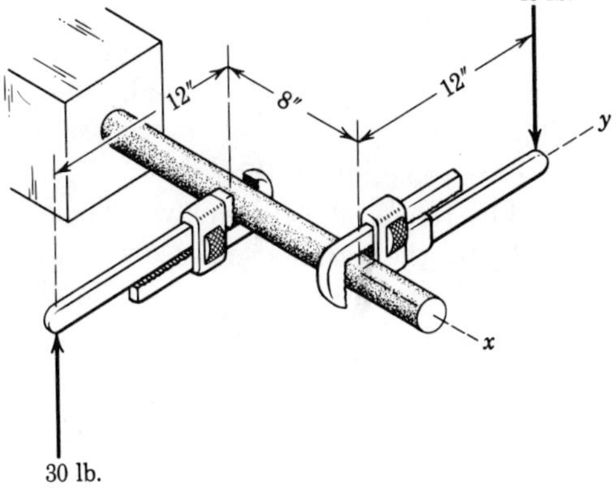

PROB. 52

* **53.** Replace the two forces shown by a force F at A and a couple M.

Ans. $F = 53.9$ lb., $M = 134.2$ lb. in.

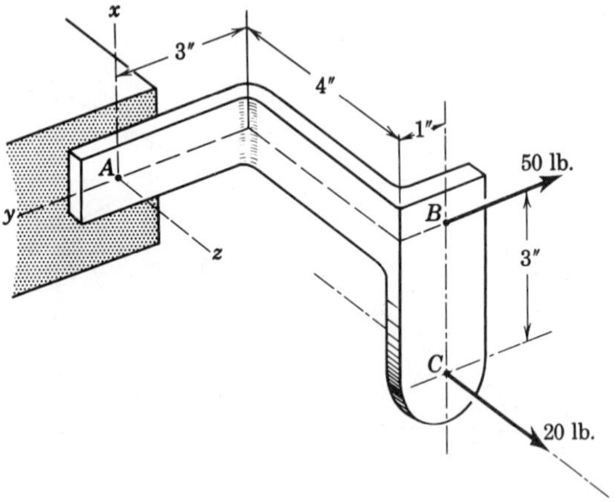

PROB. 53

16. Resultant of Coplanar Force Systems. The resultant of a system of forces is the simplest force system which can replace the original forces without altering their external effect on a rigid body. The equilibrium of a body is the condition wherein the resultant of all forces is zero, and the acceleration of a body is described by equating the force resultant to the product of mass and acceleration. Thus the determination of resultants is basic to both statics and dynamics. The properties of force, moment, and couple discussed in the preceding articles will now be used to determine the resultants of coplanar force systems.

The resultant of a system of coplanar forces may be obtained by adding the forces two at a time and then combining their sums. The three forces F_1, F_2, F_3 of Fig. 19*a* may be combined by first adding any two, such as F_2 and F_3. By the principle of transmissibility they may be moved along their lines of action to their point of concurrency A, and their sum R_1 formed by the parallelogram law. The force R_1 may then be combined with F_1 by the parallelogram law at their point of concurrency B to obtain the resultant R of the three given forces. The order of combination of the forces is immaterial as may be verified by combining them in a different sequence. The force R may be applied at any point on its established line of action.

The magnitude and direction of R may be obtained with addition by the triangle law as shown in Fig. 19*b*. Here the forces are treated as free vectors and added head-to-tail. The resultant of F_1 and F_2 is a

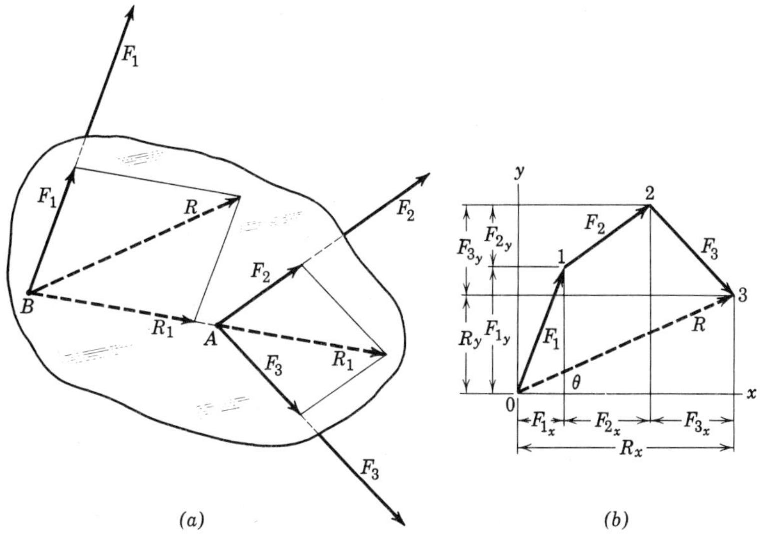

Fig. 19

vector directed from 0 to 2 and when combined with F_3 gives R correct in magnitude and direction. The polygon 0–1–2–3 is known as a *force polygon.* Algebraically these results may be obtained by forming the rectangular components of the forces in any two convenient perpendicular directions. In Fig. 19*b* the x- and y-components of R are seen to be the algebraic sums of the respective components of the three forces. Thus, in general, the rectangular components of the resultant R of a coplanar system of forces may be expressed as

$$R_x = \Sigma F_x, \qquad R_y = \Sigma F_y,$$

where (7)

$$R = \sqrt{(\Sigma F_x)^2 + (\Sigma F_y)^2}.$$

The angle made by R with the x-axis is clearly

$$\theta = \tan^{-1} \frac{\Sigma F_y}{\Sigma F_x}. \tag{8}$$

The location of the line of action of R may be computed with the aid of Varignon's theorem. Although this theorem was proved for two concurrent components of a given force, it holds for any system of forces. The moment of R, Fig. 19*a*, about some point must equal the sum of the moments of its two components F_1 and R_1 about the same point. The moment of R_1, however, must equal the sum of the moments of its components F_2 and F_3 about the same point. It follows that the moment of R about any point equals the sum of the moments of F_1, F_2, and F_3 about this same point. Application of this *principle of moments* about the point O, Fig. 20, gives the equation

$$Rd = F_1d_1 - F_2d_2 + F_3d_3$$

for this particular configuration of forces where the clockwise direction is arbitrarily taken as positive. The distance d is computed from this

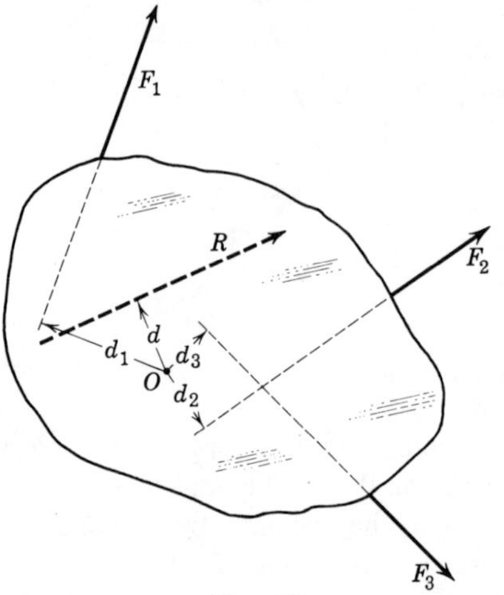

FIG. 20

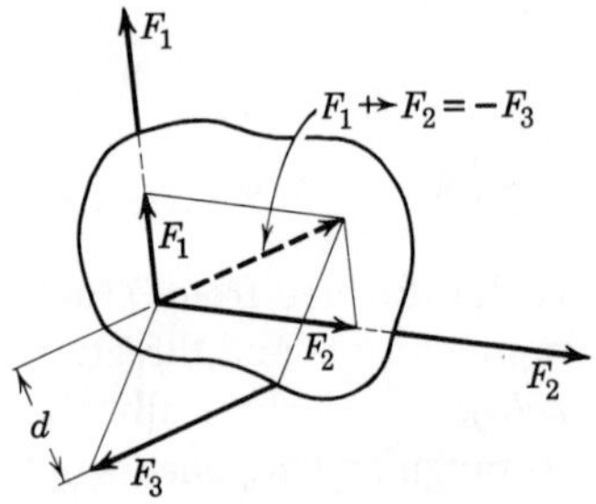

FIG. 21

relation, and R, whose magnitude and direction have been determined from Eqs. 7 and 8, may now be completely located. In general, then, the moment arm d of the resultant R is given by

$$Rd = \Sigma M_O, \tag{9}$$

where ΣM_O stands for the algebraic sum of the moments of the forces of the system about any point O.

For a system of forces all concurrent at a given point the resultant passes through this point and may be determined graphically by parallelogram or triangle addition or may be computed from Eqs. 7 and 8.

For a system of parallel forces the magnitude of the resultant is the algebraic sum of the several forces, and the position of its line of action may be obtained from the principle of moments expressed by Eq. 9.

Consider now a force system such as shown in Fig. 21, where the polygon of forces closes and consequently there is no resultant force R. Direct combination by the parallelogram law shows that for the case illustrated the resultant is a couple of magnitude F_3d. The value of the couple is equal to the moment sum about any point. Thus it is seen that the *resultant of a coplanar system of forces may be either a force or a couple*.

SAMPLE PROBLEM

54. Determine the resultant of the four forces acting on the plate shown.

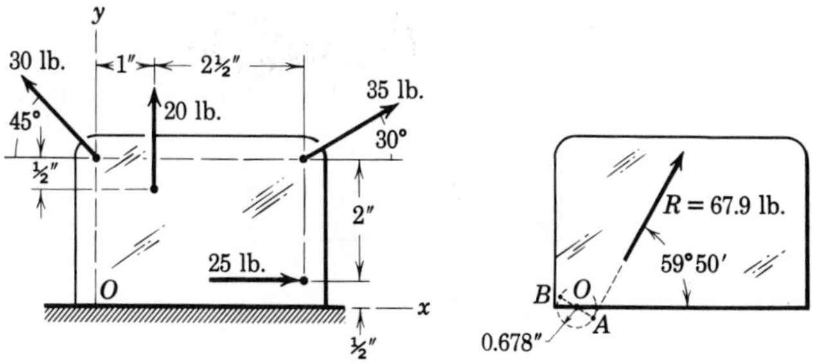

PROB. 54

Solution. Point O is selected arbitrarily as the origin of coordinates for an algebraic solution. The components R_x and R_y, the resultant R, and the angle θ_x become

$$[R_x = \Sigma F_x] \qquad R_x = -30 \cos 45° + 25 + 35 \cos 30° = 34.1 \text{ lb.},$$

$$[R_y = \Sigma F_y] \qquad R_y = 30 \sin 45° + 20 + 35 \sin 30° = 58.7 \text{ lb.},$$

$$[R = \sqrt{R_x^2 + R_y^2}] \qquad R = \sqrt{(34.1)^2 + (58.7)^2} = 67.9 \text{ lb.} \qquad \textit{Ans.}$$

$$\left[\theta_x = \tan^{-1}\frac{R_y}{R_x}\right] \qquad \theta_x = \tan^{-1}\frac{58.7}{34.1} = 59° \, 50'. \qquad \textit{Ans.}$$

The resultant is now determined in magnitude and direction. The position of its line of action is obtained from the principle of moments. With the clockwise direction as positive and point O as the moment center this principle requires

$$[Rd = \Sigma M_O] \qquad 67.9d = -30 \times 2.5 \cos 45° - 20 \times 1 + 35 \times 2.5 \cos 30°$$

$$- 35 \times 3.5 \sin 30° + 25 \times 0.5,$$

$$d = -\frac{46.0}{67.9} = -0.678 \text{ in.} \qquad \textit{Ans.}$$

The negative sign indicates that the moment of the sum is counterclockwise since the clockwise direction was taken as positive. Hence the resultant R may be applied at any point on a line making an angle of 59° 50′ with the x-axis and tangent to a circle of radius 0.678 in. about O as shown in the figure to the right of the drawing. The counterclockwise moment requires that the line of action of R be tangent at point A and not at point B as would have been the case if the moment had been positive in a clockwise sense.

Direct combination of the forces by the parallelogram law will yield the same result as just obtained, and this may be verified graphically.

PROBLEMS

55. The fixed eyebolt supports the tensions of three cables, indicated by the force vectors shown. If these three cables are removed and their combined effect on the bolt is achieved by a single cable, determine its tension T and direction θ_x. *Ans.* $T = 1850$ lb., $\theta_x = 22° 58'$

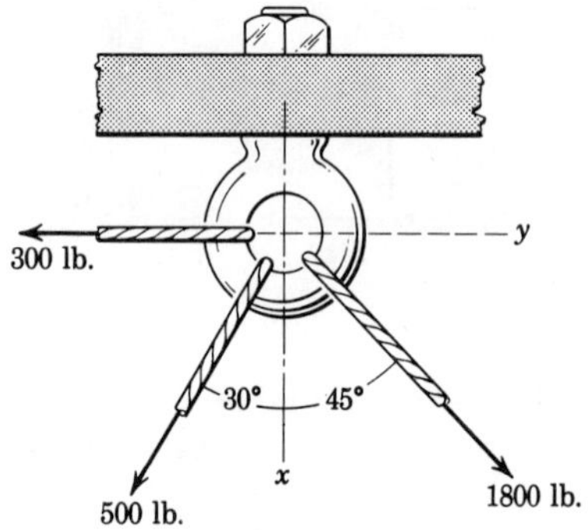

PROB. 55

56. Determine the resultant R of the four forces transmitted to the gusset plate if $\theta = 50$ deg. *Ans.* $R = 2090$ lb., $\theta_x = 72° 56'$

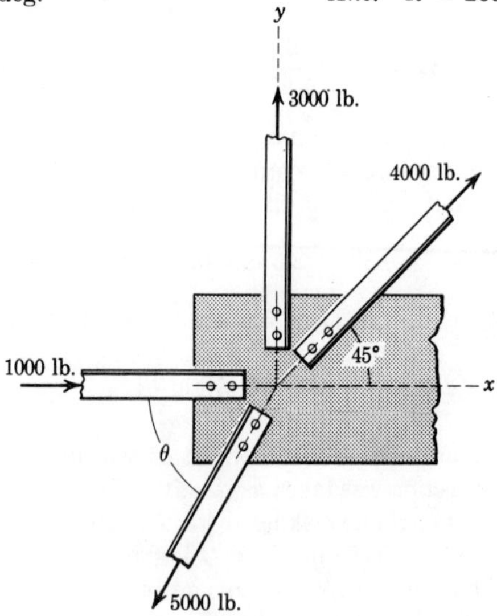

PROB. 56

57. Determine the angle θ for the figure in Prob. 56 which will yield zero resultant force in the x-direction. *Ans.* $\theta = 40° 2'$

58. Determine the resultant R of the four loads acting on the Pratt bridge truss.

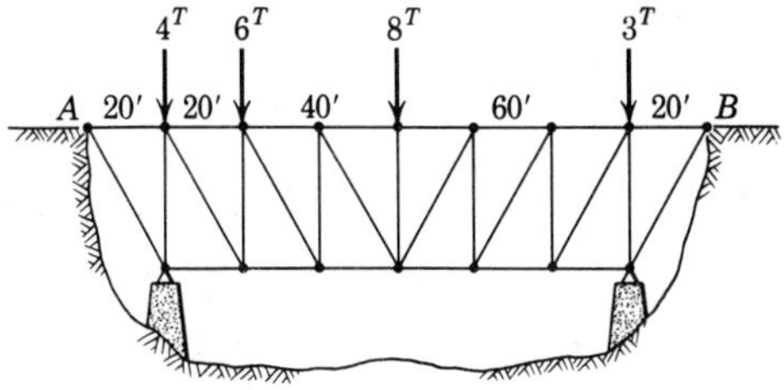

PROB. 58

59. Determine the resultant R of the roof loads shown acting on the Howe truss. *Ans.* R = 10 kips 14.0 ft. to the right of A

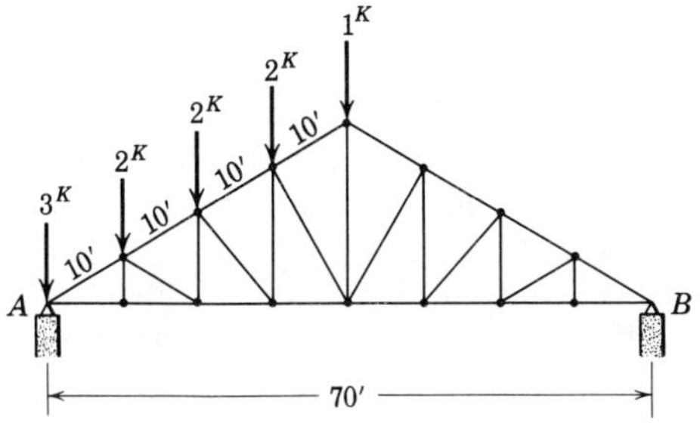

PROB. 59

60. Find the force R which could replace the four forces shown and not change the resulting reactions at the support A.

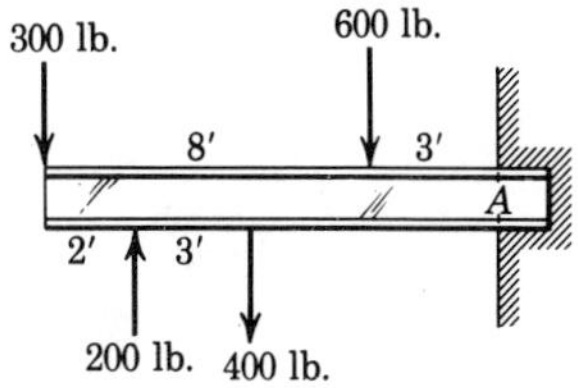

PROB. 60

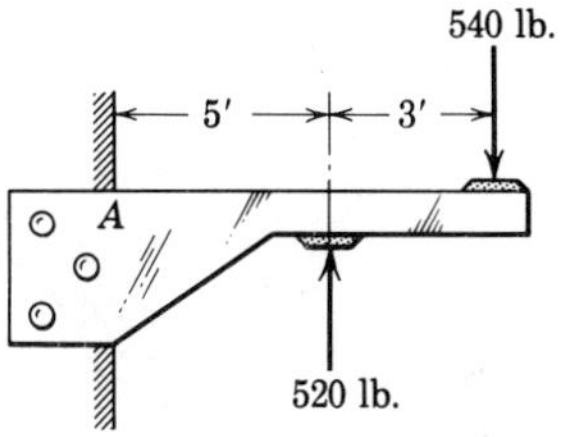

PROB. 61

61. Where would the resultant of the two applied forces act?
Ans. 86 ft. to the right of A

62. Replace the two parallel forces acting on the control lever by a single equivalent force R. *Ans.* $R = 30$ lb. through O

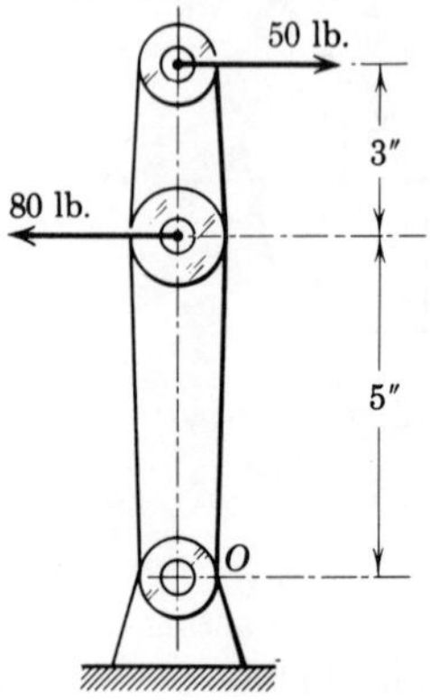

PROB. 62

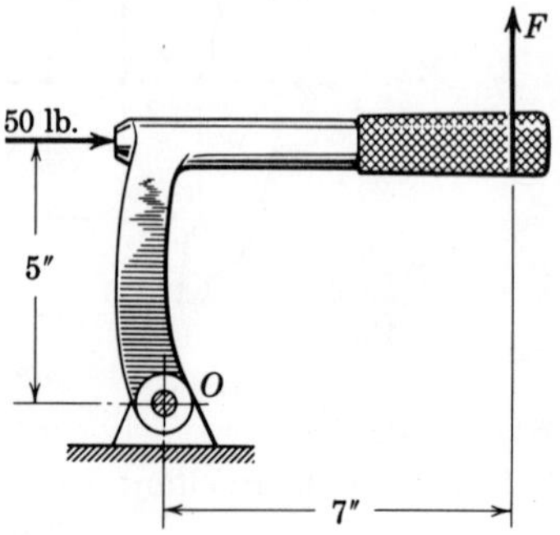

PROB. 64

63. Solve Prob. 62 graphically.

64. Find graphically the magnitude of F which will make the resultant of the two forces pass through the bearing at O.

65. Solve Prob. 64 algebraically.

66. For the bell crank shown the resultant of the vertical force F and the 30 lb. force passes through the center of the bearing at O. Compute F. Does the result depend upon θ? *Ans.* $F = 46.6$ lb.

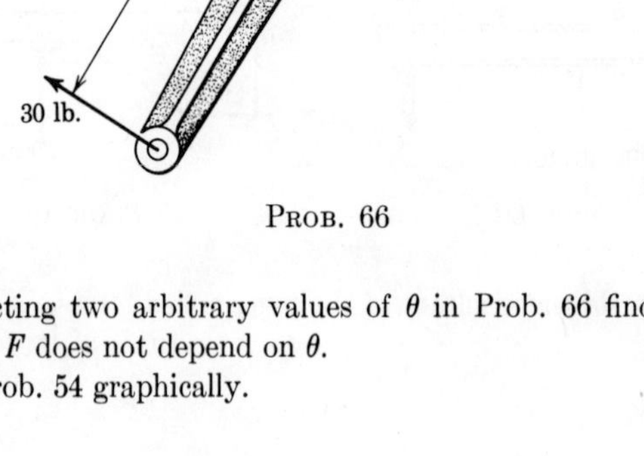

PROB. 66

67. By selecting two arbitrary values of θ in Prob. 66 find F graphically and show that F does not depend on θ.

68. Solve Prob. 54 graphically.

69. Determine the resultant of the three forces acting on the truss.

Ans. $M = 2500$ lb. ft., clockwise couple

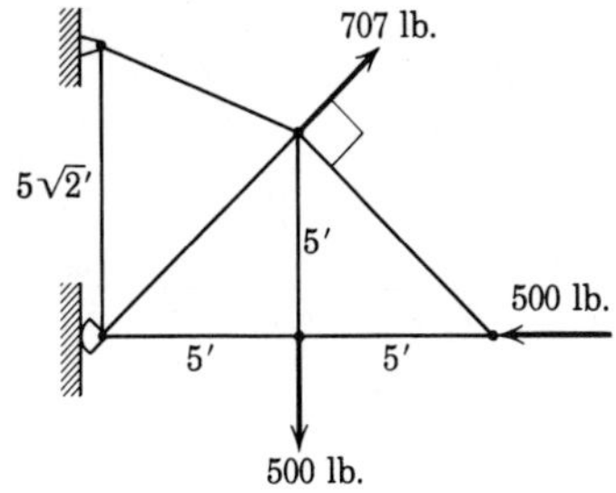

Prob. 69

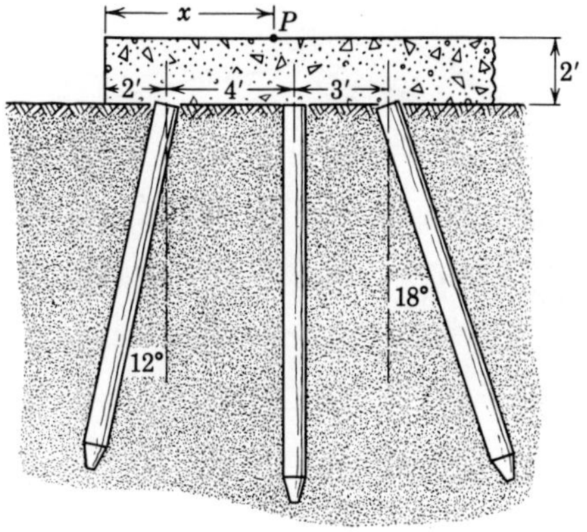

Prob. 70

70. A group of three piles supports the load under a foundation wall. If each pile supports 100 kips in the direction of the pile, determine the distance x to the point P through which the resultant of the three loads passes, and find the angle θ made by the resultant with the vertical.

71. Determine algebraically the resultant R of the two belt tensions and the 350 lb. load acting on the pulley and attached drum of the hoist. Find the distance d from R to O and specify the angle θ_x made by R with the x-axis. *Ans.* $R = 583$ lb., $d = 0.0857$ in., $\theta_x = 41° 50'$

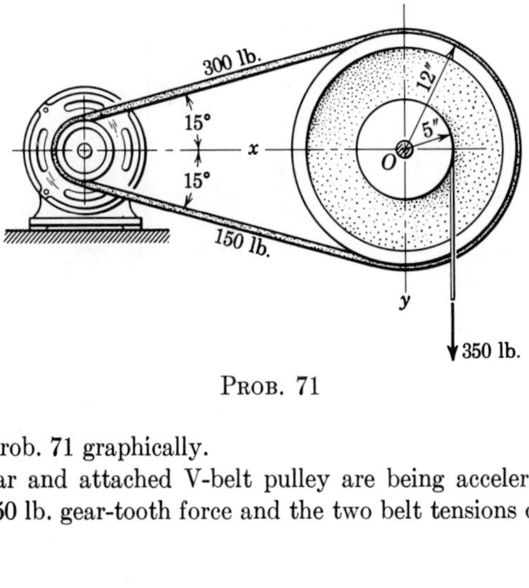

Prob. 71

72. Solve Prob. 71 graphically.

73. The gear and attached V-belt pulley are being accelerated under the action of the 50 lb. gear-tooth force and the two belt tensions of 36 lb. and 10 lb. Represent the resultant of the three forces by a force R passing through O and a couple M. What is the direction of the angular acceleration?

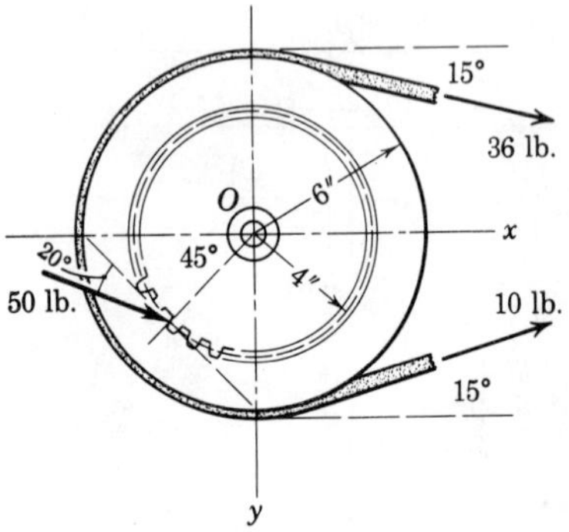

PROB. 73

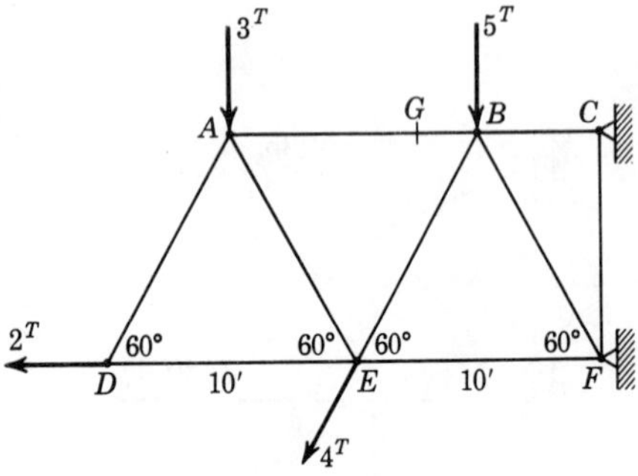

PROB. 74

74. Calculate the resultant R of the four forces acting on the cantilever truss and locate the point G on line AB through which it must pass.

Ans. $R = 12.14$ tons through G 1.11 ft. to the left of B

75. Determine the desirable width b of the concrete abutment footing which will place the resultant of the four loads through point A which is 40 per cent

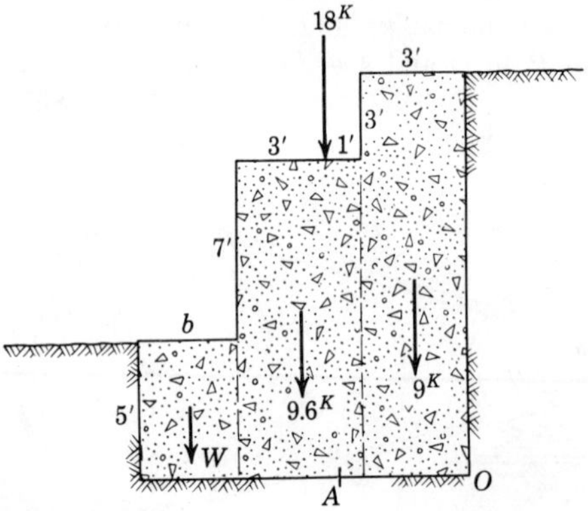

PROB. 75

of the total base dimension to the left of point O. The 9 and 9.6 kip loads and the force W represent the weights of their respective portions of the abutment and pass through the centers of each rectangle. The weight W equals $1.20b$ where b is expressed in feet.

Ans. $b = 3.4$ ft.

76. Represent the resultant of the applied loads and couple shown acting on the cantilever beam and bracket by a force R acting at A and a couple M.

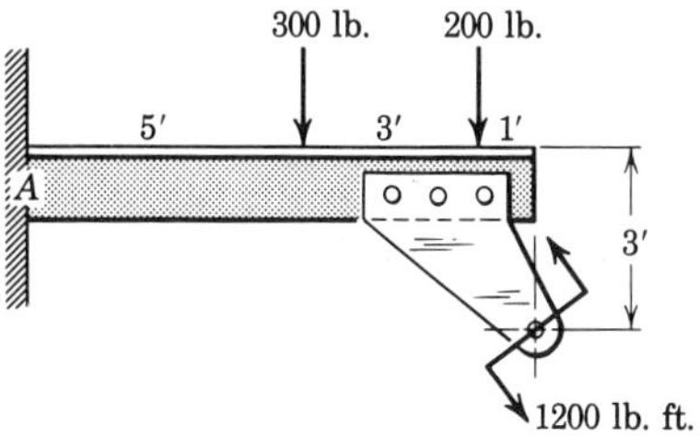

Prob. 76

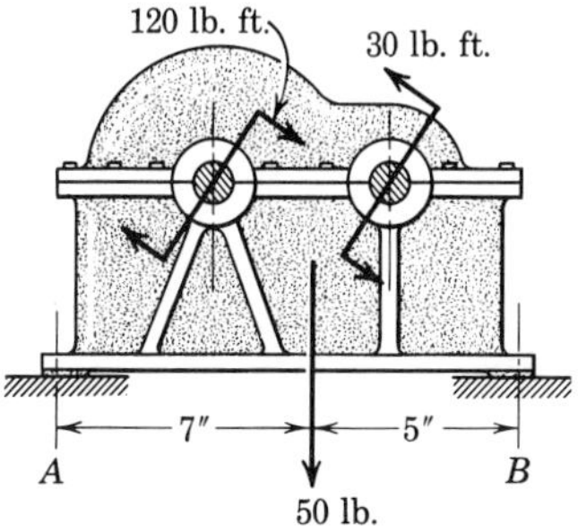

Prob. 77

77. The gear reducer shown is subjected to the two couples, its 50 lb. weight, and a vertical force at each of the mountings A and B. If the resultant of this system of two couples and three forces is zero, determine forces A and B.

Ans. A = 69.2 lb. down, B = 119.2 lb. up

78. The jet-propelled airplane is accelerating in the direction of its line of flight, and therefore the resultant of the external forces shown acting on it passes through its center of gravity G and is in the direction of flight. The total weight of the airplane is 60,000 lb., the air resistance or drag is 3000 lb., and each of its two jet engines develops a thrust of 10,000 lb. Determine the lift force L and the stabilizer force P for the conditions given.

Ans. L = 57,100 lb., P = 1990 lb.

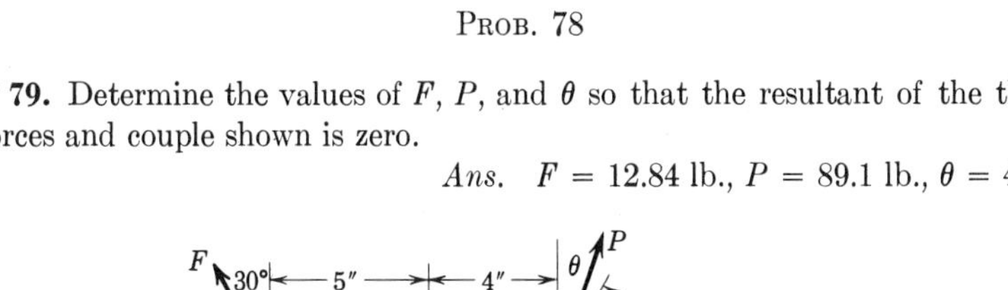

Prob. 78

* **79.** Determine the values of F, P, and θ so that the resultant of the three forces and couple shown is zero.

Ans. F = 12.84 lb., P = 89.1 lb., $\theta = 4° 8'$

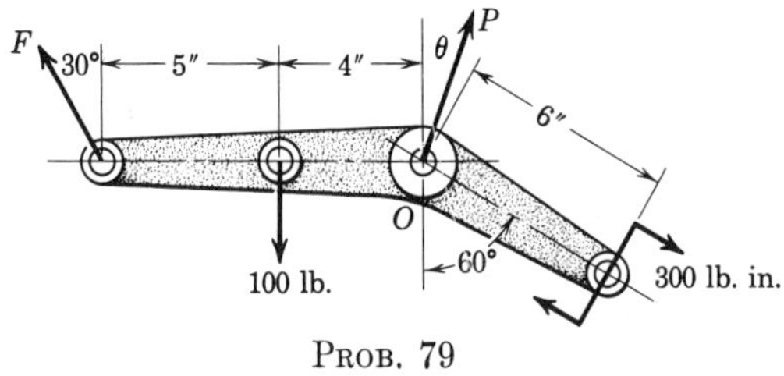

Prob. 79

* **80.** Find the magnitude of the resultant R of the forces and couple shown acting on the cantilever support.

Ans. $R = 599$ lb. through a point 2.34 ft. to the right of A

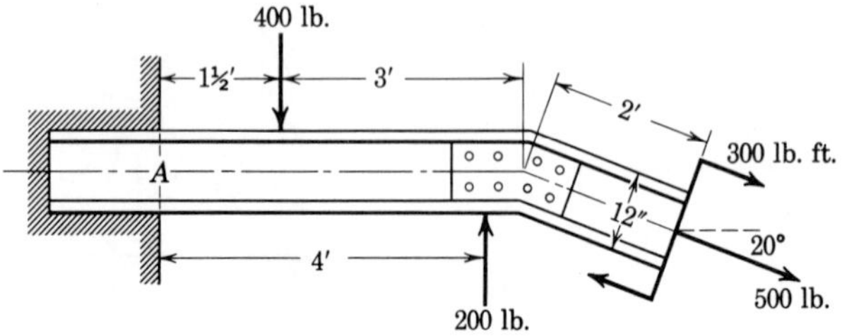

Prob. 80

17. Funicular Polygon. A graphical procedure of wide application will now be developed for obtaining the resultants of coplanar force systems. The method is used primarily for dealing with parallel forces but will be demonstrated for a more general nonparallel coplanar system. The three forces F_1, F_2, and F_3 acting on the body in Fig. 22*a* constitute an example of such a system. A procedure using what is known as *Bow's notation* is convenient for labeling the various forces. The space between each two forces is labeled by a lower-case letter so the line of action of each force is designated by two letters, such as *ab* for force F_1. The ends of the vectors which represent the forces are labeled with the corresponding capital letters. Thus force F_1 is labeled AB.

The construction is begun with the force polygon $ABCD$, Fig. 22*b*, obtained by adding the forces head-to-tail. The magnitude and direction of their resultant are given by the vector AD, but its line of action remains to be determined. Next an arbitrary point O called the *pole* is chosen either inside or outside the polygon and is joined with points A, B, C, and D by straight lines called *rays*. These rays are components of the given forces, as can be seen from the *c*-part of the illustration, where the figure is separated into its component triangles. It is seen that the force AB may be replaced by its components AO and OB. Likewise force BC may be replaced by its components BO and OC, and similarly for CD. Since forces BO and OB will cancel if they are applied collinearly and CO and OC will also cancel if collinear, the original three forces may be replaced by the two forces AO and OD whose sum is the resultant AD. It should be carefully observed that the sense of each force is designated by the sequence of the two letters which represent it.

These relations from the force polygon may now be used to obtain the correct line of action of the resultant. By starting at any convenient location, such as point 1 on the line of action of F_1, Fig. 22*a*, two lines *ao* and *bo* having the directions of rays *AO* and *OB* from Fig. 22*b* are constructed. At this point the forces *AO* and *OB* will replace *AB*.

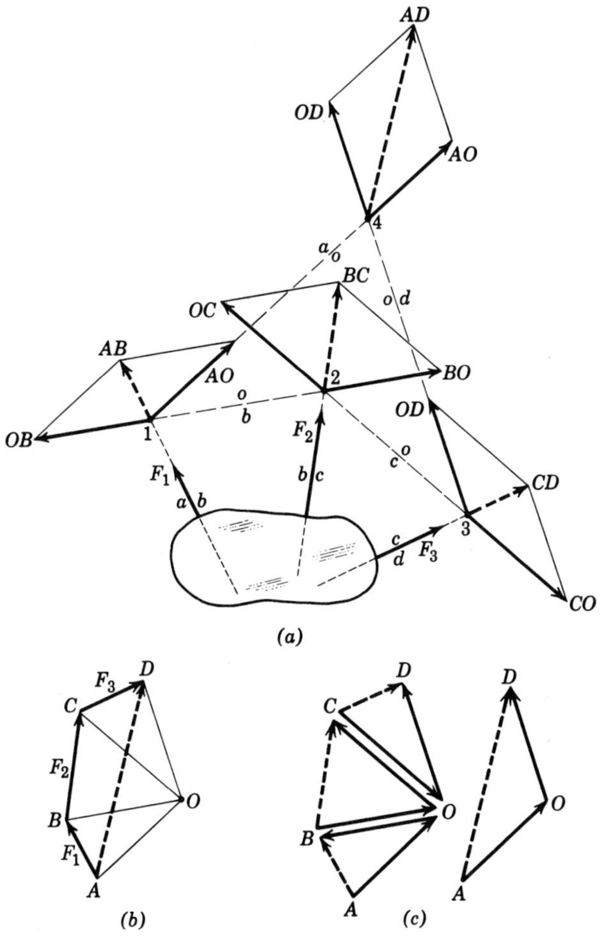

FIG. 22

At the intersection of *bo* with the line of action of F_2 the line *co* is drawn parallel to ray *CO* of the force polygon. The components *BO* and *OC* applied at this point replace the force *BC*. The forces *OB* and *BO* cancel since they are collinear. Extending line *co* yields a point of intersection with force F_3. The line *do* is drawn through point 3 parallel to *DO* in the force polygon, and the components *CO* and *OD* applied at this point replace *CD*. Forces *OC* and *CO* cancel. The only forces left are AO and OD, which have now replaced the original system. The forces AO and OD may be combined at their point of intersection to give the resultant AD, which has the correct line of action.

The parallelograms in Fig. 22*a* were drawn to illustrate the force combinations but are superfluous once the method is understood. The points 1, 2, and 3 and the directions of the lines *ao* and *od* are sufficient to determine point 4 which is a desired point on the line of action of the resultant AD. With the magnitude and direction of the resultant known from the force polygon the correct line of action is established by drawing this vector through point 4.

The lines *ao*, *bo*, *co*, and *do* are known as *strings*, and the polygon 1–2–3–4 is called a *string* or *funicular polygon*. The order in which the forces are labeled and added will not influence the result, but it is customary to use a clockwise or left-to-right alphabetical order as was done in this example. Different choices for initial starting points for the string polygon will result in polygons of differing size but all yielding a point on the same line of action of the resultant. For a system of parallel forces the force polygon becomes a straight line, and the string polygon will be the same size no matter where it is begun.

When the resultant of a coplanar force system is a couple, the polygon of the given forces will close, and the two strings whose intersection normally would give a point on the line of action of the resultant will be parallel. The magnitude of the couple will equal the value of the coincident rays on the force polygon multiplied by the perpendicular distance between their corresponding parallel strings in the string polygon.

SAMPLE PROBLEMS

81. Determine by means of a force and string polygon the resultant of the four forces shown acting on the bracket.

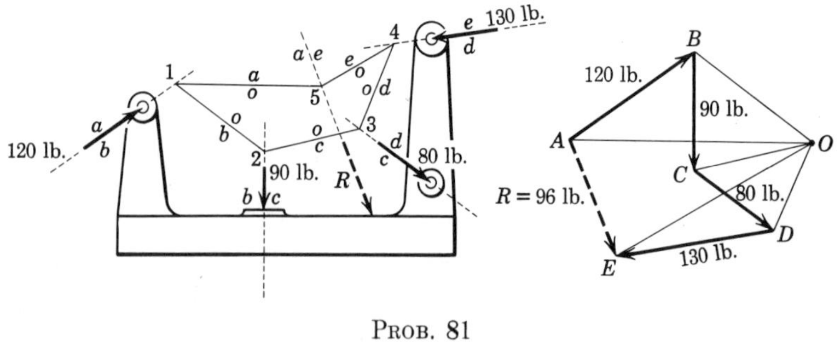

PROB. 81

Solution. The four forces are first labeled with Bow's notation, starting with the 120 lb. force. Next the force polygon *ABCDE* is constructed and an arbitrary selection of the pole *O* is made. The string polygon is begun at point 1, which is any convenient location on *ab*. Through point 1 the strings *ao* and *bo* are drawn parallel to the rays *AO* and *BO* in the force polygon. At point 2, the intersection of *bo* with *bc*, the next string *co* is drawn. Point 3 is now established at the intersection of *co* with *cd*. Point 4 is similarly obtained and the last string *eo* is drawn through this point. The intersection of *eo* and *ao* locates point 5, a point on the line of action of the resultant *R* which is labeled *AE* on the force polygon. The resultant, whose magnitude of 96 lb. and direction are determined from the force polygon, is now constructed through point 5 as indicated.

82. Determine the resultant *R* of the five vertical forces acting on the beam as shown.

Solution. The given forces are labeled with Bow's notation, beginning at the left. They are next added head-to-tail to produce the line *ABCDEF* shown to

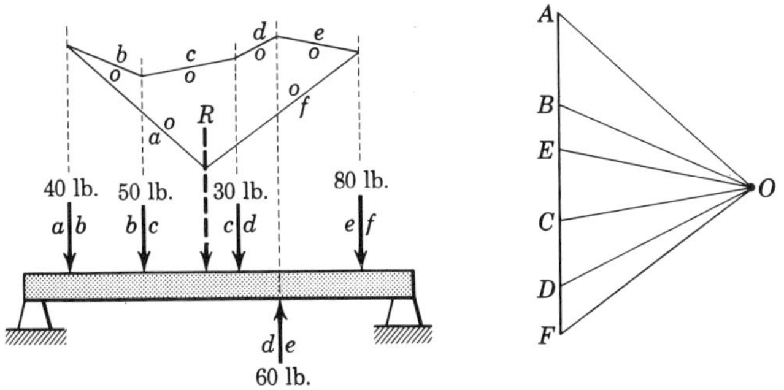

PROB. 82

the right of the beam. The arrowheads are omitted since the sense of the forces is given by the sequence of letters. The pole *O* is arbitrarily chosen, and the rays *AO, BO, CO*, etc., are drawn.

Beginning at any point on the line of action *ab*, the strings *ao* and *bo* are drawn parallel to the rays *AO* and *BO* in the force diagram. Where *bo* intersects the line of action *bc*, the string *co* is drawn, and so forth. Finally the intersection of the strings *fo* and *ao* locates a point on the line of action of the resultant *R* which is the algebraic sum of the given forces, or 140 lb. The position of *R* on the beam may be scaled from the drawing.

83. Determine the resultant of the four forces acting on the bracket shown.

Solution. The forces are labeled in any convenient order, and the force polygon *ABCDE* is then constructed. In this case it is seen that the polygon closes so that the resultant is not a force. The pole *O* is chosen at random and the rays are drawn. By starting at any position on the action line of force *AB*, such as point 1 in the figure, the strings are drawn parallel to their corresponding rays in the force polygon.

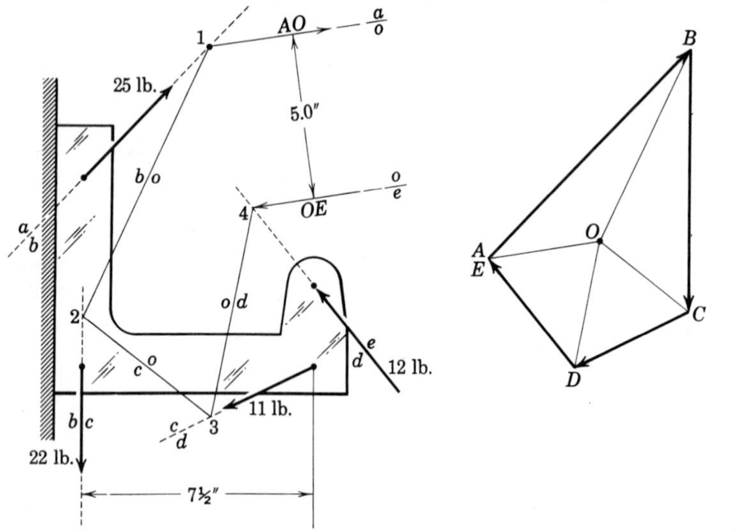

PROB. 83

The string polygon 1–2–3–4 does not close in this case since the first string *ao* is parallel to the last string *eo*. The resultant of the given forces has been reduced to the two forces *AO* and *OE*, and, since the separation of their lines of action scales 5.0 in., the resultant of the given forces is a clockwise couple *M* of magnitude $AO \times 5.0$. From the force polygon *AO* scales 10.0 lb. so that

$$M = 10.0 \times 5.0 = 50.0 \text{ lb. in. clockwise.} \qquad \textit{Ans.}$$

PROBLEMS

Solve the following problems by means of a funicular polygon.

84. Prob. 62
85. Prob. 58
86. Prob. 59
87. Prob. 60
88. Prob. 70
89. Prob. 69
90. Prob. 54
91. Prob. 71
92. Prob. 74

93. Replace the 3 ton force acting on the truss in Prob. 74 by another vertical force *F* whose magnitude is sufficient to cause the resultant *R* of the four forces to pass through the midpoint *M* of *AB*. Find *F* and *R*. (*Hint:* The string polygon should be started at point *M*, which is the only known point on the line of action of the resultant.) *Ans.* $F = 11.9$ tons, $R = 20.8$ tons.

* **94.** Solve Prob. 80 by introducing the 300 lb. ft. couple into the string polygon.

18. Resultants of Three-Dimensional Force Systems. There are many engineering problems which require analysis in three dimensions. Such analysis calls for representation of the system by a pictorial drawing or by means of two or more orthographic projections. Facility to visualize and represent the third dimension is an absolute necessity for this type of analysis.

Consider first a system of concurrent forces acting on a body. An example of such a system is shown in Fig. 23*a*, where three forces not

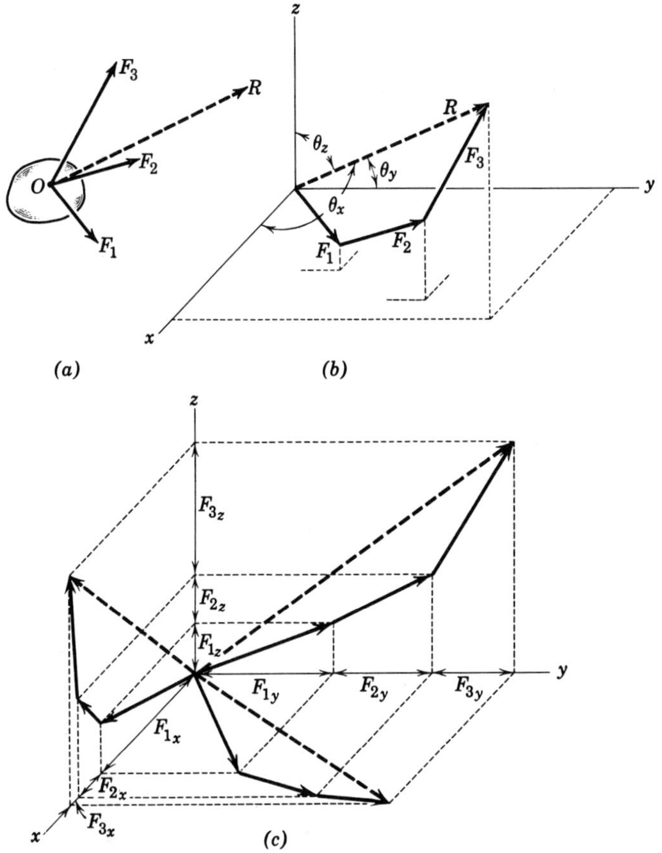

FIG. 23

in the same plane act at *O*. The resultant *R* of this system may be obtained by adding the forces head-to-tail in space as shown in Fig. 23*b*. The resultant is the vector which closes the space polygon, and its three rectangular components are seen to be the algebraic sum of the corresponding components of the given forces. Thus, in general,

$$R_x = \Sigma F_x, \qquad R_y = \Sigma F_y, \qquad R_z = \Sigma F_z,$$

and (10)

$$R = \sqrt{(\Sigma F_x)^2 + (\Sigma F_y)^2 + (\Sigma F_z)^2}.$$

If the angles made by R with the x-, y-, and z-axes are θ_x, θ_y, and θ_z, respectively, then the direction of R is specified by its direction cosines

$$\cos\theta_x = \frac{\Sigma F_x}{R}, \qquad \cos\theta_y = \frac{\Sigma F_y}{R}, \qquad \cos\theta_z = \frac{\Sigma F_z}{R}. \qquad (11)$$

The space polygon in Fig. 23*b* may be projected onto the three coordinate planes, giving three related plane polygons as shown in Fig. 23*c*. Any two of these force polygons will involve all three of the first of Eqs. 10, and hence two projections are sufficient for the full description of the force relations.

Now consider a general system of nonconcurrent forces in space acting on a body. An example of such a system is represented in Fig. 24*a*,

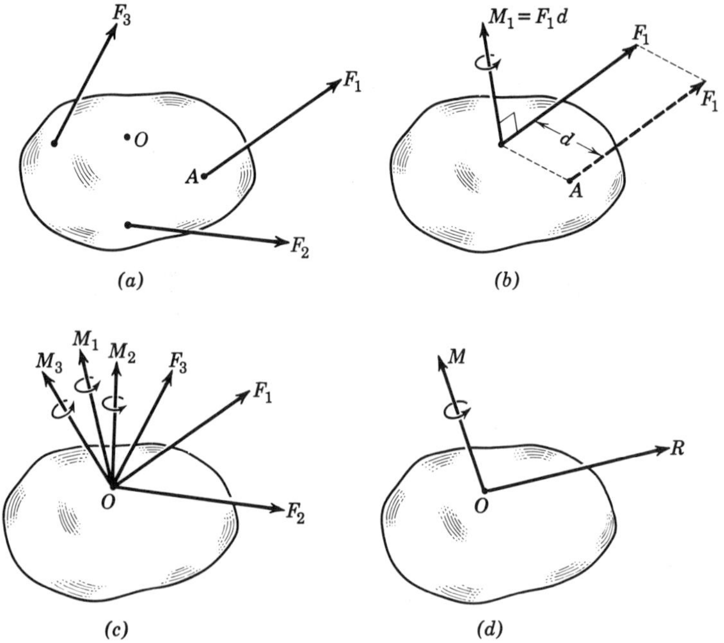

FIG. 24

where three such forces are shown. By the principles of Art. 15 the external effect on the body will be unaltered by applying F_1 at some other point, such as O, and adding the necessary couple M_1. The magnitude of this couple is $F_1 d$, where d is the perpendicular distance from O to the original line of action of F_1. This transfer for force F_1 is shown in Fig. 24*b*. The plane of the couple is the plane defined by the original line of action of F_1 and point O. The vector M_1 representing the couple is normal to this plane, and the sense is determined by the right-hand rule. The couple M_1 is a free vector but is shown at point O for convenience. The remaining two forces are transferred to point O with the addition of their two corresponding couples as shown in Fig. 24*c*. The original force system has now been reduced to a system of concurrent forces at the arbitrary point O and a corresponding number of couples. The forces may be combined to get their resultant R acting at point O, and the couples are combined vectorially to get a resultant couple M as shown in Fig. 24*d*. For a given force system the couple M will vary in magnitude and direction, depending on the choice of the reference point O, although the resultant force R remains fixed in magnitude and direction regardless of the reference point.

It has now been shown that *the resultant of any general force system can be expressed in terms of a single resultant force and a single resultant couple*. Physically the effects may be described as a push (or pull) R and a twist M. This result has a very important bearing on both the statics problem and the dynamics problem. In statics, where the equilibrium condition obtains, both R and M are zero. In dynamics the linear and rotational accelerations will be dependent on R and M, respectively.

There are several special cases of general force system resultants which occur frequently. When there is no resultant force, then the given system reduces to a couple or pure twist. When the couple vector M is perpendicular to the resultant force R, Fig. 25*a*, the two may be combined to form a single force R whose line of action is a distance

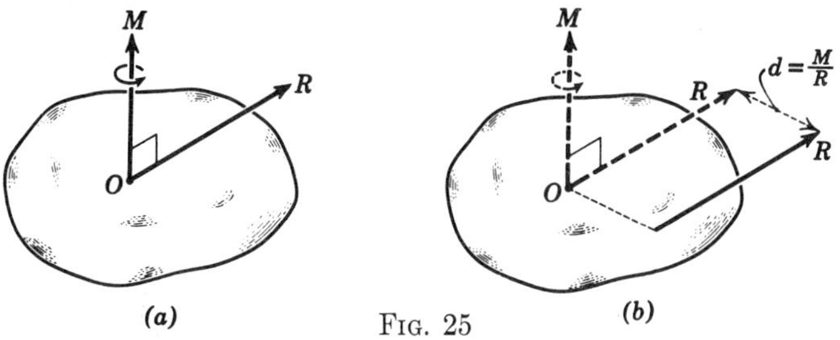

FIG. 25

$d = M/R$ from point O as shown in Fig. 25*b*. The new line of action of R must be on the side of O which makes the direction of the moment of R about O the same as that of M. When the couple M is parallel to R, Fig. 26, the combination is known as a *wrench* or *screw*. The action may be described as a push (or pull) and a twist about an axis

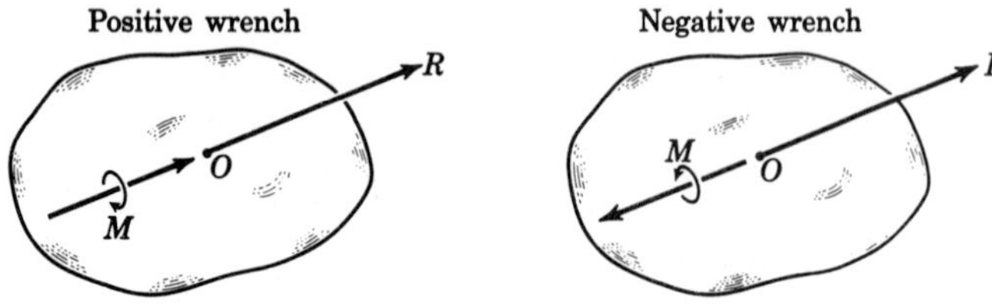

(a) (b)

FIG. 26

parallel to the push (or pull). When the force and moment vectors have the same sense, as in Fig. 26a, the wrench is said to be positive. When the vectors have the opposite sense, the wrench is negative, as indicated in Fig. 26b.

If the given forces are all parallel, the resultant R, if a force, is the algebraic sum of the several forces, and its position may be determined

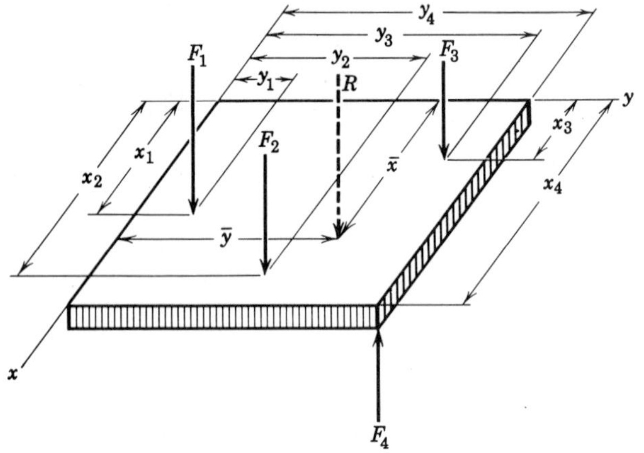

FIG. 27

by the principle of moments. Thus for the four parallel forces shown acting on the plate of Fig. 27 the resultant is

$$R = F_1 + F_2 + F_3 - F_4 = \Sigma F.$$

By the principle of moments the line of action of R is located by equating the moment of the sum to the sum of the moments about the y-

and x-axes. Thus

$$R\bar{x} = F_1x_1 + F_2x_2 + F_3x_3 - F_4x_4,$$

$$R\bar{y} = F_1y_1 + F_2y_2 + F_3y_3 - F_4y_4,$$

or in general

$$\bar{x} = \frac{\Sigma(Fx)}{\Sigma F}, \qquad \bar{y} = \frac{\Sigma(Fy)}{\Sigma F}.$$

In the event that a system of parallel forces reduces to two equal and opposite forces which are not collinear, the resultant is a couple whose vector lies in a plane perpendicular to the given forces.

SAMPLE PROBLEM

95. Replace the four forces acting on the bracket shown by a single equivalent force applied at point A and determine the corresponding couple which must also be applied.

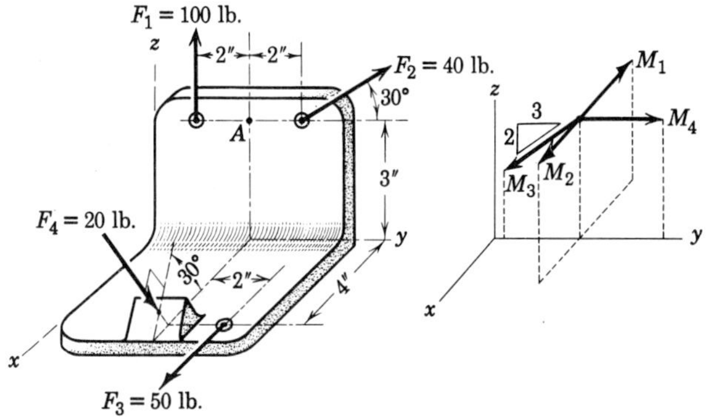

PROB. 95

Solution. The three rectangular components of the resultant force are

$[R_x = \Sigma F_x]$ $\qquad R_x = 50 - 20 \times 0.5 = 40$ lb.,

$[R_y = \Sigma F_y]$ $\qquad R_y = 40 \times 0.866 = 34.6$ lb.,

$[R_z = \Sigma F_z]$ $\qquad R_z = 100 + 40 \times 0.5 - 20 \times 0.866 = 102.7$ lb.

The resultant force is

$[R = \sqrt{R_x^2 + R_y^2 + R_z^2}]$ $\qquad R = \sqrt{(40)^2 + (34.6)^2 + (102.7)^2} = 115.5$ lb.

Ans.

The direction of R may be specified by its direction cosines:

$$\left[\cos\theta_x = \frac{R_x}{R}\right] \qquad \cos\theta_x = \frac{40}{115.5}, \qquad \theta_x = 69°\ 45',$$

$$\left[\cos\theta_y = \frac{R_y}{R}\right] \qquad \cos\theta_y = \frac{34.6}{115.5}, \qquad \theta_y = 72°\ 35',$$

$$\left[\cos\theta_z = \frac{R_z}{R}\right] \qquad \cos\theta_z = \frac{102.7}{115.5}, \qquad \theta_z = 27°\ 15'. \qquad \textit{Ans.}$$

The couple due to the transfer of F_1 to point A is

$$[M = Fd] \qquad M_1 = 100 \times 2 = 200 \text{ lb. in. (minus } x\text{-direction).}$$

Likewise the couples due to the transfer of F_2, F_3, and F_4 are

$$M_2 = 40 \times 2 \times 0.5 = 40 \text{ lb. in. (plus } x\text{-direction),}$$

$$M_3 = 50 \times \sqrt{2^2 + 3^2} = 180.3 \text{ lb. in. } (y\text{–}z \text{ plane}),$$

$$M_4 = 20 \times 4 \times 0.866 + 20 \times 3 \times 0.500 = 99.3 \text{ lb. in. (plus } y\text{-direction).}$$

These four couple vectors are shown in the right-hand part of the figure. The three rectangular components of the resultant couple are seen from the figure to be

$$M_x = -200 + 40 = -160 \text{ lb. in.,}$$

$$M_y = 99.3 - 180.3 \times \frac{3}{\sqrt{2^2 + 3^2}} = -50.7 \text{ lb. in.,}$$

$$M_z = -180.3 \times \frac{2}{\sqrt{2^2 + 3^2}} = -100 \text{ lb. in.}$$

The resultant couple is

$$\left[M = \sqrt{M_x^2 + M_y^2 + M_z^2}\right] \qquad M = \sqrt{(160)^2 + (50.7)^2 + (100)^2}$$
$$= 195.3 \text{ lb. in.} \qquad \textit{Ans.}$$

The direction of the couple may be specified by its direction cosines, which are

$$\left[\cos\theta_x = \frac{M_x}{M}\right] \qquad \cos\theta_x = \frac{-160}{195.3}, \qquad \theta_x = 145°\ 0',$$

$$\left[\cos\theta_y = \frac{M_y}{M}\right] \qquad \cos\theta_y = \frac{-50.7}{195.3}, \qquad \theta_y = 105°\ 05',$$

$$\left[\cos\theta_z = \frac{M_z}{M}\right] \qquad \cos\theta_z = \frac{-100}{195.3}, \qquad \theta_z = 120°\ 50'. \qquad \textit{Ans.}$$

The corresponding acute angles made by M with the negative directions of the x-, y-, and z-coordinate axes are 35° 0′, 74° 55′, and 59° 10′, respectively.

It should be noted that the moment M_3 due to F_3 could have been expressed in terms of its two components, $M_{3_y} = -150$ lb. in. and $M_{3_z} = -100$ lb. in., since M is most easily computed from the rectangular components of the moment vectors.

PROBLEMS

96. The concrete slab supports the six vertical loads shown. Determine the resultant of these forces and the x- and y-coordinates of a point through which it acts. *Ans.* $R = 27$ tons, $x = 7$ ft., $y = 11.92$ ft.

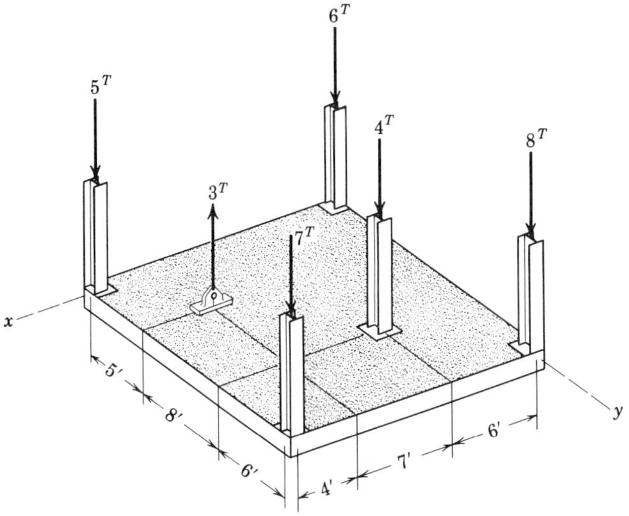

PROB. 96

97. Locate the position of the resultant of the forces shown in Prob. 96 by drawing two funicular polygons.

98. The concrete abutment supports the seven loads shown. Determine the resultant R of these forces and specify the coordinates of a point on its line of action. *Ans.* $R = 44$ tons, $x = 13.8$ in., $y = 21.5$ in.

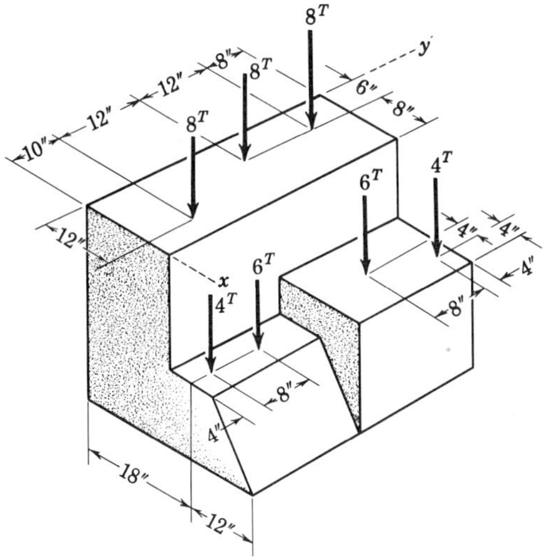

PROB. 98

99. Locate the position of the resultant of the loads shown in Prob. 98 by drawing two funicular polygons.

100. Find the resultant of the two forces shown, using point A as the point through which the resultant force shall pass.

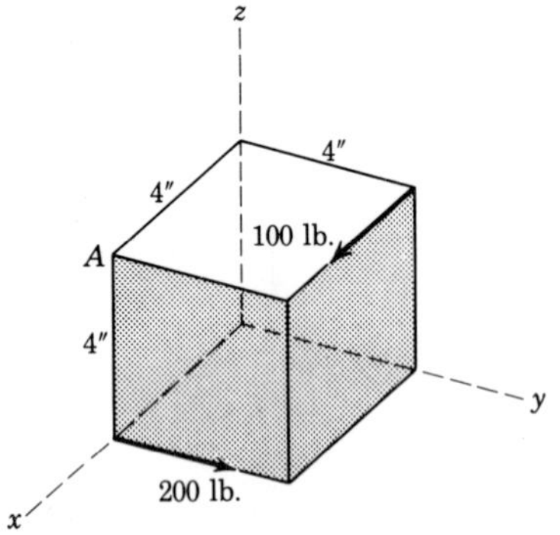

Prob. 100

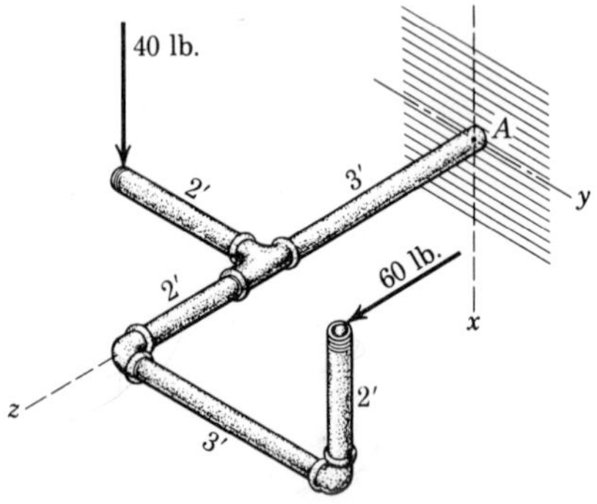

Prob. 101

101. The rigid piping shown is built into the wall and is subjected to the two forces indicated. Determine the resultant force R and moment M at point A of these two applied loads.

102. Replace the two forces shown by a single force R acting at A and a couple M. *Ans.* $R = 128$ lb., $M = 610$ lb. in.

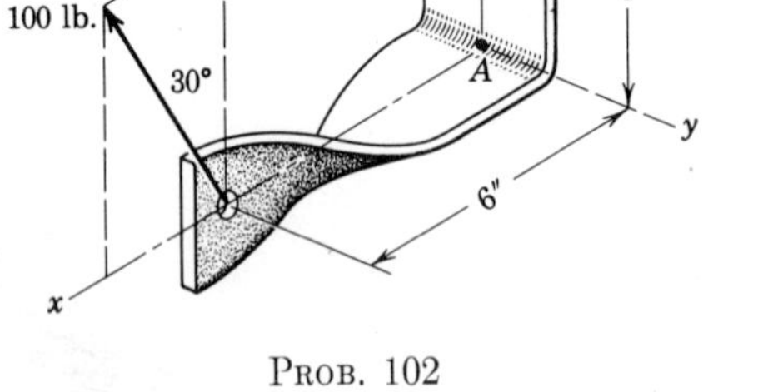

Prob. 102

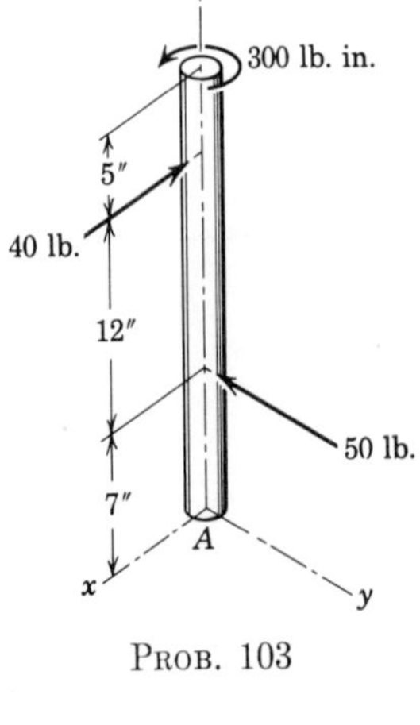

Prob. 103

103. Replace the couple and two applied forces shown acting on the vertical shaft by a resultant force R and couple M acting at point A.

104. Determine the resultant of the four forces and the couple which act on the shaft. *Ans.* Resultant is a couple $M = 589$ lb. ft.

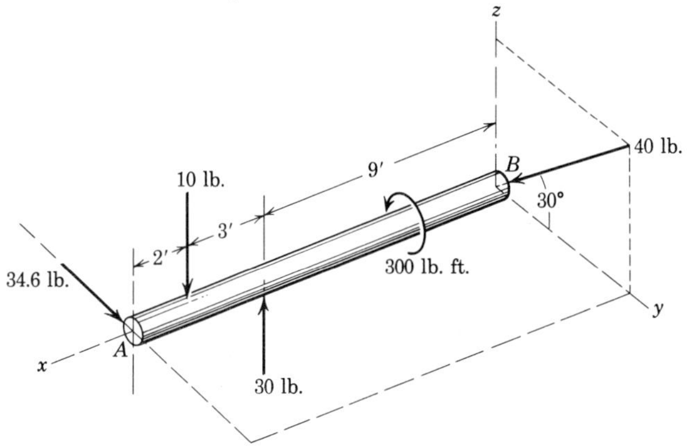

PROB. 104

105. Replace the four forces shown by an equivalent system consisting of a force R at A and a couple M.

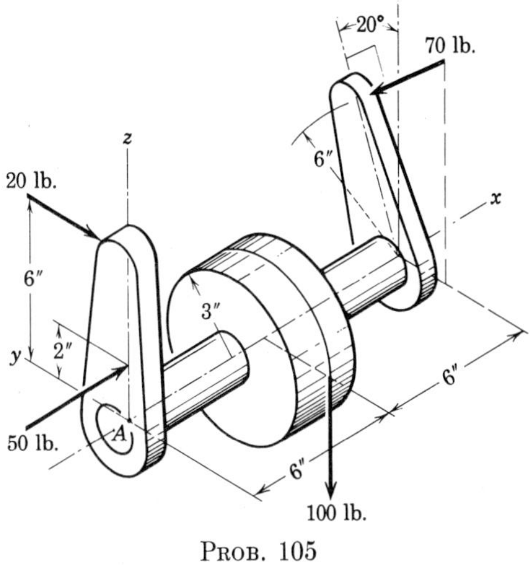

PROB. 105

* **106.** Two pipe wrenches are applied to the bent pipe as shown to screw it into the fitting at A. If a single pipe wrench applied to the pipe at A can accomplish the same job, what force F must be exerted on its handle at a moment arm of 12 in.? *Ans.* $F = 55.1$ lb.

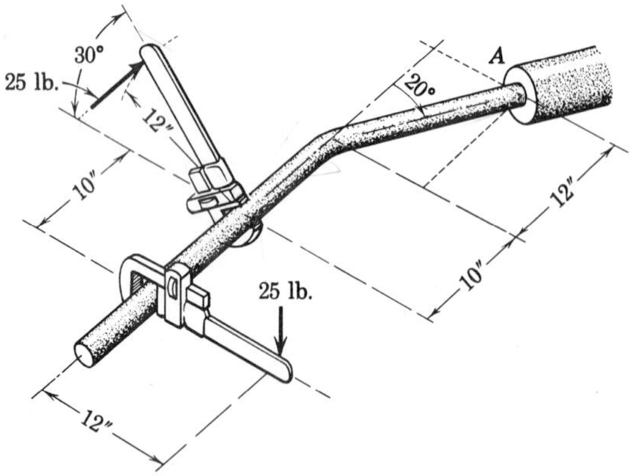

PROB. 106

107. Show that the most general force system may be expressed in terms of two nonintersecting forces.

108. Show that the most general force system, expressed as a resultant force R at a point O and a resultant couple M, is equivalent to a wrench applied along a unique line parallel to R.

CHAPTER

3

EQUILIBRIUM

19. Equilibrium. The concept of equilibrium is derived from a balance of forces. More specifically equilibrium is the condition for which the resultant of all forces acting on a given body is zero. In Art. 18 it was shown that the most general force system may be expressed in terms of a resultant force R and a resultant couple M. Thus equilibrium requires that

$$\begin{aligned} R &= 0 \\ M &= 0. \end{aligned} \tag{12}$$

Equations 12 are the necessary conditions for equilibrium.* Physically these vector equations mean that for a body in equilibrium there is as much force acting on it in one direction as in the opposite direction and that there is as much twist or moment applied to it about an axis in one sense as in the opposite sense. Thus equilibrium implies a balance of forces and a balance of moments. Graphically Eqs. 12 require that the space polygon of forces and the space polygon of corresponding couple vectors shall both close.

The equations relating force and acceleration for rigid-body motion are developed in *Mechanics, Part II: Dynamics*, from Newton's second

* When the forces acting on a body in equilibrium can be determined entirely from Eqs. 12, then these equations are also sufficient conditions. There is a certain class of problems explained in Art. 25 for which Eqs. 12, although necessary, are not sufficient.

law of motion. These equations show that, when the resultant of a force system is expressed by a single force R acting through the center of gravity and a corresponding couple M, the linear acceleration of the center of gravity of the body is proportional to R and the angular acceleration about the center of gravity is proportional to M. Hence the first of Eqs. 12 applies not only to bodies at rest, but also to any body whose center of gravity moves with a constant velocity (no acceleration). Likewise the second of Eqs. 12 describes not only a body at rest, but also one rotating about its center of gravity with a constant angular velocity. Although the subject of statics, as its name implies, concerns bodies which are static, i.e., have no motion or change in motion, the case of motion with constant linear velocity of the center of gravity and constant angular velocity about the center of gravity must be admitted when using the statical equations of equilibrium.

In order for a body to be in complete equilibrium it is necessary for both of Eqs. 12 to hold. These equations, however, represent two independent conditions, and either may hold without the other. If $R = 0$ and $M \neq 0$, the center of gravity of the body either is at rest or is moving with a constant velocity, and the body has an angular acceleration. Under these conditions it may be said that the body is in equilibrium only in so far as its linear motion is concerned. On the other hand if $R \neq 0$ and $M = 0$, the center of gravity of the body has a linear acceleration but there is no rotational acceleration. Such a body may be considered to be in rotational equilibrium. If the linear acceleration of a body is in the x-direction, then the body may be considered to be in equilibrium in the y- and z-directions since it has no acceleration in these directions. The term equilibrium, however, is most commonly used to describe a body which is completely at rest, as implied by the term statical equilibrium.

20. Free-Body Diagrams. In using Eqs. 12 it is necessary to account accurately and completely for *all* forces which are applied *on* the body in question. Error will result if one or more forces are not accounted for or if forces which do not act on the body in question are used. In analyzing the action of forces on a given body it is absolutely necessary to *isolate* the body in question by removing all contacting and attached bodies and replacing them by vectors representing the forces which they exert *on* the body isolated. Such a representation is called a *free-body diagram.* The free-body diagram is the means by which complete and accurate account of all forces acting *on* the body in question may be taken. Unless such a diagram is correctly drawn the effects of one or more forces will be easily omitted and error will result. The free-body diagram is a basic step in the solution of problems in mechanics and is *preliminary* to the application of the mathematical principles which govern the state of equilibrium or motion.

The subject of equilibrium involves application of the very basic physical laws expressed by Eqs. 12. In words these laws describe a condition wherein there is no resultant push (or pull) and no resultant twist on a body in equilibrium. The physical meaning of these laws of equilibrium is elementary, and the application of these laws for analytical solutions of equilibrium problems will also become elementary if accurate account of all forces is taken. The *free-body diagram* is the means by which this accurate account is made. An understanding of the free-body diagram method is truly the *key* to the understanding of mechanics. This comprehension cannot be gained without ample practice, but a convincing initial impression of the importance of this method of attack is extremely valuable to the beginner. When the student encounters difficulty in the problem work, the correctness of the free-body diagram is the first step to check.

The actual procedure for drawing free-body diagrams will now be explained. There are two essential parts to this procedure. (1) A clear decision must be made as to exactly what body (or group of bodies considered as a single body) is to be isolated and analyzed. An outline representing the external boundary of the body selected is then drawn. (2) *All* forces, known and unknown, which are applied *externally* to the isolated body should be represented by vectors in their correct positions. Known forces should be labeled with their magnitudes, and unknown forces should be labeled with appropriate symbols. In many instances the correct sense of an unknown force is not obvious at the outset. In this event the sense may be arbitrarily assumed. The correctness or error of the assumption will become apparent when the algebraic sign of the force is determined upon calculation. A plus sign indicates the force is in the direction assumed, and a minus sign indicates that the force is in the direction opposite to that assumed.

Before free-body diagrams are further described, it is advisable to consider the representation of the several kinds of contact forces normally encountered. Figure 28 shows the most common contacts and connections together with the proper representation of the force. In each example the force exerted *on* the body to be isolated *by* the body removed is shown. The principle of action and reaction expressed by Newton's third law must be used with extreme care in all problems in order that there be no confusion between action and the corresponding reaction. Thus in example 1, Fig. 28, the *action* of the cable on the post is the force T shown acting *on* the post. The *reaction* of the post on the

MECHANICAL ACTION OF FORCES	
Type of Contact or Connection	**Action of Force on Body Isolated**
1. Flexible cable, belt, chain, or rope Weight of cable negligible Weight of cable appreciable 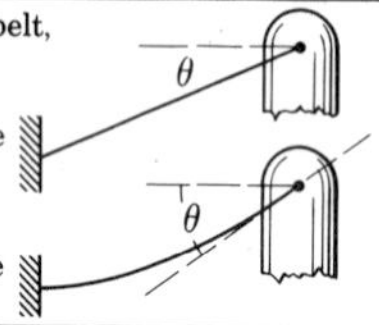	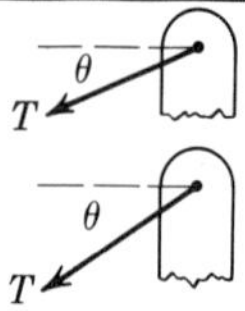 Force exerted by a flexible cable is always a tension in the direction of the cable.
2. Smooth surfaces 	 For smooth contacting surfaces the force is compressive and is normal to the surfaces.
3. Rough surfaces 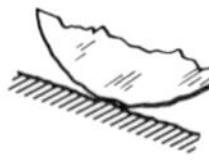	 Rough surfaces may support force which is not normal to the contacting surfaces. (Discussed in Chapter 6)
4. Ball, roller, or rocker support 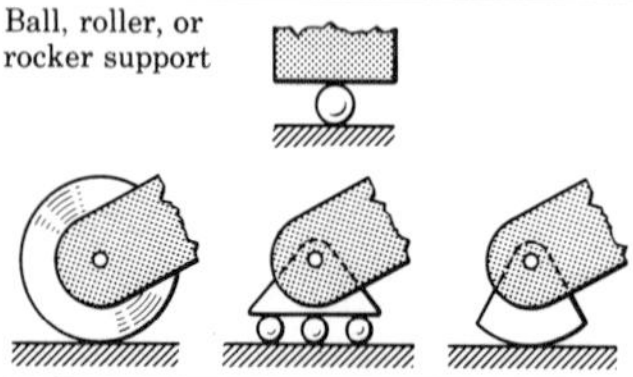	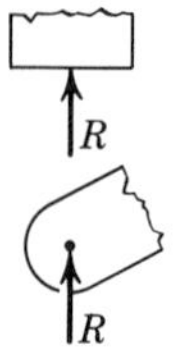 For smooth ball, roller, or rocker support the force is compressive and is normal to the contacting surfaces.
5. Smooth pin, bolt, hinge, or bearing 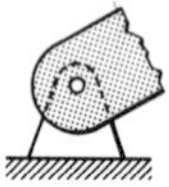	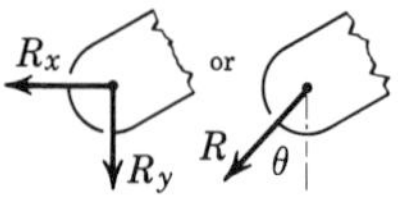 A pin connection is capable of supporting force in any direction in a plane normal to the pin axis. The force may be represented by its components or by the force at an angle θ.
6. Ball and socket or point connection 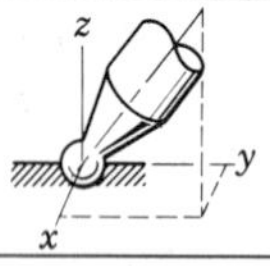	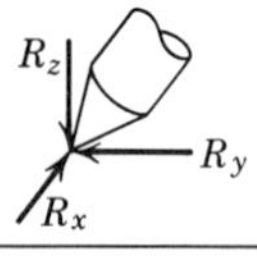 A ball and socket or point connection is capable of supporting force in any direction. The force may be represented by its three components.
7. Gravity force or weight  weight W	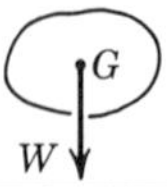 The gravitational attraction or weight always acts down toward the center of the earth and acts through the center of gravity G of the body.
8. Elastic spring 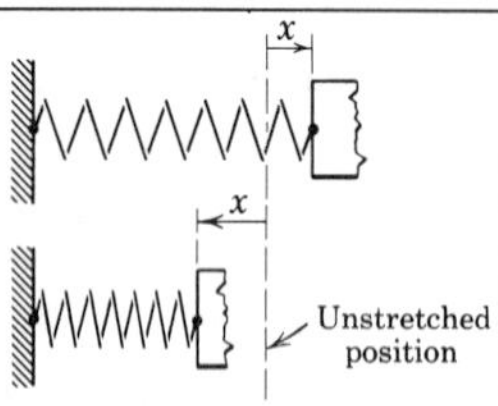	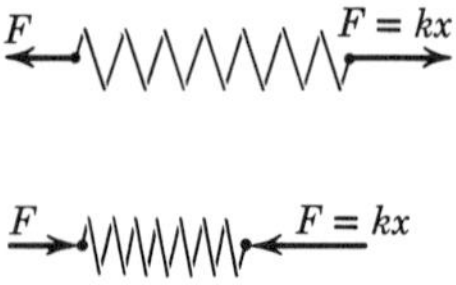 For an elastic spring the force is tension or compression and is proportional to the deformation. The constant of proportionality k is the *stiffness* or *modulus* of the spring.

FIG. 28

cable is the force T acting on the cable in the direction opposite to that shown acting on the post. Examples 2 through 6 show other types of forces applied by mechanical contact, and the characteristics of each contact are explained in the figure. Example 7 shows the force of attraction of the earth on a body. The force is actually distributed over all elements of the body but is shown as a concentrated resultant force or weight W acting through the center of gravity G. The weight of a body *always* acts *vertically down* toward the earth's center. In many instances the weight of a body is negligible compared with the other forces acting on it and is omitted from the free-body diagram and from the calculations. Example 8 shows the action of a force on an elastic spring. The force, either tensile or compressive, is proportional to the deflection of the spring. The constant of proportionality k is a property of the spring and is a measure of its stiffness. It should be made clear that the diagrams in Fig. 28, with the exception of example 8, are *not* free-body diagrams since they do not show *all* forces acting on the isolated body.

In Fig. 29 are shown five examples of complete and correct free-body diagrams. It should be carefully noted that *only those forces acting externally on the body isolated are shown.* Each of the forces indicated is in accordance with the representations of Fig. 28. The choice of reference axes should always be clearly indicated either on the sketch of the mechanism or on the free-body diagram. Many times it is convenient to indicate angles and dimensions on the free-body diagram to facilitate the resolution of forces and the computation of the moments of forces. It is well to remember, however, that the free-body diagram serves to focus accurate attention on the actual forces which act on the body, and thus the diagram should not be cluttered with extraneous information which diverts attention from the force vectors. The forces should be drawn and labeled without ambiguity. In the bottom example in Fig. 29 the horizontal component of the pin reaction at A is clearly to the left to balance P, which is to the right. The vertical component A_y, on the other hand, may be up or down, depending on the relative magnitudes of P and W. Therefore it should be arbitrarily drawn, say, down as shown, and the correctness or error of the assumed direction determined by the algebraic sign of the calculated value of A_y. It should be carefully noted that the entire frame of this example, including the pulley and cable between the pulley and the member BC, is taken as the isolated body. Only those forces applied externally to this body are shown on the free-body diagram. The force which the cable exerts on the member BC is equal and opposite to the force which BC exerts on the cable and consequently is not represented

<table>
<tr><th colspan="2">SAMPLE FREE-BODY DIAGRAMS</th></tr>
<tr><th>Mechanism</th><th>Free-Body Diagram of Isolated Body</th></tr>
<tr><td>1.
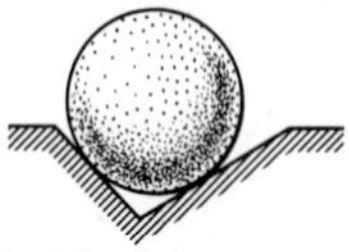
Ball of weight W resting on smooth surfaces.</td><td>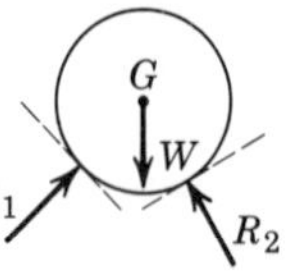
</td></tr>
<tr><td>2.
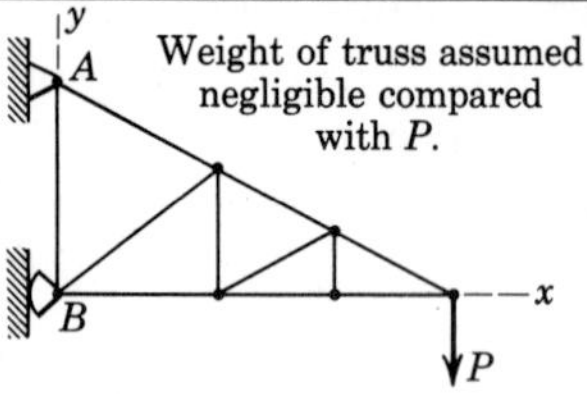

Weight of truss assumed negligible compared with P.</td><td>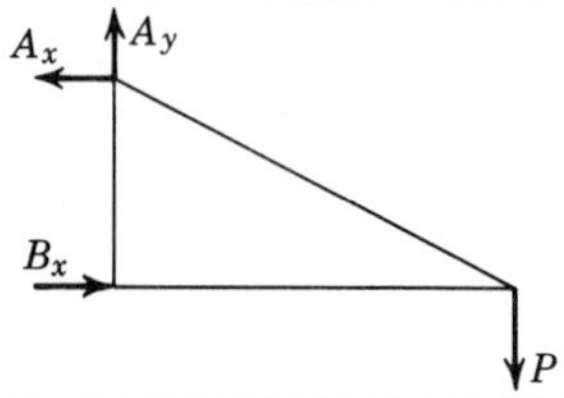
</td></tr>
<tr><td>3.
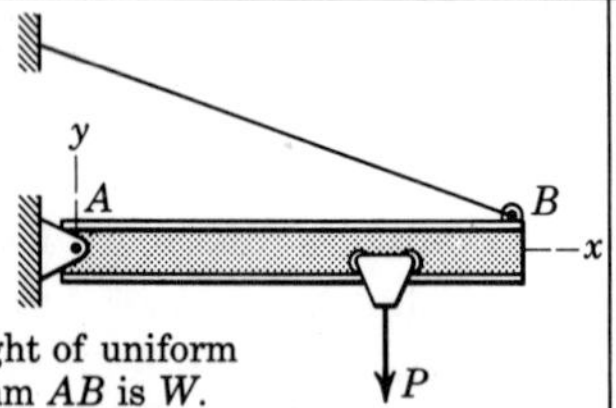

Weight of uniform beam AB is W.</td><td>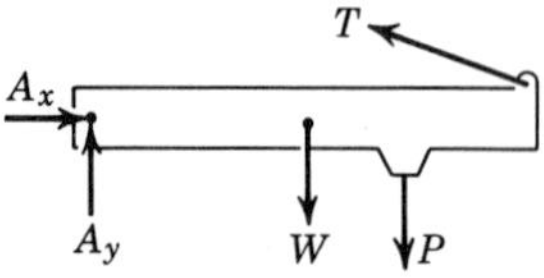
</td></tr>
<tr><td>4.
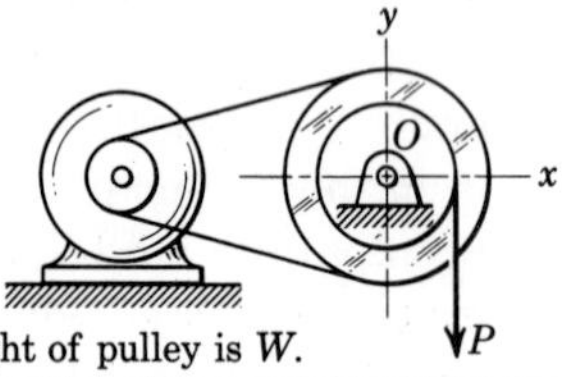

Weight of pulley is W.</td><td>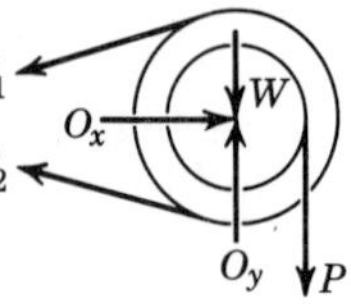
</td></tr>
<tr><td>5.
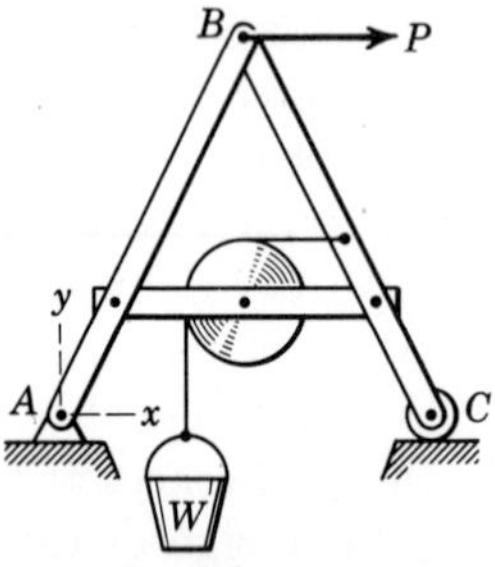

Weights of members are assumed negligible compared with applied loads.</td><td>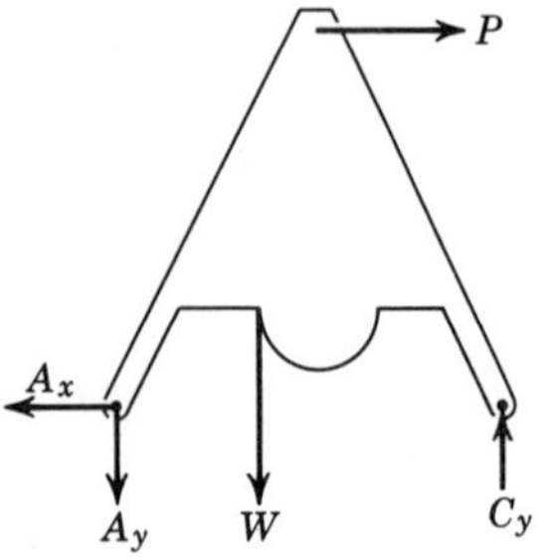
</td></tr>
</table>

FIG. 29

on the free-body diagram since it is *internal* to the body isolated. A force internal to a body is always accompanied by an equal and opposite internal reaction, and the net external effect is zero.

In addition to completing the vital step of drawing a correct free-body diagram it is extremely important to follow a clear, logical, and orderly procedure in executing the solution to the remainder of the problem. Such a procedure has been outlined in Art. 9, Chapter 1, and will be illustrated in the sample problems in the present chapter. Again it is emphatically stated that strict adherence to a well-formulated and disciplined method of attack will govern success to a large extent. The tendency of a large proportion of students in mechanics is to jump to conclusions before all factors have been accounted for. Careful attention to the drawing of a correct free-body diagram is the best insurance that account of all pertinent information has been taken. The student is *urged* to reread and study the first two articles of this chapter so that the problem work beginning with the next article will be started with an initial advantage of a proper method and procedure.

21. Equilibrium in Two Dimensions. When a body is in equilibrium under the action of forces all of which act in a single plane, say the x–y plane, Eqs. 12 become

$$R = \sqrt{(\Sigma F_x)^2 + (\Sigma F_y)^2} = 0,$$

$$M = M_z = 0.$$

These equations may be rewritten as

$$\Sigma F_x = 0,$$

$$\Sigma F_y = 0, \qquad (13)$$

$$\Sigma M_O = 0,$$

where ΣM_O represents the algebraic sum of the moments of all forces acting on the body about an axis parallel to the z-direction and passing through any point O on the body or off the body but in the x–y plane. More frequently this summation is referred to as the sum of the moments about point O. Equations 13 are the three most commonly used equations in the subject of statics. Physically they express the fact that for any body in equilibrium under the action of a coplanar system of forces there is as much force acting in any one direction as in the opposite direction and there is as much twist or moment about any point in one sense as in the opposite sense. Graphically Eqs. 13 require that the polygon of forces must close (zero resultant force) and that the string polygon must also close (zero resultant couple). Use of the string polygon will be discussed in the next article. Equations 13 are the necessary conditions for two-dimensional equilibrium, and, as may be concluded from Art. 19, they are independent conditions. Any one of the relations may hold without the other when the equilibrium is not complete.

There are two additional ways of expressing the necessary conditions for the equilibrium of forces in two dimensions. For the body shown in Fig. 30*a*, if $\Sigma M_A = 0$, then the resultant R, if it still exists, cannot

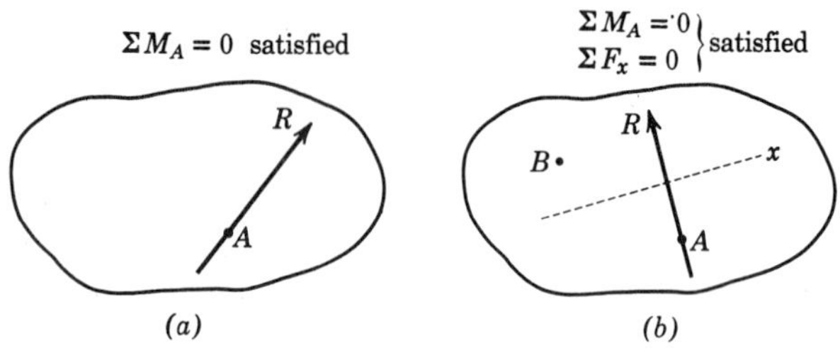

FIG. 30

be a couple but must be a force R passing through A. If now the equation $\Sigma F_x = 0$ holds, where the x-direction is perfectly arbitrary, it follows from Fig. 30*b* that the resultant force R, if it still exists, must not only pass through A, but also must be perpendicular to the x-direction as shown. Now, if $\Sigma M_B = 0$, where B is any point such that the line AB is not perpendicular to the x-direction, it is clear that R must be zero, and hence the body is in equilibrium. Therefore an alternate set of equilibrium equations is

$$\Sigma F_x = 0,$$

$$\Sigma M_A = 0, \tag{14}$$

$$\Sigma M_B = 0,$$

where the two points A and B are *not* on a line perpendicular to the x-direction.

A third formulation of the conditions of equilibrium may be made. Again, if $\Sigma M_A = 0$ for any body such as shown in Fig. 31*a*, the resultant, if it exists, must be a force R through A. In addition if $\Sigma M_B = 0$, the resultant, if one still exists, must pass through B as shown in Fig. 31*b*. Such a force cannot exist, however, if $\Sigma M_C = 0$, where C is not collinear with A and B. Hence the equations of equilibrium may be written

$$\Sigma M_A = 0,$$
$$\Sigma M_B = 0, \tag{15}$$
$$\Sigma M_C = 0,$$

where A, B, and C are any three points not on the same straight line.

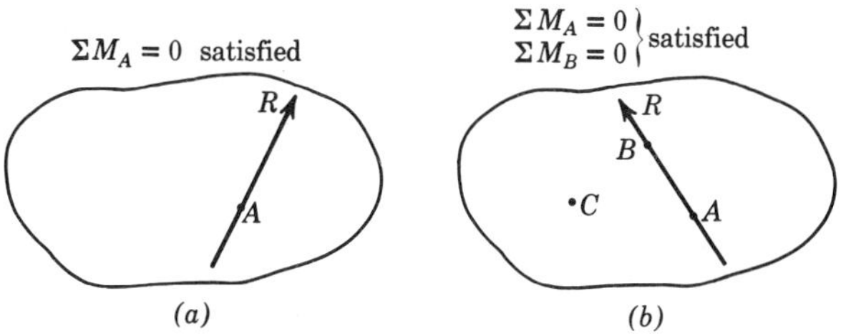

FIG. 31

When a body is in equilibrium under a system of concurrent forces, the moment sum about the point of concurrency is automatically satisfied, leaving from Eqs. 13 the relations

$$\Sigma F_x = 0, \qquad \Sigma F_y = 0.$$

These two equations, or a corresponding pair of relations from either Eqs. 14 or 15, will insure the equilibrium of concurrent forces in all cases.

In the case of equilibrium produced by parallel forces, only two conditions need be specified, and from Eqs. 13 these may be taken to be

$$\Sigma F_x = 0, \qquad \Sigma M_O = 0,$$

where the x-direction is the direction of the forces and O is any point in their plane. As an alternative two moment equations may be used, provided the line joining the moment centers is not parallel to the forces.

When a body is in equilibrium under the action of three forces only, these forces must be concurrent. If they were not concurrent, as shown in Fig. 32, then one of the forces would exert a resultant moment about the point of concurrency of the other two which would violate the requirement of zero moment about every point. Any system of coplanar forces in equilibrium may always be reduced by direct combination of the forces to a system of three forces which must therefore be concurrent. This principle of concurrency is very useful for both algebraic and graphical solutions in determining the direction of an unknown force. The only exception to this principle exists for the case where three parallel forces are in equilibrium. In this event the point of concurrency may be said to be at infinity.

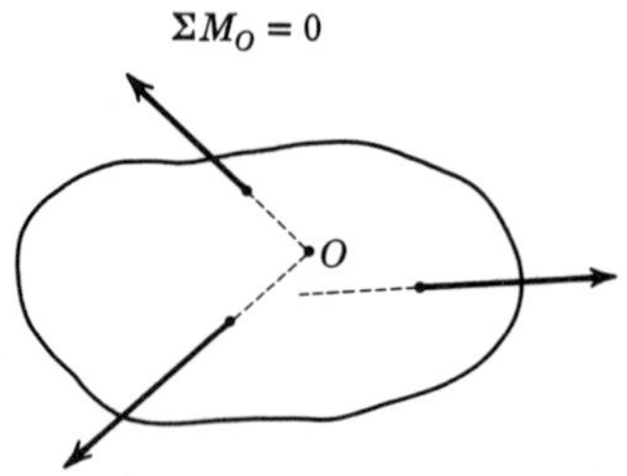

FIG. 32

The equilibrium of collinear forces requires but one equation and is considered too trivial for further comment.

It is desirable that facility with both algebraic and graphical solutions be acquired in the problem work. The sample problems which follow illustrate both methods.

SAMPLE PROBLEMS

109. Determine the force P required to prevent the wheel of weight W from rolling down the incline. Also find the force N exerted by the plane on the wheel. Neglect the weight of the yoke.

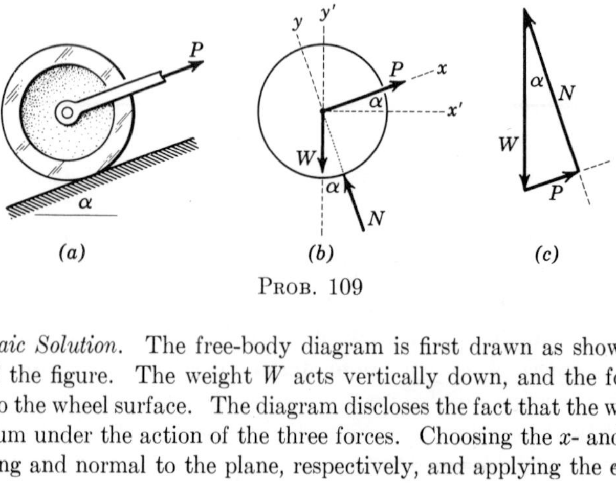

PROB. 109

Algebraic Solution. The free-body diagram is first drawn as shown in the b-part of the figure. The weight W acts vertically down, and the force N is normal to the wheel surface. The diagram discloses the fact that the wheel is in equilibrium under the action of the three forces. Choosing the x- and y-directions along and normal to the plane, respectively, and applying the equations of equilibrium give

$[\Sigma F_x = 0]$ $\quad P - W \sin \alpha = 0, \quad P = W \sin \alpha,$ *Ans.*

$[\Sigma F_y = 0]$ $\quad N - W \cos \alpha = 0, \quad N = W \cos \alpha.$ *Ans.*

If the axes were chosen as with x' and y', then the equations of equilibrium give

$[\Sigma F_{x'} = 0]$ $\quad P \cos \alpha - N \sin \alpha = 0,$

$[\Sigma F_{y'} = 0]$ $\quad P \sin \alpha + N \cos \alpha - W = 0.$

Eliminating N between the two equations and solving for P and then solving for N yield the answers just obtained, but the process was needlessly complicated by a less favorable choice of reference axes.

Graphical Solution. After the free-body diagram is completed the known force W is laid off to some convenient scale as shown in the c-part of the figure. Next lines with the known directions of P and N are constructed through the terminal points of W, and their intersection gives the solution and enables the correct magnitudes of P and N to be scaled from the drawing. It should be observed from this force polygon that the two answers may be obtained by inspection of the trigonometry of the triangle. Thus $P = W \sin \alpha$, $N = W \cos \alpha$, and also $P = N \tan \alpha$. In the case of concurrent forces a simple and approximate sketch of the force polygon will enable the required relations between the forces to be written immediately by inspection. It should also be noted that the force polygon is a graphical statement of $\Sigma F_x = 0$ and $\Sigma F_y = 0$.

110. A 50 lb. force is required to operate the foot pedal shown. Determine the tension T in the connecting link and the force exerted by the bearing O on the lever. The weight of the lever is negligible.

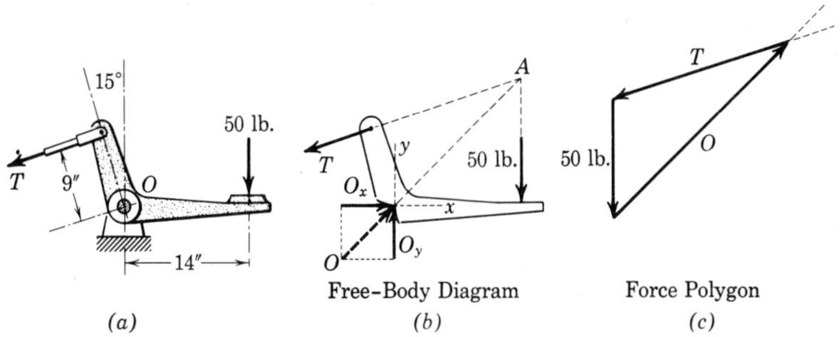

Prob. 110

Algebraic Solution. The free-body diagram is first drawn as shown in the b-part of the figure. The force exerted by the bearing on the lever at O is shown in terms of its x- and y-components. The solution is best started with the moment equation about O, which eliminates O_x and O_y from the relation. Thus

$[\Sigma M_O = 0]$ $\quad 50 \times 14 - 9T = 0, \quad T = 77.8 \text{ lb.}$ *Ans.*

The remaining two equations of equilibrium give

$$[\Sigma F_x = 0] \qquad O_x - 77.8 \cos 15° = 0, \qquad O_x = 75.1 \text{ lb.},$$

$$[\Sigma F_y = 0] \qquad O_y - 50 - 77.8 \sin 15° = 0, \qquad O_y = 70.1 \text{ lb.},$$

$$[O = \sqrt{O_x^2 + O_y^2}] \qquad O = \sqrt{(75.1)^2 + (70.1)^2}, \qquad O = 102.7 \text{ lb.} \qquad \textit{Ans.}$$

The direction of O can be specified by the angle determined by the ratio of O_x to O_y if desired.

Graphical Solution. The intersection of the 50 lb. force and the tension T defines the point A through which the reaction O must also pass, since three forces in equilibrium are concurrent. With the direction of O established, the force polygon is drawn in the *c*-part of the figure by constructing the directions of O and T through the ends of the 50 lb. vector. From the intersection of the two lines the magnitudes of T and O are scaled directly from the triangle, and the values are those obtained in the algebraic solution. In this problem the exact expressions for the unknown forces are more easily obtained from the algebraic solution than from the trigonometry of the force polygon.

111. Determine the tension T in the supporting cable and the force on the pin at A for the jib crane shown. The beam AB is a standard 18 in. I-beam weighing 65 lb./ft. of length.

Algebraic Solution. The free-body diagram of the beam is shown in the *a*-part of the figure with the pin reaction at A separated in terms of its two rectangular components. The weight of the beam is $65 \times 15 = 975$ lb. and acts through its center. In applying the moment equation about A it is simpler to consider the moments of the x- and y-components of T than it is to compute the perpendicular distance from T to A. Thus

$$[\Sigma M_A = 0] \quad (T \cos 25°)\tfrac{9}{12} + (T \sin 25°)(15 - \tfrac{4}{12})$$
$$- 2000(15 - 4.5 - \tfrac{4}{12}) - 975(7.5 - \tfrac{4}{12}) = 0,$$

from which

$$T = 3980 \text{ lb.} \qquad \textit{Ans.}$$

Equating the sum of forces in the x- and y-directions to zero gives

$$[\Sigma F_x = 0] \qquad A_x - 3980 \cos 25° = 0, \qquad A_x = 3610 \text{ lb.},$$

$$[\Sigma F_y = 0] \qquad A_y + 3980 \sin 25° - 975 - 2000 = 0, \qquad A_y = 1293 \text{ lb.},$$

$$[A = \sqrt{A_x^2 + A_y^2}] \qquad A = \sqrt{(3610)^2 + (1293)^2}, \qquad A = 3830 \text{ lb.} \qquad \textit{Ans.}$$

Graphical Solution. The principle that three forces in equilibrium must be concurrent is utilized for a graphical solution by combining the two known vertical forces of 975 lb. and 2000 lb. into a single 2975 lb. force located as shown on the modified free-body diagram of the beam in the *b*-part of the figure. The position of this resultant load may be determined graphically or algebraically.

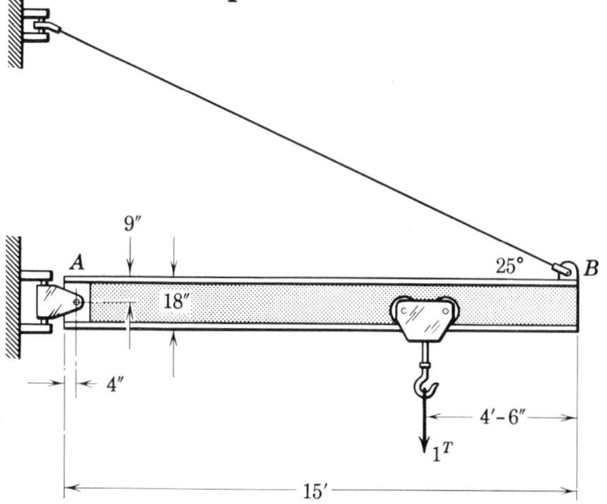

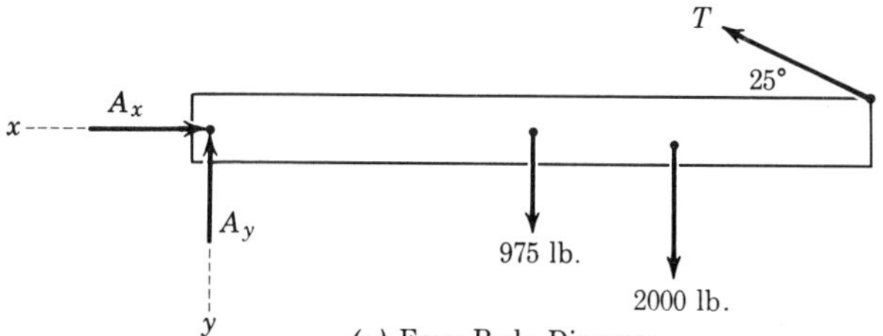

(a) Free-Body Diagram

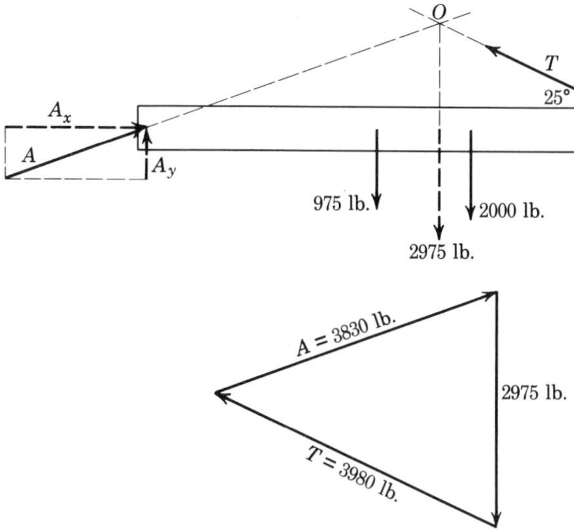

(b) Graphical solution

PROB. 111

The intersection of the 2975 lb. force with the line of action of the unknown tension T defines the point of concurrency O through which the pin reaction A must pass. The unknown magnitudes of T and A may now be found by constructing the closed equilibrium polygon of forces. After laying off the known vertical load to a convenient scale, as shown in the lower part of the figure, a line representing the given direction of the tension T is drawn through the tip of the 2975 lb. vector. Likewise a line representing the direction of the pin reaction A, determined from the concurrency established with the free-body diagram, is drawn through the tail of the 2975 lb. vector. The intersection of the lines representing vectors T and A establishes the magnitudes of both T and A which are necessary to make the vector sum of the forces equal to zero. These magnitudes may be scaled directly from the diagram. The x- and y-components of A may be constructed on the force polygon if desired.

The student should recognize that the polygon is begun with the known forces first and that the order of addition of the remaining two vectors is immaterial.

PROBLEMS

112. Which combination of rope and pulleys requires the smaller force P to raise the load W? Each pulley is free to rotate independently.

Ans. (*b*); $P = W/5$

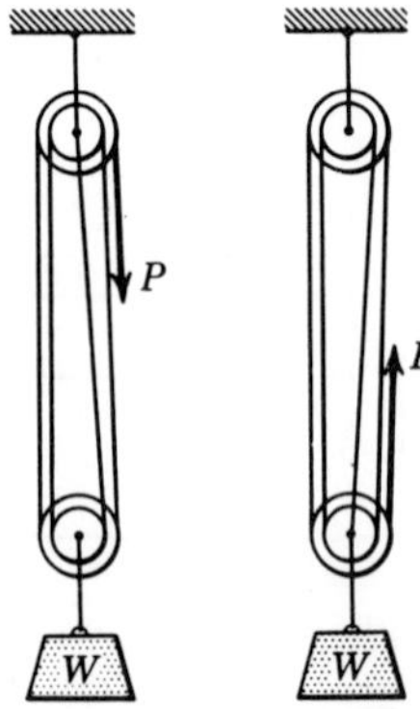

(*a*) (*b*)

PROB. 112

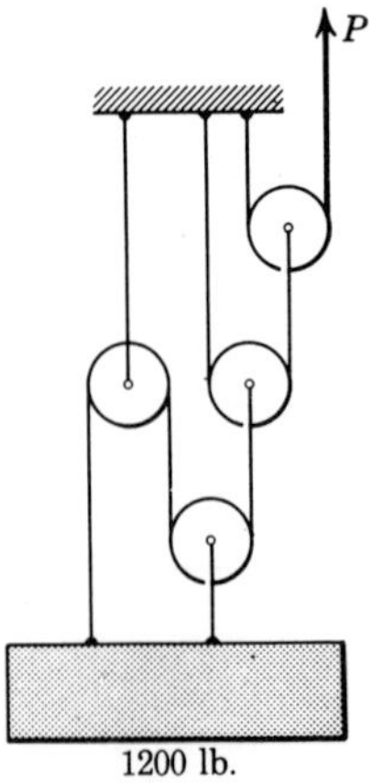

PROB. 113

113. What force P is required to raise the 1200 lb. platform?

Ans. $P = 100$ lb.

114. The 6½ yard concrete truck is weighed on a highway scale, and it is noted that the front axle supports 14,000 lb. and each of the rear axles supports 16,000 lb. Determine the distance x from the front axle to the center of gravity of the loaded truck.

Ans. $x = 107$ in.

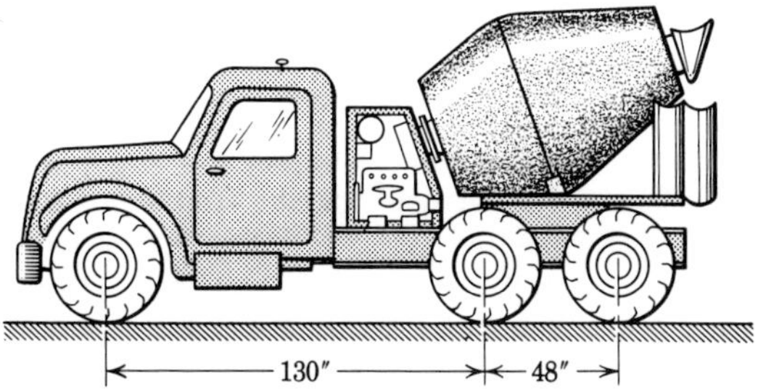

Prob. 114

115. Determine the horizontal force P applied at point A on the cable necessary to position the 1000 lb. load directly over the opening.

Ans. $P = 258$ lb.

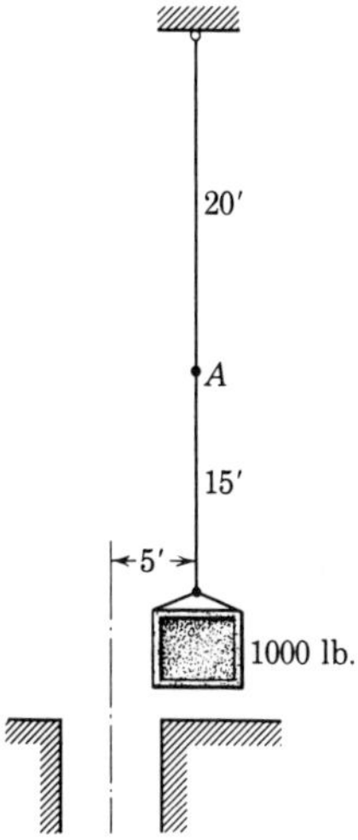

Prob. 115

116. One type of pipe cutter, shown in the figure, consists of a clamp with three sharp-edged wheels which cut through the pipe as the screw is tightened and the device is rotated around the pipe. When cutting a ¾ in. pipe (outside

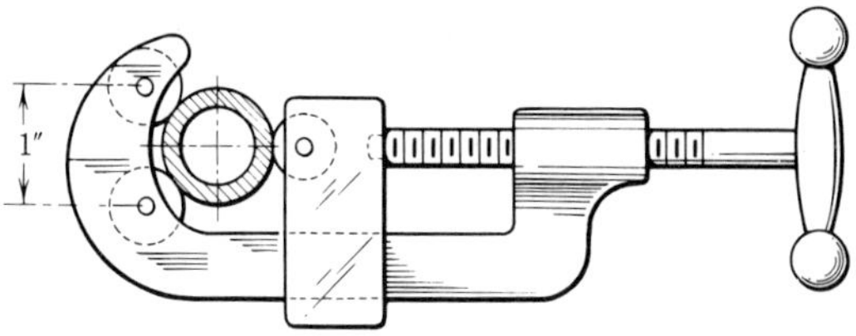

Prob. 116

diameter 1.050 in.) with a compression of 1000 lb. in the screw, determine the force R acting on each pin of the two ¾ in. diameter cutting wheels.

Ans. $R = 602$ lb.

117. The cable AB is attached to the top of a fence post and to a rigid overhead support and has an initial tension of 80 lb. To pull up the post a force of 100 lb. is then applied to the free end of the block-and-tackle rope. Point C moves to C' due to stretch in the cable and attachments. Determine the vertical component of force V applied to the post. *Ans.* $V = 1200$ lb.

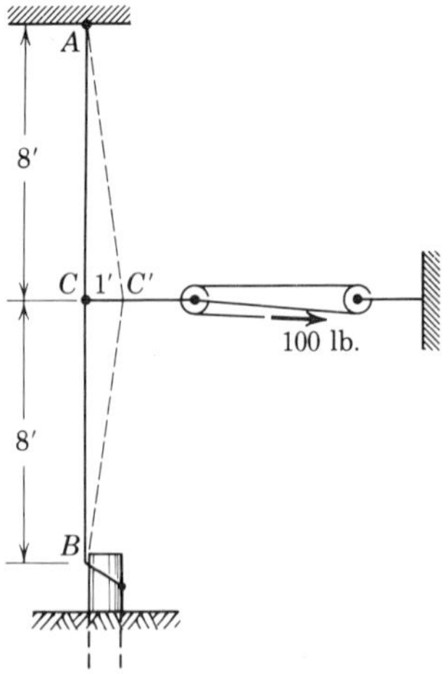

PROB. 117

118. A 300 ton refinery tower with center of gravity at section G is to be lifted from the freight cars. Two slings at A and one at B are to be used. If it is necessary to limit the tension T_2 in each cable at B to 25 tons, determine the minimum distance x.

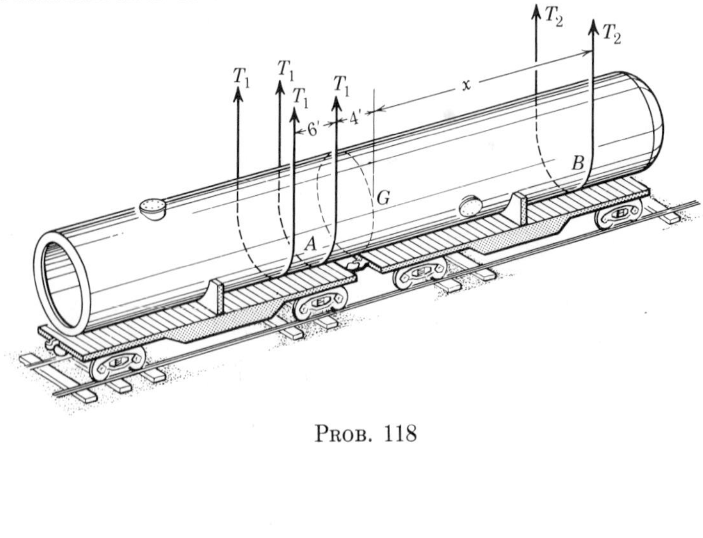

PROB. 118

119. In designing the bracket to support the 1500 lb. load the greatest shear force which either bolt will safely support is 5000 lb. Determine the minimum distance x.

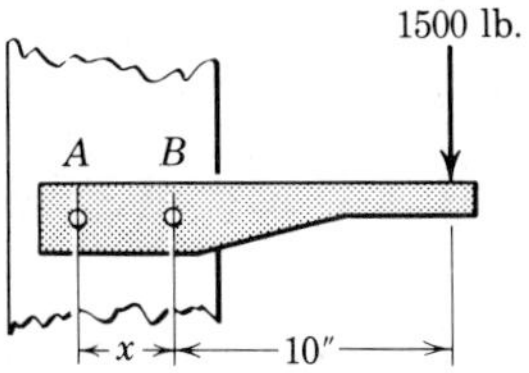

PROB. 119

120. A painter weighing 150 lb. hoists himself on a bosun's chair as shown. Determine the force P which he must apply to the rope in order to support himself. *Ans.* $P = 50$ lb.

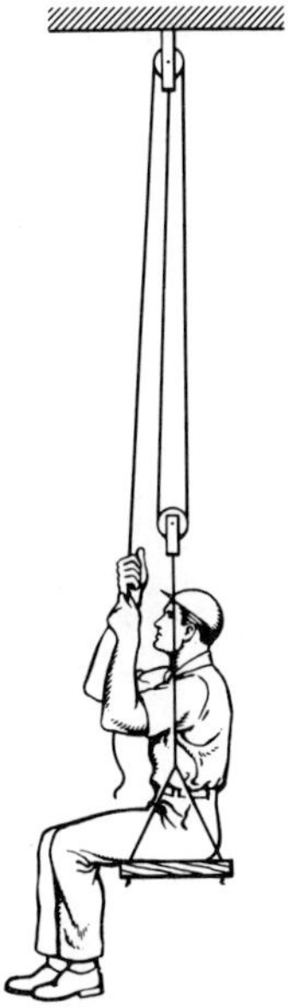

PROB. 120

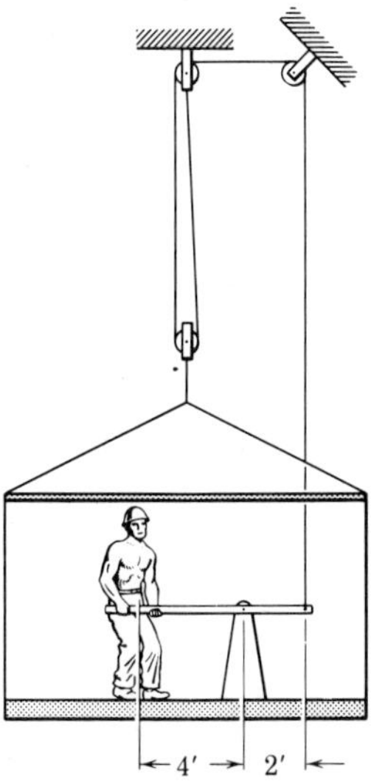

PROB. 121

121. A man weighing 160 lb. hoists himself and the 200 lb. platform by pulling up on the lever shown. Determine the reaction R between his feet and the platform.

122. If the wood clamp holds the two pieces together with a force of 100 lb., what are the vertical forces F_A and F_B in the two screws?

Ans. $F_B = 125$ lb., $F_A = 225$ lb.

123. What force P must be applied to the 200 lb. lawn roller to prevent it from gathering speed as it is rolled down the 10 deg. incline?

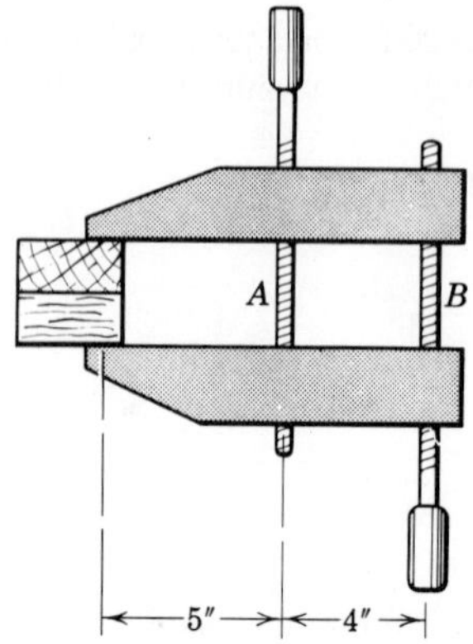

PROB. 122

PROB. 123

124. A small postal scale consists of the plate suspended at A from a link which acts as the pointer. The scale tilts according to the weight hung from the hook at B. In the unloaded position shown AB is horizontal. The scale weighs 4 oz. exclusive of pointer, and its center of gravity is $2\frac{1}{4}$ in. from A. The weight of the hook is negligible. Determine the angle θ through which the scale tilts when an 8 oz. weight is attached to the hook. *Ans.* $\theta = 60° 38'$

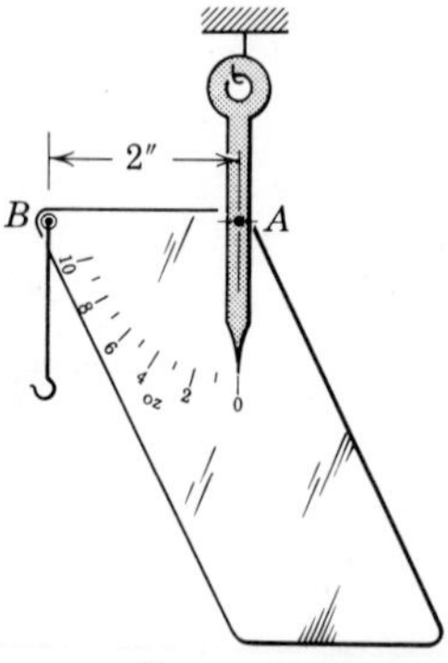

PROB. 124

125. The 50 lb. force exerts a torque or moment about the axis of the bolt of 60 lb. ft. Find the forces between the smooth jaws of the wrench and the bolt if contact is at the corners A and B of the hexagon.

Ans. A = 599 lb., B = 649 lb.

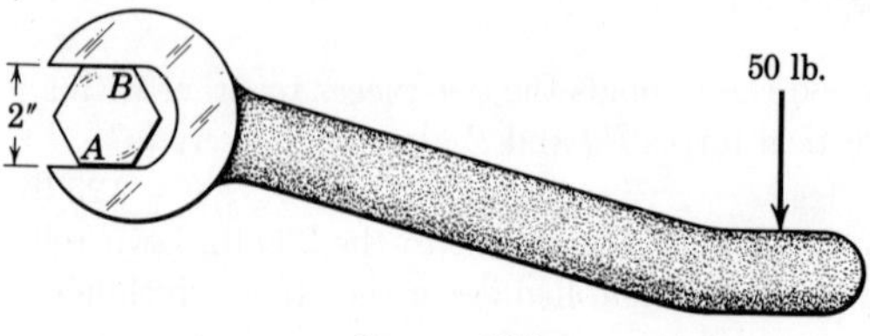

PROB. 125

126. Determine the pull P required to lift the load W for the differential chain hoist shown. The two upper pulleys are fastened together, and the chain cannot slip on the pulleys.

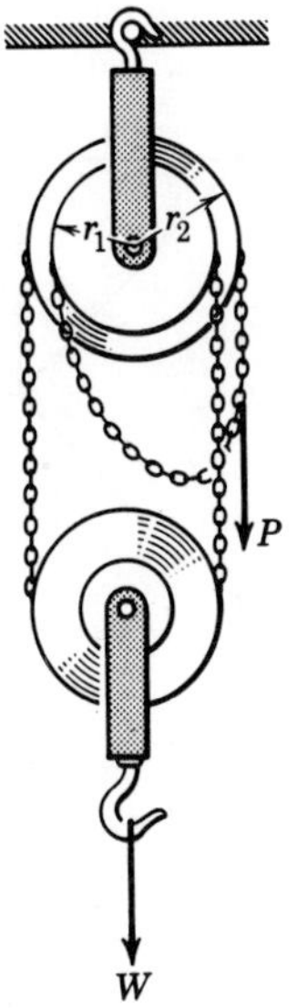

PROB. 126

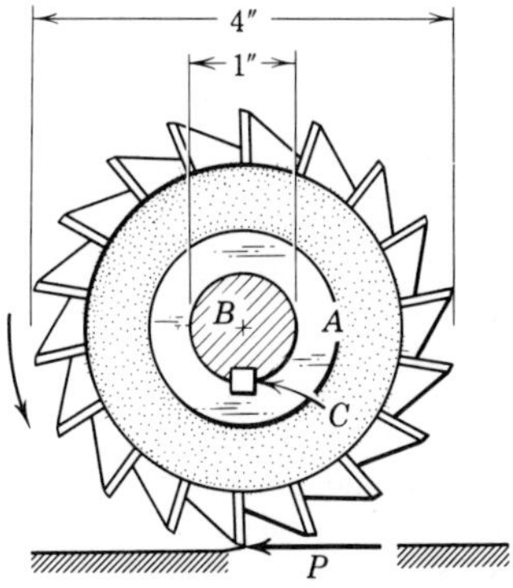

PROB. 127

127. The milling cutter A is prevented from turning on its arbor B by means of a square key which bears horizontally against the cutter at point C in the position shown. If the motor drive supplies a torque of 100 lb. ft. to the arbor, determine the force F transmitted by the key to the cutter, the reaction R between the arbor and the smooth inner periphery of the cutter, and the tooth load P. *Ans.* $F = 2400$ lb., $R = 1800$ lb., $P = 600$ lb.

128. Find the vertical load W which the pry bar can support if a 60 lb. force is applied to the bar as shown. The horizontal surface is rough enough to prevent slipping of the bar at A. Also find the friction force at A (component of reaction tangent to contact surface). *Ans.* $W = 480$ lb., $F = 20.5$ lb.

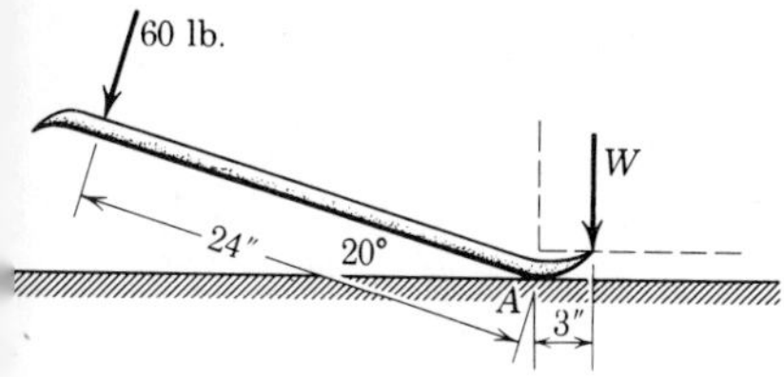

PROB. 128

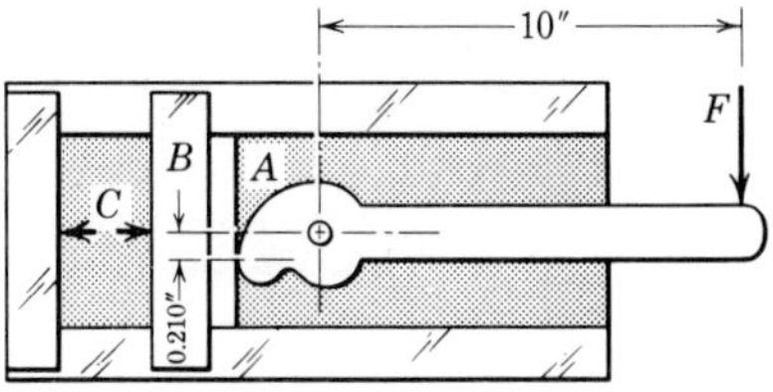

PROB. 129

129. Quick action and positive clamping are features of the cam lock vise for production work. The cam A is rotated by the force F into position against the movable jaw B, and the moment arm of the contact force about the cam pivot becomes very small. If $F = 30$ lb. for the vise shown, determine the clamping force C. All surfaces may be considered smooth.

130. A force F is applied to the handle of the positioning lever to produce a 50 lb. reaction at the contact. Determine the total force on the pin at O.

Ans. $O = 61.4$ lb.

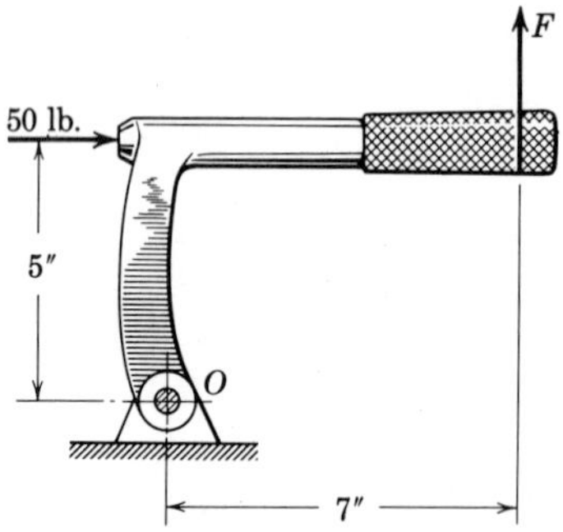

Prob. 130

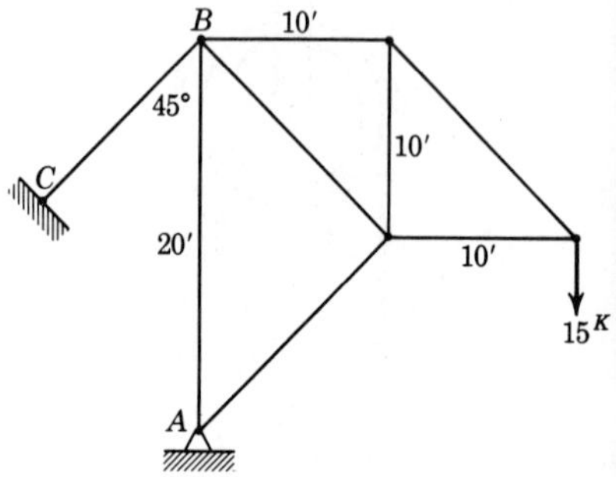

Prob. 132

131. A jet airplane weighing 6 tons is flying horizontally at a constant speed of 500 mi./hr. under a thrust of 3000 lb. from its turbo-jet engines. If the pilot increases the fuel rate to give a thrust of 4200 lb. and noses the plane upward to maintain a constant 500 mi./hr. air speed, determine the angle θ made by the new line of flight with the horizontal. Note that the air resistance in the line of flight at the particular altitude involved is a function only of air speed.

Ans. $\theta = 5° 44'$

132. Determine graphically the force on the pin at A and the tension T in the member BC due to the 15 kip load.

133. A type of hook wrench known as a pin spanner is used for turning collars and shafts. For the applied load of 30 lb. determine the forces exerted on the wrench at the pin A and at the smooth contact at B.

Ans. $A = 153$ lb., $B = 150$ lb.

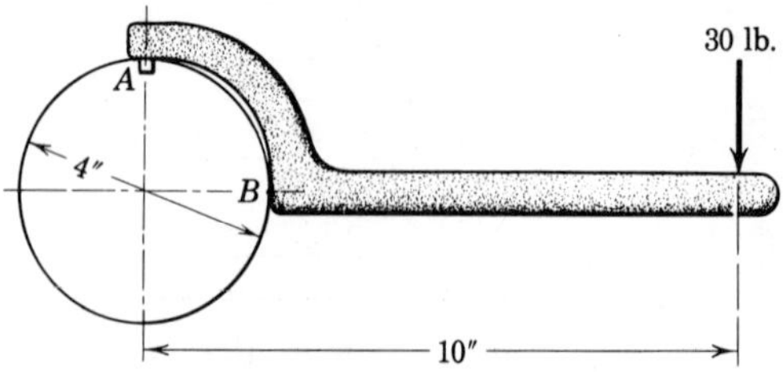

Prob. 133

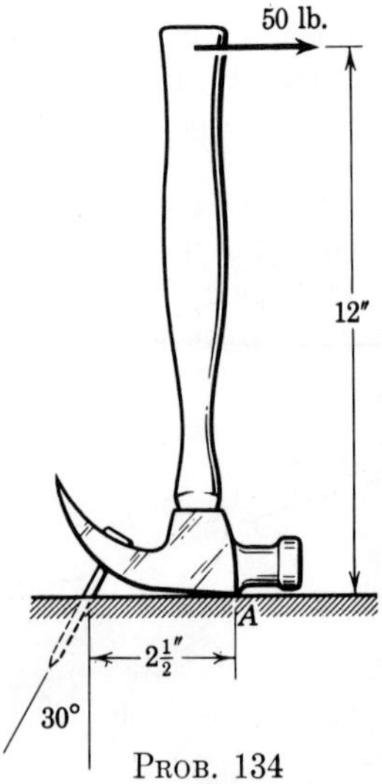

Prob. 134

134. Find the pull P exerted on the nail by the claws of the hammer and the total force R exerted by the board on the hammer head at the contact point A. The surfaces are not smooth, and it may be assumed that the force exerted on the nail is in the direction of the nail. *Ans.* $P = 277$ lb., $R = 256$ lb.

135. The uniform 2000 lb. beam is supported by cables as shown. Calculate the tensions T_1 and T_2 in the supporting ends of the cable and find the angle θ.

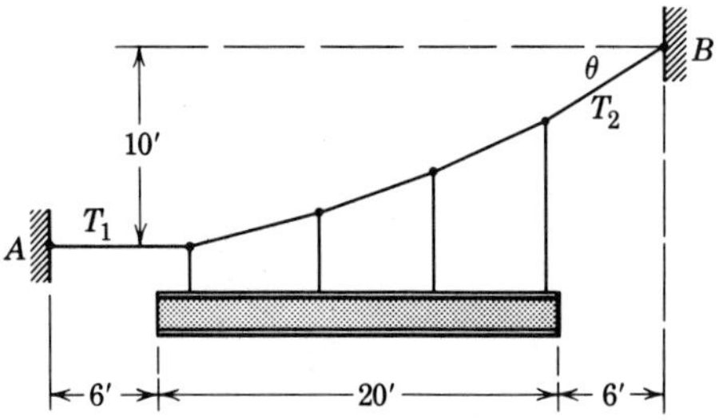

PROB. 135

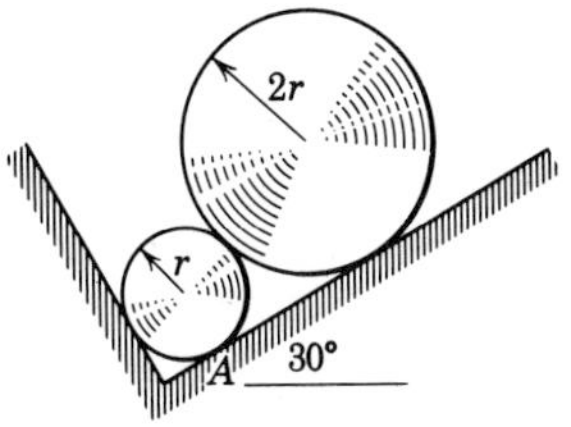

PROB. 137

136. Solve Prob. 135 graphically.

137. The large cylinder weighs 80 lb., and the small one weighs 20 lb. Determine the force of contact R between the small cylinder and the surface at A. All surfaces are smooth. *Ans.* $R = 31.5$ lb.

138. The pulley bracket is bolted down to the foundation with a negligible initial tension in each of the four bolts. Determine the tension T in each bolt at B due to the applied loads in the belt. If the bolt holes in the bracket at A are slightly oversize so that they cannot offer restraint to horizontal movement, find the shear force Q in each bolt at B.

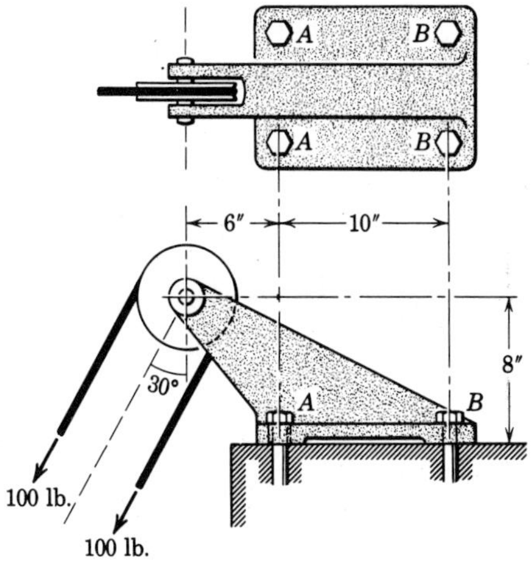

PROB. 138

139. The 100 ft. mast with center of gravity at G weighs 1800 lb. and is erected as shown. The cable passes over the pulleys at C and A and is secured to the mast at D. Determine algebraically the tension T required to support the mast in the 30 deg. position. Neglect the diameters of the two pulleys and also the weight of the struts OA and AB. Discuss any effect on T caused by securing the cable to point A in place of using a pulley at this point.

Ans. $T = 4500$ lb.

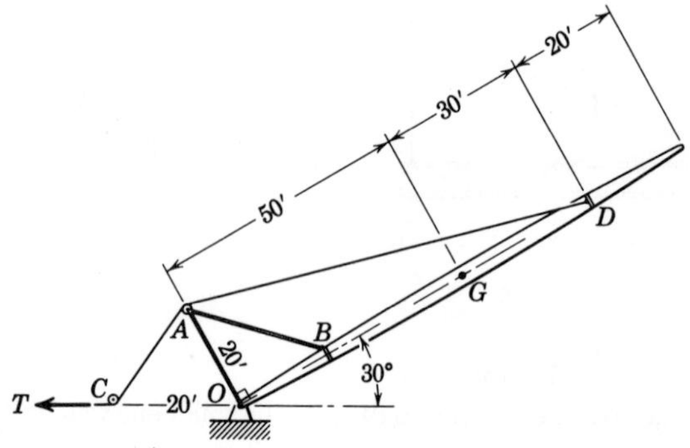

Prob. 139

140. Solve Prob. 139 graphically and determine the bearing reaction R at the bearing O.

141. Determine the least torque M which must be applied to the axle of the 20 lb. wheel to cause it to roll over the obstruction if the wheel does not slip. Calculate the corresponding friction force F (tangent to the wheel surface) exerted on the wheel at A by the obstruction.

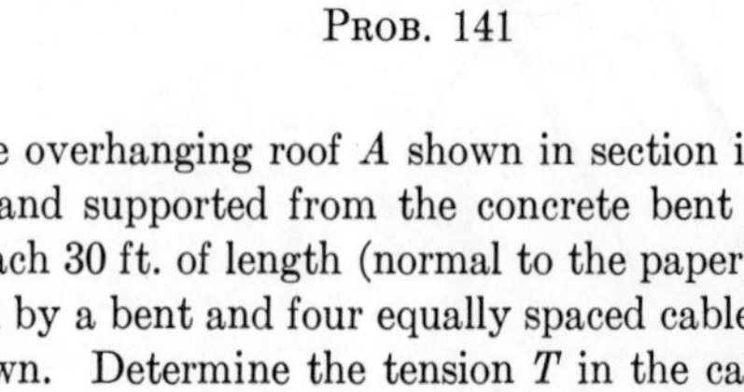

Prob. 141

142. The large overhanging roof A shown in section is constructed of reinforced concrete and supported from the concrete bent B. The roof weighs 400,000 lb. for each 30 ft. of length (normal to the paper), and each 30 ft. section is supported by a bent and four equally spaced cable-and-strut assemblies like the one shown. Determine the tension T in the cable of each assembly. The roof slab is uniform and may be considered to be hinged to the bent at C.

Ans. $T = 260{,}000$ lb.

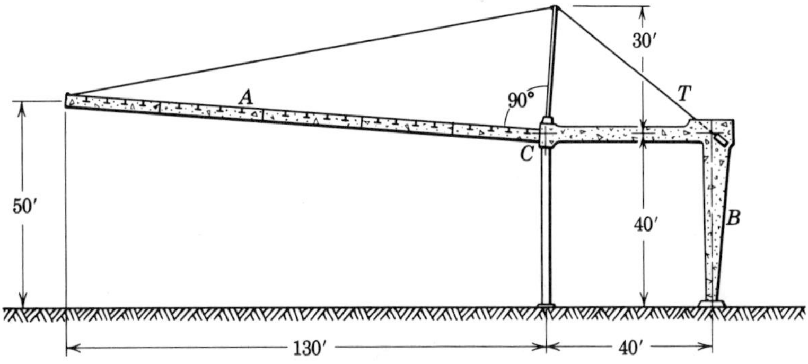

PROB. 142

143. A chain binder is used to secure loads of logs, lumber, pipe, and the like. If the tension T_1 is 500 lb. when $\theta = 30$ deg., determine the force P required on the lever and the tension T_2. Assume that the surface upon which the binder rests is perfectly smooth. *Ans.* $P = 41.7$ lb., $T_2 = 479$ lb.

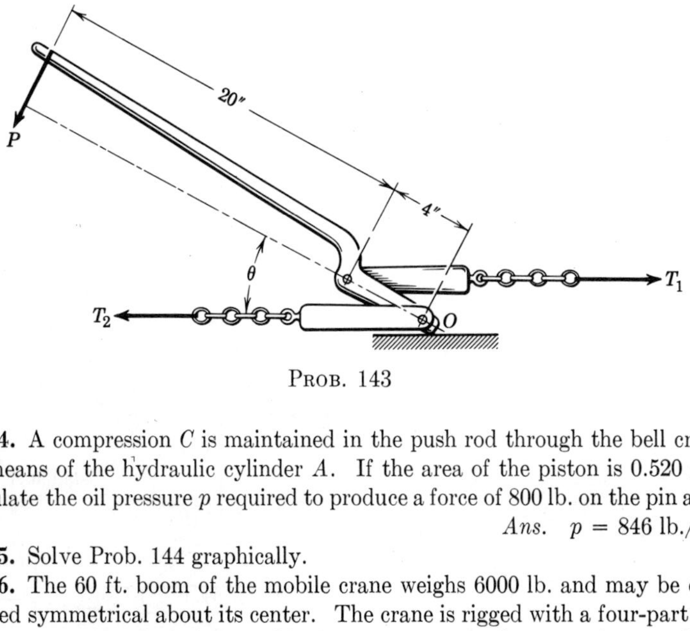

PROB. 143

144. A compression C is maintained in the push rod through the bell crank by means of the hydraulic cylinder A. If the area of the piston is 0.520 in.^{2}, calculate the oil pressure p required to produce a force of 800 lb. on the pin at O. *Ans.* $p = 846$ lb./in.^{2}

145. Solve Prob. 144 graphically.

146. The 60 ft. boom of the mobile crane weighs 6000 lb. and may be considered symmetrical about its center. The crane is rigged with a four-part line which means that the hoisting cable P passes over one sheave at A, around one sheave at B, over the second sheave at A, around the second sheave at B, and back to a fixed attachment at A. For the position shown determine the total tension T in the pendant cables which top the boom. For all practical purposes the center of gravity of the 20,000 lb. load may be taken to be directly below point A.

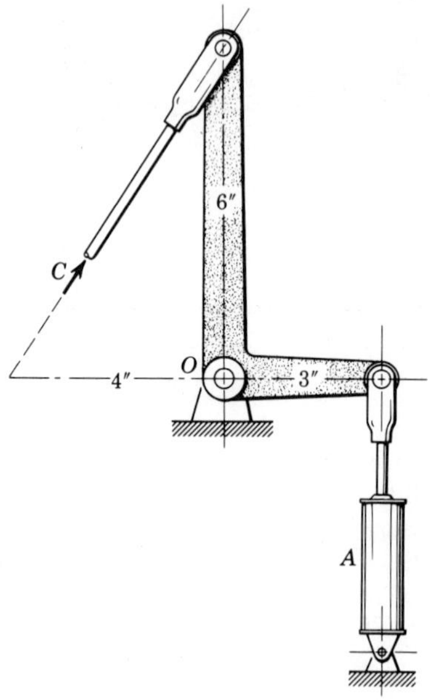

PROB. 144

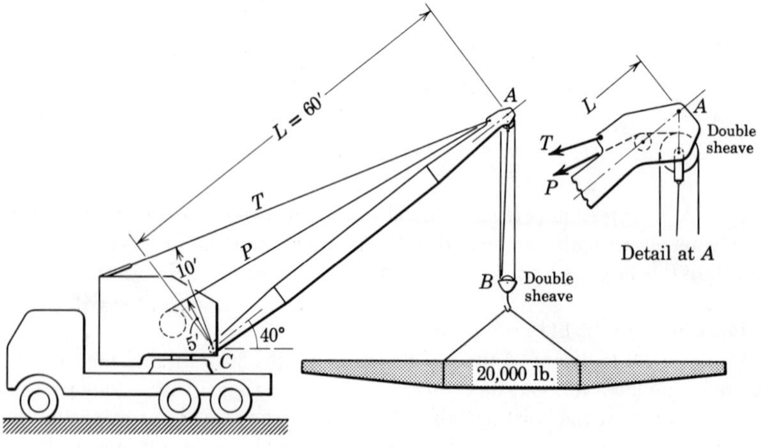

PROB. 146

147. The uniform concrete slab AB weighs 180,000 lb. and is being raised into a vertical position by means of the two cables. Calculate the tensions T_1 and T_2 for the position shown. *Ans.* $T_1 = 127{,}000$ lb., $T_2 = 135{,}500$ lb.

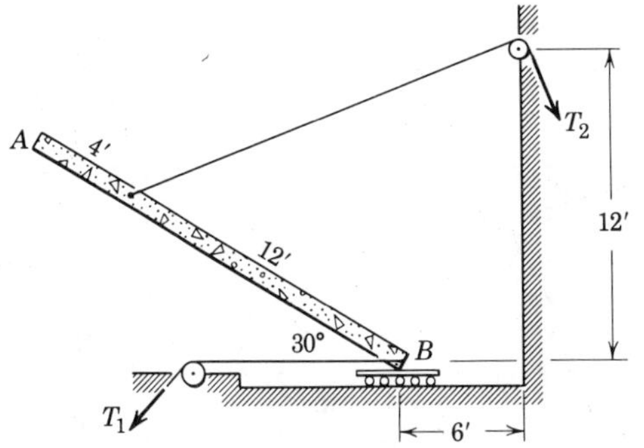

PROB. 147

148. Solve Prob. 147 graphically.

149. The screw of the heavy-duty pipe vise shown is tightened until a vertical compression of 3000 lb. is developed in the screw. If the pin at B has been removed and the vise is held in position by the link CD, determine the total force on the pin at A. The force which the link CD exerts on the frame F is directed along the line joining points C to D. *Ans.* $A = 1825$ lb.

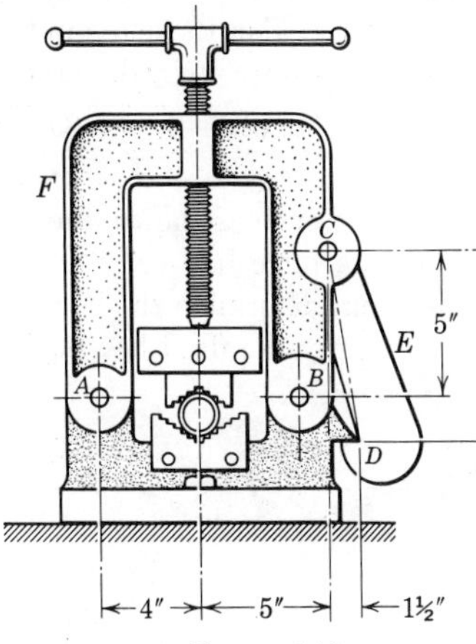

PROB. 149

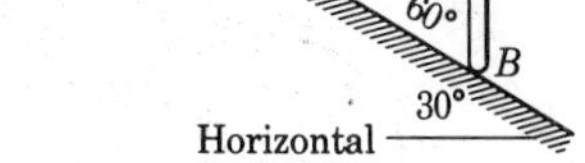

PROB. 150

150. A uniform and rigid V-frame with equal legs weighs 60 lb. and is supported by the hinge at A and a smooth surface at B. Calculate the hinge-pin reaction A.

151. Solve Prob. 150 graphically.

152. The boom weighs 1500 lb., and its center of gravity is at the midpoint of its length. Determine the tension T in the cable and the reaction on the ball joint at A. *Ans.* $T = 1760$ lb., $A = 5710$ lb.

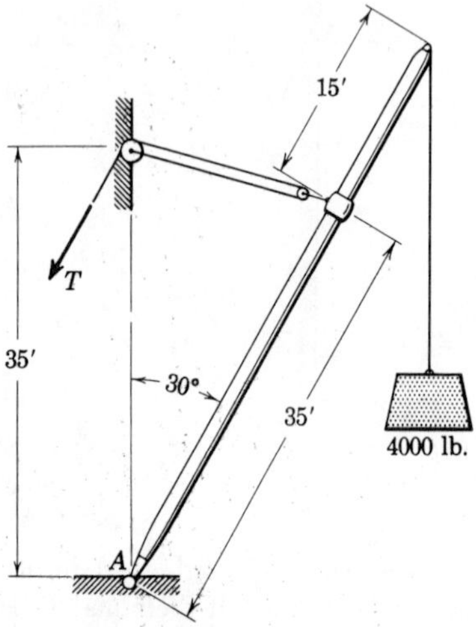

Prob. 152

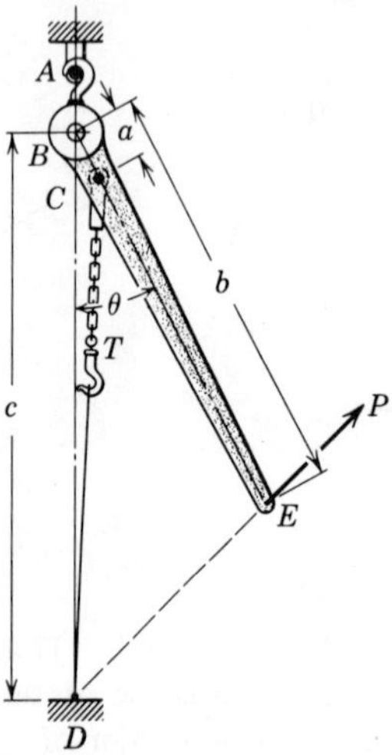

Prob. 153

153. A puller is a simple device for exerting large forces with a relatively small applied load on the handle. If the applied load P is always directed toward the point D, write an expression for the tension T in the chain in terms of P and the dimensions shown. Under the conditions stated why does the link AB remain vertical?

Ans. $T = \dfrac{Pb}{a} \dfrac{\sqrt{a^2 + c^2 - 2ac \cos \theta}}{\sqrt{b^2 + c^2 - 2bc \cos \theta}}$

154. When the 40 lb. force is applied to the tire wrench as shown, the wheel is prevented from turning by reason of the friction force between it and the ground. By using only one equation of equilibrium determine the horizontal component O_x of the reaction exerted on the wheel by the fixed bearing at O.

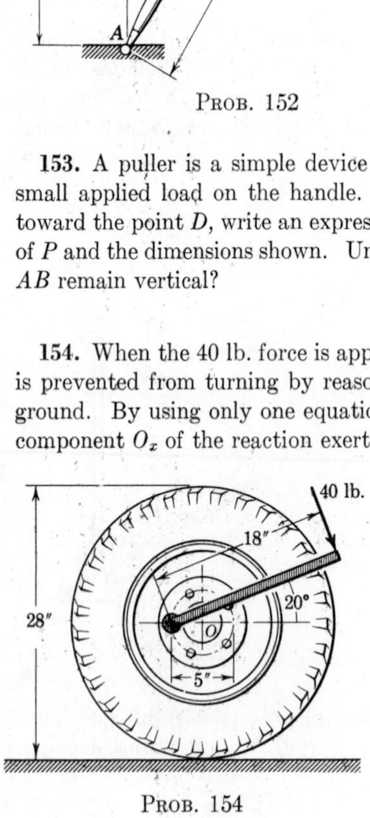

Prob. 154

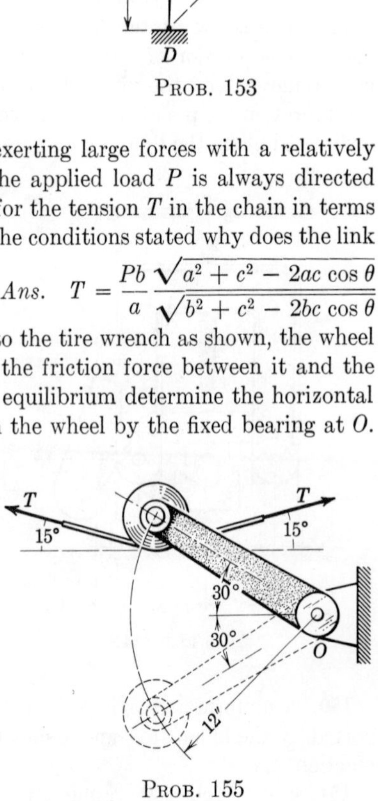

Prob. 155

155. The arm of an idler pulley is attached to one end of a coiled spring which fits over the shaft at O and is fixed at its other end. If a torque of 6 lb. in. will wind the spring through 1 deg. and if the spring is untwisted with the arm in the dotted position, determine the tension T in the belt. Neglect the weight of the arm and pulley. *Ans.* $T = 66.9$ lb.

156. The girder and brackets weigh 250 lb. and have a center of gravity at G. Determine the force acting on the pin at O while the 300 lb. force and 600 lb. ft. couple are acting. The contact force at A may be considered vertical.

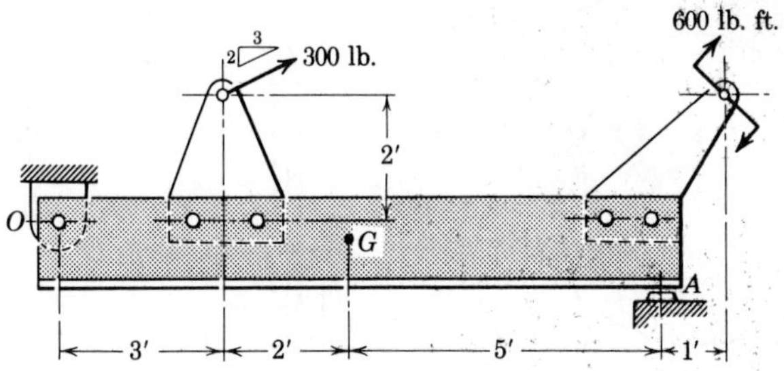

PROB. 156

157. A pipe bender consists of two grooved pulleys mounted and free to turn on a fixed frame as illustrated. For a 75 lb. force on the bent pipe compute the forces A and B on the bearings of the two pulleys similarly labeled.

Ans. $A = 290$ lb., $B = 356$ lb.

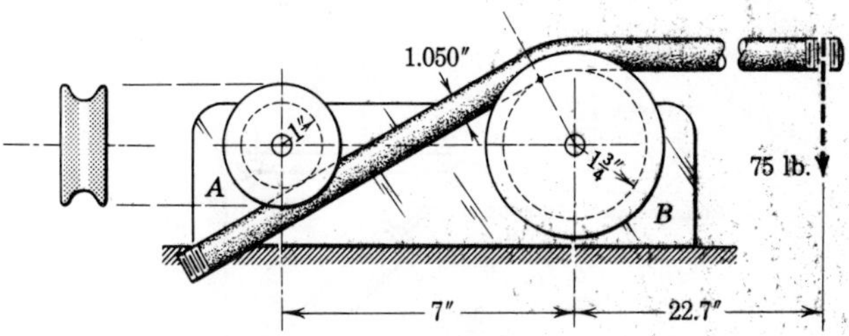

PROB. 157

158. A wedge is forced into the opening in the split ring and exerts a vertical force of 600 lb. on each end of the ring. Specify the internal force F and bending moment M (couple) acting at section C by isolating the section AC of the ring with a free-body diagram. Assume that the force on the section at C acts at the mean radius of 6 in. Do the same for section B.

Ans. $F_C = 600$ lb., $M_C = 7200$ lb. in.;
$F_B = 600$ lb., $M_B = 3600$ lb. in.

159. The curved pipe A serves as the bracket for the loaded pulley. Draw a free-body diagram of that portion of the pipe above section B, and determine all unknown actions on the pipe section.

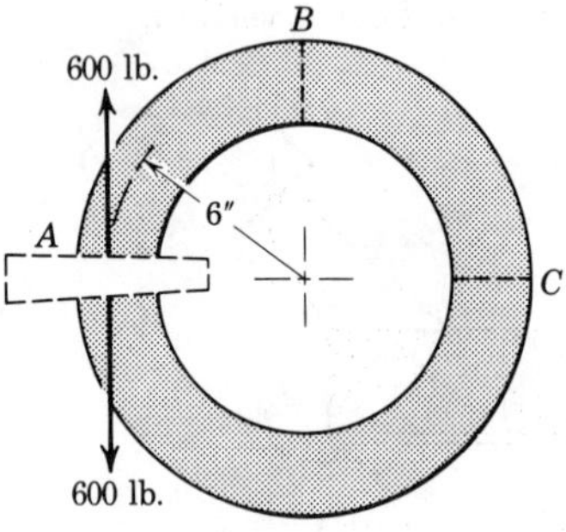

PROB. 158

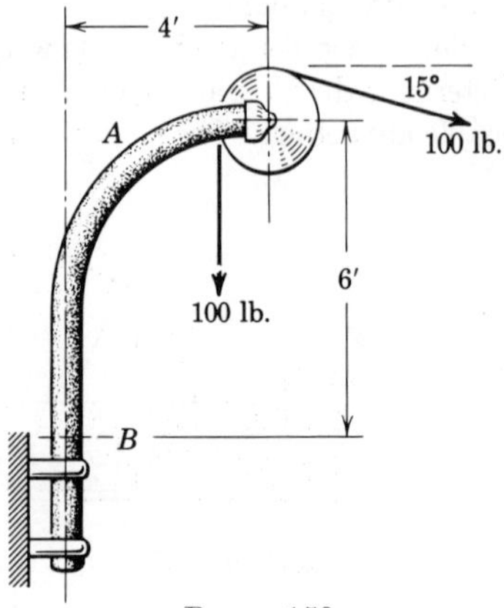

PROB. 159

160. The bar AC has a negligible weight compared with the homogeneous 100 lb. steel cylinder welded to its end. Determine the force on the pin connection at A by considering, first, the free-body diagram of the bar and weight together and, second, the free-body diagrams of the bar and weight separately.

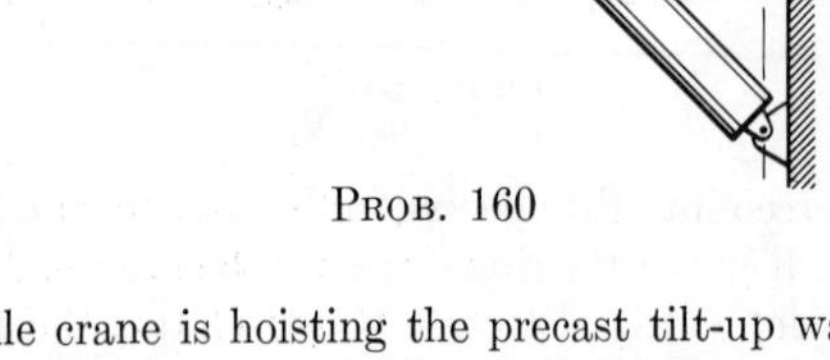

PROB. 160

161. The mobile crane is hoisting the precast tilt-up wall panel for a new building. If the uniform concrete slab weighs 24 tons, determine graphically the cable tension T when the slab reaches the position indicated. Neglect the diameter of the pulleys over which the cables run. *Ans.* $T = 5.49$ tons

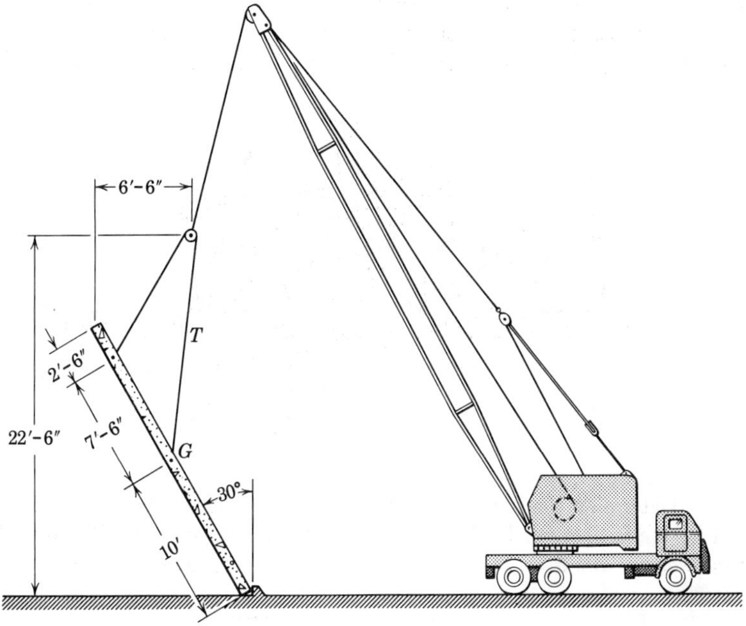

PROB. 161

162. Calculate the force F on the piston of the hydraulic cylinder A necessary to start raising the load of 1500 lb. of dirt for the front-end loader shown. Neglect the weights of the links compared with the load and take the center of gravity of the dirt to be at G. Also calculate the force on the pin at B.

Ans. $F = 4240$ lb., $B = 1524$ lb.

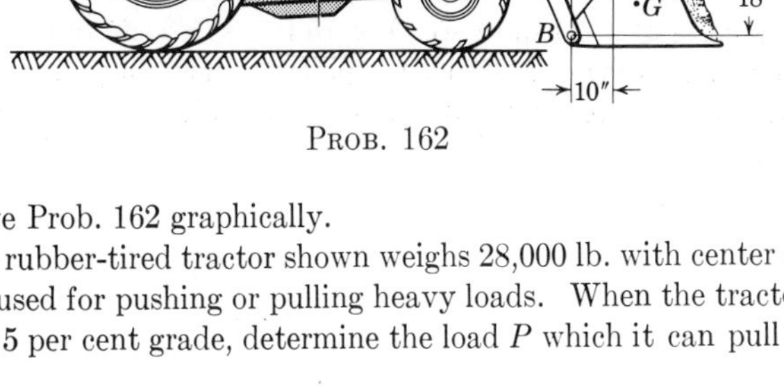

PROB. 162

163. Solve Prob. 162 graphically.

164. The rubber-tired tractor shown weighs 28,000 lb. with center of gravity at G and is used for pushing or pulling heavy loads. When the tractor is moving up the 15 per cent grade, determine the load P which it can pull at a constant velocity of 3 mi./hr. if the driving force which the ground exerts on each of its four wheels is 80 per cent of the normal force under the corresponding wheel. Also find the total normal reaction N_1 under the front pair of wheels at A.

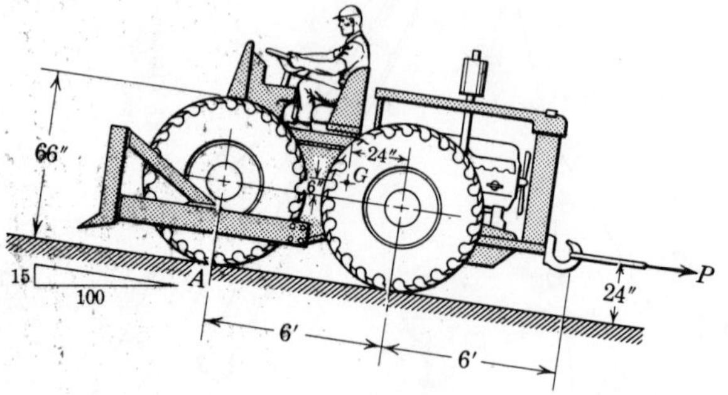

Prob. 164

165. Determine the increase ΔR in the force acting on the pin connection at A for the fixed crane due to the application of the 3 ton load. The unloaded crane weighs 4200 lb. *Ans.* $\Delta R = 9.12$ tons

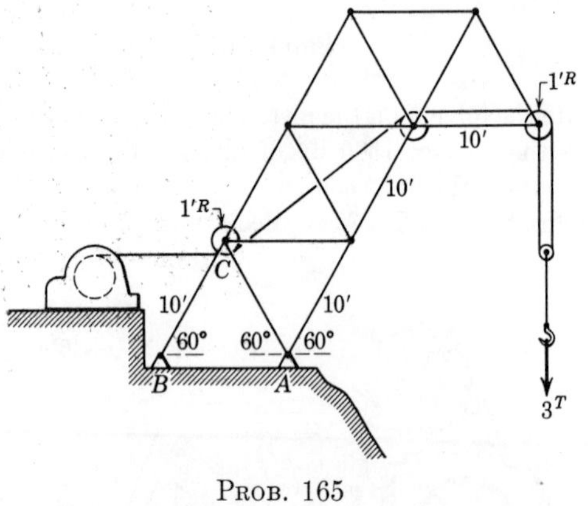

Prob. 165

166. Flexible strip steel under a constant tension of 50 lb. is fed through the guide pulleys at a constant speed of 15 ft./sec. Determine the tension T in the supporting spring which holds the plate to which the pulleys are mounted. Analyze the entire system without removing the pulleys. The plane of the plate is horizontal.

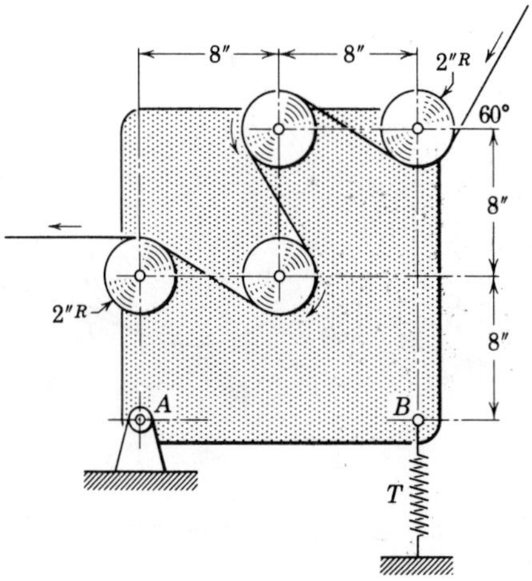

PROB. 166

167. The revolving drum of a mixer has a diameter of 20 in. and is supported by the two ball bearings A and B. Assume that the entire thrust in the direction of the axis of the bearings is taken by A and determine the total forces supported by the bearings when the drum is tilted 45 deg. and filled to capacity

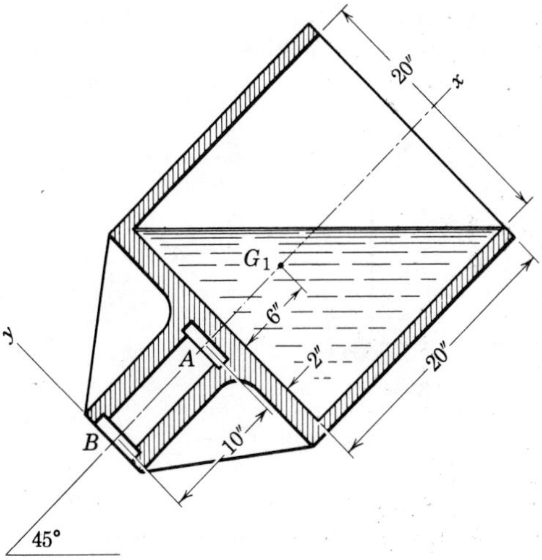

PROB. 167

with a liquid whose specific gravity is 1.20. The empty drum assembly weighs 60 lb., and its center of gravity is at G_1. (*Hint:* Use the results of Prob. 362 for the center of gravity of the liquid.)

Ans. $A_x = 139$ lb., $A_y = 276$ lb., $B_y = 137$ lb.

168. Find the minimum angle θ so that the pile of three identical smooth rollers will not collapse. *Ans.* $\theta = 10° 55'$

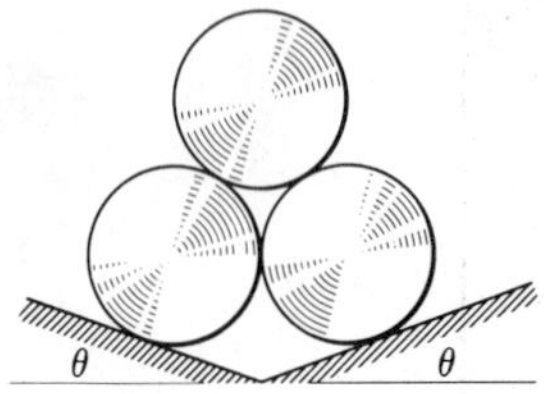

PROB. 168

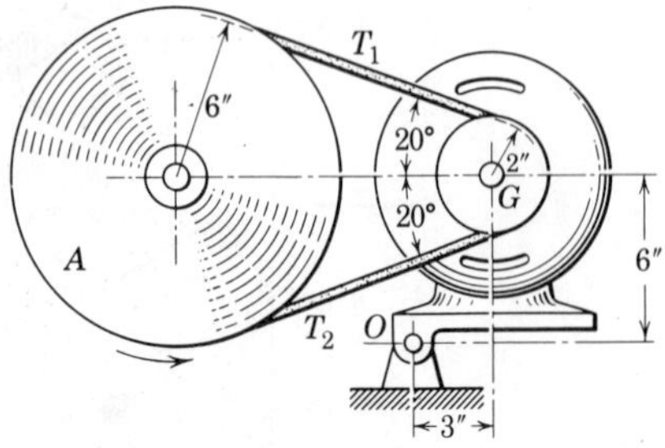

PROB. 169

* **169.** The 40 lb. electric motor with center of gravity at G is pivoted freely at O and drives the pulley A with a V-belt in a counterclockwise direction and at a constant speed. If a constant torque of 120 lb. in. is required to drive the pulley about its axis, determine the tensions T_1 and T_2 in the V-belt and find the total force on the supporting pin at O.

Ans. $T_1 = 6.0$ lb., $T_2 = 26.0$ lb., $O = 55.7$ lb.

* **170.** The 2:1 speed reducer runs at a constant speed and receives an input torque of 200 lb. in. on shaft C which turns clockwise. The output shaft D supplies a steady torque to the machine which it drives. The reducer unit weighs 30 lb. with center of gravity at G. Determine the net force exerted on the reducer base at A and B by the combined action of the foundation and bolts.

Ans. $A = 72.9$ lb. down, $B = 102.9$ lb. up

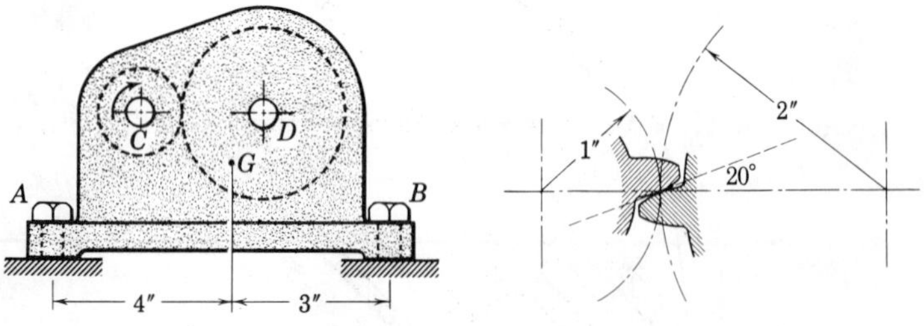

PROB. 170

171. The gear tooth action for the speed reducer of Prob. 170 is shown in the sketch accompanying the figure. Determine the resultant force exerted by each gear on its bearing.

* **172.** The "magic tube," if too short, will not stand upright on its base because of the overturning moment due to the hidden balls inside. Determine the minimum weight W of the tube so that it will not overturn. The weight of each ball is w, and $b < 2r$.

Ans. $W = 2\left(1 - \frac{r}{b}\right) w$

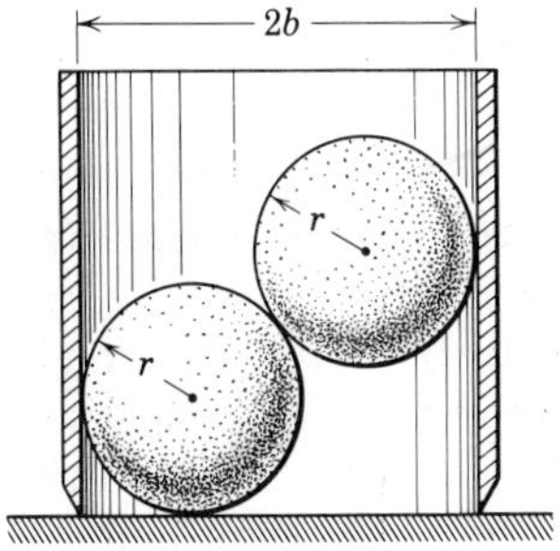

Prob. 172

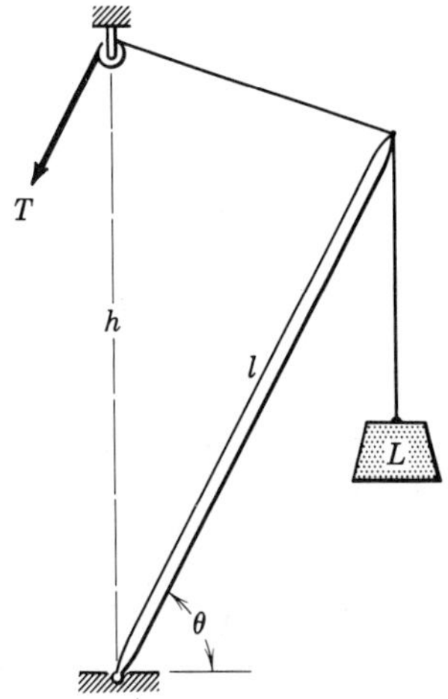

Prob. 173

* **173.** If the weight of the boom is negligible compared with the load L, find the compression C in the boom and prove algebraically that C is constant for all values of θ. Find the limiting value of the tension T as θ approaches 90 deg.

$$Ans.\quad C = \frac{l}{h}L;\ T_{\theta=90^\circ} = \pm\left(1 - \frac{l}{h}\right)L,\ h \gtrless l$$

* **174.** When erected, the movable bridge was perfectly balanced for all positions. Later the bridge roadway was paved uniformly with 2.5 tons of asphalt,

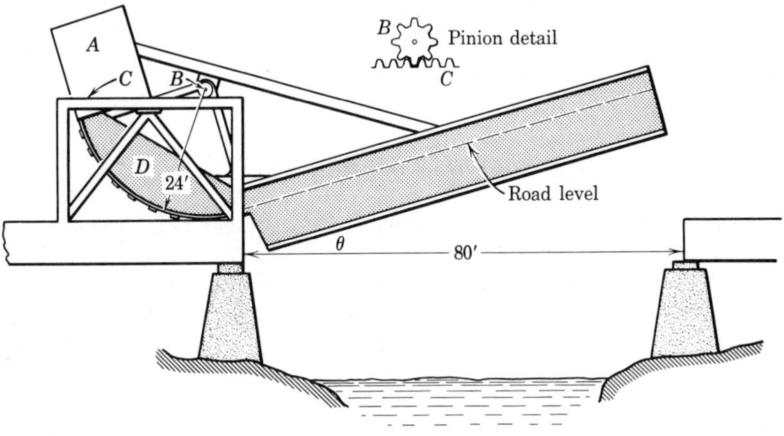

Prob. 174

but the counterweight A was not increased. The two pinions at B (one on each side of the bridge) are driven by a single connecting shaft and mesh with the fixed rack *C*. The shaft is driven by an electric motor mounted on the movable unit. This action rolls the bridge on the rocker segment *D*. Determine the torque *M* which must be applied to the pinion drive shaft in order to overcome the added roadway weight for $\theta = 20$ deg. The mean radius of each pinion is 5 in.

Ans. $M = 4050$ lb. ft.

22. Equilibrium by Funicular Polygon. In Art. 17 the resultant of a coplanar force system was found by the funicular polygon. If the resultant of the force system is zero, the body upon which it acts is in equilibrium. It follows that the force polygon must close (zero resultant force) and that the string polygon must also close (zero resultant moment or couple). In Fig. 22*a* the body would be in equilibrium under the action of F_1, F_2, F_3, and a force equal and opposite to the resultant *AD*. Such a force is called the *equilibrant.* Thus the equilibrant and the resultant force are always equal, opposite, and collinear. The equilibrant for a system of forces is that force which when added to the system produces equilibrium. In the event a system of forces has no resultant force but is not in equilibrium, the equilibrant would be a couple equal and opposite to the residual couple of the given system.

In dealing with the equilibrium of a coplanar system of forces there may be as many as three unknown quantities since Eqs. 13 represent three independent conditions to be satisfied. Thus there are several possible combinations of magnitude, direction, and line of action which may be the unknowns. No general set of rules can be stated which covers the procedure for constructing the force and string polygons for all possible combinations of unknowns. The procedures for two frequently encountered combinations are described in the sample problems which follow.

SAMPLE PROBLEMS

175. Determine by means of a funicular polygon the reactions at each end of the loaded beam of negligible weight.

Solution. The beam is drawn to scale and the lines of action of the forces are labeled as shown. Adding the known loads designated by capital letters gives the line *ABCDE*. The pole *O* is arbitrarily selected and the rays *AO, BO, CO, DO*, and *EO* are drawn. The string polygon is begun at any position, such as point 1, on the line of action of one of the known loads. The strings are constructed parallel to their corresponding rays as explained in Art. 17. By this process points 2 and 3 are located. In order that the resultant shall not be a couple, the string polygon must close. Thus the closing string *fo* may be drawn connecting points 2 and 3. It follows that the unknown ray *FO* in the force polygon may now be drawn parallel to *fo*, and point *F* is thereby determined.

The reaction on the right end is EF and scales 6.3 kips. The reaction FA on the left end scales 3.7 kips.

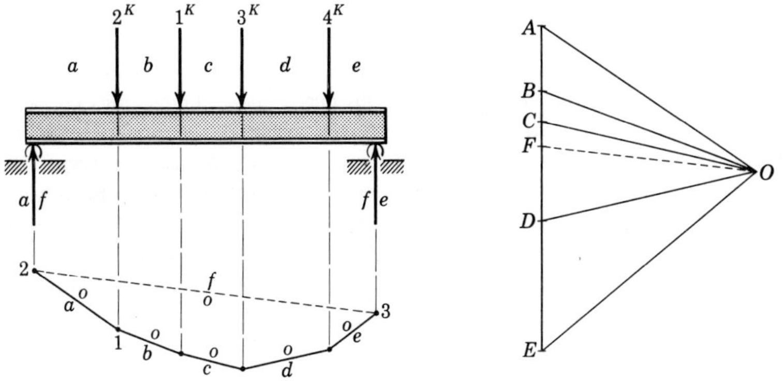

PROB. 175

176. The uniform I-beam of the jib crane weighs 900 lb. and is loaded as shown. Determine by means of a funicular polygon the reaction R at the left end of the beam and the tension T.

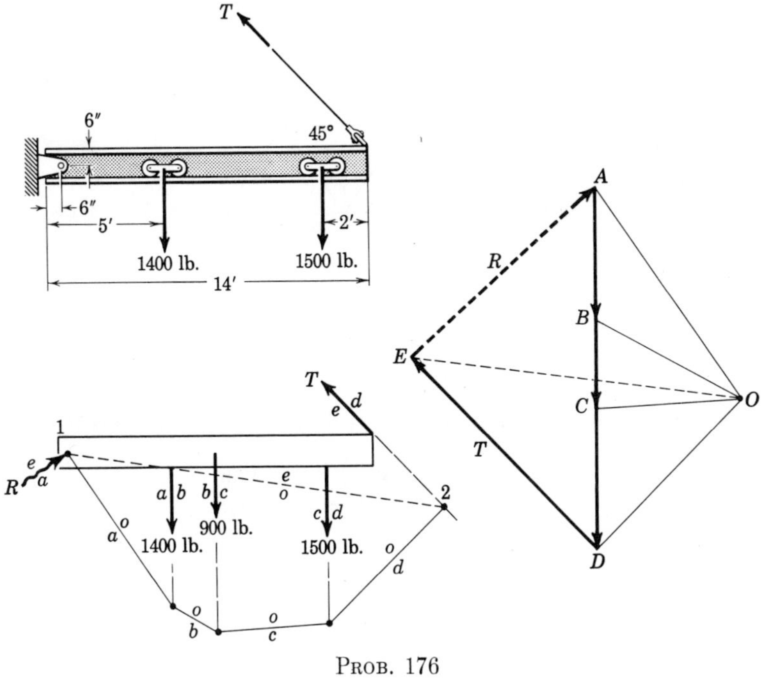

PROB. 176

Solution. The free-body diagram of the beam is drawn to scale, and the reaction R, unknown in magnitude and direction, is shown by a wavy arrow. The lines of action of the forces are labeled with small letters in the order in which they will be added, and the force polygon is begun by adding the three known forces AB, BC, and CD. A line through D with the known direction of the tension DE is also constructed. Point E is still unknown. The pole O is arbitrarily selected and the rays drawn. Point 1 is the only known point on the line of action of R so the string polygon should begin here. The strings *ao*, *bo*, *co*, and *do* are constructed parallel to their respective rays in the force polygon, and point 2 on the line of action of T is established. Since the string polygon must close for equilibrium, the closing string *eo* is drawn connecting points 1 and 2. Point E on the force polygon is now located by constructing the ray OE through O parallel to the string *oe*. The magnitude of the tension T is now established, and R, the closing leg of the polygon, is obtained in magnitude and direction. Scaling the values from the polygon gives

$$T = 2970 \text{ lb.} \qquad \text{and} \qquad R = 2700 \text{ lb.} \qquad \textit{Ans.}$$

PROBLEMS

Solve the following problems by means of a funicular polygon.

177. Determine the vertical reactions at A and B for the loaded truss.

Ans. $A = 4.2$ kips, $B = 4.8$ kips

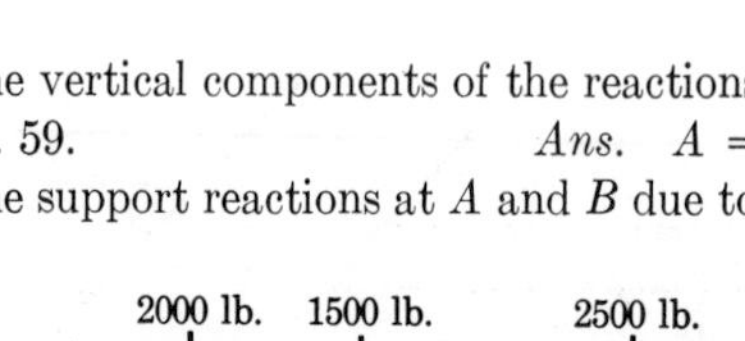

PROB. 177

178. Determine the vertical components of the reactions at A and B for the loaded truss of Prob. 59. *Ans.* $A = 8$ kips, $B = 2$ kips

179. Determine the support reactions at A and B due to the loads acting on the beam.

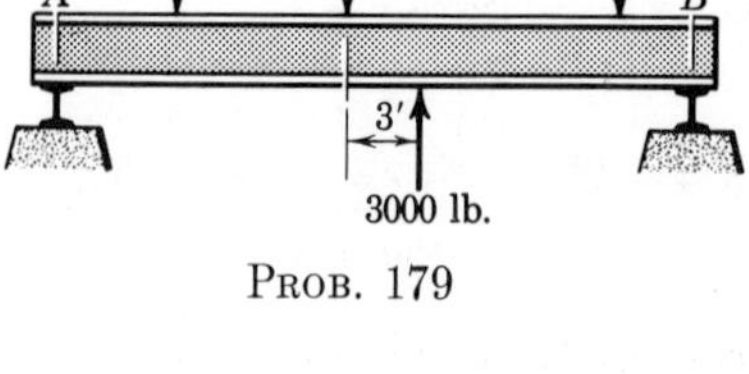

PROB. 179

180. Prob. 147.

181. Prob. 138. *Ans.* $Q = 50$ lb., $T = 92$ lb.

182. The force P maintains equilibrium for the control lever. Find P and the reaction R at the bearing O.

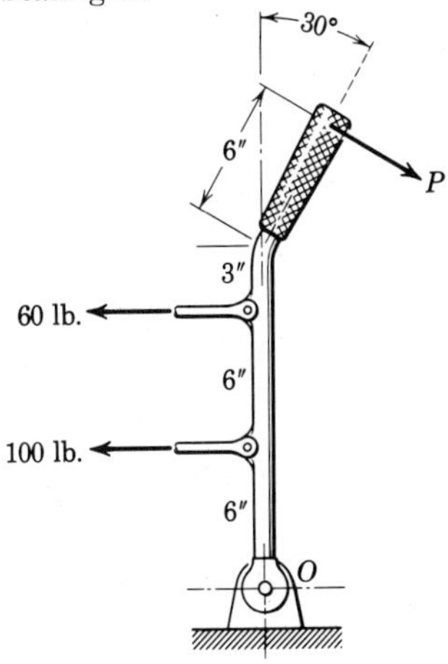

PROB. 182

183. Prob. 152.

184. In Prob. 74 determine the reactions at C and F assuming that the vertical load is supported entirely at F.

185. Cut the beam at its support, section q–q, and determine the resultant vertical force (shear) Q and the couple (bending moment) M acting on the cut section. *Ans.* $Q = 3$ tons, $M = 20$ ton ft.

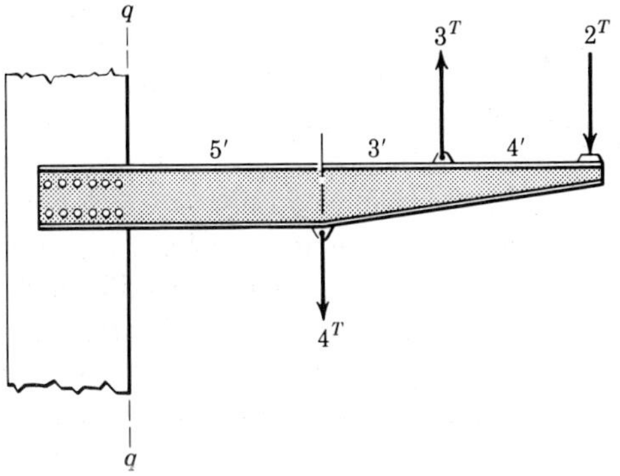

PROB. 185

186. Solve for the pin reaction at O in Prob. 156 by introducing a 600 lb. ft. couple into the known part of the string polygon in the proper sense to make the resultant zero.

187. Cut the beam in Prob. 80 at its support and determine the total force R and the couple (bending moment) M acting on the center of the cut section. *Ans.* $R = 599$ lb., $M = 870$ lb. ft.

188. Determine the magnitude of P and the corresponding acute angle θ which will cause the reaction at O to be 100 lb. in the equilibrium position shown. (*Hint:* The vertical components of P and the reaction at O can be determined independently of the horizontal components.)

Ans. $P = 107$ lb., $\theta = 23$ deg.

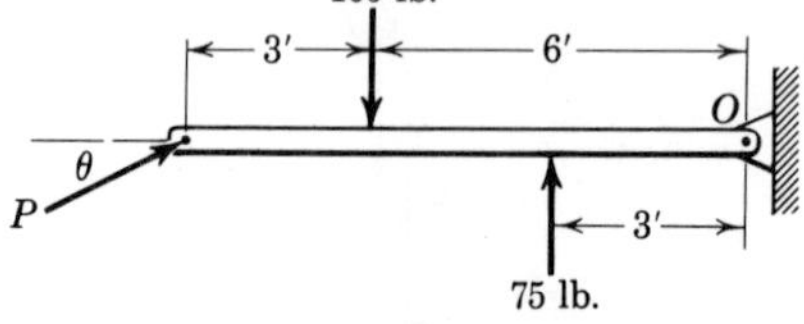

PROB. 188

23. Equilibrium in Three Dimensions. When applied to the general three-dimensional problem, the vector equations of equilibrium, Eqs. 12, may be written in scalar form as

$$\Sigma F_x = 0, \qquad \Sigma M_x = 0,$$
$$\Sigma F_y = 0, \qquad \Sigma M_y = 0, \qquad (16)$$
$$\Sigma F_z = 0, \qquad \Sigma M_z = 0.$$

The first three of these six equations state that for a body in equilibrium there is no resultant force acting on it in any of the three directions. The second three equations express the requirement that there is no resultant twist or moment about any of the coordinate axes or about axes parallel to the coordinate axes. These six equations are the *necessary conditions* for complete equilibrium. Equations 16 are entirely independent, and any of them may hold without the others, in which case the body would be in partial equilibrium only. If, for instance, $\Sigma M_x \neq 0$ but the remaining five equations are satisfied, this combination would describe a body, such as a wheel, fixed at its center of gravity but accelerating in its rotation about the x-axis.

Most three-dimensional problems are simplified if they are broken down into three related two-dimensional problems. Projection of the forces on the three coordinate planes results in the three two-dimensional systems involving the force components in the respective planes.

When equilibrium is produced by concurrent forces, the origin of coordinates is conveniently chosen at the point of concurrency. Since the moments of all forces are zero about any axis through this point, it follows that the equilibrium of concurrent forces is specified completely by the first three of Eqs. 16.

In the case of equilibrium produced by parallel forces, again only three conditions must be satisfied. If the forces are all perpendicular to the x–y plane, for example, then $\Sigma F_z = 0$. The moments of the forces about the other two axes must also be zero, so that $\Sigma M_x = 0$ and $\Sigma M_y = 0$.

SAMPLE PROBLEMS

189. Determine the compression R in the boom and the tensions T_1 and T_2 in the supporting cables if the weight of the boom is neglected compared with the applied load.

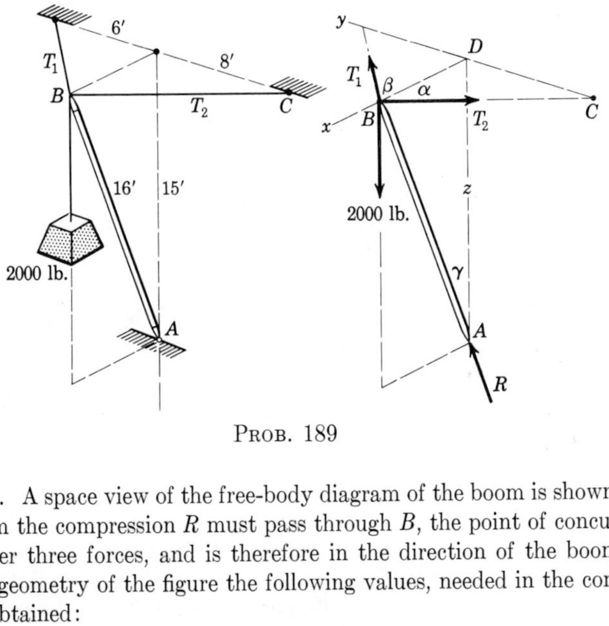

PROB. 189

Solution. A space view of the free-body diagram of the boom is shown. For equilibrium the compression R must pass through B, the point of concurrency of the other three forces, and is therefore in the direction of the boom axis. From the geometry of the figure the following values, needed in the computation, are obtained:

$$BD = 5.57 \text{ ft.}$$

$$\cos\gamma = 0.938, \qquad \sin\gamma = 0.348,$$

$$\cos\beta = 0.680, \qquad \sin\beta = 0.733,$$

$$\cos\alpha = 0.571, \qquad \sin\alpha = 0.821.$$

It may be observed that T_1 and T_2 lie in the x–y plane, and, hence, R may be computed by a force summation in the z-direction. Thus

$\Sigma F_z = 0]$ $\qquad R\cos\gamma = 2000, \qquad R = 2130$ lb. *Ans.*

Equating to zero the moments about an axis through A parallel to the y-axis eliminates R from the equation and gives

$$[\Sigma M_{A_y} = 0] \qquad (T_1 \cos \beta)15 + (T_2 \cos \alpha)15 - 2000 \times 16 \sin \gamma = 0,$$

$$0.680T_1 + 0.571T_2 = 742.$$

Equating to zero the forces in the y-direction gives

$$[\Sigma F_y = 0] \qquad T_1 \sin \beta - T_2 \sin \alpha = 0, \qquad 0.733T_1 = 0.821T_2.$$

Solution of the two equations yields

$$T_1 = 624 \text{ lb.}, \qquad T_2 = 557 \text{ lb.} \qquad \textit{Ans.}$$

The procedure used here is only one of several possible ones for obtaining the answers. In place of the moment equation about A the principle $\Sigma F_x = 0$ could have been used to obtain one of the two necessary relations between T_1 and T_2. It would be possible to avoid a simultaneous solution by equating the moments about a line passing through A and C to zero. In this event T_1 could be found from one equation. However, the added difficulty of computing moment arms to such an inclined axis would offset the small labor of a simultaneous solution in this case.

It should be noted that if the weight of the boom is not negligible the reaction at A will no longer be in the direction of AB since the forces are no longer concurrent.

190. A 50 lb. force is applied to the handle of the hoist in the direction shown. The bearing A supports the thrust (force in the direction of the shaft axis) while bearing B supports only radial load (load normal to the shaft axis). Determine the weight W which can be supported and the total radial force exerted on the shaft by each bearing.

Solution. The free-body diagram of the shaft, lever, and drum considered as a single body could be shown by a space view if desired but is represented here by its three orthogonal projections. The 50 lb. applied force is resolved into its three components, and each of the three views shows two of these components. The correct directions of A_x and B_x may be seen by inspection if it is observed that the resultant of the two 17.7 lb. forces exerts a counterclockwise moment about A. The correct directions of A_y and B_y cannot be determined until the magnitudes of the moments are obtained, so these forces may be arbitrarily assigned. The x–y projection of the bearing forces is shown by a wavy arrow since its direction is unknown. The addition of A_z and W completes the free-body diagrams. It should be noted that the three views represent three two-dimensional problems related by the corresponding components of the forces.

From the x–y projection

$$[\Sigma M_O = 0] \qquad 4W - 10 \times 43.3 = 0, \qquad W = 108.3 \text{ lb.} \qquad \textit{Ans.}$$

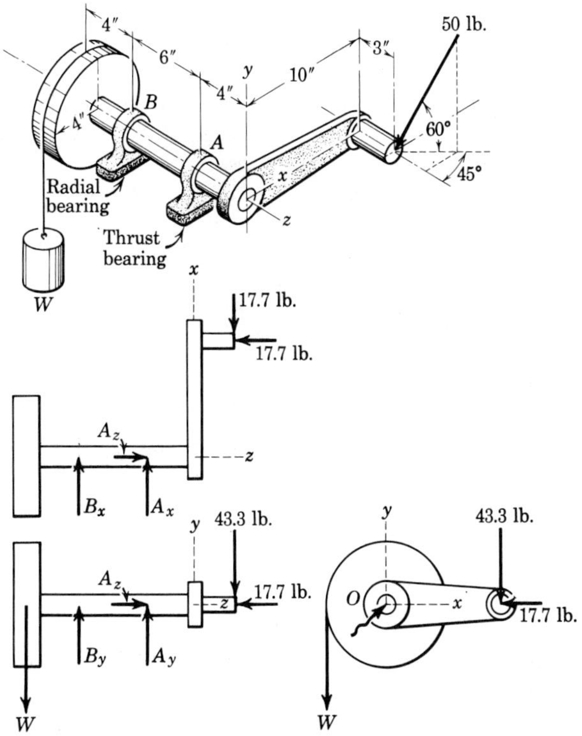

PROB. 190

From the x–z projection

$[\Sigma M_A = 0]$ $\qquad 6B_x + 7 \times 17.7 - 10 \times 17.7 = 0, \qquad B_x = 8.85$ lb.,

$[\Sigma F_x = 0]$ $\qquad A_x + 8.85 - 17.7 = 0, \qquad A_x = 8.85$ lb.

The y–z view gives

$[\Sigma M_A = 0]$ $\qquad 6B_y + 7 \times 43.3 - 10 \times 108.3 = 0, \qquad B_y = 130$ lb.,

$[\Sigma F_y = 0]$ $\qquad A_y + 130 - 43.3 - 108.3 = 0, \qquad A_y = 21.6$ lb.,

$[\Sigma F_z = 0]$ $\qquad A_z = 17.7$ lb.

The total radial forces on the bearings become

$[A_r = \sqrt{A_x^2 + A_y^2}]$ $\qquad A_r = \sqrt{(8.85)^2 + (21.6)^2} = 23.3$ lb. $\qquad$ *Ans.*

$[B = \sqrt{B_x^2 + B_y^2}]$ $\qquad B = \sqrt{(8.85)^2 + (130)^2} = 130.2$ lb. $\qquad$ *Ans.*

PROBLEMS

191. The uniform rectangular steel plate weighs 1200 lb. and is supported by the three cables so that the plate makes an angle of 23 deg. with the horizontal plane. Determine the tensions in the cables.

Ans. $T_1 = 150$ lb., $T_2 = 450$ lb., $T_3 = 600$ lb.

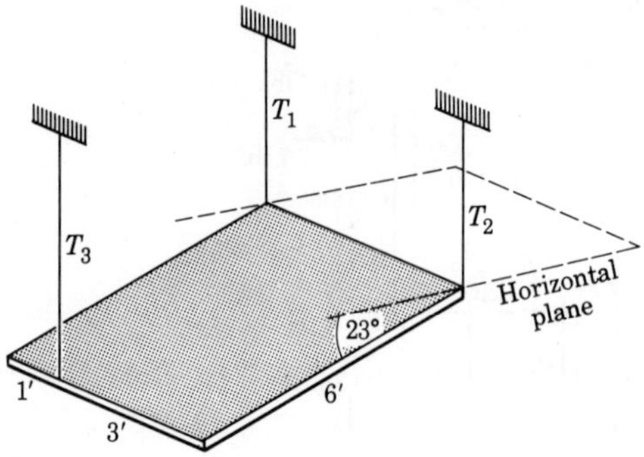

Prob. 191

192. Determine the tension T in the cables, all of which are symmetrically spaced and equally loaded. The marble slab weighs 1000 lb.

Ans. $T = 264$ lb.

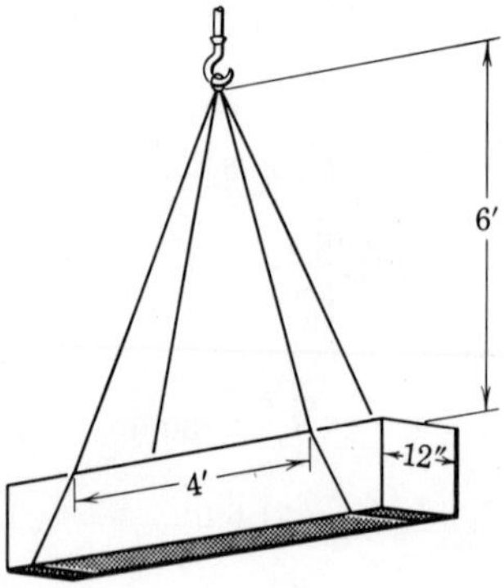

Prob. 192

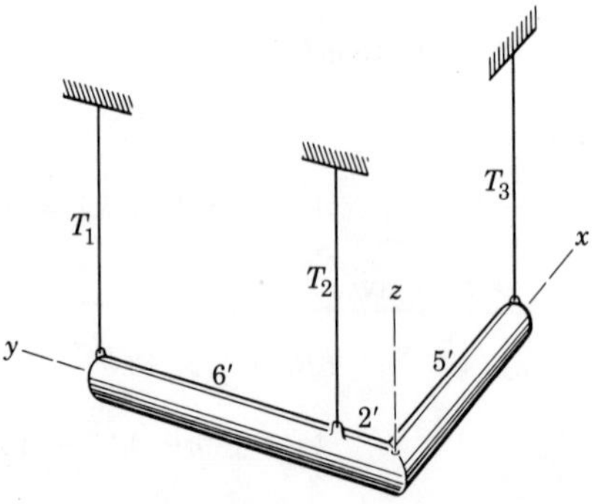

Prob. 193

193. The two sections of pipe are welded together to form a right angle bend, and they are supported in the horizontal plane as shown. If the pipe weighs 40 lb. per foot of length, determine the tensions T_1, T_2, and T_3 in the cables. Neglect the effect of the mitered joint in computing the weights of the pipes.

Ans. $T_1 = 73$ lb., $T_2 = 347$ lb., $T_3 = 100$ lb.

194. The bracket is secured to the end of the fixed shaft by a single bolt which produces sufficient force to hold it in place. Determine the resultant force and moment exerted by the bolt and shaft on the bracket.

Ans. $F = 800$ lb., $M = 9330$ lb. in.

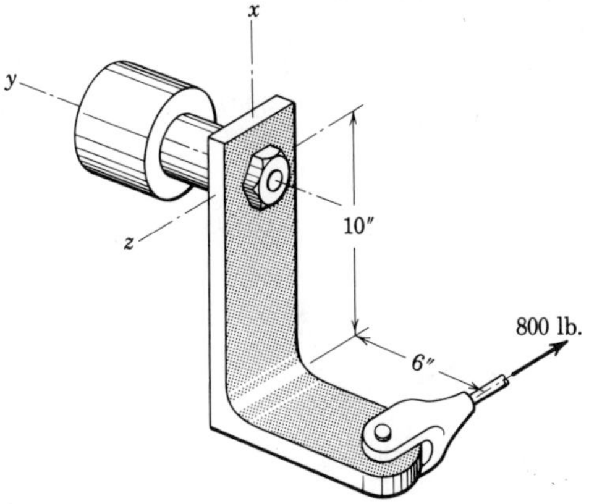

PROB. 194

195. A high-voltage power line is suspended from a transmission tower by the projecting framework shown. If the tension in the power line is 600 lb. at the insulator, determine the compression C in the legs AB and AC and the tension T in the member AD. *Ans.* $C = 246$ lb., $T = 560$ lb.

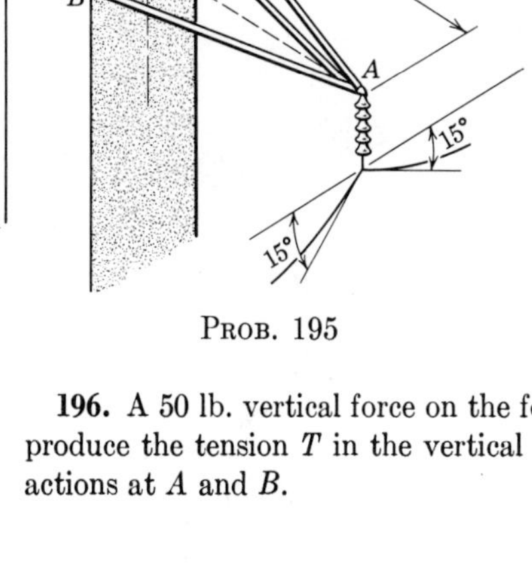

PROB. 195

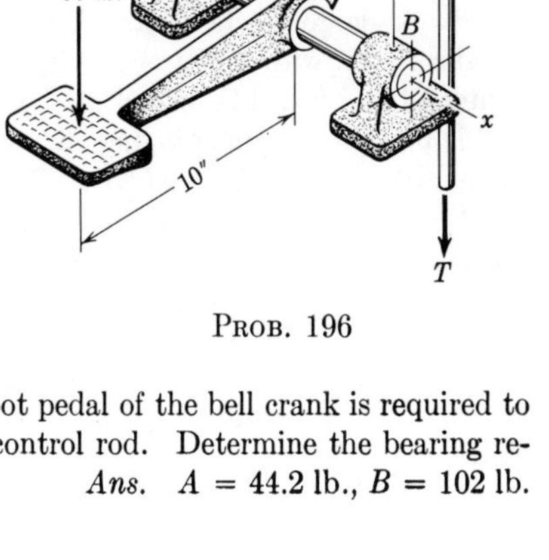

PROB. 196

196. A 50 lb. vertical force on the foot pedal of the bell crank is required to produce the tension T in the vertical control rod. Determine the bearing reactions at A and B. *Ans.* $A = 44.2$ lb., $B = 102$ lb.

197. The 40:1 right-hand worm reducer has an input torque of 10 lb. ft. applied to shaft C in the direction of rotation shown. The output shaft D rotates in the direction indicated and supplies an output torque of 40×10 lb. ft. at a constant speed. Determine the y- and z-components of force exerted on the reducer at its mounting holes by the combined action of the bolts and the foundation.

Ans. $A_y = 600$ lb. (plus y-direction), $A_z = 15$ lb. (plus z-direction), $B_y = -600$ lb. (minus y-direction), $B_z = -15$ lb. (minus z-direction)

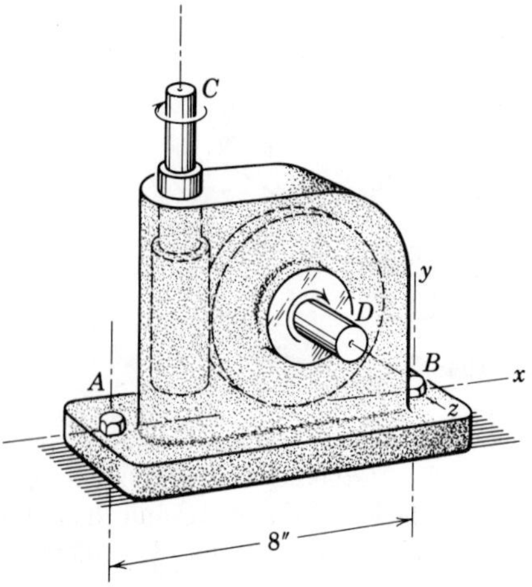

PROB. 197

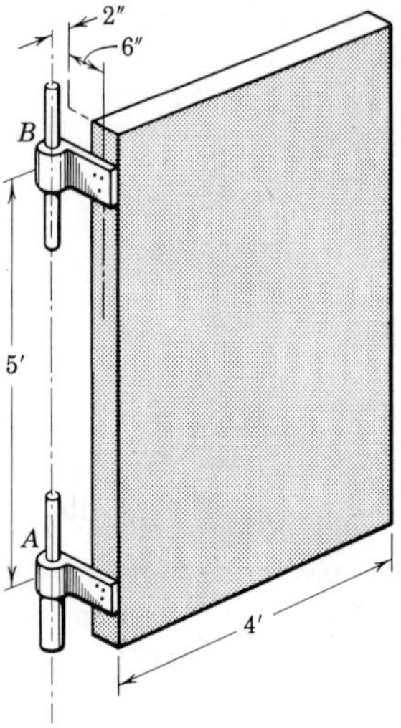

PROB. 198

198. The weight of the homogeneous 100 lb. hinged door is supported entirely at A. Determine the force exerted on the upper hinge B and the total horizontal force exerted on the lower hinge A.

Ans. $|A|_{\text{Horiz.}} = |B| = 44.4$ lb.

199. A large rectangular sign which weighs 400 lb. with center of gravity in the center of the board is hinged at A and B and is prevented from swinging under wind loads by the chains OC and OD. The two lengths of chain together are slightly longer than the dimension from C to D so that only one of the two lengths is taut under wind load. Determine the total force on the hinge pin at B during a wind loading of 300 lb. normal to the sign and acting at its center.

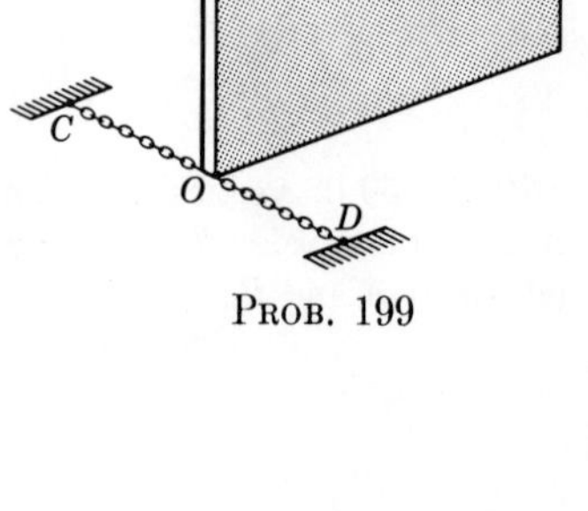

PROB. 199

200. The control lever must supply a torque of 400 lb. in. about the axis *O–O* to turn the shaft. If the lever and the shaft are in contact at *A*, find the force *F* which produces the torque, and determine the total reaction exerted on the lever by the end of the shaft at *A*.

Ans. Reaction is 57.7 lb. force and 462 lb. in. couple

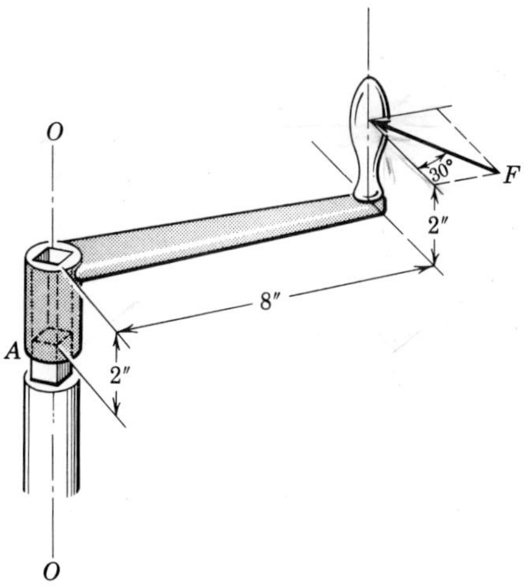

PROB. 200

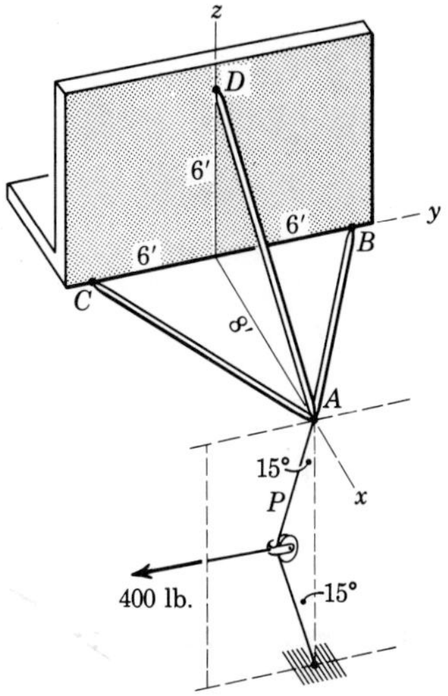

PROB. 201

201. The three struts support the cable tension *P* resulting from the 400 lb. horizontal force. Find the tension *T* or compression *C* developed in each strut.

202. Find the larger of the two tensions in the cables *AC* and *BC* for the boom hoist in the position shown. Neglect the weight of the boom.

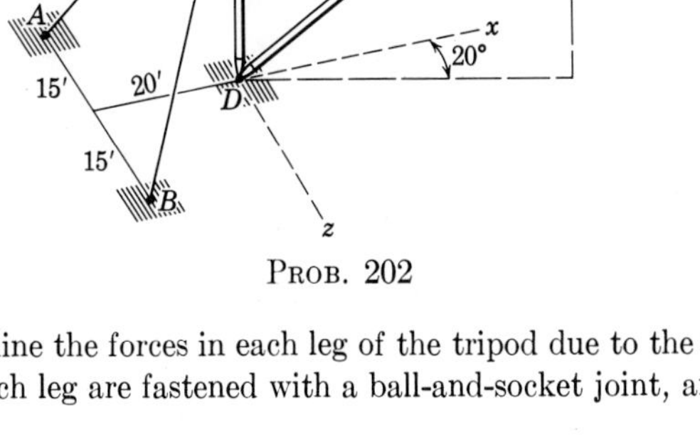

PROB. 202

203. Determine the forces in each leg of the tripod due to the 1000 lb. load. The ends of each leg are fastened with a ball-and-socket joint, and the weight of the legs is negligible compared with the applied load. Write equations which do not involve more than one unknown force at a time in any one equation. Indicate tension T or compression C.

Ans. $AD = 690$ lb. C, $AB = 488$ lb. C, $AC = 1178$ lb. T

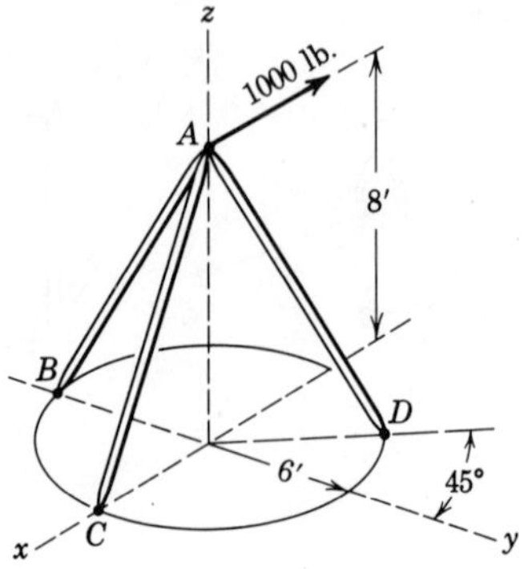

PROB. 203

204. Determine the tensions T_1 and T_2 in the cables which support the vertical mast shown.

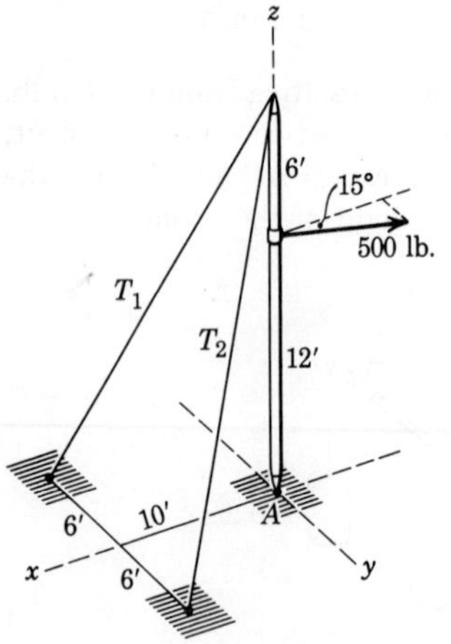

PROB. 204

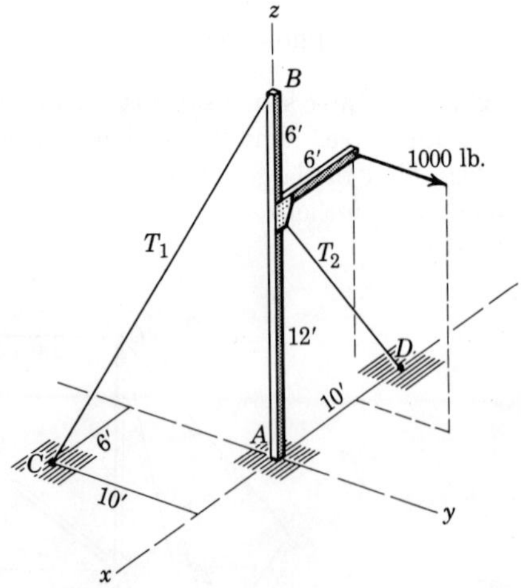

PROB. 205

205. The fitting at the base A of the mast prevents rotation of the mast and rigidly attached arm about the vertical z-axis but offers no resistance to rotation about either horizontal axis through the base. Calculate the tensions T_1 and T_2 in the supporting cables. Neglect the weight of the structure.

Ans. $T_1 = 1430$ lb., $T_2 = 937$ lb.

206. Determine the forces on the bearings A and B if the 30 lb. force is required to turn the crankshaft of the single-cylinder engine against the compression in the cylinder for the position shown. The axis of the 10 in. connecting rod is shown by the dotted line.

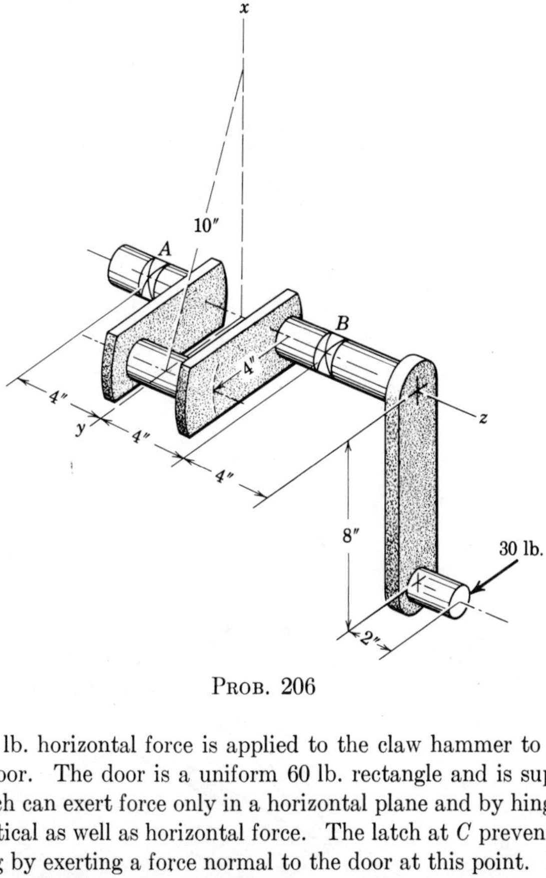

PROB. 206

207. A 40 lb. horizontal force is applied to the claw hammer to pull a nail out of the door. The door is a uniform 60 lb. rectangle and is supported by hinge A which can exert force only in a horizontal plane and by hinge B which supports vertical as well as horizontal force. The latch at C prevents the door from opening by exerting a force normal to the door at this point. Determine the force A supported by the upper hinge.

208. The skylight shown weighs 80 lb. with center of gravity in the center of the rectangle. The chain which operates the sprocket and attached shaft to raise the skylight engages with the teeth of the sprocket and cannot slip. Determine the forces A and B which the two bearings exert on the control shaft if the skylight is held in the position shown by a force P applied to the chain.

Ans. $A = 160$ lb., $B = 17.8$ lb.

209. The shaft, lever, and handle are welded together and constitute a single rigid body. Their combined weight is 60 lb. with center of gravity at G. The assembly is mounted in the bearings A and B, and rotation is prevented by the link CD. Determine the forces exerted on the shaft by the bearings A and B

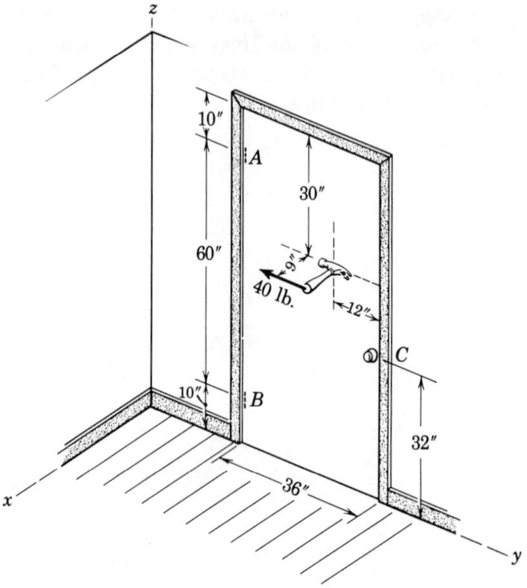

Prob. 207

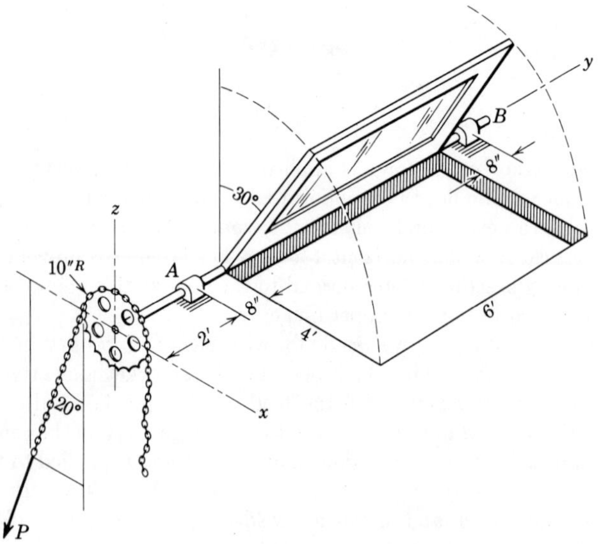

Prob. 208

while the 24 lb. ft. couple is applied to the handle as shown. Would the bearing reactions change if the couple were applied to the end of the shaft AB rather than to the handle? *Ans.* $A = 28.0$ lb., $B = 24.4$ lb

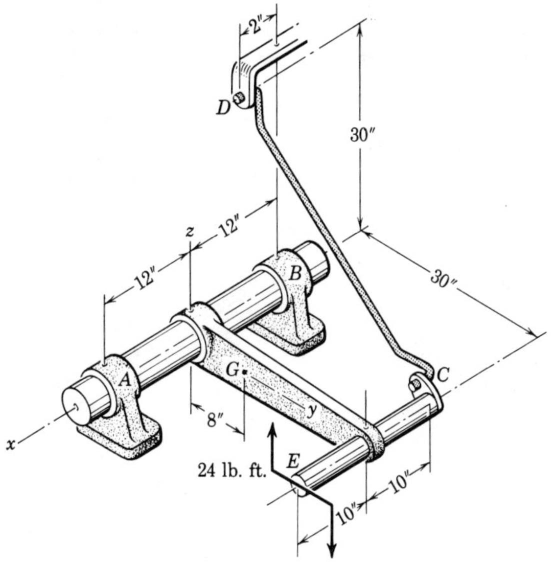

PROB. 209

210. Replace the 24 lb. ft. couple in Prob. 209 by a vertically downward force (minus z-direction) of 50 lb. applied at E and compute the forces exerted on the shaft by the bearings A and B.

211. The post, attached shelf, and electric motor together weigh 280 lb. and have a combined center of gravity at G. The load driven by the motor produces

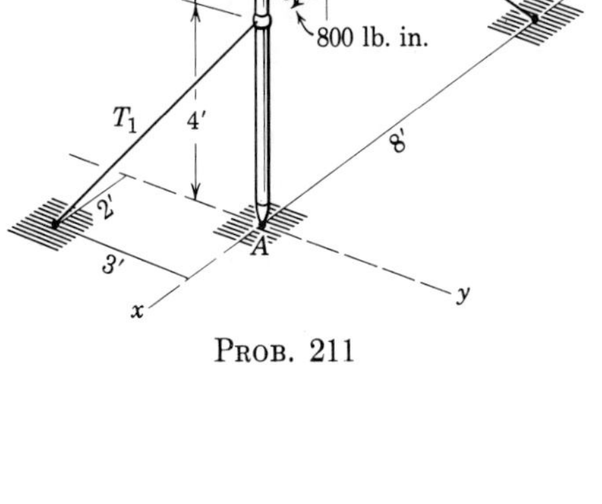

PROB. 211

the reacting couple of 800 lb. in. on the motor shaft as indicated. Determine the tensions T_1 and T_2 in the supporting cables. Assume that the post is supported by a ball-and-socket joint at A. *Ans.* $T_1 = 92.7$ lb., $T_2 = 24.3$ lb.

212. The 1000 lb. mast is supported by a ball-and-socket joint at A and is restrained by the two cables shown. Determine the tensions T_1 and T_2 in the cables and the total force acting on the joint at A.

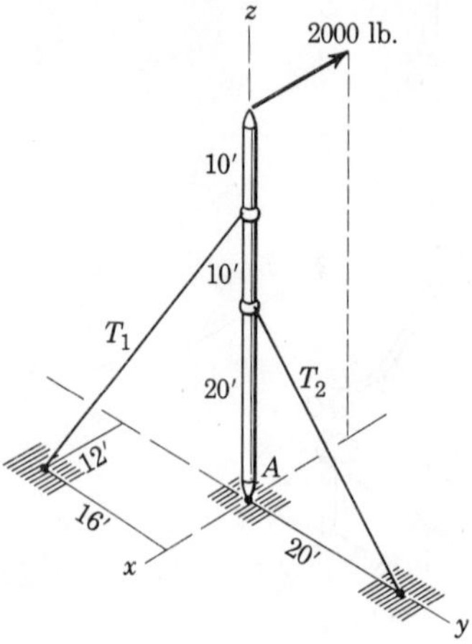

PROB. 212

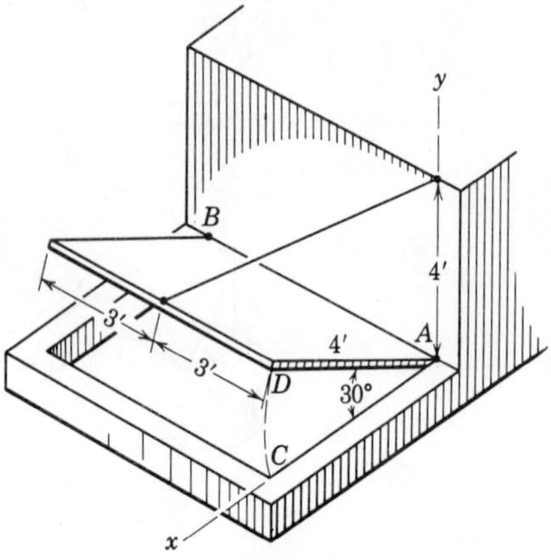

PROB. 213

213. A homogeneous trap door weighing 60 lb. is hinged at A and B and secured by a cable in the position shown. Determine the tension T in the cable and the forces acting on the two hinges perpendicular to the hinge axis AB. Assume all thrust in the direction of AB is supported by hinge A.

Ans. $T = 37.5$ lb., $A_{xy} = 39.7$ lb., $B = 15$ lb.

214. Three identical smooth steel balls of radius r and weight W are placed in a smooth hemispherical bowl of radius R. Determine the force of contact P between the balls for their equilibrium position.

$$Ans.\quad P = \frac{2Wr}{3\sqrt{R^2 - 2Rr - \dfrac{r^2}{3}}}$$

215. If a fourth identical ball is placed centrally on the three balls of Prob. 214, determine the maximum value of R so that the lower three balls will not separate. *Ans.* $R = (1 + 2\sqrt{11})r = 7.63r$

216. The figure shows the top view of a door partly open. A force of 20 lb. normal to the plane of the door is required on the knob to hold the door in the open position against the action of the spring-loaded link CD of the door closer. The link CD is horizontal and is mounted at the top of the door. The door is a uniform 60 lb. panel, 6 ft. 8 in. high and 36 in. wide. The top hinge A is 9 in. below the top of the door, and the bottom hinge B is 9 in. above the bottom. The knob is 36 in. above the bottom. If the lower hinge supports the entire weight of the door, determine the tension T in CD and find the force supported by hinge A for the 30 deg. position.

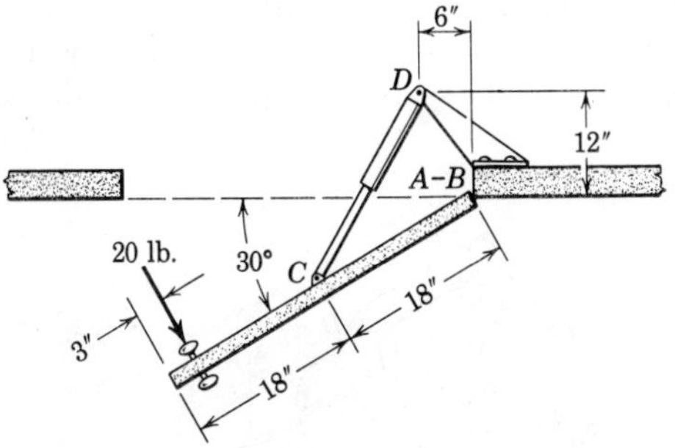

PROB. 216

* **217.** The uniform boom AD weighs 400 lb. and is secured to the wall at A by a ball-and-socket connection. If a force of 300 lb. is required on the rope to support the load W in the position shown, determine the tensions T_1 and T_2 and the total force acting on the connection at A.

Ans. $T_1 = 820$ lb., $T_2 = 434$ lb., $A = 950$ lb.

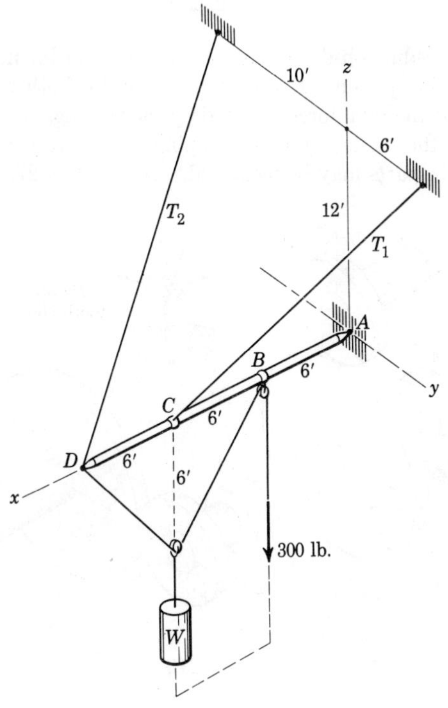

PROB. 217

* **218.** A steel shaft is mounted in a lathe between centers A and B and is driven from the face plate C in the direction shown by the tang of the clamped dog D. The lathe tool E exerts a force of 200 lb. on the shaft at a mean radius

of 2 in. and in a direction given by $\beta = 70$ deg. and $\alpha = 10$ deg. Determine the radial components A_r and B_r (normal to the shaft axis) of the forces exerted by the centers at A and B on the shaft when the tang is in the position illustrated.
Ans. $A_r = 123$ lb., $B_r = 106$ lb.

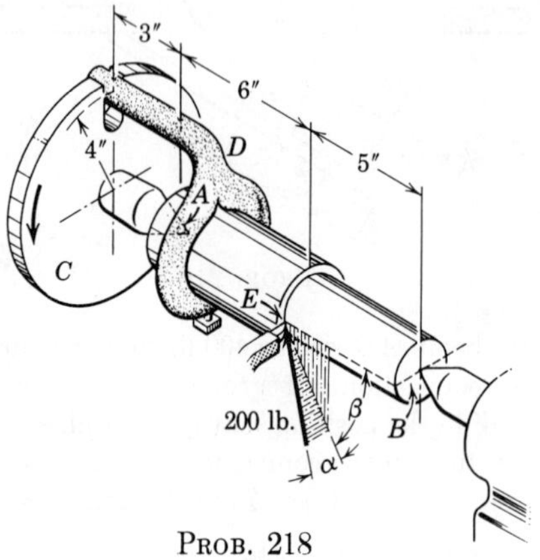

PROB. 218

*** 219.** The 4:1 reduction drive has a torque of 1000 lb. in. supplied to the shaft of the driving pinion. If the tooth action for both pairs of gears is as shown, determine the total forces exerted by the bearings A and B on the shaft. The bearings for the shafts of the driving pinion and driven gear are not shown. The weights of the parts may be neglected. *Ans.* $A = 279$ lb., $B = 1580$ lb.

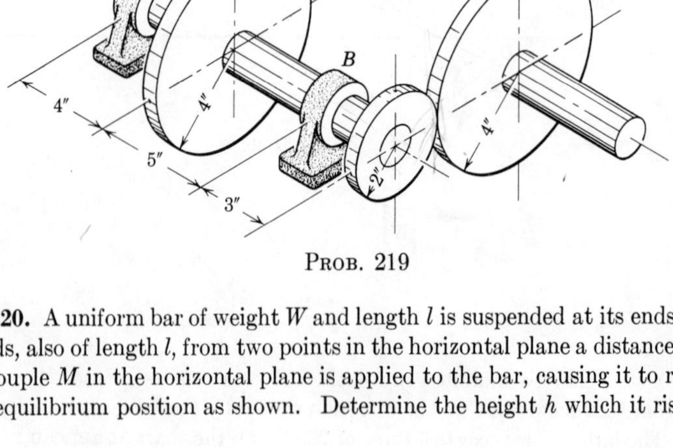

PROB. 219

*** 220.** A uniform bar of weight W and length l is suspended at its ends by two cords, also of length l, from two points in the horizontal plane a distance l apart. A couple M in the horizontal plane is applied to the bar, causing it to rotate to an equilibrium position as shown. Determine the height h which it rises from its original untwisted position. What value of M is required to raise the bar the maximum amount l?

Ans. $h = l\left(1 - \sqrt{1 - \frac{4M^2}{W^2l^2}}\right), \; M_{h\to l} = \frac{Wl}{2}$

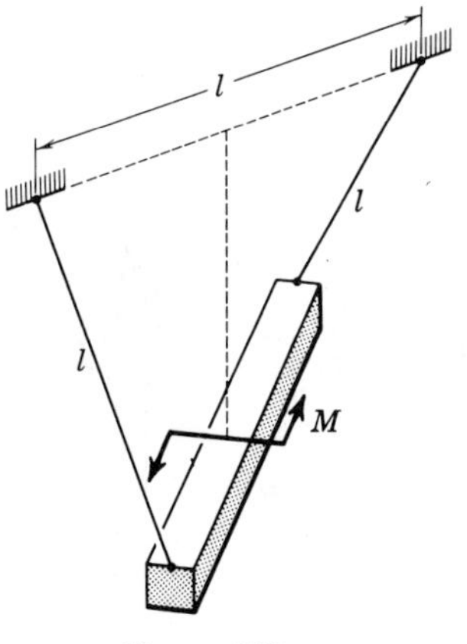

Prob. 220

* **221.** A flexible shaft is bent through 180 deg. in the horizontal plane, and an input torque of 100 lb. in. is applied at one end as shown. After the initial angular twist of the shaft has taken place, one revolution of the input end will be accompanied by one revolution of the output end, and the output torque will equal the input torque. The shaft housing is mounted in a self-aligning support at A which is capable of exerting only a single radial force normal to the

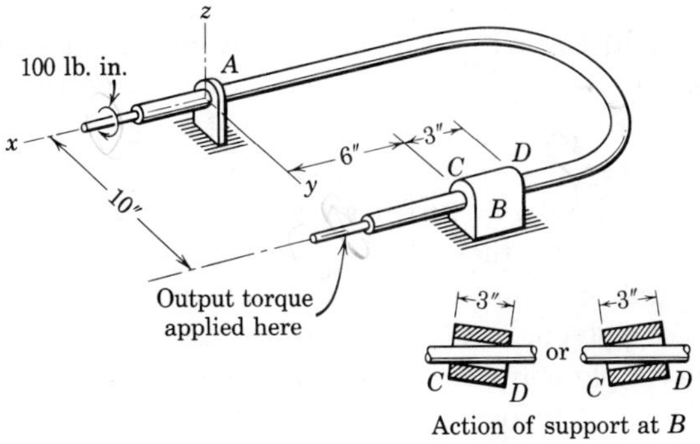

Prob. 221

shaft axis. Support B, on the other hand, is a loose-fitting sleeve and can support the shaft and housing as shown in the separate sectional views. It may be assumed that the shaft housing acts like a rigid tube for any position in which it is bent. Determine the forces exerted by the supports on the shaft housing. Neglect the weight of the shaft.

Ans. A = 20 lb. down, C = 60 lb. up, D = 40 lb. down

* **222.** If the flexible shaft described in Prob. 221 is bent into the position illustrated with the present problem and the supports are of the type used with Prob. 221, determine the forces exerted by the supports on the shaft.

Ans. $A = 25$ lb. plus x-direction,
$C = 325$ lb. minus x-direction,
$D = 300$ lb. plus x-direction

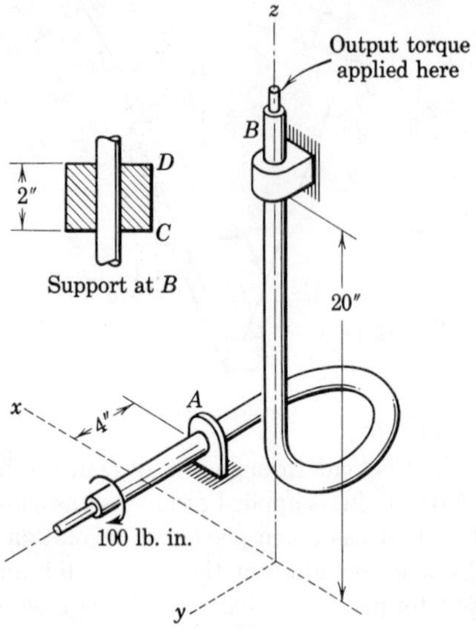

PROB. 222

24. Graphical Solution for Three-Dimensional Equilibrium. The necessary conditions for equilibrium expressed vectorially by Eqs. 12 require that the space polygon of external forces, considered as free vectors, must close and the space polygon of moment or couple vectors must also close. For two-dimensional problems closure of the force and string polygons satisfies these two requirements as was shown in Art. 22. Extension of this procedure to cover the three-dimensional case involves a closed space polygon of forces to insure zero resultant force and a closed space couple polygon to insure zero resultant couple. The construction of these polygons on paper could be accomplished by drawing the three related orthogonal projections of the two space polygons on the three coordinate planes. Such a process involving both polygons is awkward and does not offer an attractive method of solution.

Fortunately many three-dimensional problems involve the equilibrium of concurrent forces or forces which can be easily reduced to a concurrent system. Under these conditions the requirement of zero resultant moment is automatically satisfied, and closure of the space polygon of forces is the only condition which need be considered.

Closure of the force polygon is best accomplished by constructing its orthogonal projections and treating each as a two-dimensional problem. In many instances only two projections are needed, although for some problems all three projections are required.

It is essential before proceeding further that several basic laws of projective geometry be reviewed. In Fig. 33*a* the directed line segment

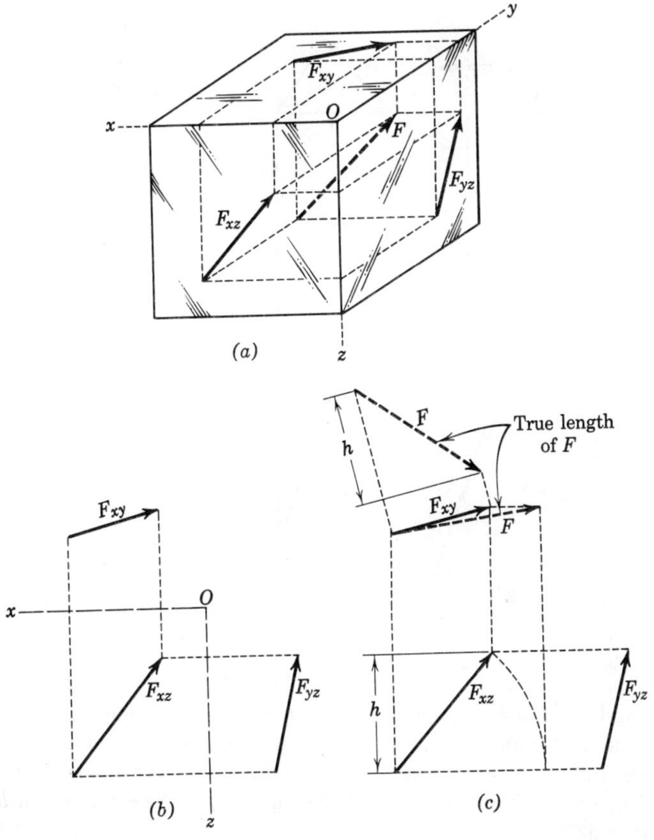

FIG. 33

representing the force F may be located in space by its three coordinate projections. By severing the edge O_y and unfolding along O_x and O_z there result the normal three views of third-angle projection as shown in Fig. 33*b*. The magnitude of the force is obtained in Fig. 33*c* from an auxiliary projection which shows the true length of the vector. This true length may also be found by rotation as shown.

Application of the graphical method is best illustrated by actual examples, two of which are worked in detail in the sample problems which follow.

SAMPLE PROBLEMS

223. Solve Prob. 189 graphically.

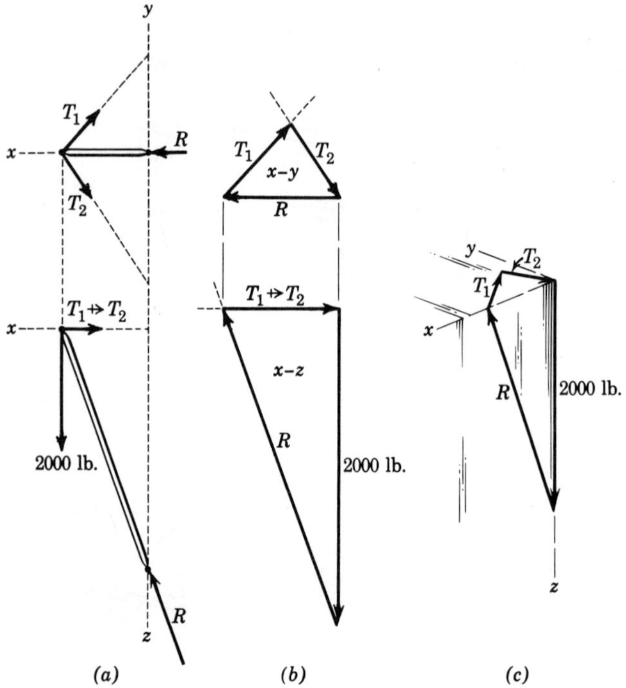

PROB. 223

Solution. Two views of the boom are laid off to scale in the *a*-part of the figure, and the free-body diagram of each view is completed by drawing the corresponding x–z and x–y projections of all forces on the two figures. In the x–z plane the x-components of T_1 and T_2 will appear as a single force and are labeled $T_1 \nrightarrow T_2$. Equilibrium of the boom requires the compression R to act along its axis.

The triangle of forces in the x–z plane is constructed in the *b*-part of the figure by starting with the known 2000 lb. load. From this figure the magnitude of R is obtained since the vector R is seen in its true length. The top or x–y view of the space polygon of forces is drawn next, and the forces are added in the *same sequence* as in the x–z projection. The 2000 lb. load does not appear in this view so that only the horizontal projection of R plus the two tensions T_1 and T_2 are involved. Again the triangle is drawn by starting with the known projection of R. The values of T_1, T_2, and R are scaled from the views which show them in their true length, and they are $T_1 = 624$ lb., $T_2 = 557$ lb. $R = 2130$ lb.

In the *c*-part of the figure is shown the space polygon of forces which was represented first by the two projections. Any order of addition of the forces may be used except that it is usually necessary to start with the known loads first.

224. If the weight of the mast is neglected compared with the applied load, determine graphically the two cable tensions T_1 and T_2 and the force R acting at the ball joint at A.

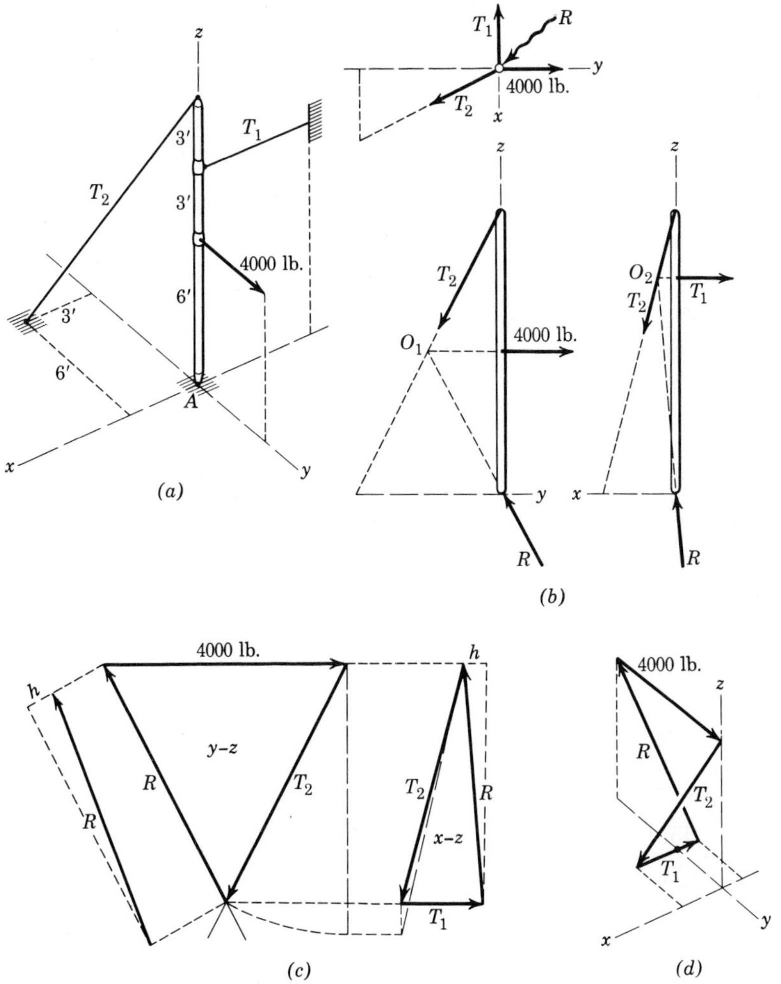

Prob. 224

Solution. The three orthogonal projections of the mast and cables are constructed to scale and used for the three views of the free-body diagram of the mast. In the y–z projection only three forces appear, so that their projections in this view must satisfy the principle of concurrency of three forces in equilibrium. Thus the direction of the y–z projection of R is drawn through point O_1. Actually the three forces all pass through a line through O_1 perpendicular to the y–z plane. The y–z projection of the space polygon of forces may now be drawn as shown in the c-part of the figure. The two resulting vectors R and T_2 are not seen in their true length so their proper magnitudes are not yet obtained.

From the x–z view of the free-body diagram the proper direction of the projection of R is obtained by constructing it through the point of concurrency O_2 of the three vectors. The x–z view of the force polygon is now drawn with the aid of the previous construction and the x–z free-body diagram. By starting with R its x–z projection is constructed parallel to that determined in the free-body diagram, and its terminal points must lie in the same horizontal planes as its established terminal points in the y–z view. Next T_2 and T_1 are drawn with their proper directions to complete the triangle.

The magnitude of T_1 may be scaled directly from the x–z triangle and is

$$T_1 = 1330 \text{ lb.} \qquad \textit{Ans.}$$

The true lengths of R and T_2 must be constructed since neither of the views shows either one in its true length. The true length of R is constructed in the auxiliary projection and is found to be

$$R = 4490 \text{ lb.} \qquad \textit{Ans.}$$

The true length of T_2 is found by rotation (to illustrate the second method) and is shown in the dotted line whose magnitude is

$$T_2 = 4580 \text{ lb.} \qquad \textit{Ans.}$$

The space polygon of forces represented initially by its two projections is shown by way of further illustration in the d-part of the figure.

PROBLEMS

Solve the following problems graphically.

225. Prob. 192. **226.** Prob. 195.
227. Prob. 198. **228.** Prob. 201.
229. Prob. 202.

230. Prob. 203. (*Hint:* View the frame so that two of the legs appear as one.)

* **231.** Prob. 214 for $W = 4$ lb. and $R = 4r = 8$ in.

* **232.** Prob. 215 if the radius of each sphere is 2 in. and $W = 4$ lb.

* **233.** Prob. 204. (*Hint:* Note that in the x–y view of the free-body diagram the x–y component of the reaction A is parallel to the 500 lb. force.)

* **234.** Prob. 205. (*Hint:* Determine the direction of the reaction at A by choosing two views of the free-body diagram for which the principle of concurrency of three forces in equilibrium may be used.)

25. Statically Indeterminate Problems. In all the problems and examples of equilibrium treated so far, care has been taken to select only those situations for which the necessary conditions of equilibrium (Eqs. 12 or 16) were also sufficient conditions. There is a class of problems for which these equations, although necessary, are not sufficient for determining all forces acting on a body in equilibrium. Bodies which have more supports than are necessary to maintain an equilibrium configuration belong to this class and are called *statically indeterminate*. This term means that the statical equations of equilibrium are insufficient to determine all the forces acting.

When any supporting element of a body can be removed without destroying the equilibrium position, the body is statically indeterminate with that member in place. Such a member or supporting element is said to be *redundant*. The more redundant elements present the greater the degree of statical indeterminancy.

Bodies which are statically indeterminate require, in addition to the statical equations of equilibrium, certain relations between the externally applied forces and the resulting strains or movements of the body. These additional relations involve the physical properties of the body and are studied under the heading of strength of materials and other subjects.

Four simple examples of statically indeterminate bodies together with their free-body diagrams are shown in Fig. 34. In the first example there are only two equations of equilibrium for the parallel force system but there are three unknown reactions. The beam will remain in equilibrium if the support at B is removed. The load-deformation properties of the beam must be accounted for if the three reactions are to be computed. In example 2 each pin reaction will have an x- and a y-component for a given load P. Thus there are four unknowns, one more than the three equations of equilibrium will separate. The components A_y and B_y can be computed by the moment equation applied about either end, but A_x and B_x cannot be computed separately. If either pin connection were replaced by a roller, the beam would still retain its equilibrium configuration, and the three unknown forces could be determined. The A-frame in example 3 is statically indeterminate for the same reason as for example 2. If the pin at B is replaced by a roller, the frame would still be in equilibrium, and all external reactions could be computed. Or, if the horizontal supporting member were removed, the frame would not collapse and a solution could be made. In like manner the truss in the last example is statically indeterminate. Removal of the member AB or substitution of a rocker at B would eliminate the redundant supporting element, and the truss would be statically determinate.

It is essential to be able to recognize when a problem is statically indeterminate; otherwise effort may be wasted in attempting an impossible solution with the aid of the equilibrium equations only. If a

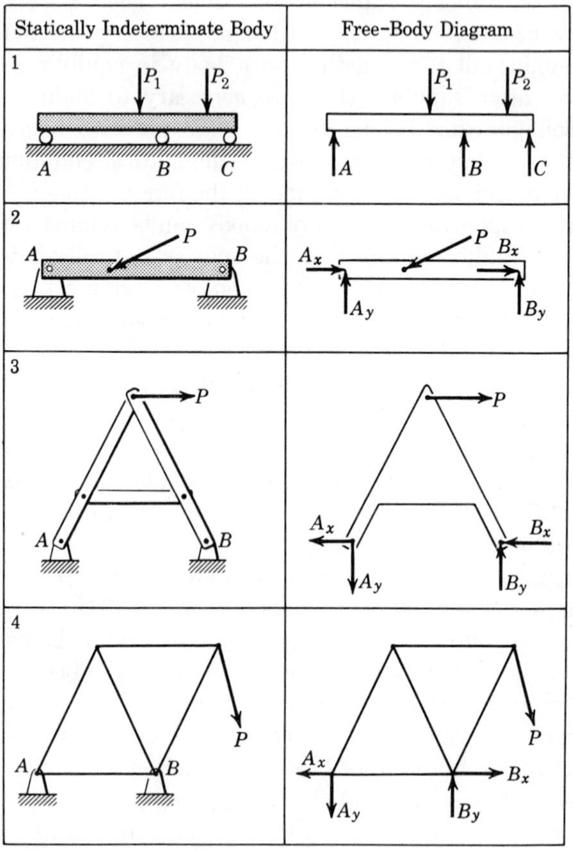

FIG. 34

body is in equilibrium with the minimum number of supports to maintain its position, the equations of equilibrium are not only necessary but are also sufficient conditions for the determination of all forces external to the body in question.

CHAPTER

4

STRUCTURES

26. Structures. In Chapter 3 attention was centered on the equilibrium of a single rigid body or upon a system of connected members which, when taken as a whole, was analyzed as a single rigid body. In such problems a free-body diagram of this single body showing all forces external to the body isolated was drawn preliminary to the application of the force and moment equations of equilibrium. In the present chapter attention is directed toward the determination of the forces internal to a structure, i.e., forces of action and reaction between the connected members. An engineering structure is any connected system of members built to serve a purpose and to withstand safely the loads applied to it. In the force analysis of structures it is necessary to dismember the structure and to analyze separate free-body diagrams of individual members or combinations of members in order to determine the forces internal to the structure. This analysis calls for very careful observance of Newton's third law which states that each action is accompanied by an equal and opposite reaction. The analysis of three types of structures, namely trusses, frames, and machines, is treated. In this treatment only *statically determinate* structures will be considered, i.e., structures for which the statical equations of equilibrium, Eqs. 16, are sufficient conditions, as well as necessary conditions, for equilibrium.

27. Trusses. A framework composed of members joined at their ends to form a rigid structure is known as a truss. Bridges, roof supports, derricks, and other such structures are common examples of trusses. Structural members used are I-beams, channels, angles, bars, and special shapes which are fastened together at their ends by riveted connections, welded joints, or large bolts or pins. Several examples of commonly used trusses are shown in Fig. 35.

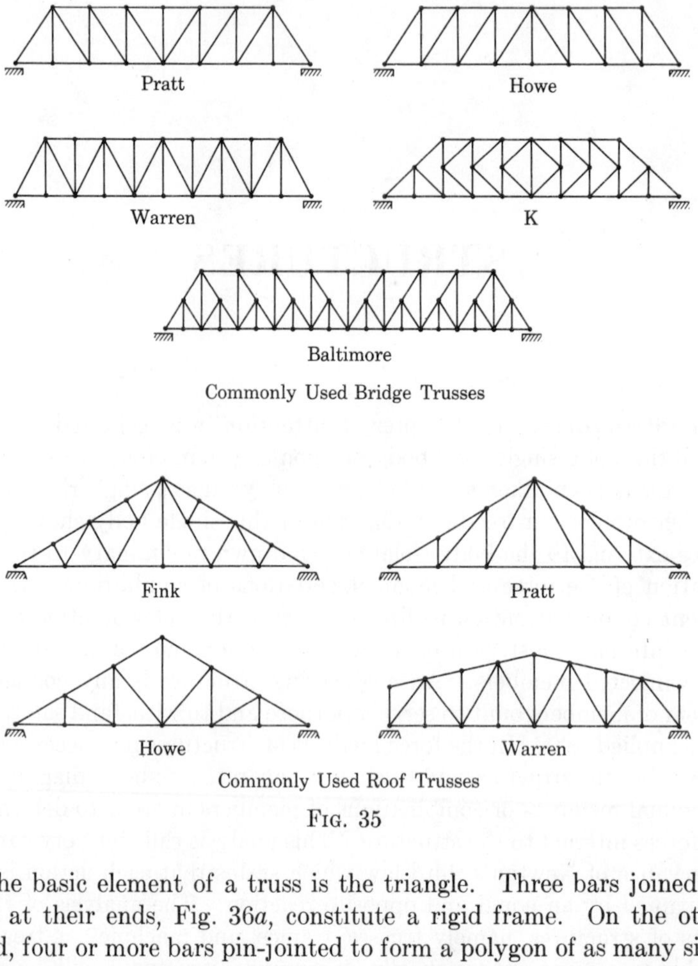

Commonly Used Bridge Trusses

Commonly Used Roof Trusses

FIG. 35

The basic element of a truss is the triangle. Three bars joined by pins at their ends, Fig. 36*a*, constitute a rigid frame. On the other hand, four or more bars pin-jointed to form a polygon of as many sides constitute a nonrigid frame. The nonrigid frame in Fig. 36*b* can be made stable or rigid with an additional diagonal bar joining *A* and *D* or *B* and *C* and thereby forming two triangles. The structure may be extended by adding additional units of two end-connected bars, such as *DE* and *CE* or *AF* and *DF*, Fig. 36*c*, which are pinned to two fixed joints, and in this way the entire structure will remain rigid. The term rigid is used in the sense of noncollapsible and also in the sense of negligible deformation of the members due to induced internal strains. Structures which are built from a basic triangle in the manner described are known as *simple trusses.* When more members are present than are needed to prevent collapse, the truss is statically indeterminate. A statically indeterminate truss cannot be analyzed by the equations of

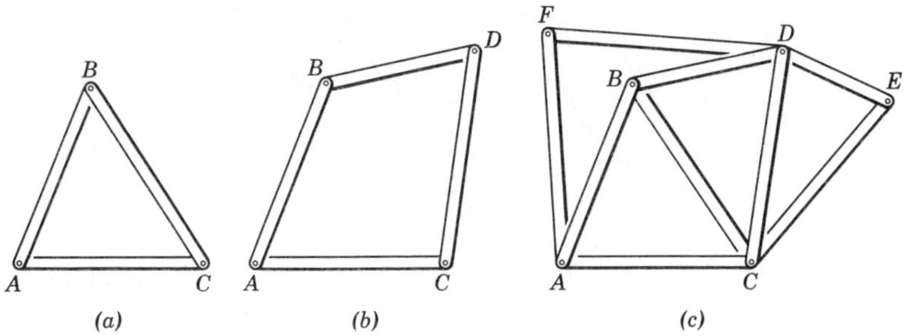

FIG. 36

equilibrium alone. Such additional members or supports which are not necessary for maintaining the equilibrium position are called *redundant.*

The design of a truss involves the determination of the forces in the various members and the selection of appropriate sizes and structural shapes to withstand the forces. There are several assumptions made in the force analysis of simple trusses. First, all members are assumed to be *two-force members.* A two-force member is one in equilibrium under the action of two forces only. These two forces are applied at the ends of the member and are necessarily equal, opposite, and *collinear* for equilibrium. The member may be in tension or compression, as shown in Fig. 37. It should be noted that in representing the equilibrium of a portion of a two-force member the tension T or compression C acting on the cut section is the same for all sections. It is assumed here that the weight of the member is small compared with the force it supports. If such is not the case or if the small effect of the weight is to be accounted for, the weight W of the member, if uniform, may be assumed to be replaced by two forces, each $W/2$, acting at each end of the member. These forces, in effect, are treated as loads externally applied to the pin connections. Accounting for the weight of a member in this way gives the correct result for the average tension or compression along the member but will not account for the effect of bending of the member.

When riveted or welded connections are used to join structural members, the assumption of a pin-jointed connection is usually satisfactory

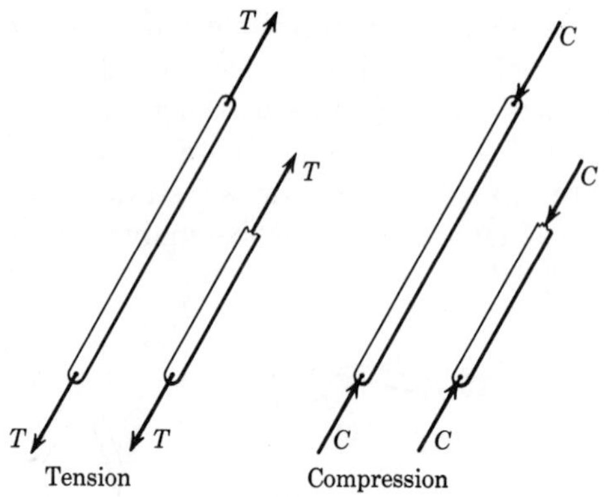

FIG. 37

if the centerlines of the members are concurrent at the joint as in Fig. 38.

It is furthermore assumed in the analysis of simple trusses that all external forces are applied at the pin connections. This condition is satisfied in most trusses. In bridge trusses the deck is usually laid on cross beams that are supported at the joints.

Provision for expansion and contraction due to temperature changes and for deformations resulting from applied loads is usually made at

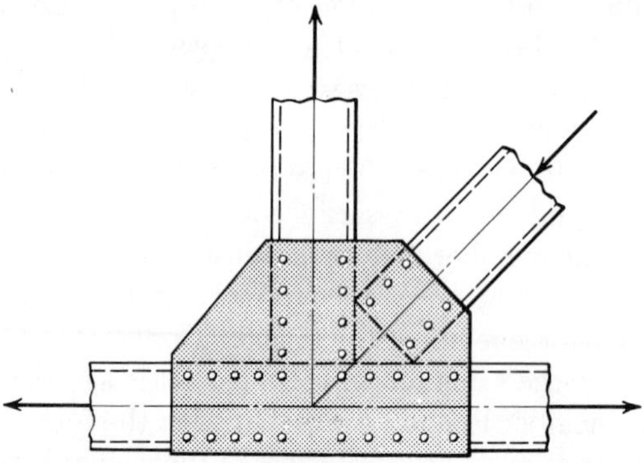

FIG. 38

one of the supports for large trusses. A roller, rocker, or some kind of slip joint is provided. Trusses and frames wherein such provision is not made are statically indeterminate, as explained in Art. 25.

Three methods for the force analysis of simple trusses will be given, and reference will be made to the simple truss shown in Fig. 39a for each of the three methods. The free-body diagram of the truss as a whole is shown in Fig. 39*b*, and for this example a system of Bow's notation is used here to designate each member and all forces. The spaces external to the truss between points of application of the external forces are labeled with small letters in a clockwise order. Next the triangular spaces within the truss are labeled in any order. The applied load L may now be designated by the corresponding capital letters AB, and the support reactions R_1 and R_2 are designated as BC and CA, respectively. The external reactions are usually determined by computation from the equilibrium equations applied to the truss as a whole before proceeding with the force analysis of the remainder of the truss.

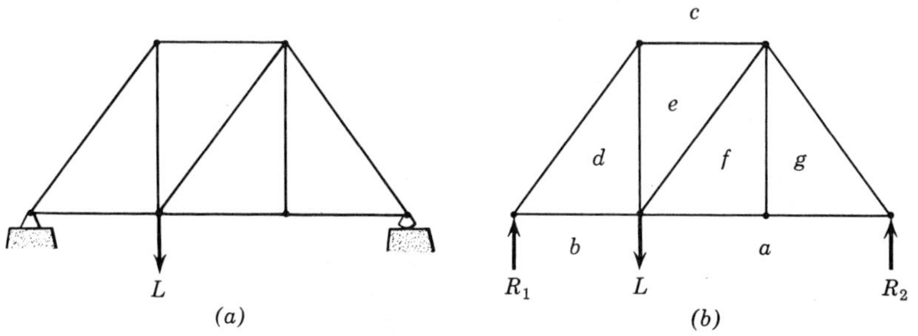

FIG. 39

28. Method of Joints. Although any convenient notation may be used to designate each member and joint in a simple truss, such as the labeling of each joint by a letter or number, Bow's notation is employed for illustration here by reason of its convenience for the graphical analysis to be explained in the next article for this same truss. With Bow's notation each joint is uniquely designated by the clockwise sequence of letters surrounding the joint. Thus the pin at the left support, Fig. 39*b*, is designated as joint *bcd*, and the joint at which the load L is applied is denoted by *abdef*. The *method of joints* consists of satisfying the conditions of equilibrium for the forces acting on the connecting pin of each joint. The method therefore deals with the equilibrium of concurrent forces, and only two independent equilibrium equations are involved. The analysis is begun with any joint where at least one known load exists and where not more than two unknown forces are present. Solution may be started with the pin at the left end, and its free-body diagram is shown in Fig. 40. The proper directions of the forces should be evident for this simple case by inspection. The free-body diagrams of portions of members *cd* and *db* are also shown to indicate clearly the mechanism of the action and reaction. The member *db* actually makes contact on the left side of the pin, although the force DB is drawn from the right side and is shown acting away from the pin. Thus, if the force arrows are consistently drawn on the *same* side of the pin as the member, then tension (such as DB) will always be indicated by an arrow *away* from the pin, and compression (such as CD) will always be indicated by an arrow *toward* the pin. The magnitude of CD is obtained from the equation $\Sigma F_y = 0$, and DB is then found from $\Sigma F_x = 0$.

Joint *dce* must be analyzed next since it now contains only two unknowns CE and ED. Joints *bdefa*, *afg*, *cgfe*, and *agc* are subsequently

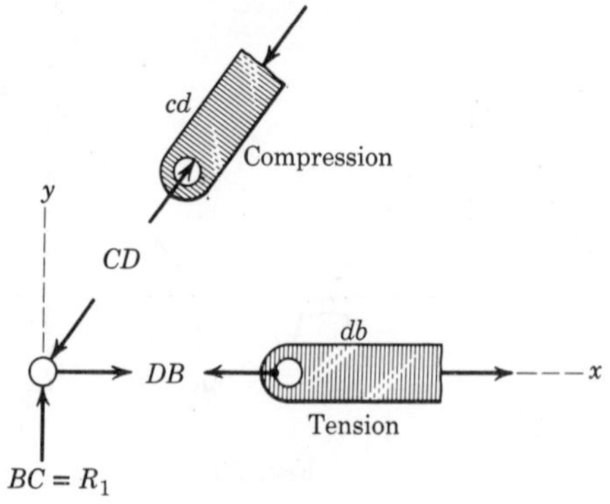

FIG. 40

analyzed in that order. The free-body diagram of each joint and its corresponding force polygon which represents graphically the two equilibrium conditions $\Sigma F_x = 0$ and $\Sigma F_y = 0$ are shown in Fig. 41. The numbers indicate the order in which the joints are analyzed. The force polygons shown have a particular significance which will be described in the next article. It should be noted that, when joint *agc* is finally reached, the computed reaction R_2 must be in equilibrium with the forces in members *ag* and *gc*, determined previously from the two neighboring joints. This requirement will provide a check on the correctness of the work. It should also be noted that isolation of joint *afg* quickly discloses the fact that the force in *fg* is zero when the equation $\Sigma F_y = 0$ is applied. The force in this member would not be zero, of course, if an external load were applied at *afg*.

It is often convenient to indicate the tension T and compression C of the various members directly on the original truss diagram by drawing arrows away from the pins for tension and toward the pins for compression. This designation is illustrated at the bottom of Fig. 41.

In some instances it is not possible to assign initially the correct direction of one or both of the unknown forces acting on a given pin. In this event an arbitrary assignment may be made. A negative value from the computation indicates that the assumed direction should be reversed.

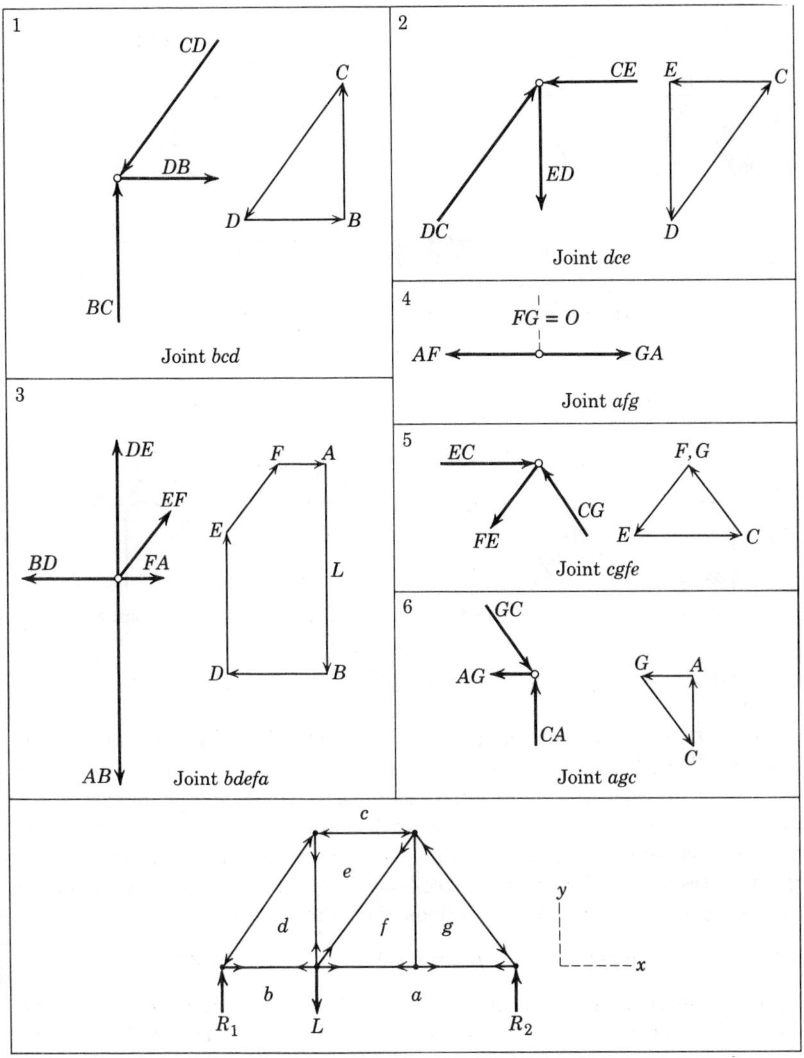

FIG. 41

SAMPLE PROBLEM

235. Compute the force in each member of the loaded cantilever truss.

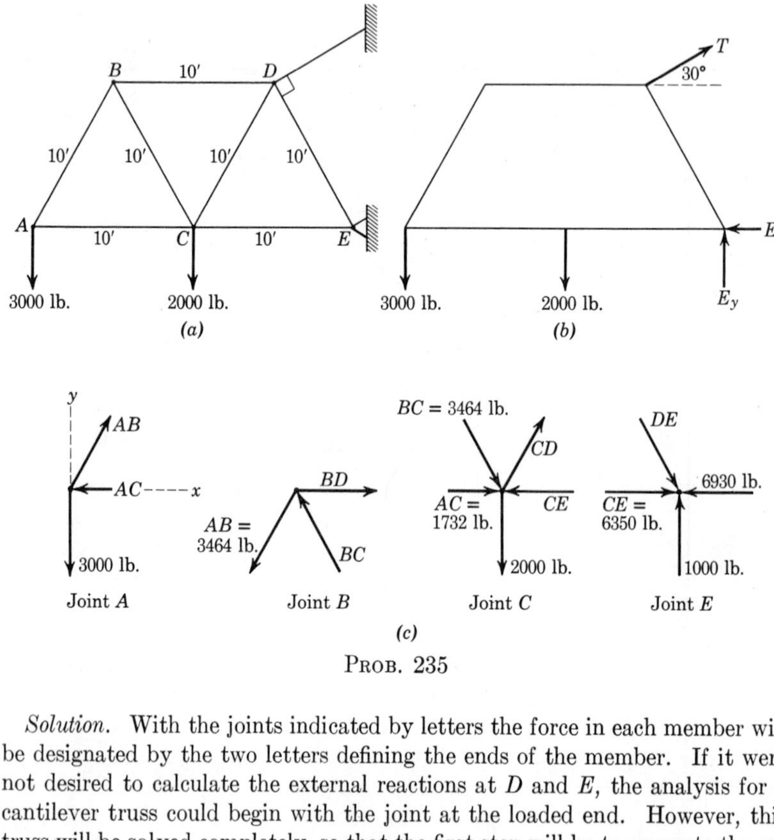

PROB. 235

Solution. With the joints indicated by letters the force in each member will be designated by the two letters defining the ends of the member. If it were not desired to calculate the external reactions at D and E, the analysis for a cantilever truss could begin with the joint at the loaded end. However, this truss will be solved completely, so that the first step will be to compute the external forces at D and E from the free-body diagram of the truss as a whole in the b-part of the figure. The equations of equilibrium give

$$T = 8000 \text{ lb.}, \qquad E_x = 6930 \text{ lb.}, \qquad E_y = 1000 \text{ lb.}$$

In the c-part of the figure are drawn the free-body diagrams showing the forces acting on each of the connecting pins. The correctness of the assigned directions of the forces is verified when each joint is considered in sequence. There should be no question as to the correct direction of the forces on joint A. Equilibrium requires

$[\Sigma F_y = 0]$ $\qquad 0.866AB - 3000 = 0, \qquad AB = 3464$ lb. T, $\qquad$ *Ans.*

$[\Sigma F_x = 0]$ $\qquad AC - 0.5 \times 3464 = 0, \qquad AC = 1732$ lb. C. $\qquad$ *Ans.*

Joint B must be analyzed next since there are more than two unknown forces on joint C. The force BC must provide an upward component in which case BD must balance the force to the left. Again the forces are obtained from

$[\Sigma F_y = 0]$ $\quad 0.866BC - 0.866 \times 3464 = 0, \quad BC = 3464$ lb. C, *Ans.*

$[\Sigma F_x = 0]$ $\quad BD - 0.5 \times 2 \times 3464 = 0, \quad BD = 3464$ lb. T. *Ans.*

Joint C now contains only two unknowns, and these are found as before:

$[\Sigma F_y = 0]$ $\quad 0.866CD - 0.866 \times 3464 - 2000 = 0,$

$CD = 5774$ lb. T, *Ans.*

$[\Sigma F_x = 0]$ $\quad CE - 1732 - 0.5 \times 3464 - 0.5 \times 5774 = 0,$

$CE = 6350$ lb. C. *Ans.*

Lastly from joint E there results

$[\Sigma F_y = 0]$ $\quad 0.866DE = 1000, \quad DE = 1154$ lb. C, *Ans.*

and the equation $\Sigma F_x = 0$ checks.

PROBLEMS

236. Determine the force in each member of the truss.
Ans. $AB = BC = 1000$ lb. C, $AD = DC = 866$ lb. T, $BD = 1000$ lb. T

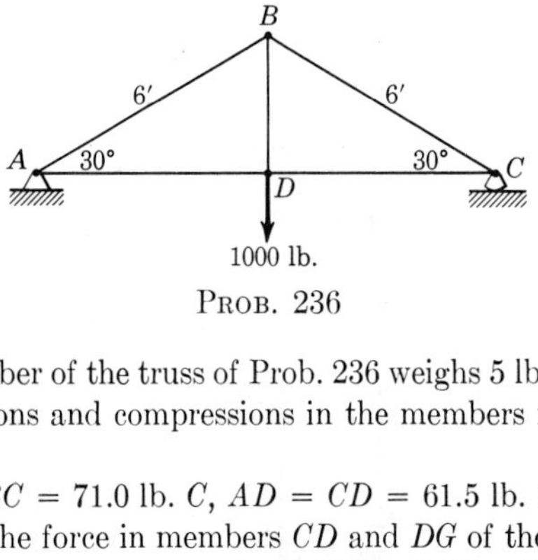

PROB. 236

237. If each member of the truss of Prob. 236 weighs 5 lb. per foot of length, determine the tensions and compressions in the members resulting from their weights alone.
Ans. $AB = BC = 71.0$ lb. C, $AD = CD = 61.5$ lb. T, $BD = 33.5$ lb. T

238. Determine the force in members CD and DG of the Howe truss.
Ans. $CD = 18$ kips T, $DG = 4.24$ kips C

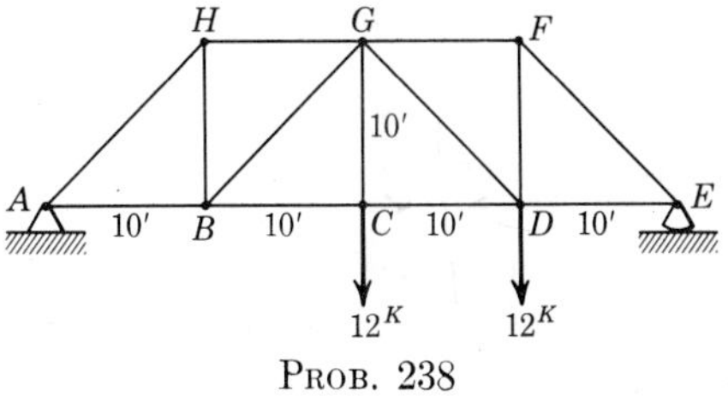

PROB. 238

239. Determine the force in members BE and EF of the cantilever truss.

Ans. $EF = 2308$ lb. C, $BE = 3464$ lb. C

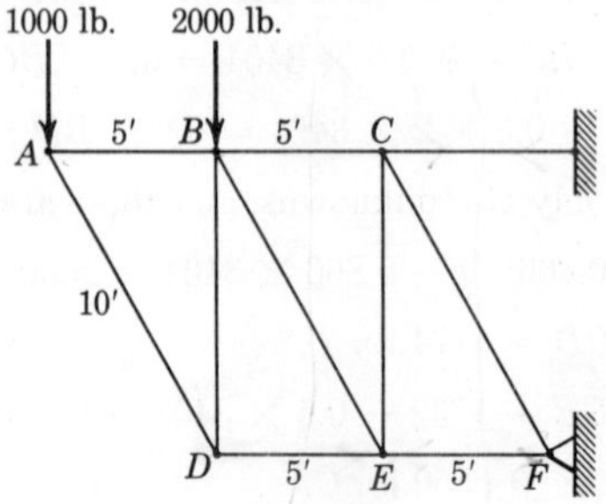

PROB. 239

240. Determine the force in members FJ and FK for the loaded Pratt truss.

Ans. $FJ = 12$ kips C, $FK = 7.5$ kips T

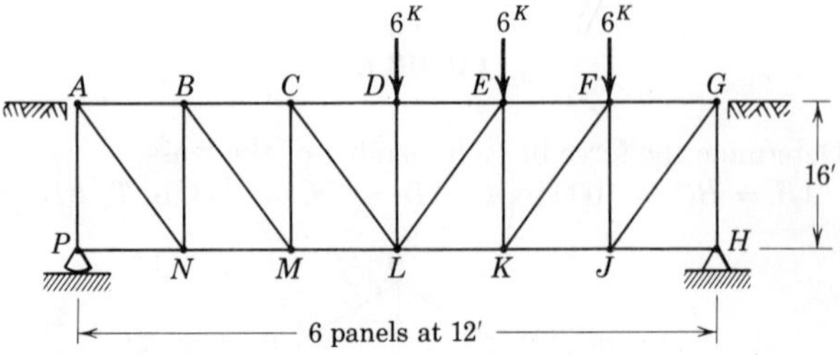

PROB. 240

241. Determine the force in members DE and JE for the deck truss shown.

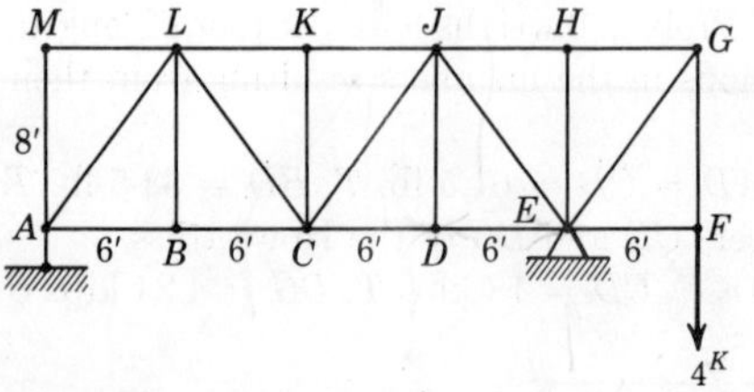

PROB. 241

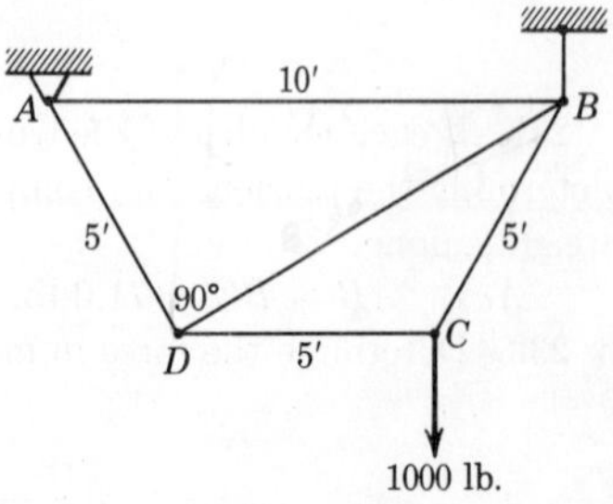

PROB. 242

242. Calculate the force in members AB and DB.

Ans. $AB = 144$ lb. C, $DB = 500$ lb. C

243. Determine the force in members CD and DE for the signboard truss due to a horizontal wind load of 800 lb. on the sign. A separate analysis considering the sign as a beam shows that $\frac{5}{8}$ of this load is transferred to the midpoint B and the remainder is divided equally between A and C. The truss is composed of 45 deg. right triangles.

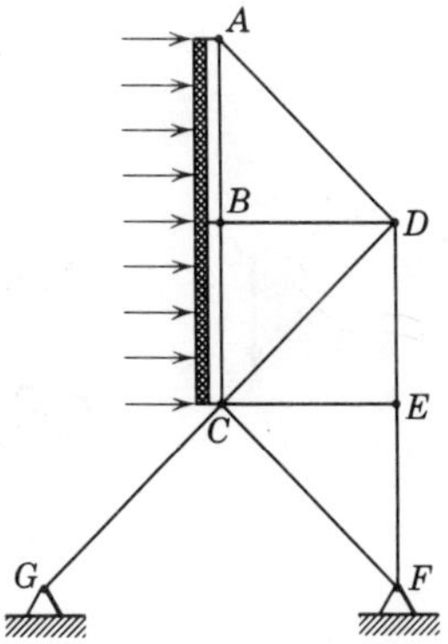

Prob. 243

244. Calculate the force in members BE, CE, and FE for the small hoisting truss. *Ans.* $BE = CE = 0$, $FE = 950$ lb. C

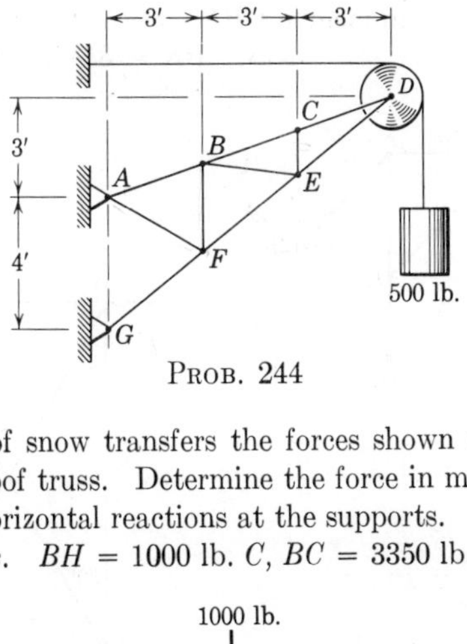

Prob. 244

245. The weight of snow transfers the forces shown to each of the upper joints of the Pratt roof truss. Determine the force in members BH, BC, and CH. Neglect any horizontal reactions at the supports.

Ans. $BH = 1000$ lb. C, $BC = 3350$ lb. C, $CH = 1414$ lb. T

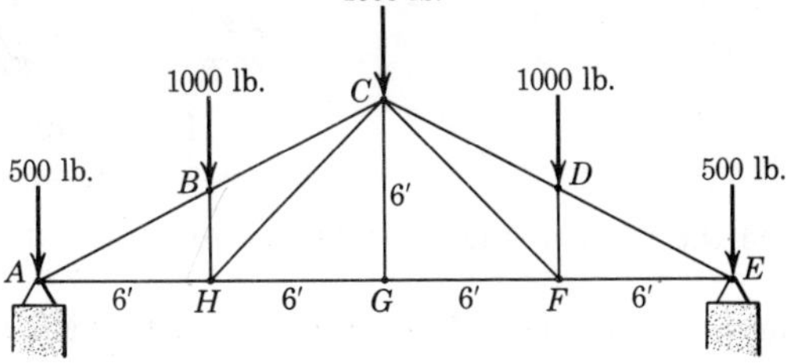

Prob. 245

246. Determine the force in members BC and CF for the crane truss.

Ans. $BC = 7.50$ kips T, $CF = 3.33$ kips T

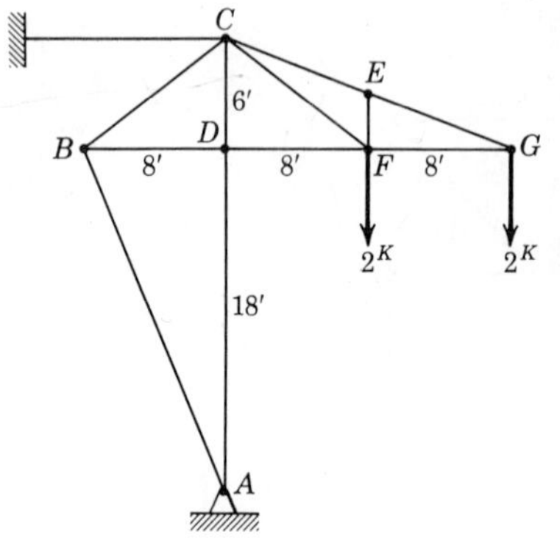

PROB. 246

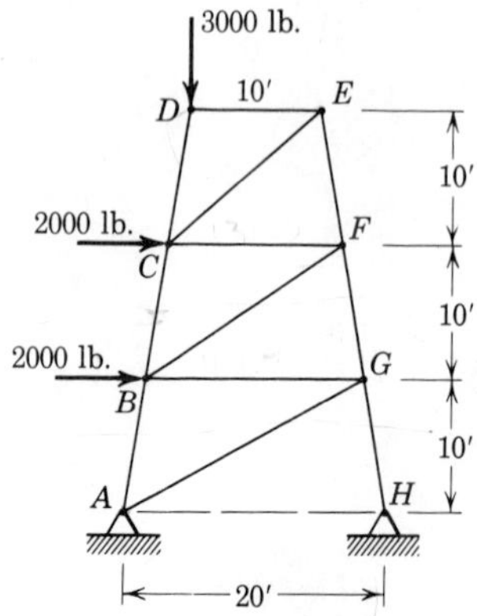

PROB. 247

247. Calculate the force in members CE and BC.

248. Calculate the force in members BK and GE for the tower truss.

Ans. $BK = 3540$ lb. C, $GE = 9240$ lb. T

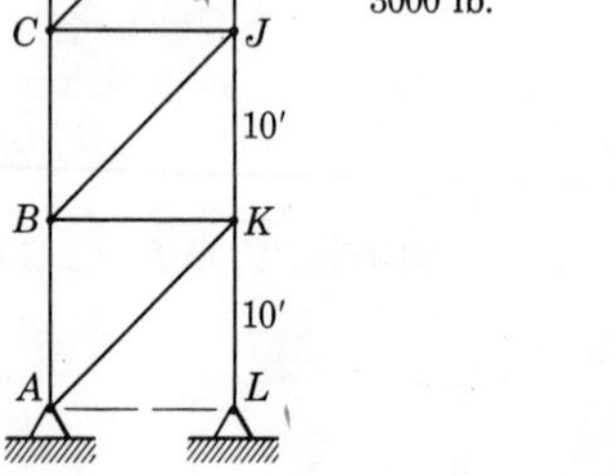

PROB. 248

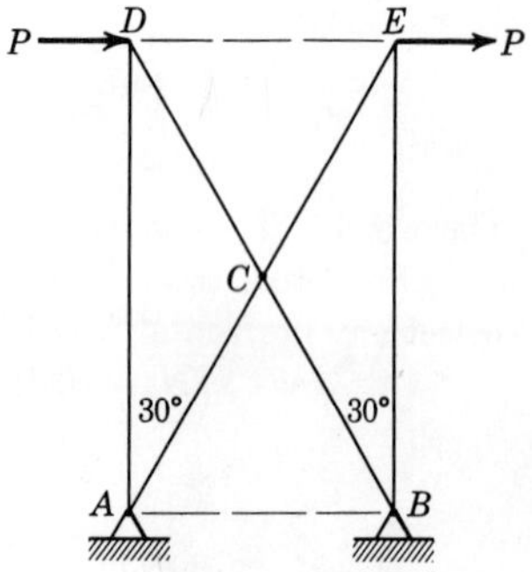

PROB. 249

249. Determine the force in each member of the truss in terms of the load P.

250. Calculate the components of the reactions at A and B acting on the truss.

Ans. $A_x = B_x = 500$ lb. left, $A_y = 1500$ lb. down, $B_y = 1500$ lb. up

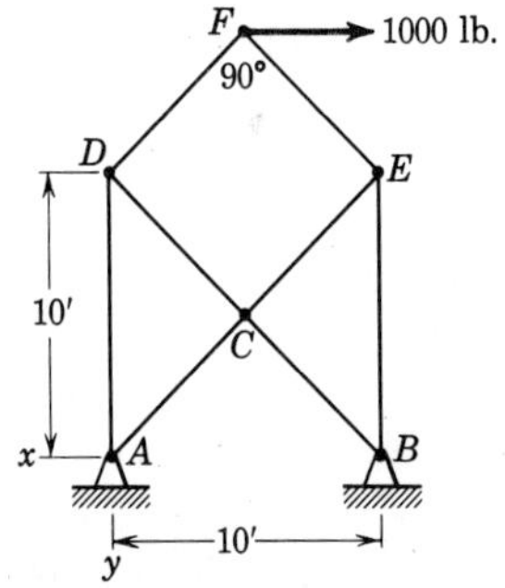

PROB. 250

251. The Howe truss supports a roof loaded by the pressure of a wind blowing in the direction marked W. The weather side of the roof is subjected to positive pressure while the lee side is subjected to negative pressure due to the

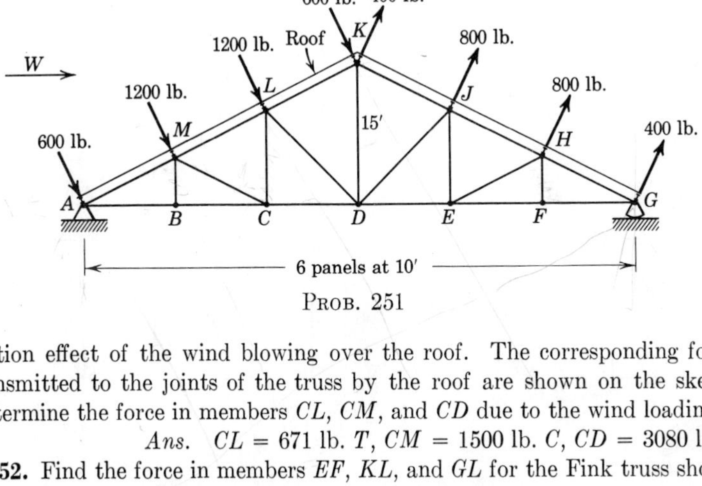

PROB. 251

suction effect of the wind blowing over the roof. The corresponding forces transmitted to the joints of the truss by the roof are shown on the sketch. Determine the force in members CL, CM, and CD due to the wind loading.

Ans. $CL = 671$ lb. T, $CM = 1500$ lb. C, $CD = 3080$ lb. T

252. Find the force in members EF, KL, and GL for the Fink truss shown. (*Hint:* Note that the forces in BP, PC, DN, etc., are zero.)

Ans. $EF = 40.4$ kips C, $KL = 20.0$ kips T, $GL = 10.0$ kips T

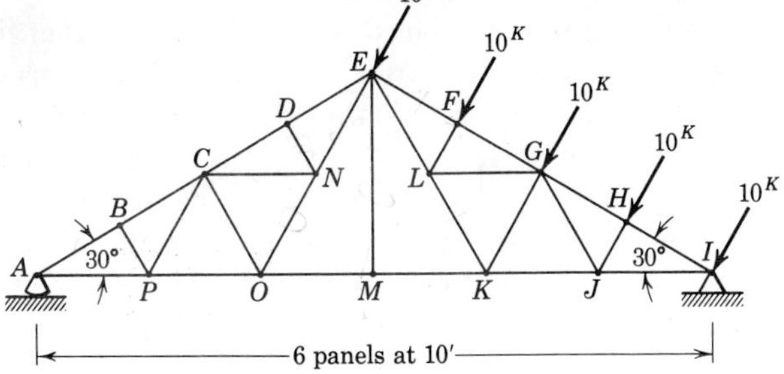

PROB. 252

29. Graphical Solution; Maxwell Diagram. A graphical procedure of wide use for determining the tensions and compressions in the various members of a simple truss will now be explained, using the truss of Fig. 39 for illustration. The procedure is based on the method of joints, and for this reason the explanation in the previous article should be thoroughly understood.

The force polygons which represent the equilibrium of each joint of the truss of Fig. 39 are shown in Fig. 41. These polygons have been formed by vector addition of the forces consistently taken in a clockwise order around each respective joint. This consistent order makes it possible to superimpose all the polygons on a single diagram as shown in Fig. 42*a*. The resulting figure is called the *Maxwell diagram* * for this

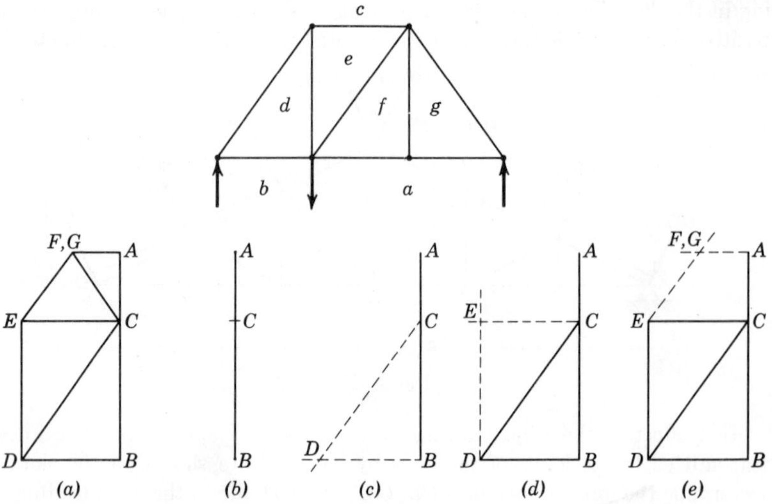

FIG. 42

truss, and it contains all the force polygons for each joint. The arrowheads have been omitted since the direction of the force in a member will depend on which of two joints is considered.

The Maxwell diagram may be constructed directly from the original truss without the necessity for prior calculation of the forces in the internal members. The diagram requires the use of Bow's notation, and a clockwise order for labeling the external forces on the truss is generally used. As a first step the external reactions are determined, usually by calculation. Next the equilibrium polygon of forces external to the truss as a whole is drawn. If the loads and reactions are all parallel, this polygon becomes a line, shown in Fig. 42*b* for the present truss.

* The method was published by James Clerk Maxwell in 1864.

The force polygon of a joint where only two unknown forces act, such as *bcd*, is first drawn. This is accomplished, Fig. 42*c*, by merely constructing a line through *B* with the known direction of *db* and a line through *C* with the known direction of *cd*. The intersection of these two lines locates point *D*, and the resulting triangle *BCD* is the force polygon for joint *bcd*, previously shown in step 1 of Fig. 41.

The adjacent joint *dce* upon which only two unknown forces act is analyzed next. A line is now drawn through *D*, Fig. 42*d*, with the direction of member *de* on the truss, and another line is constructed through *C* with the direction of member *ce*. The intersection gives point *E* and completes the force polygon for joint *dce*, obtained earlier in step 2 of Fig. 41. Point *F* on the diagram, Fig. 42*e*, is similarly found from the intersection of a line through *E* with the direction of *ef* and a line through *A* with the direction of *fa*. The resulting polygon *ABDEF* (step 3, Fig. 41) represents the equilibrium of forces on joint *abdef*. From joint *afg* it is seen that *G* must lie on a horizontal line through *A* and on a vertical line through *F*. Thus *G* is coincident with *F*, which checks the fact that the force in member *fg* is zero. Finally the equilibrium of joint *agc* gives the polygon *AGC*. Since these three points are already obtained it is necessary only to connect *G* with *C*, and thus the completed polygon of Fig. 42*a* is obtained. If the construction has been accurately carried out, the direction of *GC* will coincide with the direction of the member *gc*, thus providing a check on the correctness of the diagram.

Once the Maxwell diagram is constructed, it is a simple matter to obtain the magnitude of the force in any member and determine whether it is tension or compression. The force which the member *ef* of the sample truss exerts on the joint *abdef*, for instance, is the vector from *E* to *F* on the Maxwell diagram. The direction is *away* from the joint so that the member is in *tension*. The force which the same member exerts on the joint *cgfe* is the vector from *F* to *E* and likewise indicates tension since it is away from the joint. It should be carefully noted that the proper sequence of letters for the force vector is obtained from a *clockwise* travel about the joint in question. A counterclockwise diagram could, of course, be used with equal success, provided this direction was consistently used in the notation and the interpretation. Such a diagram would result in an upside-down mirror image of the clockwise construction but is not used in practice.

Although the load line (or polygon) of external forces is normally the first step in the construction of the Maxwell diagram, in some cases it may be just as convenient or even necessary to begin the construction without the initial determination of the external reactions.

SAMPLE PROBLEM

253. Draw the Maxwell diagram for the truss of Sample Prob. 235.

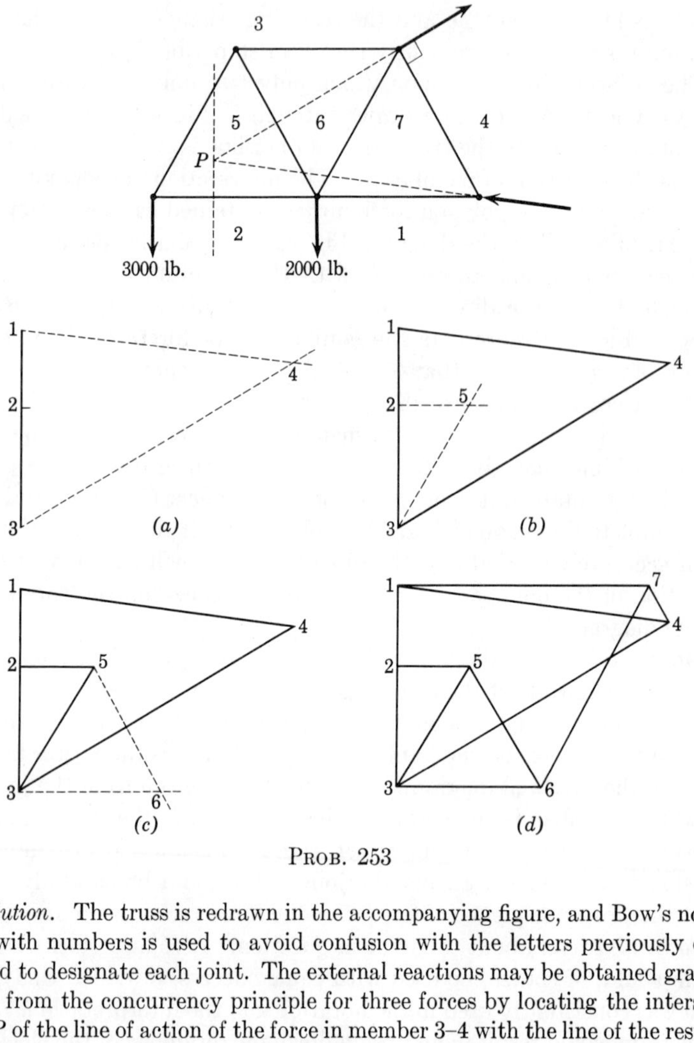

Prob. 253

Solution. The truss is redrawn in the accompanying figure, and Bow's notation with numbers is used to avoid confusion with the letters previously employed to designate each joint. The external reactions may be obtained graphically from the concurrency principle for three forces by locating the intersection P of the line of action of the force in member 3–4 with the line of the resultant of the two applied loads. The reaction 4–1 must pass through this point. The force polygon representing the equilibrium of the truss as a whole is next drawn as shown in the a-part of the illustration.

The Maxwell diagram is constructed on the force polygon. By starting with the left end of the truss, point 5 is seen to lie on a horizontal line through point 2 and on a line through point 3 having the direction of 3–5 as illustrated in the *b*-part of the drawing. The triangle 2–3–5 represents in that order the force polygon for joint 2–3–5. The same three forces are described in the figure for Prob. 235 for joint *A*. Point 6 is located in similar manner in the *c*-part of the figure. Point 7 may be obtained from joint 1–7–4 and the diagram completed by joining points 6 and 7 as shown in the *d*-part of the illustration. The line joining points 6 and 7 is parallel to the member 6–7, which forms a check on the work.

In interpreting the diagram to obtain the force in member 6–5, for example, it is first necessary to consider one of the two joints to which this member is attached. If joint 3–6–5 is chosen, the polygon 3–6–5 is traced on the Maxwell diagram in that order, and the force which member 6–5 exerts on the pin is up and to the left (from 6 to 5). This is a compressive force since it is toward the pin. Scaling the diagram gives a magnitude for the line 6–5 in agreement with that already obtained. If joint 1–2–5–6–7 had been considered, the force would be designated 5–6 (clockwise order around the joint). The direction of the force is from 5 to 6 on the Maxwell diagram, which is toward the joint and is likewise compression.

PROBLEMS

Solve the following problems by drawing the complete Maxwell diagram. Relabel as needed with Bow's notation.

254. Prob. 236.

255. Determine the force in each member of the truss with the aid of a free-hand sketch of the Maxwell diagram.

Ans. $AE = EC = 2P$, T; $DE = EB = 2P$, T; $AB = P\sqrt{3}$, C; $BC = P$, C

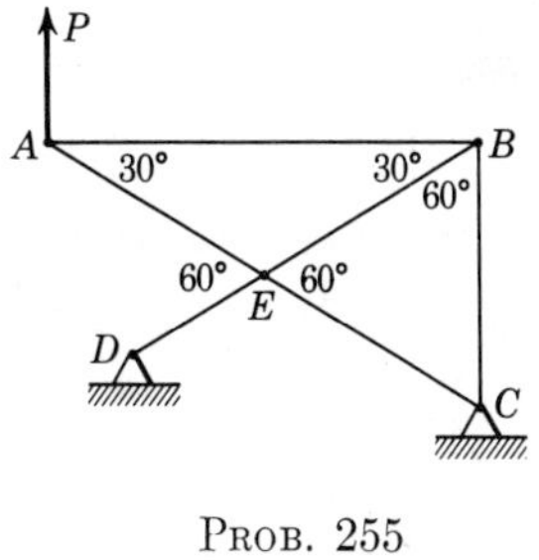

PROB. 255

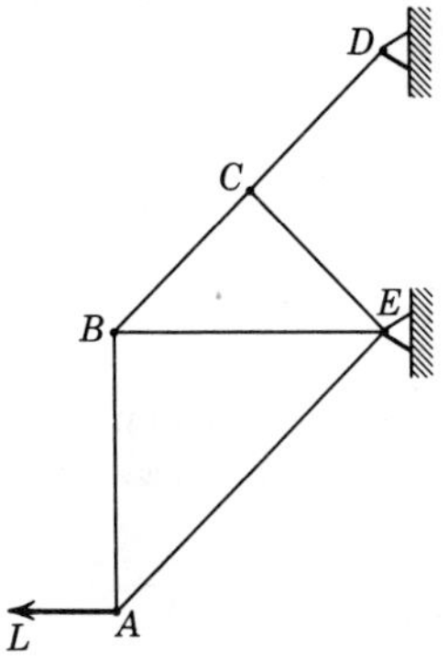

PROB. 256

256. Determine the force in members *BE* and *BC* from a free-hand sketch of the Maxwell diagram. All angles are 45 or 90 deg.

Ans. $BE = L$, T; $BC = L\sqrt{2}$, C

257. Prob. 239.

258. Prob. 238.

259. Prob. 245.

260. Prob. 243.

261. Prob. 246.

262. Determine the force in members JD and HD for the crane truss.

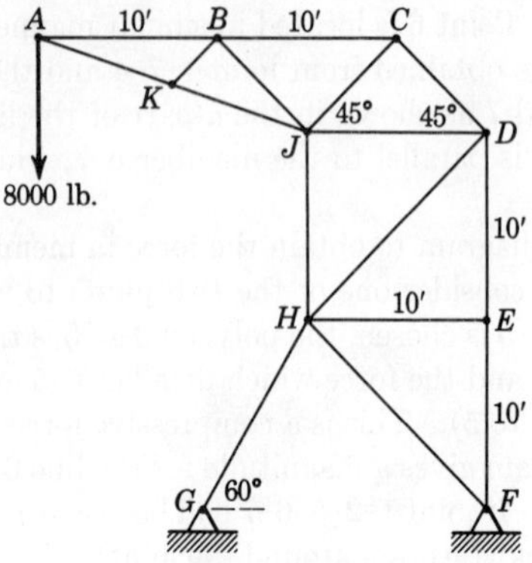

PROB. 262

263. Prob. 250. **264.** Prob. 248.
265. Prob. 252.

266. Find the force in member DE for the loaded truss shown.

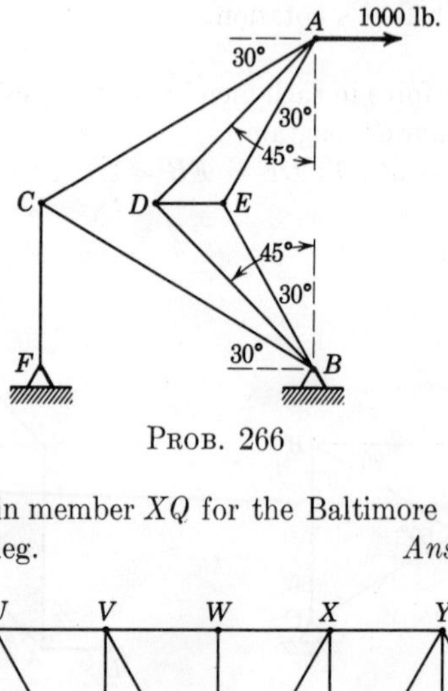

PROB. 266

* **267.** Find the force in member XQ for the Baltimore truss where all angles are 30, 60, 90, or 120 deg. *Ans.* $XQ = 2.89$ kips C

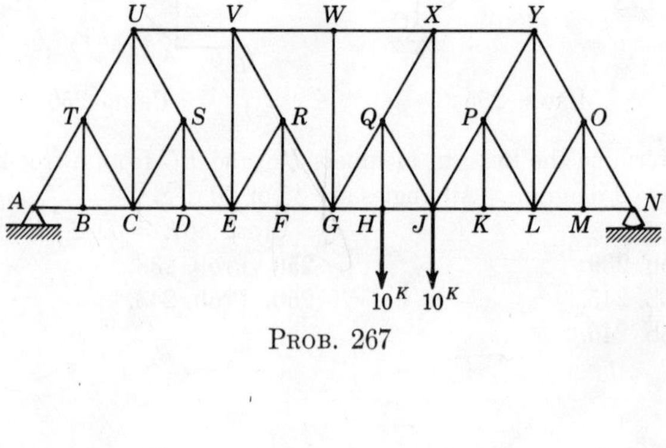

PROB. 267

* **268.** The hinged frames *ACE* and *DFB* are connected by two hinged bars *AB* and *CD* which cross without being connected. Draw the Maxwell diagram and determine the force in *AB*. *Ans.* $AB = 377$ lb. *C*

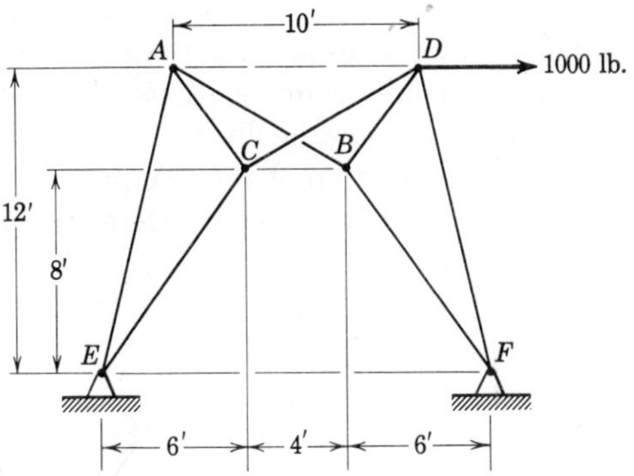

PROB. 268

* **269.** Draw the Maxwell diagram for the Fink truss of Prob. 252 loaded in the manner shown here. Find the force in member *LG*. (*Hint:* For the right side of the truss the force in *EF* is unaffected by replacing members *FL* and *GL* by a member from *F* to *K*. The diagram can be completed with the temporary member and modified to account for the resubstitution of the original two members. By reason of symmetry only one-half of the diagram need be drawn.) *Ans.* $LG = 4.33$ kips *T*

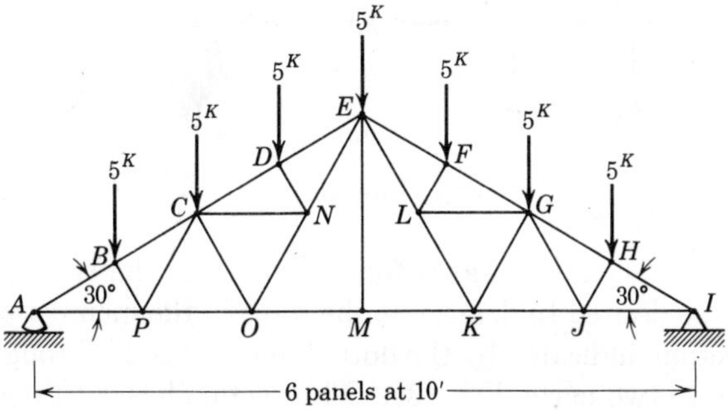

PROB. 269

30. Method of Sections. In the method of joints and in the graphical method advantage is taken of only two of the three equilibrium equations since the procedures involve concurrent forces at each joint. The third equilibrium principle may be used to advantage by considering an entire section of the truss as a free body in equilibrium under the action of a nonconcurrent system of forces. This *method of sections* has the basic advantage that the force in almost any desired member may be found directly from an analysis of a section which has cut that member. Thus it is not necessary to proceed with the calculation from joint-to-joint until the member in question has been reached. In choosing a section of the truss it should be noted that in general not more than three members whose forces are unknown may be cut since there are only three available equilibrium relations which are independent.

The method of sections will now be illustrated for the truss in Fig. 39, which was used in the explanation of the two previous methods. The truss is shown again in Fig. 43*a* for ready reference. The external re-

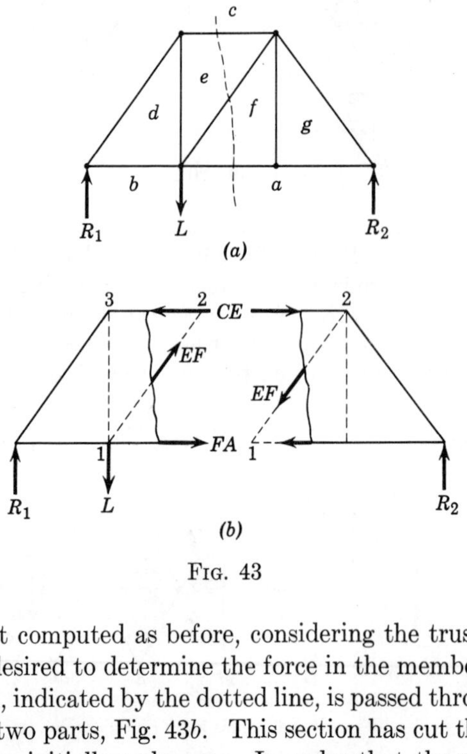

FIG. 43

actions are first computed as before, considering the truss as a whole. Now let it be desired to determine the force in the member *ef*. An imaginary section, indicated by the dotted line, is passed through the truss cutting it into two parts, Fig. 43*b*. This section has cut three members whose forces are initially unknown. In order that the portion of the truss on each side of the section will remain in equilibrium it is necessary to apply to each cut member the force which was exerted on it by the member cut away. These forces, either tensile or compressive, will always be in the direction of the respective members for simple trusses composed of two-force members. The left-hand section is in equilibrium under the action of the applied load L, the end reaction R_1, and the three forces exerted on the cut members by the right-hand section which has been removed. The forces may usually be drawn with their proper senses by a visual approximation of the equilibrium requirements. Thus in balancing the moments about point 1 the force CE is clearly to the left, which makes it compression since it acts toward the cut section of member ce. The load L is greater than the reaction R_1 so that the force EF must be up and to the right to supply the needed upward component for vertical equilibrium. Force EF is therefore tension since it acts away from the cut section. With the approximate magnitudes of R_1 and L in mind the balance of moments about point 2 requires that FA be to the right. A casual glance at the truss should lead to the same conclusion when it is realized that the lower horizontal member will stretch under the tension caused by bending. The equation of moments about joint 1 eliminates three forces from the relation, and CE may be determined directly. The force EF is calculated from the equilibrium equation for the y-direction. Lastly FA may be determined by balancing moments about point 2. In this way each of the three unknowns has been determined independently of the other two.

The right-hand section of the truss, Fig. 43*b*, is in equilibrium under the action of R_2 and the same three forces in the cut members applied in the directions opposite to those for the left section. The proper sense for the horizontal forces may easily be seen from the balance of moments about points 1 and 2.

It is essential to understand that in the method of sections an entire portion of the truss is considered as a single body in equilibrium. Thus the forces in members internal to the section are not involved in the analysis of the section as a whole. In order to clarify the free body and the forces acting externally on it, the section is preferably passed through the members and not the joints.

Either section of a truss may be used for the calculations, but the one involving the least number of forces will usually yield the simpler solution.

The moment equations may be used to great advantage in the method of sections, and a moment center through which as many forces pass as possible should be chosen. It is not always possible to assign an unknown force in the proper sense when the free-body diagram of a section is drawn. With an arbitrary assignment made, a positive answer will verify the assumed sense and a negative result will indicate that the force is in the sense opposite to that assumed. Any system of notation desired may be used, although usually it is found convenient to letter the joints and designate a member and its force by the two letters defining the ends of the member.

SAMPLE PROBLEMS

270. Calculate the forces in members BC, BD, and CE for the truss of Probs. 235 and 253, which is relabeled with this present problem.

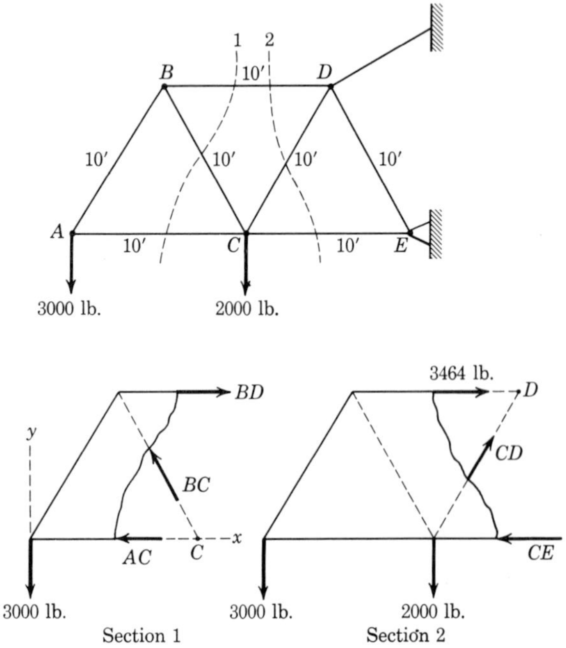

PROB. 270

Solution. Section 1 cuts only three members whose forces are unknown, and the free-body diagram of the portion of the truss to the left of the section is drawn. A force summation in the y-direction gives

$[\Sigma F_y = 0]$ $\qquad 0.866BC - 3000 = 0, \qquad BC = 3464$ lb. C. $\qquad$ *Ans.*

Using C as a moment center gives

$[\Sigma M_C = 0]$ $\qquad 8.66BD - 3000 \times 10 = 0, \qquad BD = 3464$ lb. T. $\qquad$ *Ans.*

Section 2 may be used to find the force in CE. From the free-body diagram of the portion of the truss to the left of section 2 is obtained

$[\Sigma M_D = 0]$ $\quad 8.66CE - 2000 \times 5 - 3000 \times 15 = 0, \qquad CE = 6350$ lb. C. *Ans.*

For a loaded cantilever truss, such as illustrated in this problem, it should be noted that the forces in the members may be obtained without calculation of the support reactions.

271. Calculate the force in member DJ of the Howe roof truss illustrated. Neglect any horizontal components of force at the supports.

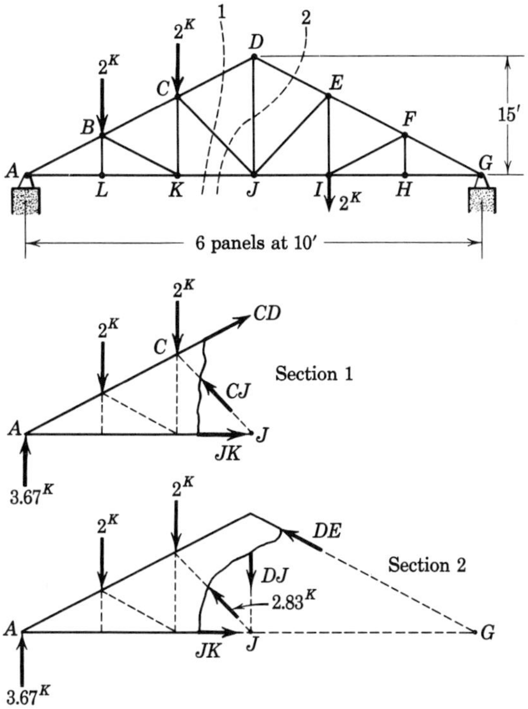

PROB. 271

Solution. It is not possible to pass a section through DJ without cutting four members whose forces are unknown. Although three of these cut by section 2 are concurrent at J and therefore the moment equation about J could be used to obtain the fourth, DE, the force in DJ cannot be obtained from the remaining two equilibrium principles. It is necessary to consider first the adjacent section 1 before considering section 2.

The free-body diagram for section 1 is drawn and includes the reaction of 3.67 kips at A, which is previously calculated from the equilibrium of the truss as a whole. In assigning the proper directions for the forces acting on the three cut members a balance of moments about A eliminates the effects of CD and JK and clearly requires that CJ be up and to the left. A balance of moments about C eliminates the effect of the three forces concurrent at C and indicates that JK must be to the right to supply sufficient counterclockwise moment. Again it should be fairly obvious that the lower chord is under tension due to the bending tendency of the truss. Although it should also be apparent that the top chord is under compression, the force in CD will be arbitrarily assigned as tension. There is no harm in assigning one or more of the forces in the wrong direction as long as the calculations are consistent with the assumption. A negative answer will show the need for reversing the direction of the force.

By the analysis of section 1, CJ is obtained from

$$[\Sigma M_A = 0] \quad (0.707CJ)30 - 2 \times 10 - 2 \times 20 = 0, \qquad CJ = 2.83 \text{ kips } C.$$

In this equation the moment of CJ is calculated by considering its horizontal and vertical components acting at point J. Equilibrium of moments about J requires

$$[\Sigma M_J = 0] \qquad (0.894CD)15 + 3.67 \times 30 - 2 \times 10 - 2 \times 20 = 0,$$

$$CD = -3.73 \text{ kips.}$$

The moment of CD about J is calculated here by considering its two components as acting through D. The minus sign indicates that CD was assigned in the wrong direction. Thus

$$CD = 3.73 \text{ kips } C. \qquad \textit{Ans.}$$

If desired, the direction of CD may be changed on the free-body diagram and the algebraic sign of CD reversed in the calculations, or else the work may be left as it stands with a note stating the proper direction.

From the free-body diagram of section 2, which now includes the known value of CJ, a balance of moments about G is seen to eliminate DE and JK. Thus

$$[\Sigma M_G = 0] \quad 30DJ + 2 \times 40 + 2 \times 50 - 3.67 \times 60 - 2.83 \times 0.707 \times 30 = 0,$$

$$DJ = 3.33 \text{ kips } T. \qquad \textit{Ans.}$$

Again the moment of CJ is determined from its components considered as acting at J. The answer for DJ is positive so that the assumed tensile direction was correct. An analysis of the joint D alone also verifies this conclusion.

Although the procedure used here is undoubtedly the shortest for obtaining DJ, the student should consider other possibilities. It may be observed that, if for some other problem the 2 kip load at I were not present but the other loads remained the same, the forces in IE and JE (as well as in HF and IF) would be zero. In this event a section through members CD, DJ, JE, and IJ would involve only three unknown forces, and a solution for DJ could be obtained with a single moment equation about A.

PROBLEMS

Solve the following problems by the method of sections.

272. Determine the force in members BE and DE for the truss of Prob. 239.
Ans. $BE = 3464$ lb. C, $DE = 577$ lb. C

273. Calculate the force in members JH, JD, and CD for the Warren bridge truss. *Ans.* $JH = 12.96$ kips C, $JD = 2.92$ kips T, $CD = 11.33$ kips T

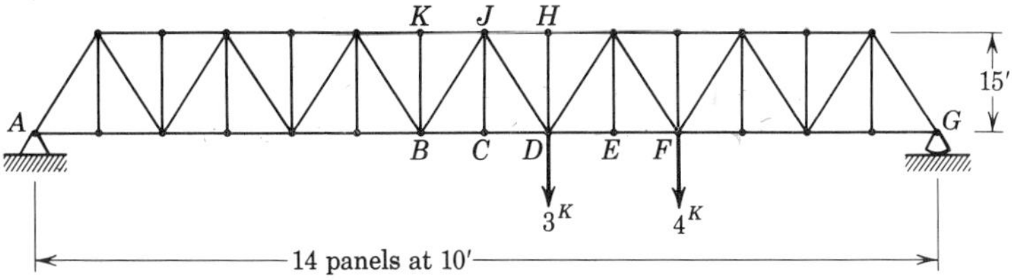

PROB. 273

274. Determine the force in members HG, CG, and BG for the truss of Prob. 238. *Ans.* $HG = 9$ kips C, $CG = 12$ kips T, $BG = 12.73$ kips C

275. Determine the force in members DF, CE, and BE for the truss of Prob. 250. Solve for each force from an equation which contains that force as the only unknown.

276. Calculate the force in members EH and CH for the truss of Prob. 248. *Ans.* $EH = 16{,}600$ lb. C, $CH = 5000$ lb. T

277. The truss shown is composed of 45 deg. right triangles. The crossed members in the center two panels are slender tie rods incapable of supporting

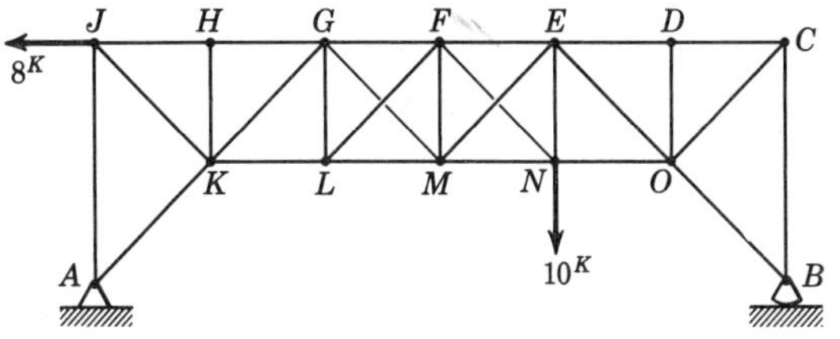

PROB. 277

compression. Retain the two rods which are under tension and compute the magnitude of their tensions. Also find the force in member MN.

278. Calculate the force in members JH and JD for the truss of Prob. 262. Solve for each force from an equation which contains that force as the only unknown.

279. Calculate the force in member CJ with only one free-body diagram and one equation of equilibrium.

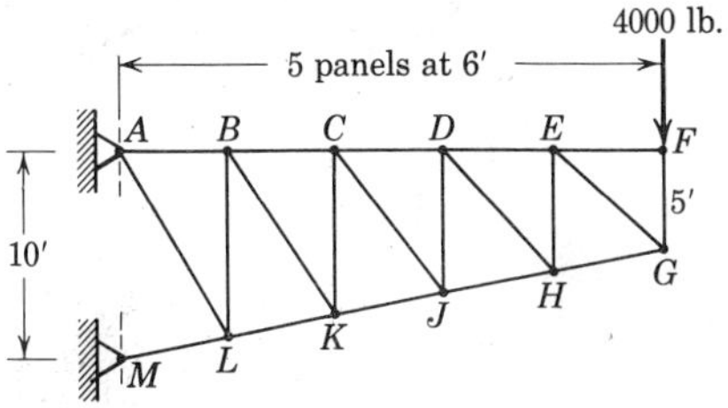

PROB. 279

280. Determine the force in member BF for the truss of Prob. 247 by using only one free-body diagram and one equation of equilibrium. *Ans.* $BF = 2570$ lb. T

281. After analyzing joint G for the truss in Prob. 245, determine the force in members CH and FG from only one section of the truss.

282. Calculate the force in members BC, CD, and DF for the truss of Prob. 246. *Ans.* $BC = 7.50$ kips T, $CD = 8.50$ kips C, $DF = 8$ kips C

283. Calculate the force in member CF of the loaded truss. All angles are 30, 60, 90, or 120 deg.

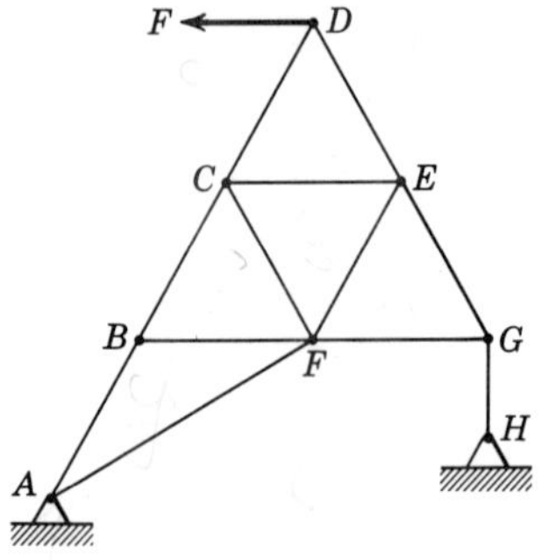

PROB. 283

284. Find the force in member JQ for the truss of Prob. 267.

* **285.** Determine the force in members DG, EG, FG, and MG for the cantilever crane truss. What can be said regarding the statical determinateness of the truss?

Ans. $DG = 5$ kips C, $EG = 30$ kips C, $FG = 11.55$ kips C, $MG = 23.1$ kips C

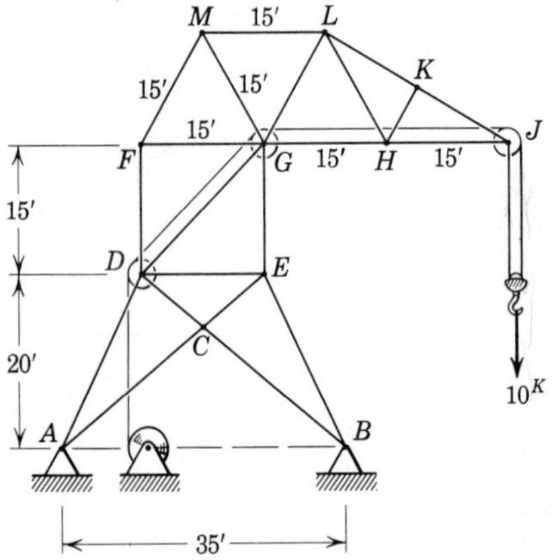

PROB. 285

* **286.** The single-leaf bascule bridge is exactly balanced with a counterweight of 1800 tons located as shown. Determine the force in JG as the bridge starts to lift, assuming that the weights of the members are negligible compared with the weight of the uniform roadway. Treat all intersections of the truss members as pin joints connecting two-force members, and assume each

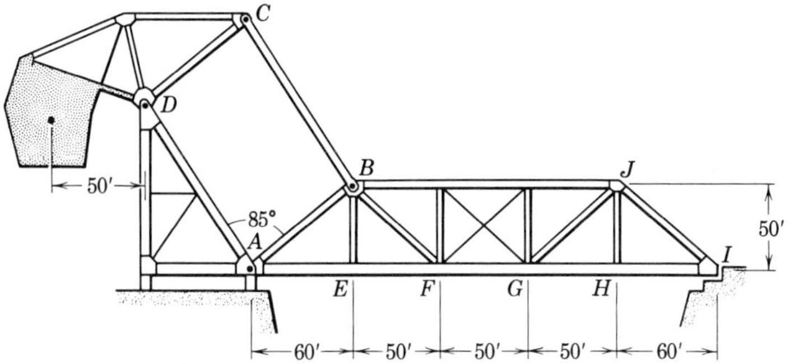

PROB. 286

of the joints A, E, F, G, H, I carries half the weight of the roadway on each side of the joint. Figure $ABCD$ is a parallelogram. *Ans.* $JG = 297$ tons C

* **287.** Prob. 268.

* **288.** In the traveling bridge crane shown all crossed members are slender tie rods incapable of supporting compression. Determine the force in members DF and EF and find the horizontal reaction on the truss at A. Show that, if $CF = 0$, $DE = 0$ also.

Ans. $DF = 76.8$ tons C, $EF = 36.4$ tons C, $A_x = 10.1$ tons to the right

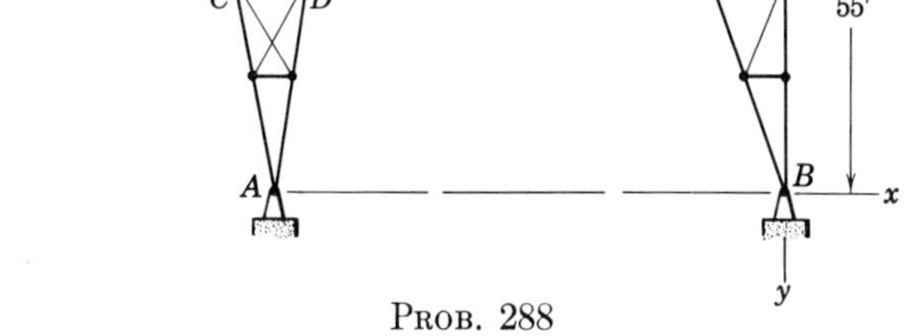

PROB. 288

31. Space Trusses. All members of the trusses described in the preceding four articles have been in a single plane so that the equilibrium problem has been two dimensional. There are, however, many types of construction which utilize a system of two-force members in space joined together at their ends to form a rigid structure. Such a configuration of bars is known as a *space truss*.

In a plane truss it has already been seen that a triangle of pin-connected bars forms a rigid, noncollapsible unit. A space truss, on the other hand, requires six bars joined at their ends to form the edges of a tetrahedron for the fundamental noncollapsible unit. In Fig. 44*a* the two bars *AD* and *BD* joined at *D* require a third support *CD* to keep the triangle *ABD* from rotating about *AB*. In Fig. 44*b* the supporting base is replaced by three more bars *AB*, *BC*, and *AC* to form a tetrahedron independent of the foundation for its own rigidity. Added units

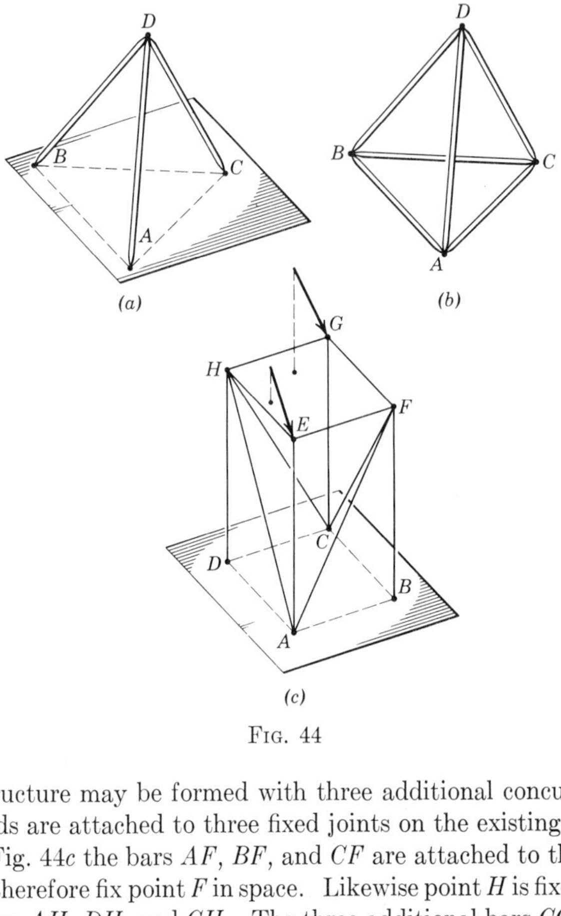

FIG. 44

to the structure may be formed with three additional concurrent bars whose ends are attached to three fixed joints on the existing structure. Thus in Fig. 44*c* the bars *AF*, *BF*, and *CF* are attached to the foundation and therefore fix point *F* in space. Likewise point *H* is fixed in space by the bars *AH*, *DH*, and *CH*. The three additional bars *CG*, *FG*, and *HG* are attached to the three fixed points *C*, *F*, and *H* and therefore fix *G* in space. Point *E* is similarly established. The structure is entirely rigid, and the two applied loads shown will result in forces in all of the members.

Ideally there must be point support, such as represented by a ball-and-socket joint, for the connections of a space truss in order that there be no bending in the members. Again, as in riveted and welded connections for plane trusses, if the center lines of joined members intersect at a point, the assumption of two-force members under simple tension and compression may be justified.

If a space truss is loaded and supported at the joints in such a way that the entire truss is not statically indeterminate, the forces in all members may be found by the methods of equilibrium already developed. The method of joints may be used in a manner similar to that employed with plane trusses except that the *three* equilibrium equations

$$\Sigma F_x = 0, \qquad \Sigma F_y = 0, \qquad \Sigma F_z = 0$$

must be satisfied at each joint. It is necessary to start at some joint where at least one known force acts and not more than three unknown forces are present. Adjacent joints upon which not more than three unknown forces act may be analyzed in turn. A method of sections could also be employed wherein all six of the equations of equilibrium would be used, but this method is tedious by reason of the labor of computing moment arms in space.

32. Frames and Machines. Structures and mechanisms composed of joined members any one of which has more than two forces acting on it cannot be analyzed by the methods developed for simple trusses. Such members are multiforce members (three or more forces), and in general the forces will *not* be in the direction of the members. In the previous chapter the equilibrium of multiforce bodies was discussed and illustrated, but attention was focused on the equilibrium of a *single* rigid body. In this present article attention is focused on the equilibrium of *interconnected* rigid bodies which contain multiforce members. The forces acting on each member of a connected system are found by isolating the member with a free-body diagram and applying the established equations of equilibrium. The *principle of action and reaction* must be carefully observed when representing the forces of interaction on the separate free-body diagrams. If the structure contains more members or supports than are necessary to prevent collapse, then, as in the case of trusses, the problem is statically indeterminate, and the principles of equilibrium although necessary are not sufficient for solution.

If the frame or machine constitutes a rigid unit by itself, the analysis is best begun by establishing all the forces external to the structure considered as a single rigid body. The structure is then dismembered and the equilibrium of each part is considered. The equilibrium equations for the several parts will be related through the terms involving the forces of interaction. If the structure is not rigid by itself but depends on its external supports for rigidity, then it is usually necessary to consider first the equilibrium of a portion of the system which itself is inherently rigid.

It will be found that in most cases the analysis of frames and machines is facilitated by representing the forces in terms of their rectangular components. This is particularly so when the dimensions of the parts are given in mutually perpendicular directions. The advantage of this representation is that the calculation of moment arms is accordingly simplified. It is not always possible to assign all forces or their components in the proper sense when drawing the free-body diagrams, and it becomes necessary to make an arbitrary assignment. In this ¯nt it is *absolutely necessary* that a force be *consistently* represented on the diagrams for interacting bodies which involve the force in question. Thus for two bodies which are connected by the pin A, Fig. 45a,

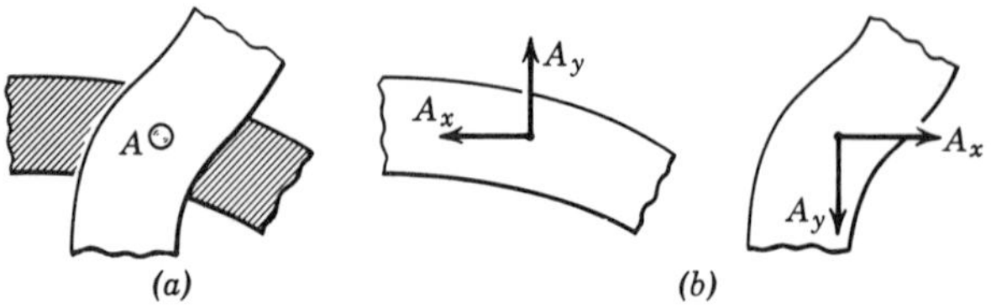

FIG. 45

when separated the components must be consistently represented in the *opposite* directions, Fig. 45b. The assigned directions may prove to be wrong when the algebraic signs of the components are determined upon calculation. If A_x, for instance, should turn out to be negative, it is actually acting in the direction opposite to that originally represented. Accordingly it would be necessary to reverse the direction of the force on *both* members and to reverse the sign of this force term in the equations. Or the representation may be left as originally made, and the proper sense of the force will be understood from the negative sign.

Finally, situations occasionally arise where it is necessary to solve two or more equations simultaneously in order to separate the unknowns. In most instances, however, simultaneous solutions may be avoided by careful choice of the member or group of members for the free-body diagram and by a careful choice of moment centers which will eliminate undesired terms from the equations. The method of solution described in the foregoing paragraphs is illustrated in the following sample problem.

SAMPLE PROBLEM

289. Determine the x- and y-components of all forces acting on each member of the hoisting frame. The weights of the parts are small compared with the load carried.

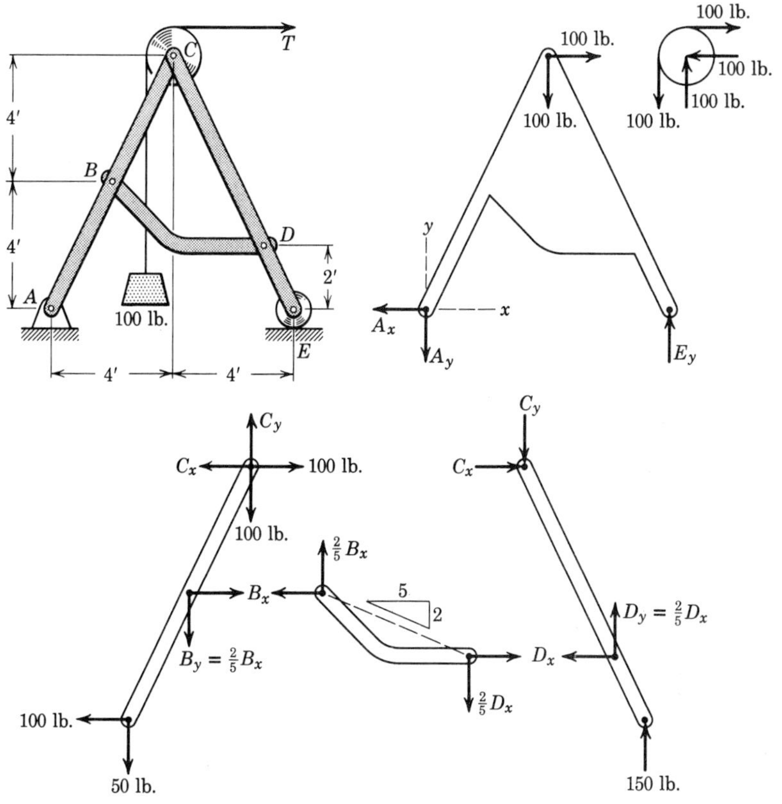

PROB. 289

Solution. The frame is a noncollapsible unit if the external supports are removed, so the reactions external to the frame as a whole will be computed first. The free-body diagram of the entire frame minus the pulley is shown in the figure. The forces acting at C are obtained from the free body of the pulley shown separately. The equations of equilibrium for the frame give

$[\Sigma M_A = 0]$ $\quad 8E_y - 4 \times 100 - 8 \times 100 = 0, \quad E_y = 150 \text{ lb.},$

$[\Sigma F_y = 0]$ $\quad A_y + 100 - 150 = 0, \quad A_y = 50 \text{ lb.},$

$[\Sigma F_x = 0]$ $\quad A_x = 100 \text{ lb.}$

The members are now separated and *all* forces acting on each member are represented. The diagrams are best arranged in their approximate relative position to aid in designating the common forces of interaction. The forces exerted by the pulley on the frame can be considered as applied to either of the two members and are shown acting on AC in this solution. Or if desired a separate free-body diagram of the pulley shaft which connects the members could be drawn to account for the action of the applied loads and the reactions of the two members at C. It is suggested that the equivalence of this alternate representation be studied. It is somewhat difficult to visualize the proper direction of the components of the interactions at C, so C_x and C_y are arbitrarily but consistently assigned as shown. The member BD is a two-force member when its weight is neglected. Therefore the components at B and D must be in a ratio such that their resultants are in the direction of the line joining points B and D. Since the slope of line BD is 2 to 5, the ratio of B_y to B_x and D_y to D_x is also 2 to 5. It should be noted that the shape of the actual member between B and D is of no consequence in considering its equilibrium.

For member AC the moment equation about C will yield B_x. Thus the equilibrium of AC requires

$$[\Sigma M_C = 0] \qquad 2 \times \tfrac{2}{5}B_x + 4B_x + 4 \times 50 - 8 \times 100 = 0, \qquad B_x = 125 \text{ lb.,} \qquad \textit{Ans.}$$

$$[\Sigma F_x = 0] \qquad 100 + 125 - 100 - C_x = 0, \qquad C_x = 125 \text{ lb.,} \qquad \textit{Ans.}$$

$$[\Sigma F_y = 0] \qquad C_y - 100 - \tfrac{2}{5} \times 125 - 50 = 0, \qquad C_y = 200 \text{ lb.} \qquad \textit{Ans.}$$

The values of C_x and C_y are positive, so that the directions were correctly guessed on the free-body diagrams.

From member BD it is clear that

$$[\Sigma F_x = 0] \qquad D_x = B_x = 125 \text{ lb.,} \qquad \textit{Ans.}$$

from which

$$D_y = B_y = \tfrac{2}{5} \times 125 = 50 \text{ lb.} \qquad \textit{Ans.}$$

All forces acting on CE have been found from the two other members. As a check on the correctness of the work the equilibrium of CE may be checked. Thus

$$[\Sigma M_C = 0] \qquad 3 \times \tfrac{2}{5} \times 125 + 4 \times 150 - 125 \times 6 = 0, \qquad \textit{(Check)}$$

$$[\Sigma F_x = 0] \qquad 125 - 125 = 0, \qquad \textit{(Check)}$$

$$[\Sigma F_y = 0] \qquad 150 + \tfrac{2}{5} \times 125 - 200 = 0. \qquad \textit{(Check)}$$

If desired the total reactions at each connection may be obtained by combining the two force components.

PROBLEMS

290. Determine the force F supported by the pin at A when the 100 lb. force acts on the linkage as shown. *Ans.* $F = 269$ lb.

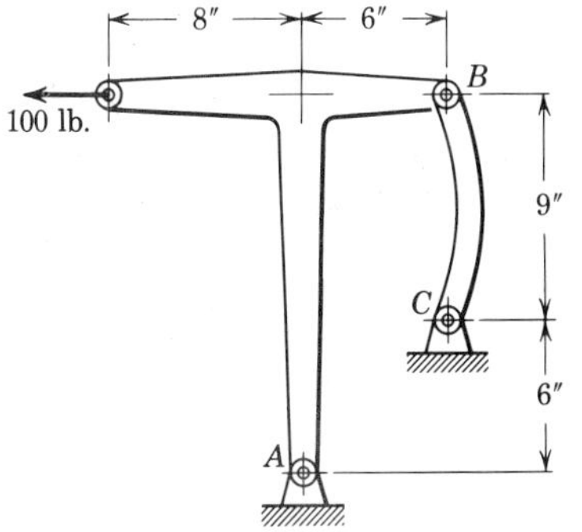

PROB. 290

291. Find the force supported by the pin at C. *Ans.* $C = 178$ lb.

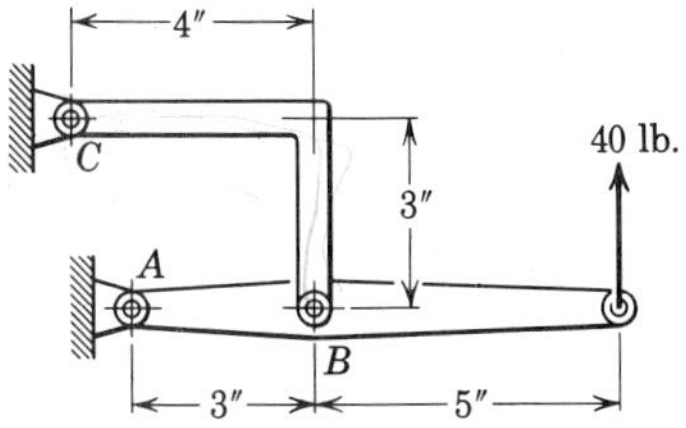

PROB. 291

292. Calculate the force supported by the pins at A and C for the connected links under the action of the applied couple. *Ans.* $A = C = 49.9$ lb.

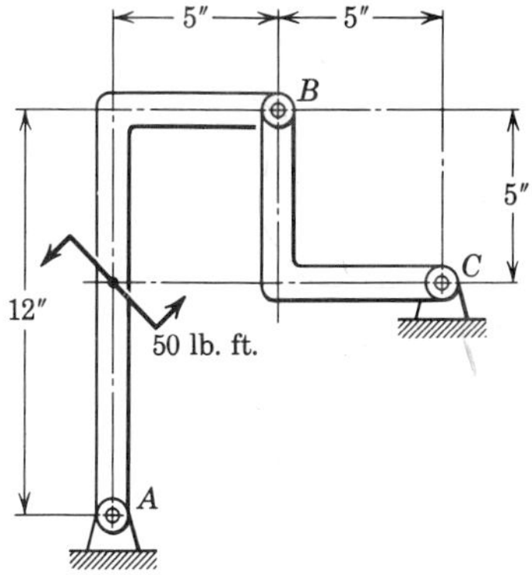

PROB. 292

293. If the handles of the pliers are gripped with a force of 50 lb. as shown, determine the compressive force P on the tube and the reaction R on the pin at A. *Ans.* $P = 150$ lb., $R = 180$ lb.

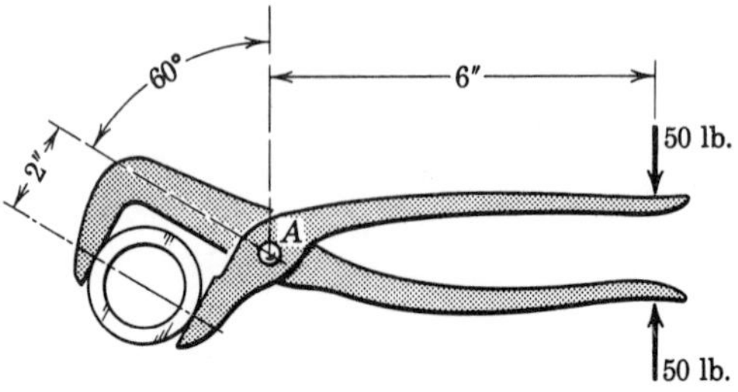

PROB. 293

294. Compound-lever snips, shown in the figure, are often used in place of regular tinners' snips when large cutting forces are required. For the gripping force of 75 lb. what is the cutting force P at a distance of 1 in. along the blade from the pin at A?

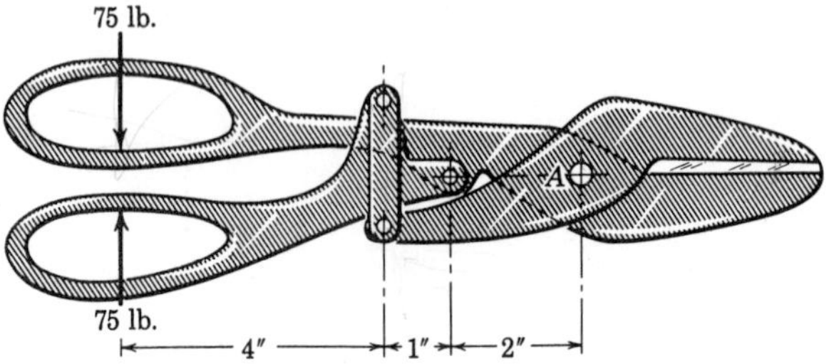

PROB. 294

295. Determine the compression P in the screw in terms of the clamping force F and the angle θ.

Ans. $P = F\left(\frac{a}{b} + \tan\theta\right)$

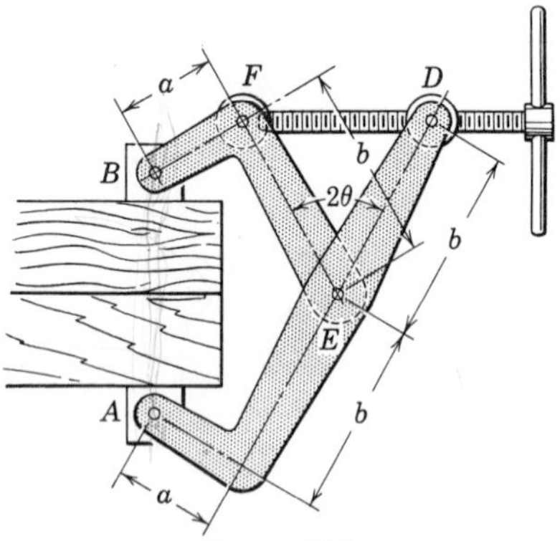

PROB. 295

296. A nail is used as the supporting pin at A for the limiting torque wrench, and the maximum force which the nail can support before it shears places an upper limit on the torque which can be supplied by the wrench. If the nail to be used can support a maximum total shear force of 400 lb., determine the limiting torque M which the wrench can supply to the bolt, and find the corresponding force P which the operator must exert on the handle. What would be the effect of increasing the dimension c, other conditions remaining the same?

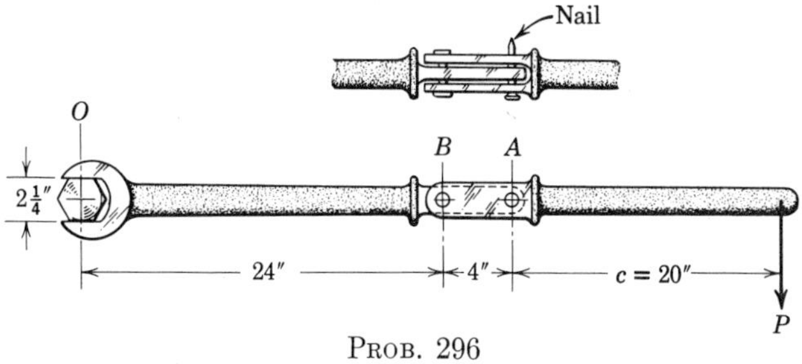

PROB. 296

297. A dual-grip clamp shown in the figure is used to provide added clamping force with a positive action. If the vertical screw is tightened to produce a clamping force of 1000 lb. and then the horizontal screw is tightened until the force at A is doubled, find the total clamping force P and the reaction R on the pin at B. *Ans.* $P = 2000$ lb., $R = 2400$ lb.

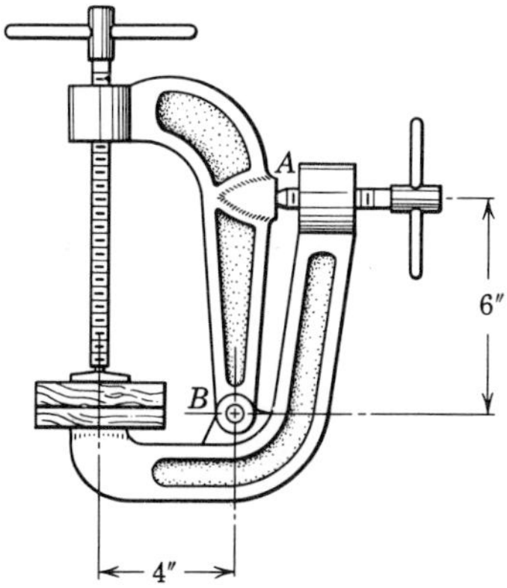

PROB. 297

298. The platform is raised or lowered by the hand-operated winches shown. Each handle may be engaged directly to the drum in any position by means of a ratchet device. If each man weighs 180 lb. and the platform and winches together weigh 120 lb., determine the force P which each man must exert on the handle in the position shown to elevate the platform, and find the corresponding force R between each man's feet and the platform.

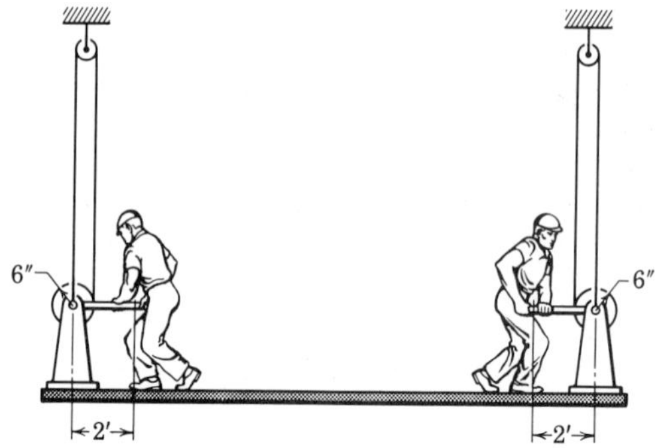

PROB. 298

299. Neglect the weight of the three-hinged arch compared with the applied load and compute the total hinge reaction at A. *Ans.* $A = 14.9$ tons

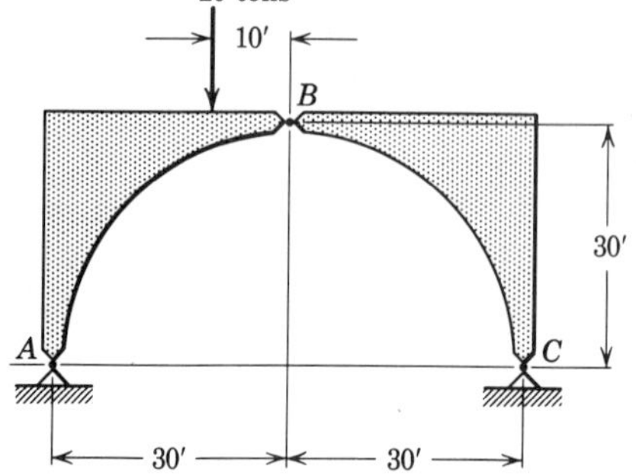

PROB. 299

300. A car mover for rolling freight cars consists of a long hand-operated lever with toggle action as shown in the figure. For a 50 lb. force applied to

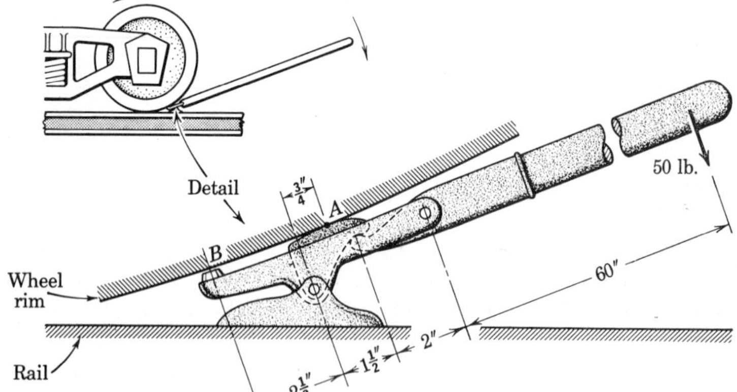

PROB. 300

the handle find the forces F_A and F_B exerted on the wheel by the mover. Assume that the upper-shoe contact is at A and that the lower shoe does not slip on the rail. Neglect the curvature of the wheel rim between A and B.

301. Calculate the force in member BE from a free-body diagram of member ABC. Neglect the weights of the members. *Ans.* $BE = 6000$ lb. C

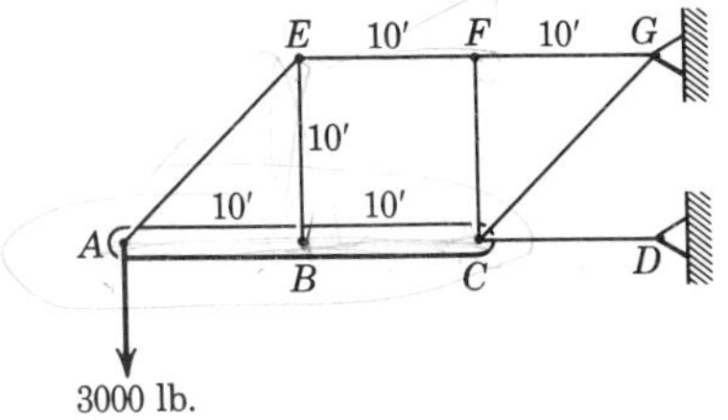

PROB. 301

302. Determine the force Q exerted on each side of the bolt by the cutters if the handles are subjected to loads of 100 lb.

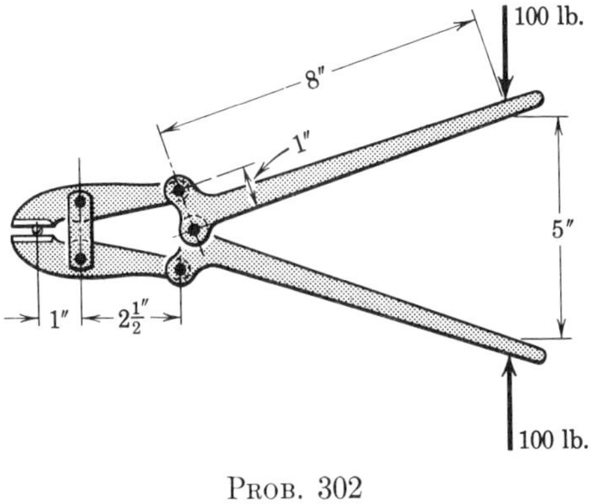

PROB. 302

303. For the paper punch shown find the punching force Q corresponding to a hand grip P. *Ans.* $Q = P\frac{b}{a}$

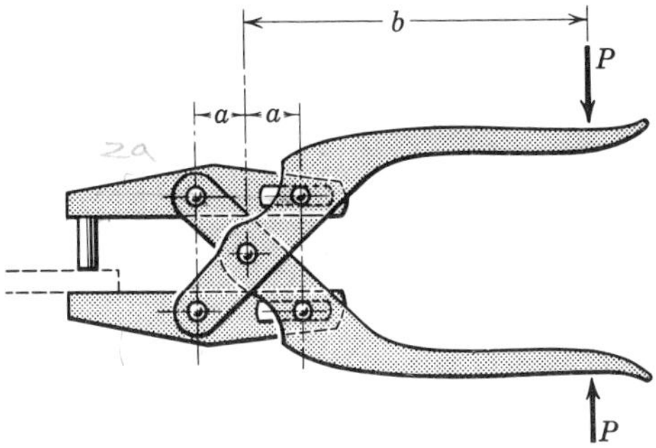

PROB. 303

304. Determine the vertical clamping force at E in terms of the applied load P for the toggle clamp in the operating position shown. *Ans.* $E = 5.25P$

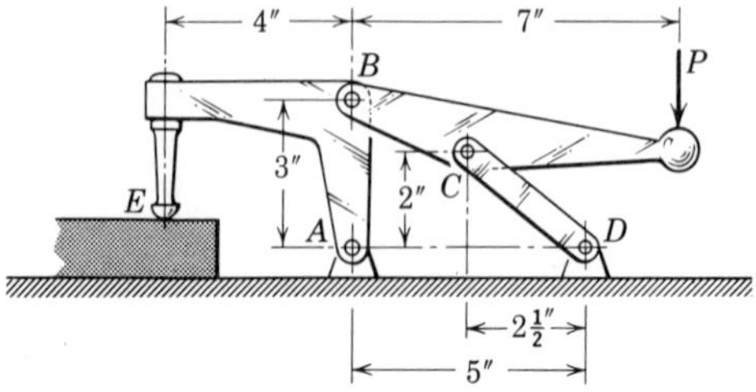

Prob. 304

305. Find the force acting on the pin at C for the lifting tongs.

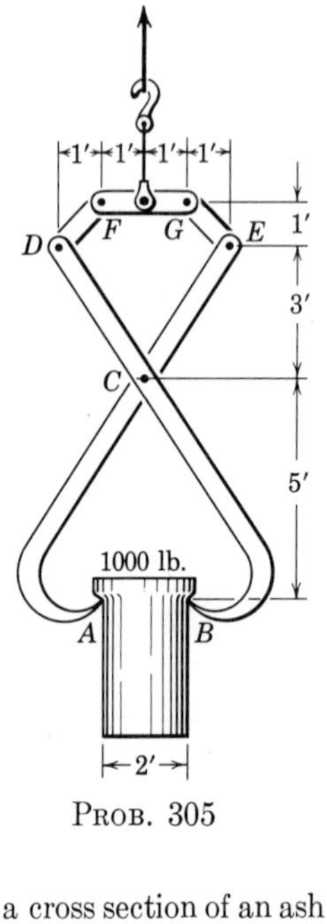

Prob. 305

306. In the figure is shown a cross section of an ash dumping pit. The hinged cover doors are actuated by the hydraulic cylinder, and the lower edge of the door at A moves on rollers with negligible friction in a horizontal guide. Each door is a uniform steel plate weighing 2000 lb. Determine the force P exerted on the piston of the hydraulic cylinder to support the doors for an angle of $\theta \doteq 30$ deg. *Ans.* $P = 5320$ lb.

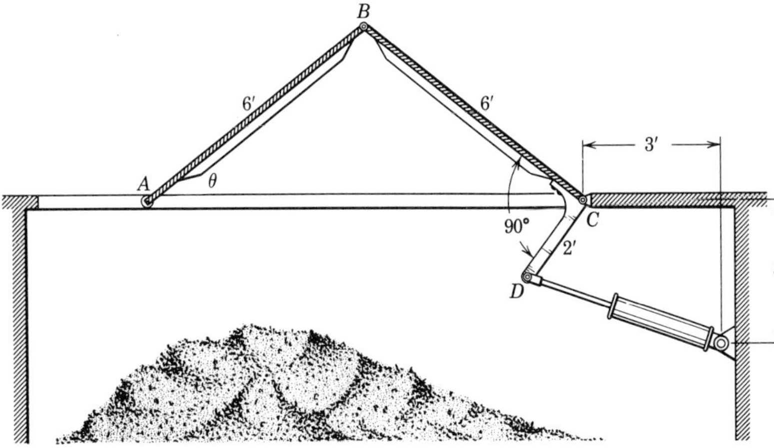

Prob. 306

307. An extension ladder of the form shown rests against a smooth vertical wall at D. The contact between the two parts of the ladder at C may also be assumed to be smooth. If a 180 lb. man with center of gravity at G climbs to the position shown, find the total force on the hinge at B. Each section of the ladder weighs 40 lb. with center of gravity at its midlength. The small dimension a may be neglected in the calculations. *Ans.* $B = 265$ lb.

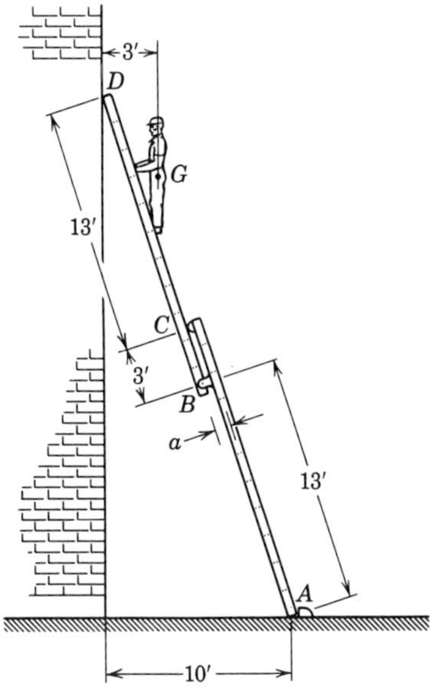

Prob. 307

308. Neglect the weight of the frame and compute the x- and y-components of all forces on each member.

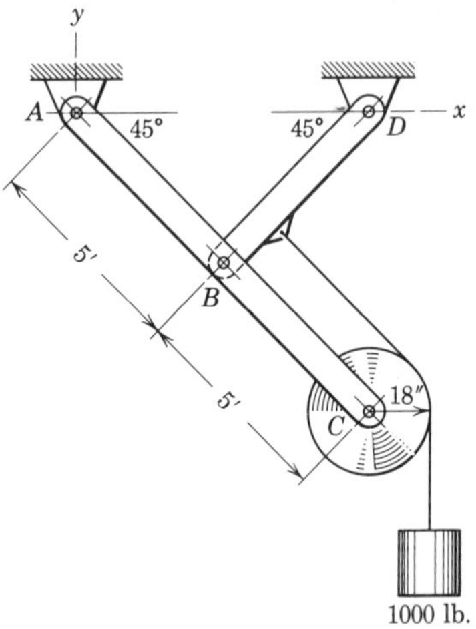

PROB. 308

309. A passenger-car front-end suspension is shown in the sketch. The weight of the frame F is included in the vertical loading of 1500 lb. The weights of the links AB and DC and the springs E are small compared with the applied load and may be neglected. The weight of each wheel, brake, and steering

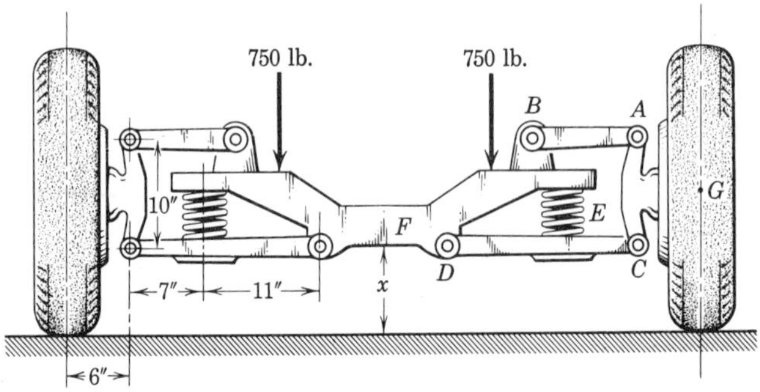

PROB. 309

knuckle assembly AC is 60 lb. and is assumed to act through G. In the equilibrium position shown each of the springs E is compressed 3 in. It is assumed that there is no shock absorber at B, and therefore no moment is applied to AB. Determine the compression P in the link AB and the constant k of the spring E.

310. Determine the shearing force Q applied to the bar if a 50 lb. force is applied to the handle for $\theta = 30$ deg. For a given applied force what value of θ gives the greatest shear? *Ans.* $Q = 1835$ lb., $\theta = 0$ for max. Q

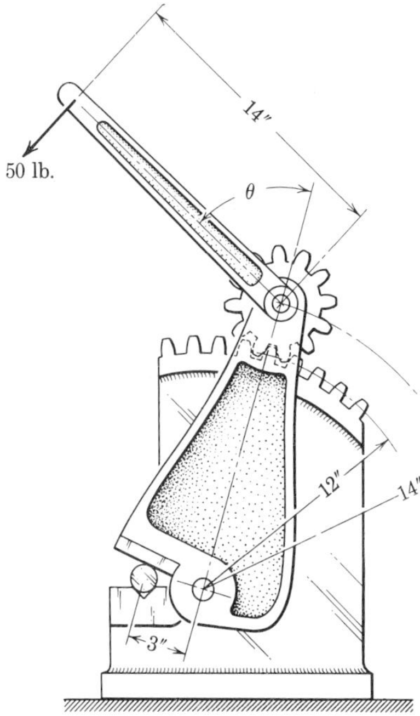

PROB. 310

311. Determine the punching force P for the aircraft rivet squeezer shown if a 50 lb. grip is used. *Ans.* $P = 3600$ lb.

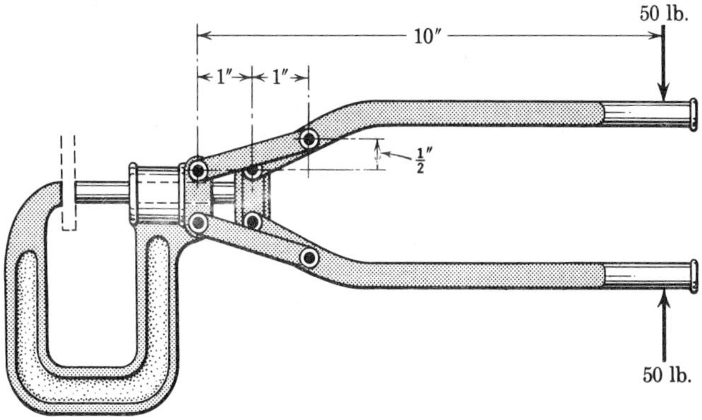

PROB. 311

312. The control lever F is rigidly keyed to the fixed shaft A. The rod B of the release handle controls lever C which is fastened to a collar concentric with the shaft. The collar turns independently of the shaft. For the condition of equilibrium illustrated a clockwise torque of 30 lb. ft. is applied to the shaft by the lever, and the collar independently resists a clockwise rotation with a moment of 24 lb. in. Draw a free-body diagram of the triangular plate, the handle, the 90 deg. lever, and the man's arm, and find all forces on each part. The weights of the parts are negligible.

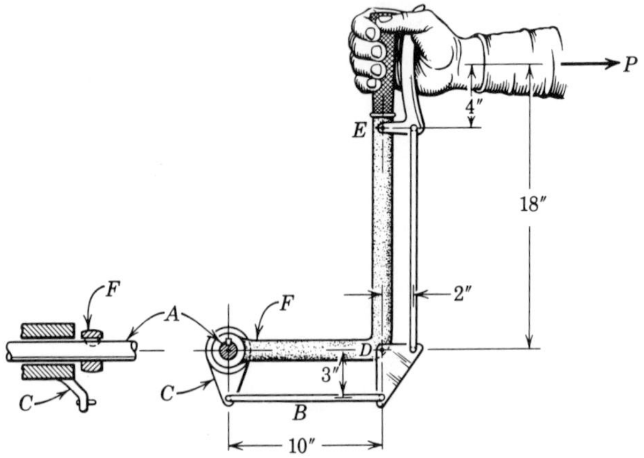

PROB. 312

313. The rubber-tired loader weighs 50,000 lb. empty and handles 5 yd.³ of dirt with center of gravity at G. Duplicate linkage exists on each side of the machine. If the loader handles dirt weighing 80 lb./ft.³, determine for the particular position shown the force P on the piston of each hydraulic cylinder AB and the force on the pins C and E on one side of the machine.

Ans. $P = 21{,}300$ lb., $C = 22{,}000$ lb., $E = 11{,}600$ lb.

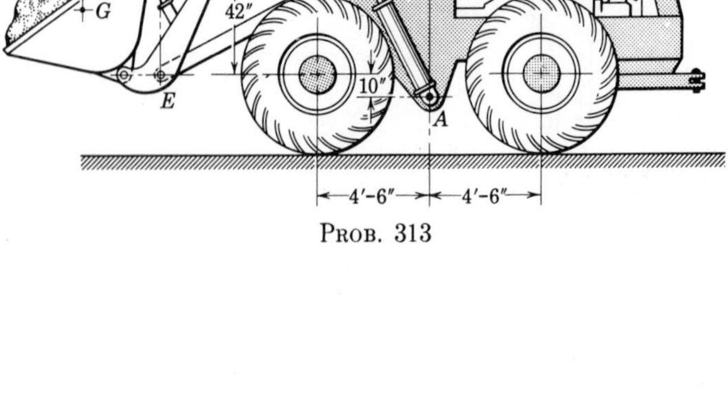

PROB. 313

314. A force of 20 lb. is required on the crank of the hand drill to start the drill in the position shown with a thrust P applied to the handle. The gear ratio is 3 to 1. Determine the moment M about the axis of the drill which must be supplied by the hand grip to prevent the handle from turning.

Ans. M = 56.7 lb. in.

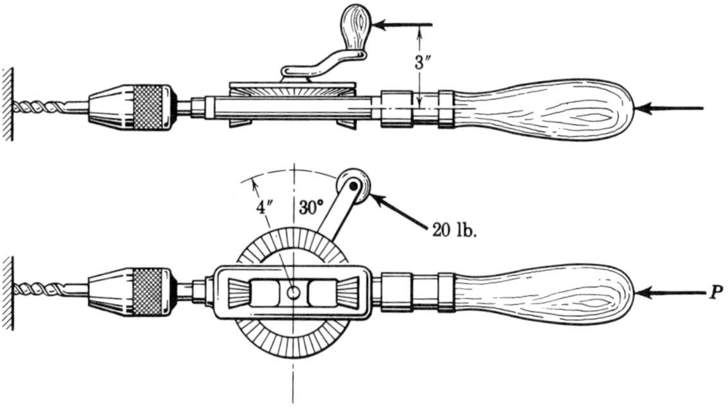

Prob. 314

315. The elevation of the bulldozer scoop is controlled mainly by the link ABC which is pinned to the fixed frame of the machine at C and operated by the hydraulic cylinder F. The lower end of the cylinder is pinned to the frame at J. The tilt of the scoop is controlled mainly by the link DE which is

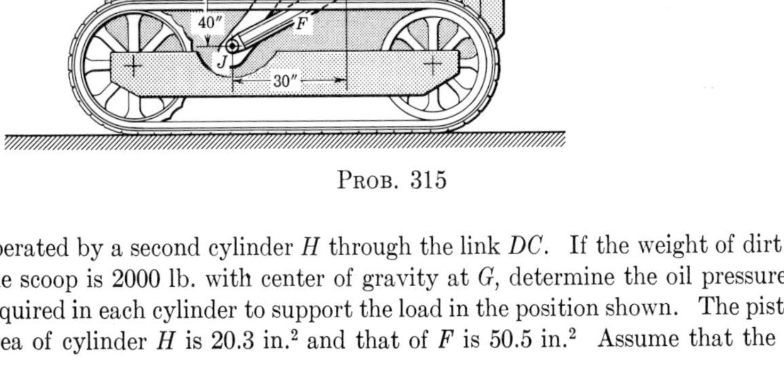

Prob. 315

operated by a second cylinder H through the link DC. If the weight of dirt in the scoop is 2000 lb. with center of gravity at G, determine the oil pressure p required in each cylinder to support the load in the position shown. The piston area of cylinder H is 20.3 in.^{2} and that of F is 50.5 in.^{2} Assume that the oil pressure acts on one side only of the piston at any one time. Note that the scoop is supported by a duplicate set of links on each side of the bulldozer. Neglect the weight of the links compared with the load supported.

Ans. $p_H = 52.3$ lb./in.^{2}, $p_F = 85.4$ lb./in.^{2}

* **316.** In the small jib crane each of the three structural members is uniform and weighs 400 lb. The connections at B, C, and D may be assumed to be pin joints. The gear drum and pinion are mounted in bearings fastened to the mast. The upper mast bearing is capable of exerting horizontal support only.

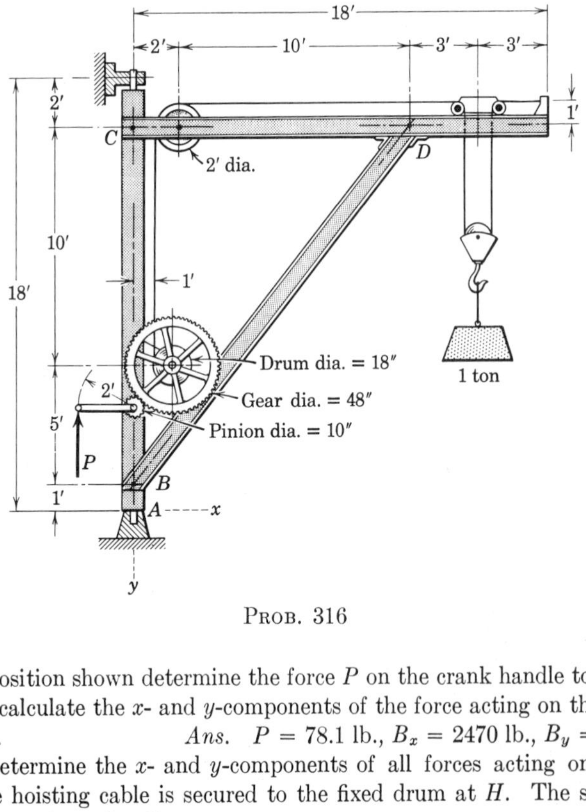

PROB. 316

For the position shown determine the force P on the crank handle to raise the load and calculate the x- and y-components of the force acting on the connection at B. *Ans.* $P = 78.1$ lb., $B_x = 2470$ lb., $B_y = 3280$ lb.

* **317.** Determine the x- and y-components of all forces acting on member GE. The hoisting cable is secured to the fixed drum at H. The sheaves at D and G are of equal radius.

Ans. $C_x = 325$ lb., $C_y = 1249$ lb., $E_x = E_y = 49.6$ lb. Total forces at D are $D_x = 575$ lb., $D_y = 699$ lb.

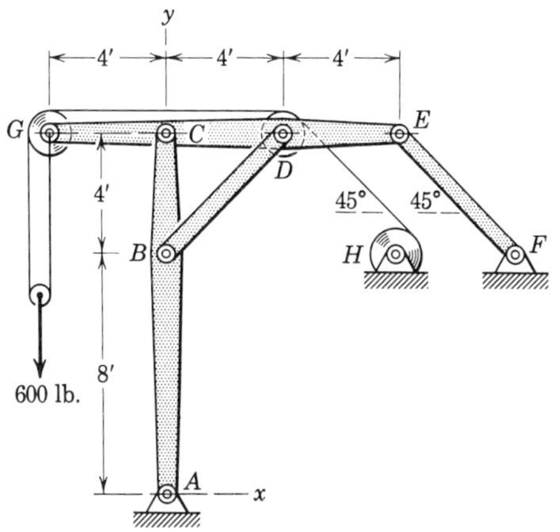

PROB. 317

* **318.** Determine the total reaction at *C* if the connections at *C*, *D*, *E*, and *F* act as ball-and-socket joints. The bearings at *A* and *B* provide no support in the direction of *AB*. *Ans.* $C = 78.2$ lb.

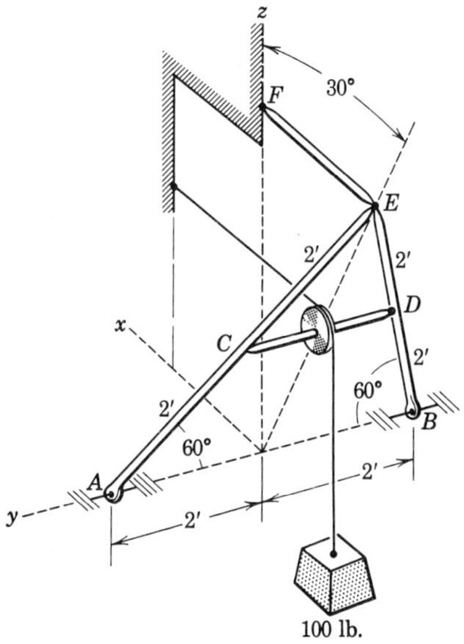

PROB. 318

* **319.** The frame shown rests on a smooth horizontal surface, and the connections at *D*, *E*, *F*, *G*, and *H* act as ball-and-socket joints. Determine the total force acting on the connection at *D* due to the 500 lb. load applied at *F*.
Ans. $D = 257$ lb.

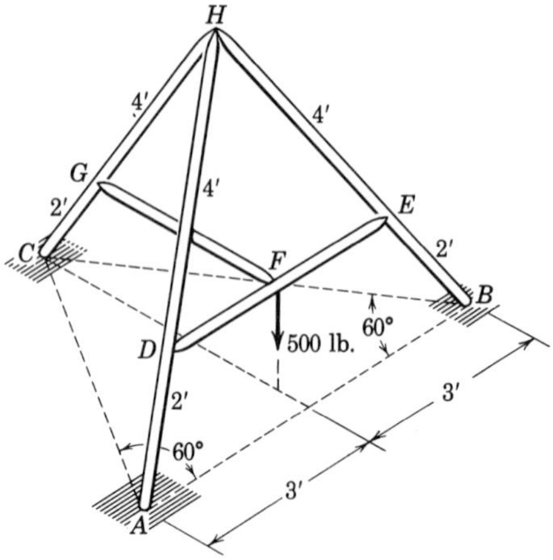

PROB. 319

33. Beams with Concentrated Loads. Structural members which offer resistance to bending caused by applied loads are known as beams. Most beams are long prismatical bars, and the loads are usually applied normal to the axes of the bars. Beams are undoubtedly the most important of all structural members, and the basic theory underlying their design must be thoroughly understood. The analysis of the load-carrying capacities of beams consists, first, in establishing the equilibrium requirements of the beam as a whole and any portion of it considered separately. Second, the relations between the resulting forces and the accompanying internal resistance of the beam to support these forces are established. The first part of this analysis requires the application of the principles of statics, while the second part of the problem involves the strength characteristics of the material and is usually treated in the study of strength of materials. This article concerns the first aspect of the problem only.

Beams supported in such a way that the external support reactions can be calculated by the methods of statics alone are called *statically determinate* beams. A beam that has more supports than are necessary to provide equilibrium is said to be *statically indeterminate*, and it is necessary to consider the load-deformation properties of the beam in addition to the equations of statical equilibrium to determine the support reactions. In Fig. 46 are shown examples of both types of beams. In this article only statically determinate beams are analyzed.

In the analysis of simple trusses the resultant of the forces acting on the section of a cut member was a single force, either tension or compression, in the direction of the member. Bending either was negligible or was absent. In the analysis of beams the resultant of the forces acting on a transverse section of the beam cannot, in general, be represented in terms of a single force but must be expressed by a force and a couple. It should be recalled from Chapter 2 that the resultant of any coplanar force system is expressible as a resultant force acting at any

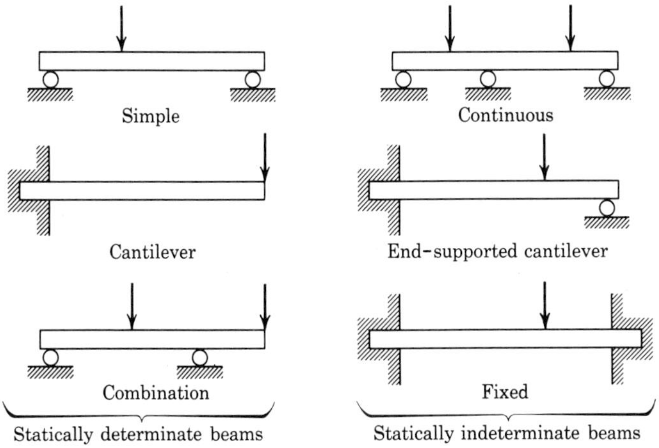

FIG. 46

point and a corresponding couple. In some beams the actual distribution of force over a cross section is exceedingly complex and requires for a complete description extended analysis involving the load-deformation properties of the beam materials. In the present discussion only the *resultant* of the force distribution across any section of a statically determinate beam will be considered. This resultant, required for equilibrium of the portion of the beam on each side of the section, may be expressed in terms of a force and a couple.

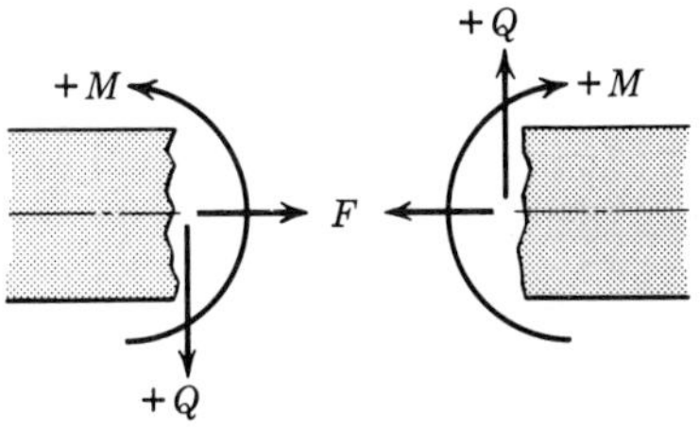

FIG. 47

In Fig. 47 are shown two portions of a beam cut by an imaginary section transverse to the beam. The resultant force acting on either section is represented in terms of its two components Q and F and is shown as acting at the *center line* of the beam. The force Q, tangent to the section, is a *shear* force. The *average shear stress* over the cross section is Q/A, where A is the area of the section. The force F as shown is a tensile force, and the *average tensile stress* over the section is F/A. The couple M is known as the *bending moment* at this section. It should be noted that the directions of Q, F, and M are reversed on the two sections by the principle of action and reaction. Most beams are supported and loaded by forces normal to the beam axis, and in this case the tensile force F or a compressive force C is either zero or negligible.

It is of advantage to adopt conventions for the positive directions of Q and M. Figure 47 shows the conventions generally used for the positive sense of moment and shear. It is frequently impossible to ascertain at a glance whether the shear and moment on a certain section of a loaded beam are positive or negative. For this reason it will be found advisable to represent Q and M in their positive directions on the free-body diagrams and let the algebraic signs of the calculated values indicate the proper direction.

As an aid to the physical interpretation of the bending couple M consider the beam shown in Fig. 48 bent by the two equal and opposite

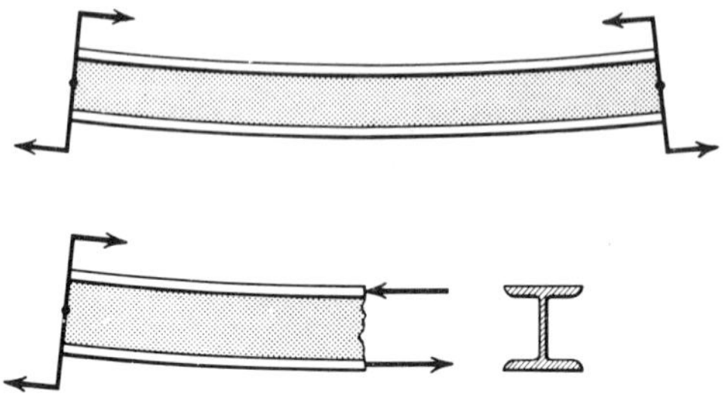

Fig. 48

moments applied at the ends. The cross section of the beam is taken to be that of an H-section with a very narrow center web and heavy top and bottom flanges. For this beam the load carried by the small web may be neglected compared with that carried by the two flanges. It should be perfectly clear that the upper flange of the beam is shortened and is under compression while the lower flange is lengthened and is under tension. The resultant of the two forces, one tension and the other compression, acting on any section is a couple and is the value of the bending moment on the section. If a beam of some other cross section were loaded in the same way, the distribution of force over the cross section would be different, but the resultant would be the same couple.

The variation of shear force Q and bending moment M over the length of a beam provides information necessary for the analysis of the beam. In particular, the maximum magnitude of the bending moment is usually the primary consideration in the design or selection of a beam, and its value and position should be determined. The variations in shear and moment are best shown graphically, and the expressions for Q and M when plotted against the length of the beam give the *shear-force* and *bending-moment diagrams* for the beam.

The first step in the calculation of the shear and moment relations is to establish the values of all external reactions on the beam by applying the equations of equilibrium to a free-body diagram of the beam as a whole. Next, a portion of the beam, either to the right or to the left of an arbitrary transverse section, is isolated with a free-body diagram, and the equations of equilibrium are applied to this isolated portion of the beam. These equations will yield expressions for the shear force Q and bending moment M acting at the cut section on the part of the beam isolated. The part of the beam which involves the least number of forces, either to the right or to the left of the arbitrary section, usually yields the simpler solution. Finally it is important to note that the calculations for Q and M on each section chosen must be consistent with the positive convention illustrated in Fig. 47.

There are many possible combinations of loading and supports. In each case the method and procedure described here and illustrated in the sample problems which follow will always work.

SAMPLE PROBLEMS

320. Draw the shear-force and bending-moment diagrams for the beam shown in the *a*-part of the illustration and determine the maximum magnitude of the bending moment and its location.

Solution. From the free-body diagram of the beam in part *b* the reactions are

$$[\Sigma M_{R_1} = 0] \qquad 7R_2 - 4 \times 400 - 10 \times 200 = 0, \qquad R_2 = 514.3 \text{ lb.},$$

$$[\Sigma F_y = 0] \qquad R_1 + 514.3 - 400 - 200 = 0, \qquad R_1 = 85.7 \text{ lb.}$$

The free-body diagram of the part of the beam to the left of section A is shown in part c of the figure. The shear Q and moment M are shown in their positive directions. Equilibrium requires

$$[\Sigma F_y = 0] \qquad Q = 85.7 \text{ lb.},$$

$$[\Sigma M_A = 0] \qquad M = 85.7x.$$

These values hold between $x = 0$ and $x = 4$ ft.

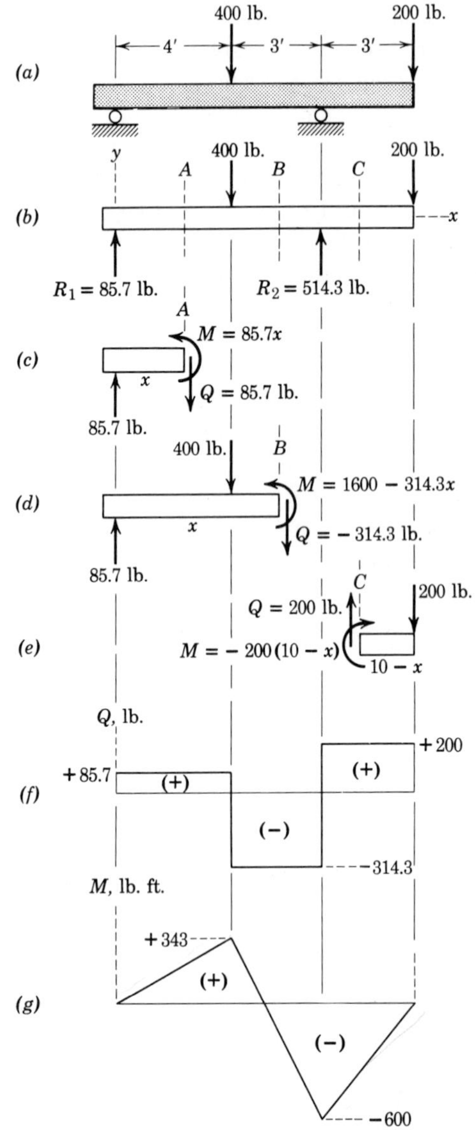

400 lb.
200 lb.
4′
3′
3′
(a)
y
A
B
C
(b)
x
$R_1 = 85.7$ lb.
$R_2 = 514.3$ lb.
(c)
$M = 85.7x$
$Q = 85.7$ lb.
85.7 lb.
(d)
400 lb.
$M = 1600 - 314.3x$
$Q = -314.3$ lb.
(e)
$Q = 200$ lb.
$M = -200(10 - x)$
$10 - x$
(f)
Q, lb.
+85.7
(+)
(−)
+200
−314.3
(g)
M, lb. ft.
+343
−600

Prob. 320

The next interval is analyzed by the free-body diagram of the entire portion of the beam to the left of section B. Again Q and M are shown in their positive directions, part d. Equilibrium gives

$$[\Sigma F_y = 0] \qquad Q + 400 - 85.7 = 0, \qquad Q = -314.3 \text{ lb.},$$

$$[\Sigma M_B = 0] \qquad M + 400(x - 4) - 85.7x = 0, \qquad M = 1600 - 314.3x.$$

Lastly, from the simpler of the two diagrams for section C, shown in part e of the figure, literal application of the equilibrium equations gives

$$[\Sigma F_y = 0] \qquad Q = 200 \text{ lb.},$$

$$[\Sigma M_C = 0] \qquad M + 200(10 - x) = 0, \qquad M = -200(10 - x).$$

It should be noted that M and Q are shown in their positive directions on the free-body diagram.

In parts f and g are plotted the shear-force and bending-moment diagrams for the three intervals of the beam. The maximum magnitude of the moment and its position are clearly

$$M = 600 \text{ lb. ft. at } x = 7 \text{ ft.} \qquad \textit{Ans.}$$

321. The hoisting drum is temporarily locked to its shaft which in turn is rigidly attached to the boom. Determine the variation of shear force (normal to the boom axis) and bending moment over the length of the boom.

Solution. The forces external to the boom are first determined with the aid of the free-body diagram shown. The tension T and the reaction at A are represented by their components along and normal to the boom. Isolation of the pulley alone enables the reactions on the boom at the pulley shaft to be correctly drawn. The 1000 lb. bearing force is represented by its components along and normal to the boom. The 1500 lb. ft. twist is applied through the shaft fixed in the boom.

Two sections A and B are required. Isolation of the part of the boom below section A and isolation of the part above section B are separately shown with all forces and moments external to both parts indicated. On each of the two free-body diagrams Q and M are shown in their positive directions, and, to be consistent, the axial force F is also shown positive as tension. The values of Q, M, and F for the two sections are *not* equal since they act on different sections and do not constitute actions and reactions.

For the lower member,

$$[\Sigma F_y = 0] \qquad Q = 358 \text{ lb.},$$

$$[\Sigma M_A = 0] \qquad M = 358x,$$

$$[\Sigma F_x = 0] \qquad F = -1380 \text{ lb.}$$

For the upper member,

$[\Sigma F_y = 0]$ $\qquad Q = -508$ lb.,

$[\Sigma M_B = 0]$ $\qquad M = 508(20 - x)$,

$[\Sigma F_x = 0]$ $\qquad F = -880$ lb.

The shear-force and bending-moment diagrams are shown at the bottom of the figure. The discontinuity in M at $x = 10$ ft. is due to the applied moment at that point. The increment of this discontinuity, 5080 minus 3580, equals this applied moment. Below the pulley the axial force is 1380 lb. compression, and above the pulley the axial force is 880 lb. compression.

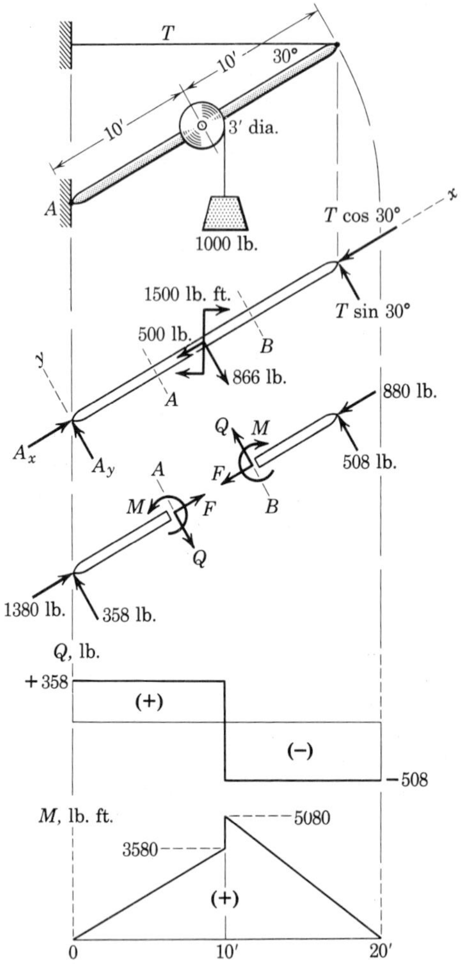

Prob. 321

PROBLEMS

Neglect the weight of the beams in the following problems.

322. Draw thc shear and moment diagrams for the simply supported beam and determine the maximum moment M.

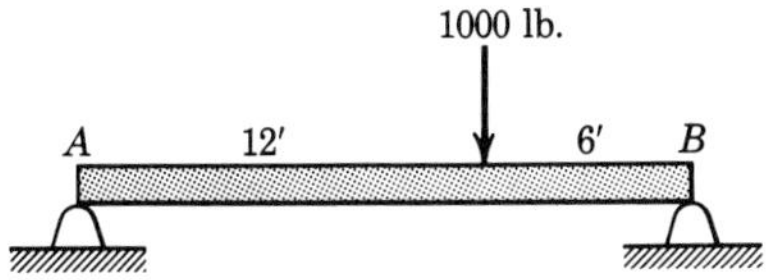

PROB. 322

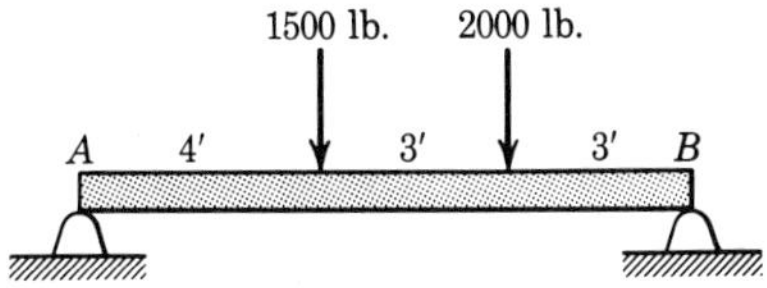

PROB. 323

323. Draw the shear and moment diagrams for the combination beam and determine the maximum moment M. *Ans.* $M = 6000$ lb. ft.

324. Draw the shear and moment diagrams for the cantilever beam.

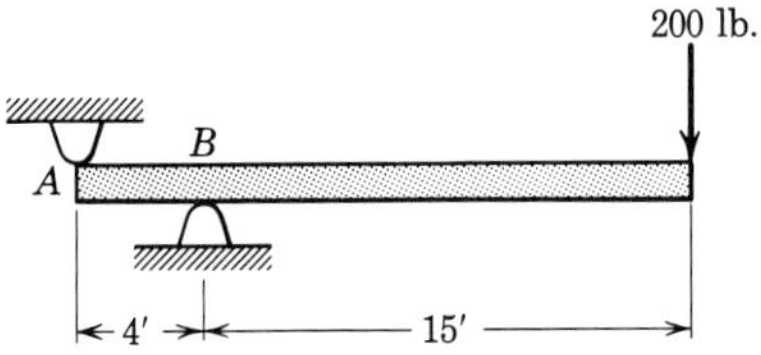

PROB. 324

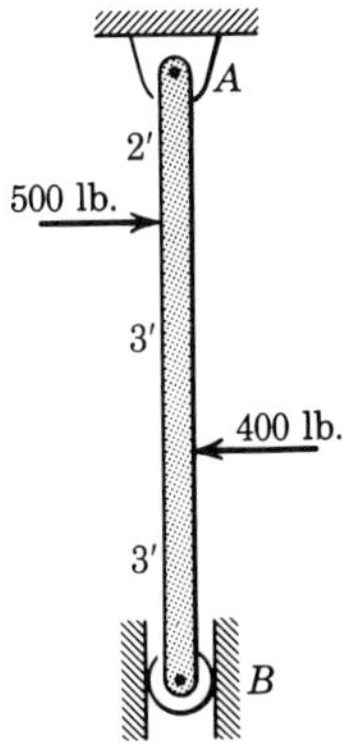

PROB. 325

325. Draw the shear and moment diagrams for the vertical member and find the maximum moment M.

326. Draw the shear and moment diagrams for the cantilever beam.

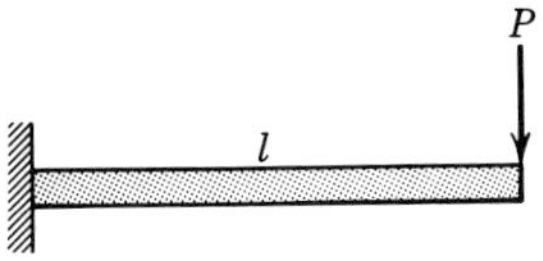

PROB. 236

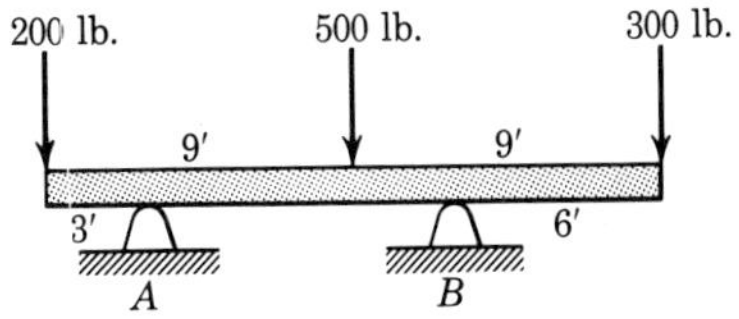

PROB. 327

327. Draw the shear and moment diagrams for the loaded beam and find the maximum magnitude of the moment M. *Ans.* $M = 1800$ lb. ft.

328. Draw the shear and moment diagrams for the beam loaded in its center by the couple C. What is the magnitude of the bending moment M on a section of the beam which approaches the midpoint?

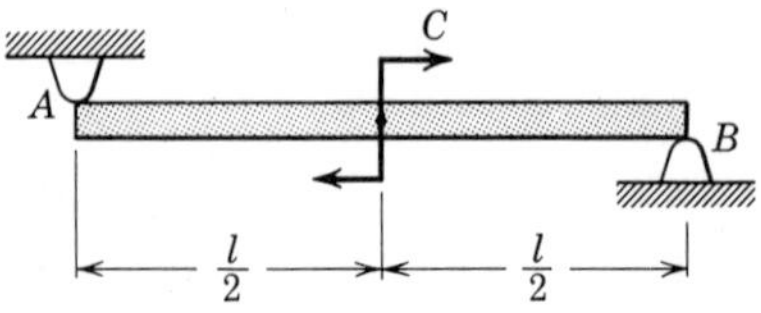

PROB. 328

329. Draw the shear and moment diagrams for the beam loaded as shown.

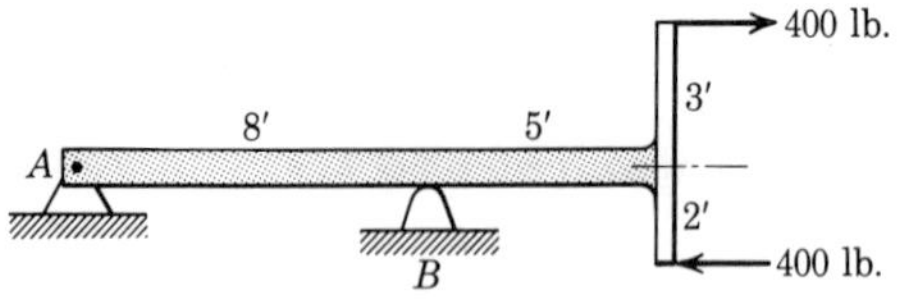

PROB. 329

330. Draw the shear and moment diagrams for the beam AB loaded through the attached curved strut.

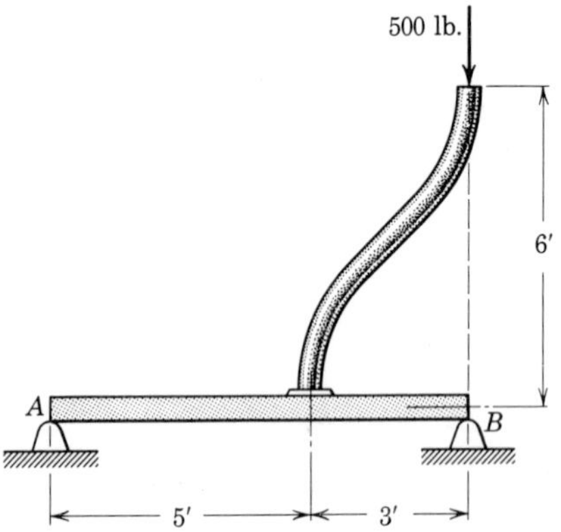

PROB. 330

331. Determine the bending moment M at section A from the moment diagram of the beam BC. *Ans.* $M = 500$ lb. ft.

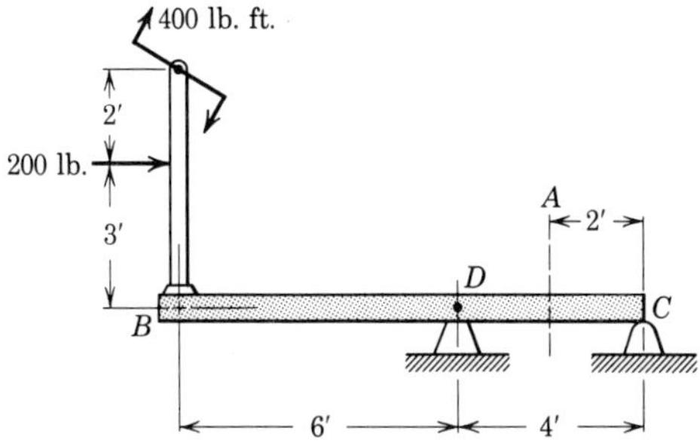

PROB. 331

332. The resistance of a beam of uniform width to bending is found to be proportional to the square of the beam depth y. For the cantilever beam shown the depth is h at the support. Find the required depth y as a function of the length x in order that the resistance to bending offered by the beam at the support will be the same for all sections.

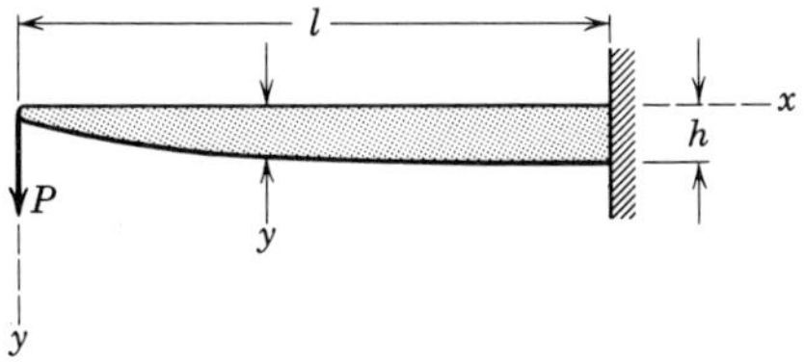

PROB. 332

333. A curved beam has the form of a semicircular arc and is centrally loaded as shown. Determine the shear Q (perpendicular to the arc) and the bending moment M as functions of θ. Assume that the horizontal surface is perfectly smooth.

Ans. $Q = \dfrac{P}{2} \cos\theta,\ M = \dfrac{Pr}{2}(1 - \sin\theta)$

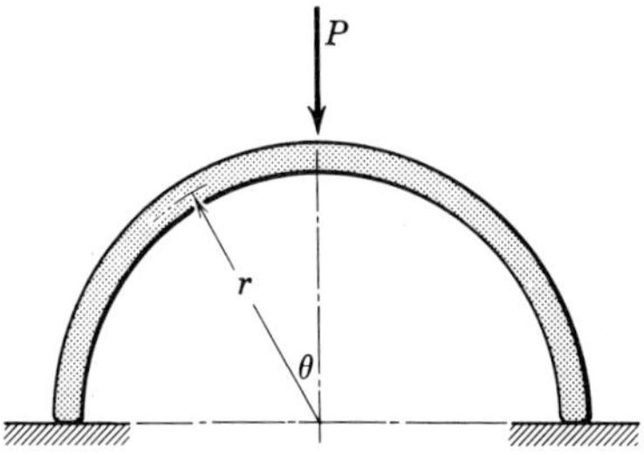

PROB. 333

334. Find the maximum bending moment M in the arm AB and its distance x from A.

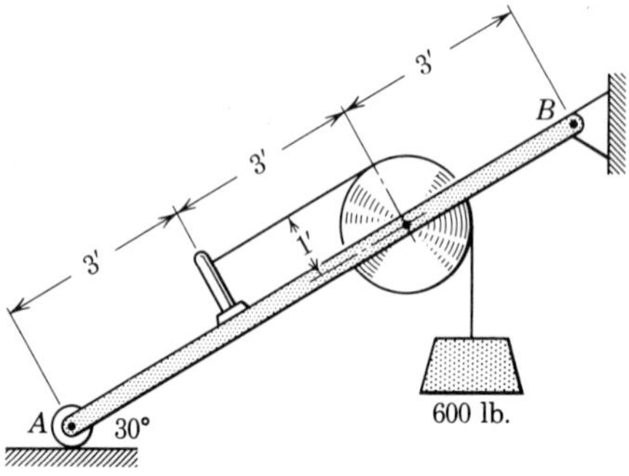

PROB. 334

* **335.** Determine the maximum bending moment M and the corresponding value of x in the crane beam and indicate the section where this moment acts.

Ans. $M_A = \dfrac{W}{4l}(l - a)^2, \; x = \dfrac{a + l}{2}$

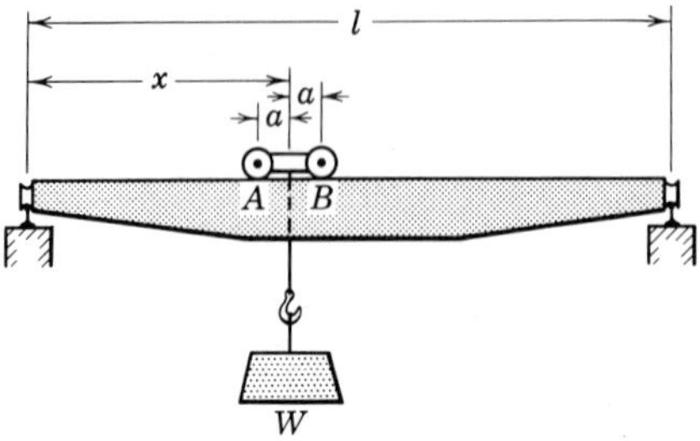

PROB. 335

* **336.** A curved bar with the dimensions shown is in the form of a circular segment. Determine the shear Q normal to the axis of the bar and the bending moment M as functions of x.

$$Ans. \quad Q = \frac{2Pax}{a^2 + L^2/4}, \; M = P\left[\sqrt{\left(\frac{a^2 + L^2/4}{2a}\right)^2 - x^2} + \frac{4a^2 - L^2}{8a}\right]$$

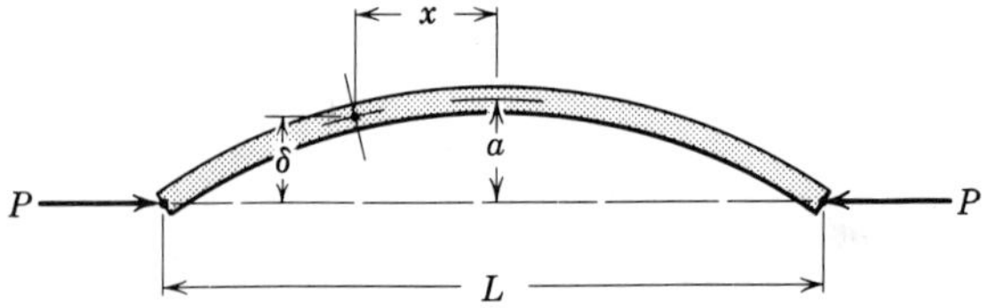

PROB. 336

CHAPTER
5

DISTRIBUTED FORCES

34. Introduction. In the preceding chapters all forces have been assumed to be concentrated and have been represented by single vector arrows at the points of application or along the unique lines of action of the forces. Actually, no "concentrated" forces exist, since every real force applied to a body is distributed over some finite area or volume. In the case of force applied to a surface it is clear that, when the dimensions of the area upon which the force is distributed are negligible compared with the other dimensions of the body, the concept of a concentrated force raises no question. On the other hand force may be applied over a surface area of considerable size, and the variation in the distribution of the force acting over the area must be accounted for. There is also force which is distributed over the volume of a body, such as the earth's gravitational force or electrical and magnetic forces.

A distributed force is measured at any point by its intensity. Thus force distributed over an area is known as *pressure* or *stress* and is measured as force per unit area on which it acts (lb./in.^{2}). The term *pressure* is usually used to denote the intensity of distributed force due to the action of fluids, whereas the term *stress* is more generally used to denote internal distributed force in solids. Force distributed over the volume of a body is known as *body force* and is measured as force per unit of volume (lb./in.^{3}).

35. Center of Gravity. The most common distributed force is the force of attraction of the earth. This body force is distributed over all parts of every object in the earth's field of influence. The resultant of this distribution of body force is known as the *weight* of the body, and it is necessary to determine its magnitude and position for bodies whose weights are appreciable.

Consider a three-dimensional body of any size, shape, and weight. If it is suspended, as shown in Fig. 49, by a cord from any point such as A, the body will be in equilibrium under the action of the tension in the cord and the resultant of the gravity or body forces acting on all the particles. This resultant is clearly collinear with the cord, and it will be assumed that its position will be marked, say, by drilling a hole of negligible size along its line of action. The experiment is repeated by suspension at other points such as B and C, and in each case the line of action of the resultant is marked. For all practical purposes these lines of action will be concurrent at a point which is known as the *center of gravity* or *center of mass* of the body. An exact analysis, however, would take into account the fact that the directions of the gravity forces for the various particles of the body differ slightly because of the fact that they converge toward the center of attraction of the earth. Also, since the particles are at different distances from the earth, the intensity of the earth's force field is not exactly constant over the body. These considerations lead to the conclusion that the lines of action of the gravity force resultants in the experiments just described will not quite be concurrent, and therefore no unique center of gravity exists in the exact sense. This condition is of no practical importance as long as we deal with bodies whose dimensions are small compared with those of the earth. We therefore assume a uniform and parallel field of force due to the earth's gravitational attraction, and this condition results in the concept of a unique center of gravity.

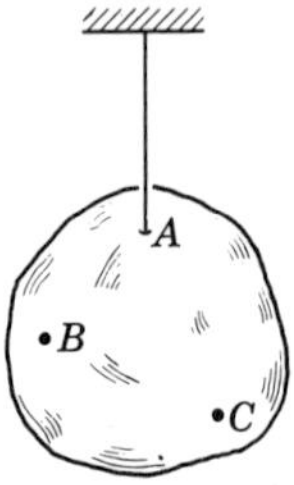

Fig. 49

The position of the center of gravity as a unique point may be determined by experiment, but its existence must not be inferred from this result alone. It may be proved in the following way. Consider any two particles of weight dW_1 and dW_2 in a body as shown in Fig. 50. The line AB joining these particles makes an angle θ with the horizontal plane, and the particles are separated a distance $a + b$. The resultant dR of dW_1 and dW_2 is their sum and can be located by Varignon's theorem. Taking moments about

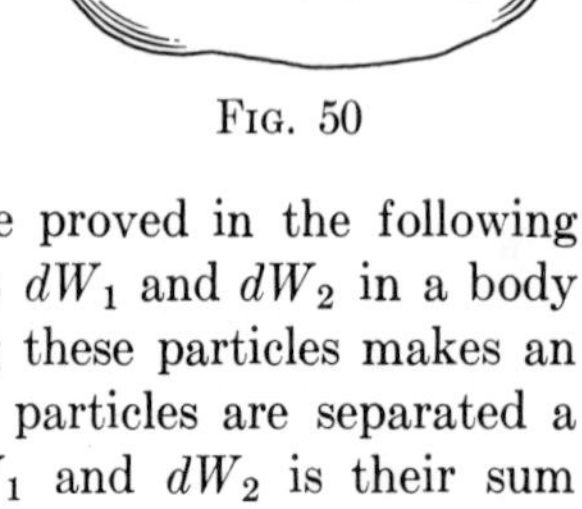

Fig. 50

B gives

$$(dW_1 + dW_2)b \cos \theta = dW_1(a + b) \cos \theta,$$

or

$$b = \frac{dW_1}{dW_1 + dW_2} (a + b).$$

The point C on line AB through which the resultant passes is now located, and the result is independent of θ. Hence regardless of the orientation of the body the resultant of dW_1 and dW_2 will always pass through point C. Combining dR with the weight of a third particle will define another unique point through which the new resultant will always pass. This process is continued until all particles are accounted for and a point is obtained whose coordinates are independent of the orientation of the body. This point is the center of gravity of the body.

To locate mathematically the center of gravity G of any body, Fig. 51, an equation may be written which states, by Varignon's theorem, that the moment about any axis of the resultant W of the gravity forces equals the sum of the moments about the same axis due to the gravity forces dW acting on each particle. If the center of gravity is designated by G, its coordinates by $\bar{x}$, $\bar{y}$, and $\bar{z}$, and the total weight by W, the moment principle gives

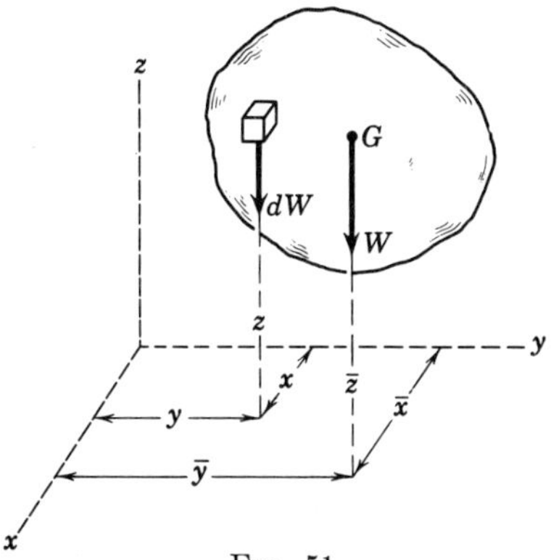

FIG. 51

$$\bar{x} = \frac{\int x \, dW}{W},$$

$$\bar{y} = \frac{\int y \, dW}{W}, \qquad (17)$$

$$\bar{z} = \frac{\int z \, dW}{W}.$$

The numerator of each expression represents the *sum of the moments*,

and the product of W and the corresponding coordinate of G represents the *moment of the sum*. The third equation is obtained by revolving the body and reference frame 90 deg. about a horizontal axis so that the z-axis is horizontal.

In most problems the calculations may be simplified by an intelligent choice of reference axes. In general the axes should be placed so as to simplify the equations of the boundaries as much as possible. Thus polar coordinates will usually simplify any problem having circular boundaries. Another important clue may be taken from considerations of symmetry. Whenever there exists a line or plane of symmetry, a coordinate axis or plane should be chosen to coincide with this line or plane. The center of gravity will always lie on such a line or plane since the moments due to symmetrically located elements will always cancel, and the body can be considered as being composed of pairs of these elements. Thus the axis of a right circular cone is such a line of symmetry, and the central vertical plane in the fore-and-aft direction of a ship's hull is such a plane of symmetry.

The proper choice of the differential element for the integration process is important. Whenever possible a first-order differential element of volume should be selected so that only one integration will be required to cover the entire figure. Regardless of the element used, the coordinate x, y, or z which is multiplied by dW in the numerator of Eqs. 17 is the coordinate to the *center of gravity of the element.* When a first-order element is not convenient, a second-order quantity should be selected in preference to a third-order element. As an example of these remarks consider the calculation of the center of gravity of a right circular cone. An element $dx\ dy\ dz$ could be chosen and a triple integration carried out. The process would be relatively laborious. On the other hand if a first-order element defined by a coaxial circular slice of differential thickness were selected, only one simple integration would be required in moving the element from vertex to base. Other considerations in the selection of the element and integration limits are best shown by actual examples, several of which follow the next article.

In the event the density μ is not constant but can be expressed as a function of the coordinates, it will be necessary to account for this variation in the calculation of both the numerators and denominators of Eqs. 17.

36. Centroids of Lines, Areas, and Volumes. Whenever the density μ of a body is uniform throughout, it will be a constant factor in both the numerators and denominators of Eqs. 17 and will therefore cancel. The expressions then define a purely geometrical property of the body, since any reference to its physical properties is absent. The term *centroid* is used when the calculation concerns a geometrical shape only. When speaking of an actual physical body, the term *center of gravity* or *center of mass* is used. If the density is uniform, the positions of the centroid and center of gravity are identical; whereas if the density varies, these two points will, in general, not coincide.

In the case of a slender rod or wire of length L and weight μ per unit length the body approaches a line, and $dW = \mu\, dL$. Therefore if μ is constant Eqs. 17 become

$$\bar{x} = \frac{\int x\, dL}{L}, \quad \bar{y} = \frac{\int y\, dL}{L}, \quad \bar{z} = \frac{\int z\, dL}{L}. \tag{18}$$

When the body has a small thickness and approaches a surface of area A whose weight per unit area is μ, then $dW = \mu\, dA$, and again if μ is constant, Eqs. 17 give

$$\bar{x} = \frac{\int x\, dA}{A}, \quad \bar{y} = \frac{\int y\, dA}{A}, \quad \bar{z} = \frac{\int z\, dA}{A}. \tag{19}$$

If the surface is curved, as with a shell, all three coordinates will be involved. If it is a plane surface, only the two coordinates of that plane will be involved.

In the case of a body of volume V and density μ the element is $dW = \mu\, dV$. The density μ will cancel if it is constant, and

$$\bar{x} = \frac{\int x\, dV}{V}, \quad \bar{y} = \frac{\int y\, dV}{V}, \quad \bar{z} = \frac{\int z\, dV}{V}. \qquad (20)$$

A summary of the centroidal coordinates for some of the commonly used shapes is given in Table D4, Appendix D.

SAMPLE PROBLEMS

337. *Centroid of a Circular Arc.* Locate the centroid of a line segment in the form of a circular arc as shown in the figure.

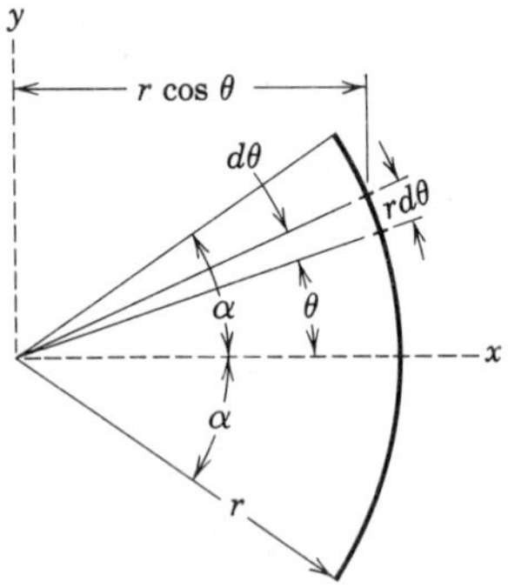

PROB. 337

Solution. Choosing the x-axis as an axis of symmetry makes $\bar{y} = 0$. A differential element of arc has a length $dL = r\, d\theta$, and the x-coordinate of the element is $r \cos \theta$. Applying the first of Eqs. 18 gives

$$\left[L\bar{x} = \int x\, dL\right] \qquad (2\alpha r)\bar{x} = \int_{-\alpha}^{\alpha} (r \cos \theta) r\, d\theta,$$

$$2\alpha r \bar{x} = 2r^2 \sin \alpha,$$

$$\bar{x} = \frac{r \sin \alpha}{\alpha}. \qquad \textit{Ans.}$$

For $2\alpha = \pi/2$, $\bar{x} = 0.900r$; for a semicircular arc $2\alpha = \pi$, which gives $\bar{x} = 2r/\pi$.

338. *Centroid of a Triangular Area.* Locate the centroid of the area of a triangle of base b and altitude h.

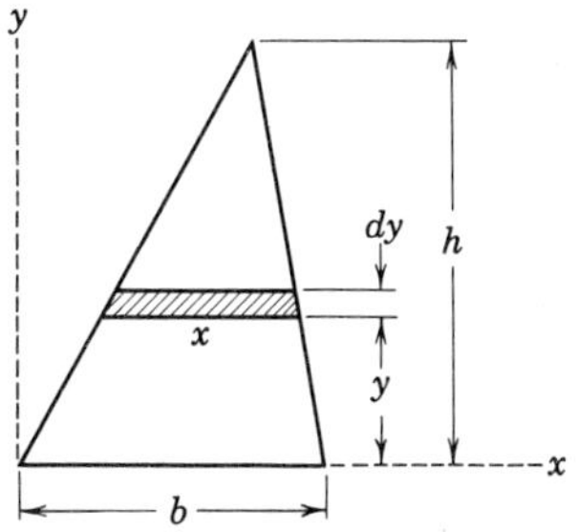

PROB. 338

Solution. The x-axis is taken to coincide with the base. A differential strip of area $x\,dy$ is chosen. By similar triangles $x/(h-y) = b/h$. Applying the second of Eqs. 19 gives

$$\left[A\bar{y} = \int y\,dA\right] \qquad \frac{bh}{2}\,\bar{y} = \int_0^h y\,\frac{b(h-y)}{h}\,dy = \frac{bh^2}{6},$$

and

$$\bar{y} = \frac{h}{3}. \qquad \textit{Ans.}$$

This same result holds with respect to either of the other two sides of the triangle considered as a new base with corresponding new altitude. Thus it can be said that the centroid lies at the intersection of the medians, since the distance of this point from any side is one third the altitude of the triangle with that side considered as base.

It should be noted that the differential strip is a trapezoid, and its area becomes $x\,dy$ only in the limit for which dy approaches zero. In setting up the expression for the elemental area, then, the small triangular end sections are omitted since they involve the higher-order term $dx\,dy$.

339. *Centroid of the Area of a Circular Sector.* Locate the centroid of the area of a circular sector with respect to its vertex.

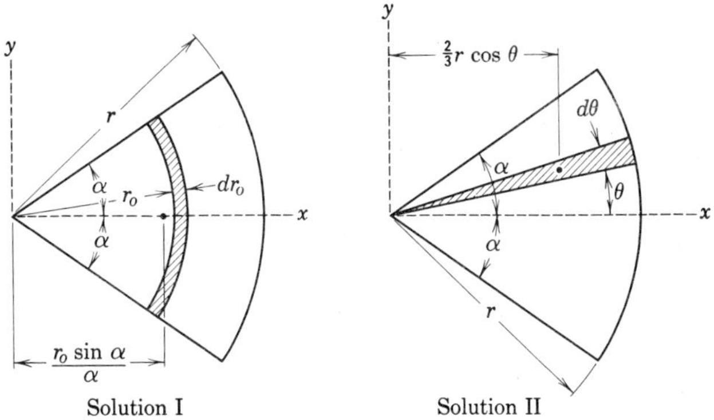

Solution I Solution II

PROB. 339

Solution I. The x-axis is chosen as an axis of symmetry, and $\bar{y}$ is therefore automatically zero. The area may be covered by moving an element in the form of a segment of the circular ring, shown in the figure, from the center to the outer periphery. The radius of the ring is r_0 and its thickness is dr_0. In the first of Eqs. 19 the coordinate x is the coordinate to the *centroid* of the element dA. From Prob. 337 this distance is $\dfrac{r_0 \sin \alpha}{\alpha}$, where r_0 replaces r. Thus the first of Eqs. 19 gives

$$\left[A\bar{x} = \int x\,dA\right] \qquad \frac{2\alpha}{2\pi}(\pi r^2)\bar{x} = \int_0^r \left(\frac{r_0 \sin \alpha}{\alpha}\right)(2r_0\alpha\,dr_0),$$

$$r^2\alpha\bar{x} = \tfrac{2}{3}r^3 \sin \alpha,$$

$$\bar{x} = \frac{2}{3}\frac{r \sin \alpha}{\alpha}. \qquad \textit{Ans.}$$

For a semicircular area $2\alpha = \pi$ and $\bar{x} = 4r/3\pi$.

Solution II. The area may also be covered by swinging a triangle of differential area about the vertex and through the total angle of the sector. This triangle, shown in the illustration, has an area $dA = (r/2)(r\,d\theta)$ where higher-order terms are neglected. Again the x-coordinate of dA is measured to the centroid of the element, and from Prob. 338 this coordinate is seen to be $2r/3$ multiplied by $\cos \theta$. Applying the first of Eqs. 19 gives

$$\left[A\bar{x} = \int x\,dA\right] \qquad (r^2\alpha)\bar{x} = \int_{-\alpha}^{\alpha} (\tfrac{2}{3}r \cos \theta)(\tfrac{1}{2}r^2\,d\theta),$$

$$r^2\alpha\bar{x} = \tfrac{2}{3}r^3 \sin \alpha,$$

and as before

$$\bar{x} = \frac{2}{3}\frac{r \sin \alpha}{\alpha}. \qquad \textit{Ans.}$$

It should be noted that, if a second-order element $r\,dr\,d\theta$ is chosen, one integration with respect to θ would yield the ring with which *Solution I* began. On the other hand integration with respect to r_0 initially would give the triangular element with which *Solution II* began.

340. Locate the centroid of the area under the curve $x = ky^3$ from $x = 0$ to $x = a$.

Solution I. A vertical element of area $dA = y\,dx$ is chosen as shown in the left part of the figure. The x-coordinate of the centroid is found from the first of Eqs. 19. Thus

$$\left[A\bar{x} = \int x\,dA\right] \qquad \bar{x}\int_0^a y\,dx = \int_0^a xy\,dx.$$

Substituting $y = (x/k)^{1/3}$ and $k = a/b^3$ and integrating gives

$$\frac{3ab}{4}\bar{x} = \frac{3a^2b}{7}, \qquad \bar{x} = \tfrac{4}{7}a. \qquad \textit{Ans.}$$

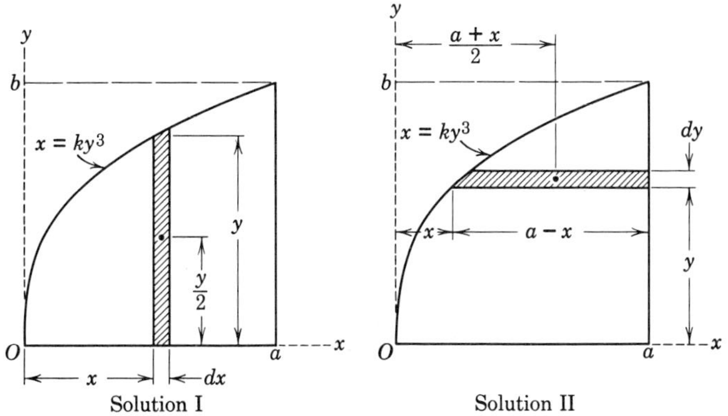

PROB. 340

In solving for $\bar{y}$ by the second of Eqs. 19 the coordinate y is *not* the coordinate to the curve $x = ky^3$ but is the y-distance to the centroid of the element dA. Thus the value $y/2$, which locates the centroid of the rectangular element, must be used. The moment principle becomes

$$\left[A\bar{y} = \int y\,dA\right] \qquad \frac{3ab}{4}\bar{y} = \int_0^a \left(\frac{y}{2}\right) y\,dx.$$

Substituting $y = (x/k)^{1/3}$ and integrating gives

$$\frac{3ab}{4}\bar{y} = \frac{3ab^2}{10}, \qquad \bar{y} = \tfrac{2}{5}b. \qquad \textit{Ans.}$$

Solution II. The horizontal element of area shown in the right-hand part of the figure may be employed in place of the vertical element. In calculating $\int x\,dA$ the x-coordinate of the centroid of the element must be used. This distance is $x + \frac{a - x}{2} = \frac{a + x}{2}$. Thus

$$\left[A\bar{x} = \int x\,dA\right] \qquad \bar{x}\int_0^b (a - x)\,dy = \int_0^b \left(\frac{a + x}{2}\right)(a - x)\,dy.$$

The value of $\bar{y}$ is found from

$$\left[A\bar{y} = \int y\,dA\right] \qquad \bar{y}\int_0^b (a - x)\,dy = \int_0^b y(a - x)\,dy.$$

The evaluation of these integrals will check the previous results for $\bar{x}$ and $\bar{y}$.

341. *Hemispherical Volume.* Locate the centroid of the volume of a hemisphere of radius r with respect to its base.

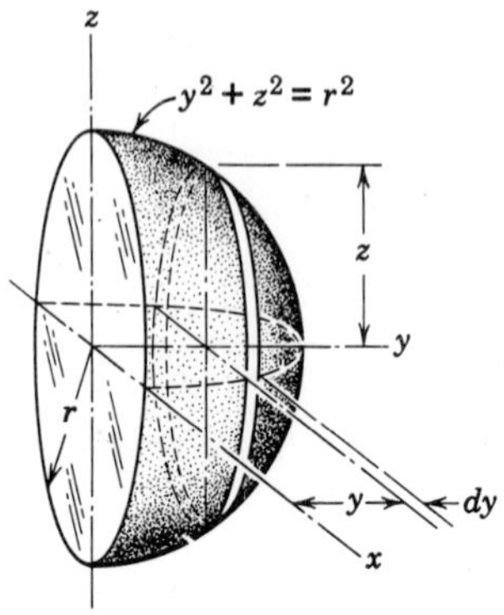

PROB. 341

Solution. With the axes chosen as shown in the figure $\bar{x} = \bar{z} = 0$ by symmetry. The simplest volume element is a circular slice of thickness dy parallel to the x–z plane. Since the hemisphere intersects the y–z plane in the circle $y^2 + z^2 = r^2$, the radius of the circular slice is $z = +\sqrt{r^2 - y^2}$. The volume of the elemental slice becomes

$$dV = \pi(r^2 - y^2)\,dy.$$

The second of Eqs. 20 requires

$$\left[V\bar{y} = \int y\,dV\right] \qquad \bar{y}\int_0^r \pi(r^2 - y^2)\,dy = \int_0^r y\pi(r^2 - y^2)\,dy.$$

Integrating gives

$$\tfrac{2}{3}\pi r^3\bar{y} = \tfrac{1}{4}\pi r^4, \qquad \bar{y} = \tfrac{3}{8}r. \qquad \textit{Ans.}$$

PROBLEMS

342. Locate the center of gravity of the wire bent into the circular shape shown. *Ans.* $\bar{x} = -1.273$ in., $\bar{y} = 1.273$ in.

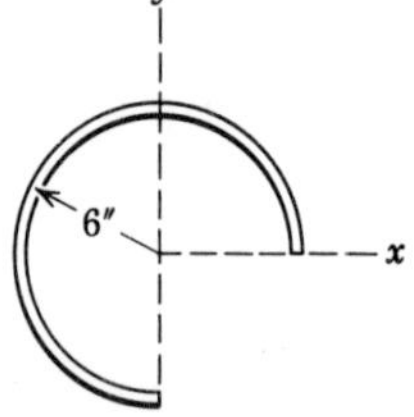

PROB. 342

343. Locate the centroid of the area bounded by the curve $x = y^3$, the y-axis, and the line $y = 1$. *Ans.* $\bar{x} = \frac{2}{7}$, $\bar{y} = \frac{4}{5}$

344. Find the distance $\bar{z}$ from the vertex of a right circular cone to the centroid of its volume. *Ans.* $\bar{z} = \frac{3}{4}h$

345. Determine the height h of the center of gravity of the cylindrical shell segment above the horizontal surface upon which it rests. *Ans.* $h = 0.45$ in.

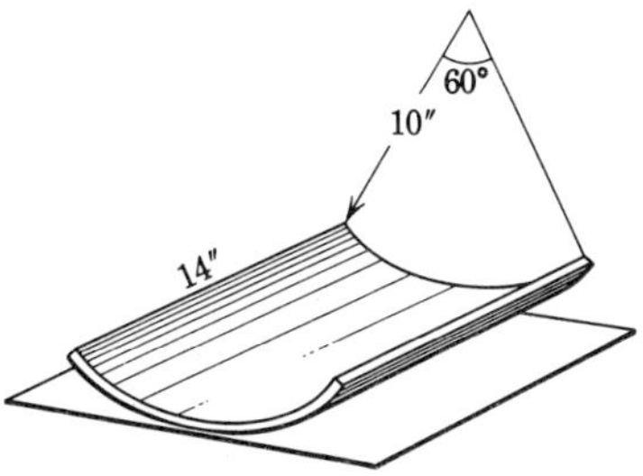

PROB. 345

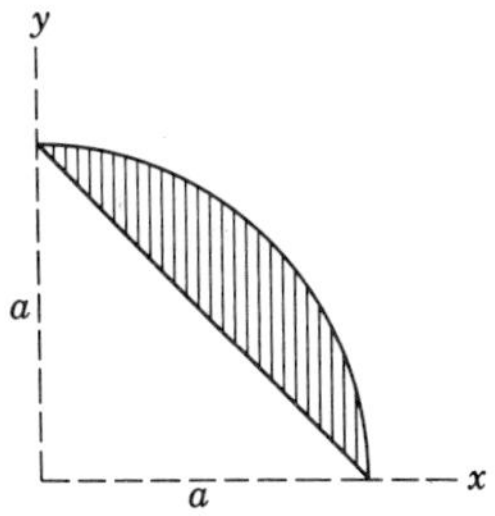

PROB. 346

346. Calculate the coordinates of the centroid of the shaded area bounded by the circular arc and the chord.

347. Locate the centroid of the elliptical area shown.

Ans. $\bar{x} = \dfrac{4a}{3\pi}, \ \bar{y} = \dfrac{4b}{3\pi}$

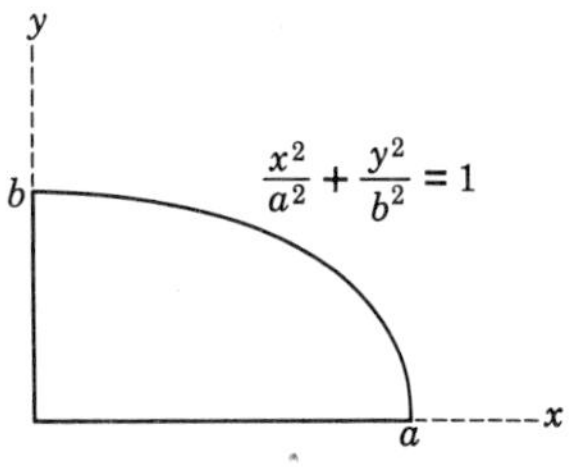

PROB. 347

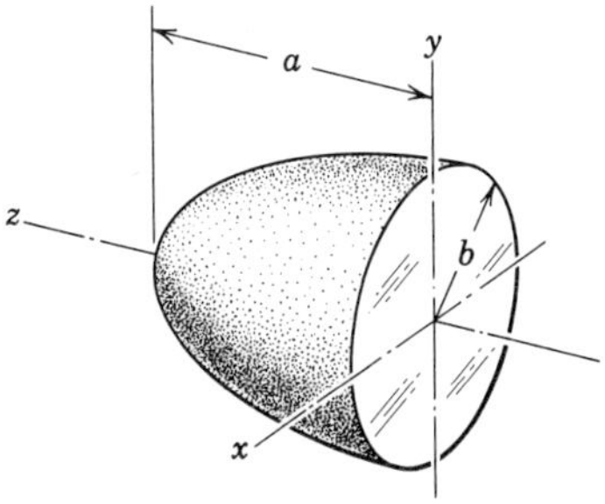

PROB. 348

348. A parabola is revolved about the z-axis to obtain the paraboloid shown. Locate the centroid of its volume with respect to the base $z = 0$.

Ans. $\bar{z} = \dfrac{a}{3}$

349. Determine the distance $\bar{h}$ from the centroid of the lateral area of any cone or pyramid of altitude h to the base of the figure.

350. Determine the distance $\bar{z}$ from the base of any cone or pyramid of altitude h to the centroid of its volume.

Ans. $\bar{z} = \dfrac{h}{4}$

351. Calculate the y-coordinate of the centroid of the area under the curve $y = a \cos \pi x/l$ between $x = 0$ and $x = l/2$.

352. Locate the center of gravity of the homogeneous hemispherical shell of radius r and negligible wall thickness.

Ans. $\bar{z} = \dfrac{r}{2}$

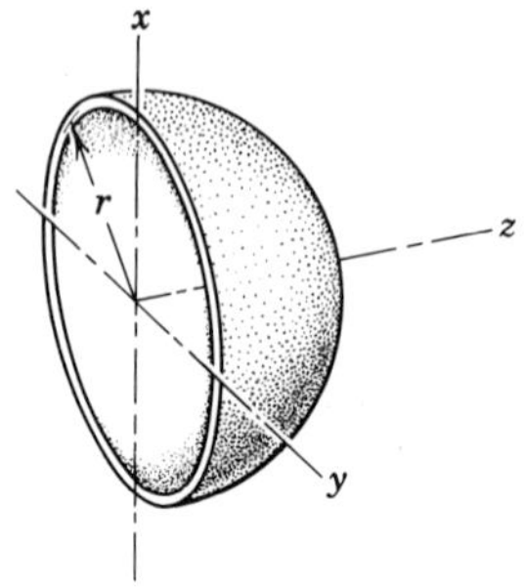

PROB. 352

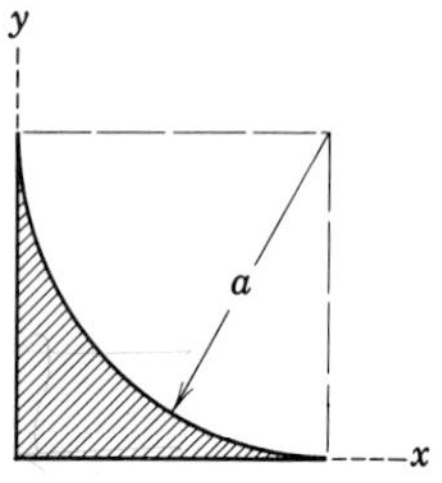

PROB. 353

353. Locate the centroid of the area shown in the figure by direct integration.

Ans. $\bar{x} = \dfrac{10 - 3\pi}{4 - \pi}\dfrac{a}{3}$

354. Locate the centroid of the shaded area between the ellipse and the circle.

Ans. $\bar{x} = \dfrac{4(a + b)}{3\pi}$

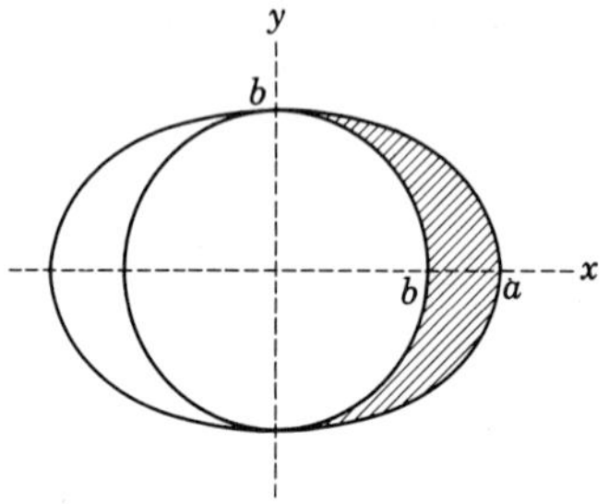

PROB. 354

355. Locate the centroid of the parabolic arc extending from $x = 0$ to $x = 1$.

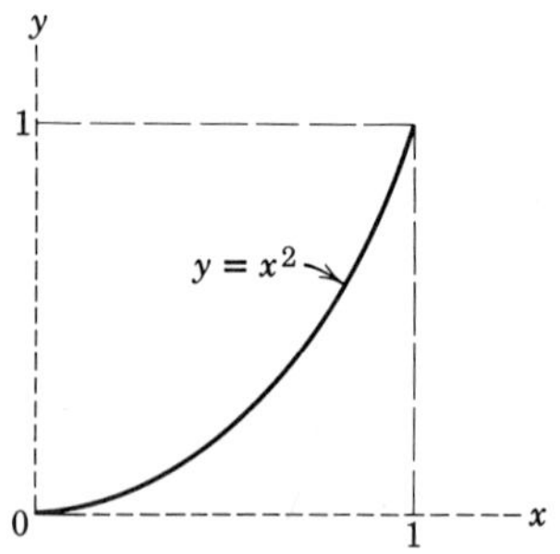

PROB. 355

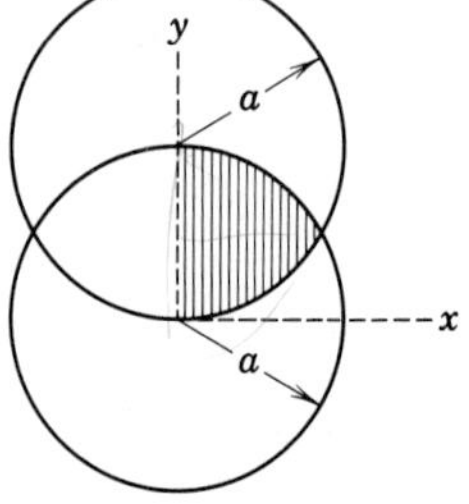

PROB. 356

356. Locate the x-coordinate of the centroid of the shaded area shown.

357. The density of a solid right circular cone of altitude h varies linearly with distance along the cone axis from a certain value at the vertex to double this value at the base. Determine the distance $\bar{h}$ from the vertex to the center of gravity of the cone.

358. Locate the centroid of the volume generated by revolving the right triangle of altitude a about its base b through an angle θ.

Ans. $\bar{r} = \dfrac{a \sin(\theta/2)}{\theta}$, $\bar{z} = \dfrac{b}{4}$

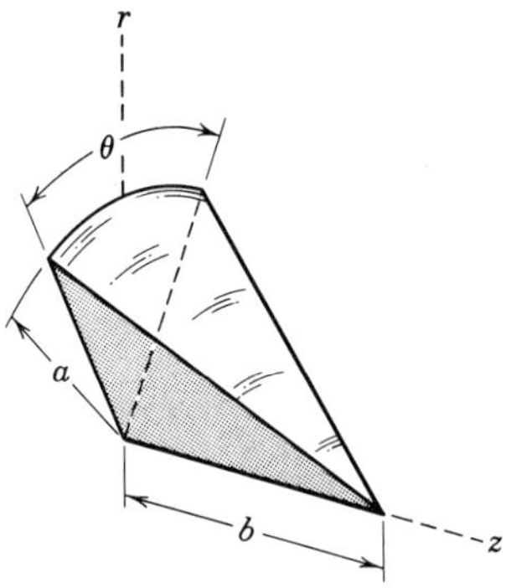

Prob. 358

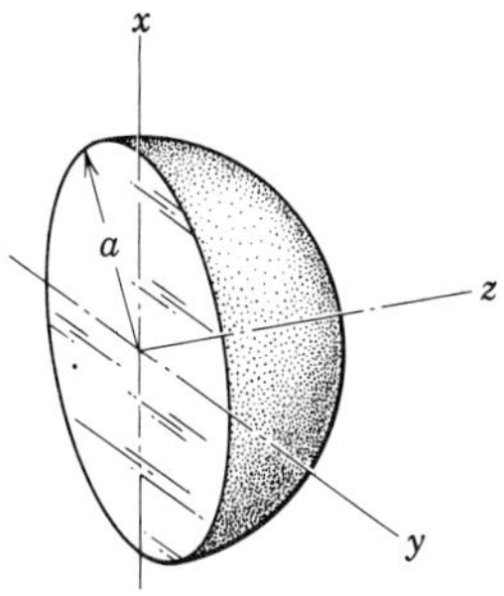

Prob. 359

* **359.** The density of a sphere decreases uniformly with radial distance from μ_0 at the center to one-half this value at the surface $r = a$. If the sphere is cut on a diametral plane as shown, determine the distance $\bar{z}$ from this base plane to the center of gravity of either hemisphere. (*Hint:* Use the results of Prob. 352 in setting up the element of volume.)

* **360.** Determine the position of the center of gravity of the thin conical shell shown.

Ans. $\bar{x} = \frac{2}{3}h$, $\bar{z} = \dfrac{4r}{3\pi}$

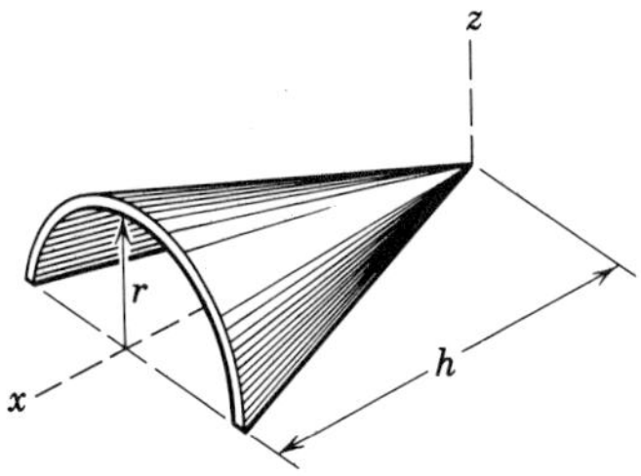

Prob. 360

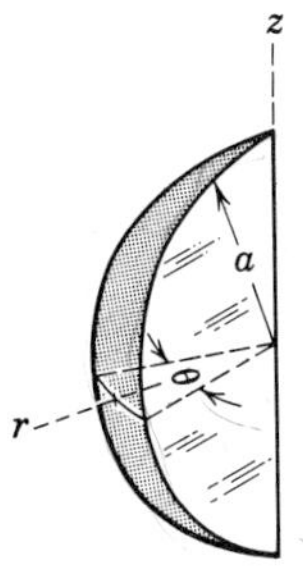

Prob. 361

* **361.** Determine the distance $\bar{r}$ to the center of gravity of the solid spherical wedge shown.

Ans. $\bar{r} = \dfrac{3}{8} \dfrac{\pi a \sin(\theta/2)}{\theta}$

* **362.** A cylindrical body of radius r and height h is divided in half by a diagonal slice as shown. Locate the center of gravity of the part indicated.

Ans. $\bar{x} = \frac{1}{4}r$, $\bar{z} = \frac{5}{16}h$

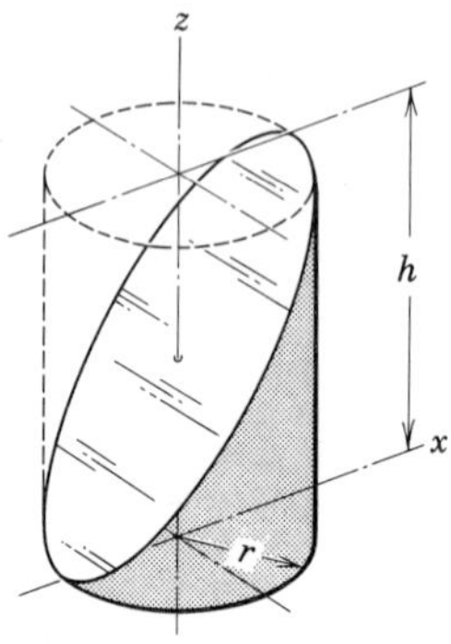

PROB. 362

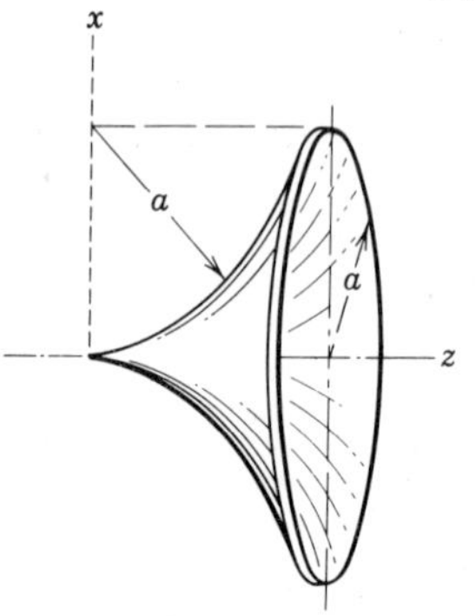

PROB. 363

* **363.** Locate the center of gravity of the bell-shaped shell of uniform but negligible thickness.

Ans. $\bar{z} = \dfrac{a}{\pi - 2}$

* **364.** Determine the position of the centroid of the volume within the bell-shaped shell of Prob. 363.

Ans. $\bar{z} = \dfrac{r}{2(10 - 3\pi)}$

* **365.** Determine the coordinates of the centroid of the volume generated by revolving the area shown in section through the 90 deg. angle.

Ans. $\bar{x} = \bar{y} = \dfrac{16 - 3\pi}{4\pi}a$, $\bar{z} = \dfrac{a}{4}$

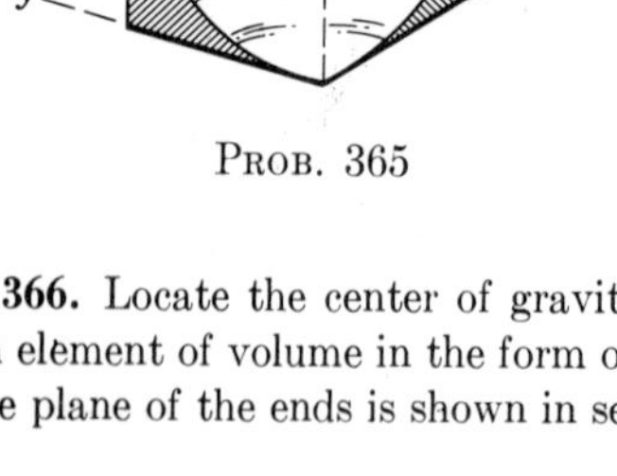

PROB. 365

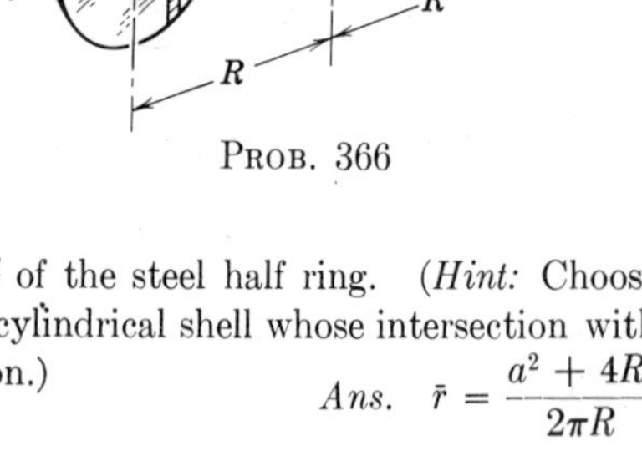

PROB. 366

* **366.** Locate the center of gravity G of the steel half ring. (*Hint:* Choose an element of volume in the form of a cylindrical shell whose intersection with the plane of the ends is shown in section.)

Ans. $\bar{r} = \dfrac{a^2 + 4R^2}{2\pi R}$

37. Composite Bodies and Figures. When a body or figure can be conveniently divided into several parts of simple shape, the principle of Varignon may be used if each part is treated as a finite element of the whole. Thus for a body whose several parts weigh W_1, W_2, W_3, $\cdots$, and whose separate coordinates of the centers of gravity of these parts in, say, the x-direction are $\bar{x}_1$, $\bar{x}_2$, $\bar{x}_3$, $\cdots$, the moment principle gives

$$(W_1 + W_2 + W_3 + \cdots)\overline{X} = W_1\bar{x}_1 + W_2\bar{x}_2 + W_3\bar{x}_3 + \cdots,$$

where $\overline{X}$ is the x-coordinate of the center of gravity of the whole. Similar relations hold for the other two coordinate directions. These sums may be expressed in condensed form and written as

$$\overline{X} = \frac{\Sigma W\bar{x}}{\Sigma W},$$

$$\overline{Y} = \frac{\Sigma W\bar{y}}{\Sigma W}, \qquad (21)$$

$$\overline{Z} = \frac{\Sigma W\bar{z}}{\Sigma W}.$$

Analogous relations hold for composite lines, areas, and volumes, where the W's are replaced by L's, A's, and V's, respectively. It should be pointed out that, if a hole or cavity is considered as one of the component parts of a composite body or figure, the corresponding weight or area represented by the cavity or hole is considered a negative quantity.

SAMPLE PROBLEM

367. Locate the center of gravity of the bracket-and-shaft combination. The vertical face is made from sheet metal which weighs 5 lb./ft.^{2}, the material of the horizontal base weighs 8 lb./ft.^{2}, and the steel shaft has a weight density of 0.283 lb./in.^{3}

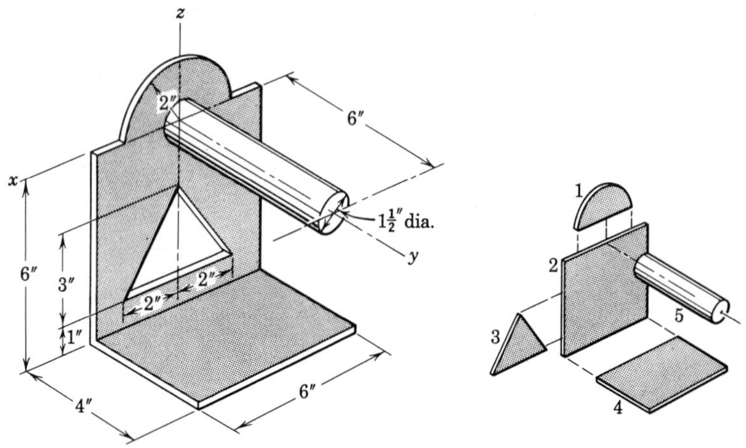

PROB. 367

Solution. The composite body may be considered to be composed of the five elements shown in the right-hand part of the illustration. The triangular part will be taken as a negative area. For the reference axes indicated it is clear by symmetry that the x-component of the center of gravity is zero.

The weight W of each part and the coordinates $\bar{y}$ and $\bar{z}$ of their respective centers of gravity are determined. The terms involved in applying Eqs. 21 are best handled in the form of a table as follows:

Part	W, lb.	$\bar{y}$, in.	$\bar{z}$, in.	$W\bar{y}$, lb. in.	$W\bar{z}$, lb. in.
1	0.218	0	0.849	0	0.185
2	1.25	0	−3.00	0	−3.75
3	−0.208	0	−4.00	0	0.832
4	1.33	2.00	−6.00	2.66	−7.98
5	3.00	3.00	0	9.00	0
Totals	5.59			11.66	−10.71

Equations 21 are now applied and the results are

$$\left[\bar{Y} = \frac{\Sigma W\bar{y}}{\Sigma W}\right] \qquad \bar{Y} = \frac{11.66}{5.59} = 2.08 \text{ in.,}$$

$$\left[\bar{Z} = \frac{\Sigma W\bar{z}}{\Sigma W}\right] \qquad \bar{Z} = \frac{-10.71}{5.59} = -1.92 \text{ in.}$$

PROBLEMS

368. Locate the center of gravity of the slender rod bent into the shape shown. *Ans.* $\bar{Y} = -0.966$ in.

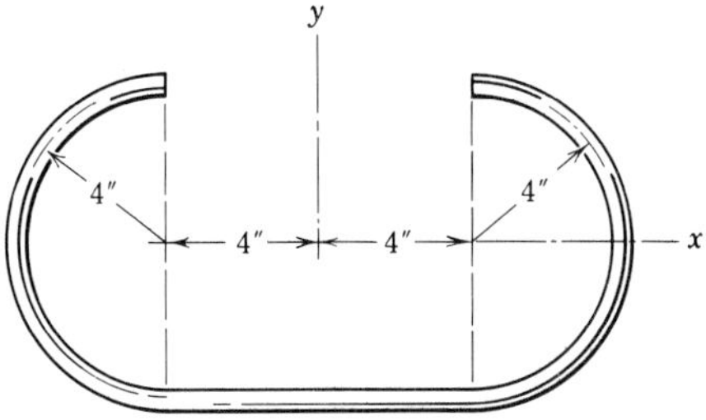

PROB. 368

369. Determine the distance a from the center of the square to the centroid of the shaded area. *Ans.* $a = 0.404$ in.

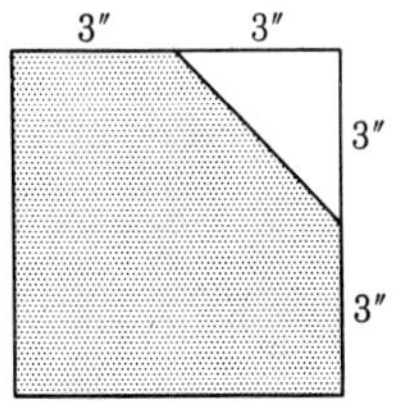

PROB. 369

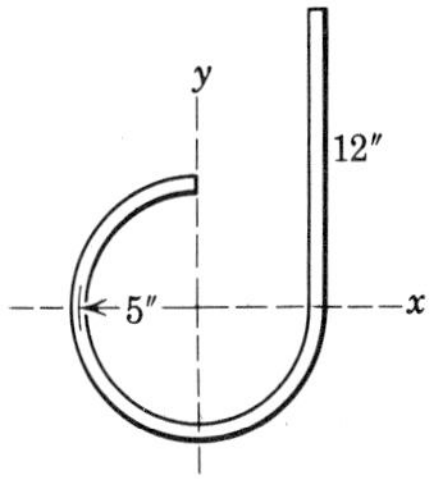

PROB. 370

370. A steel rod is bent into the form of a hook as shown. Locate the position of the center of gravity. *Ans.* $\bar{X} = 0.984$ in., $\bar{Y} = 1.321$ in.

371. Determine the distance $\bar{H}$ from the top of the cover plate to the centroid of the built-up structural section.

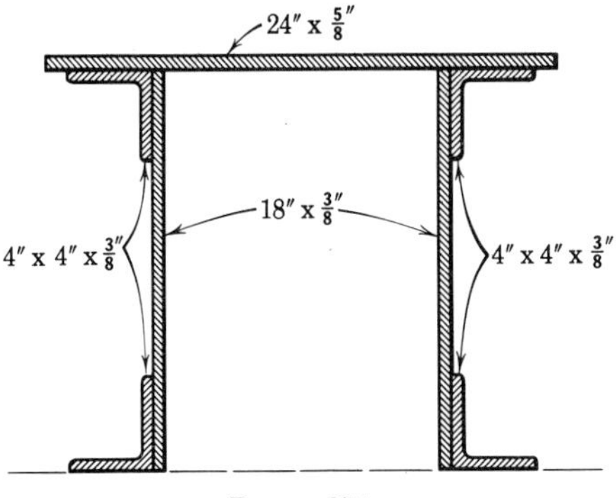

PROB. 371

372. A quarter-circular steel bar weighing 5 lb. is welded to the 8 lb. half-circular disk as shown. Locate the center of gravity of the combination. The cross-sectional dimensions of the bar and the thickness of the plate may be neglected compared with the other dimensions.

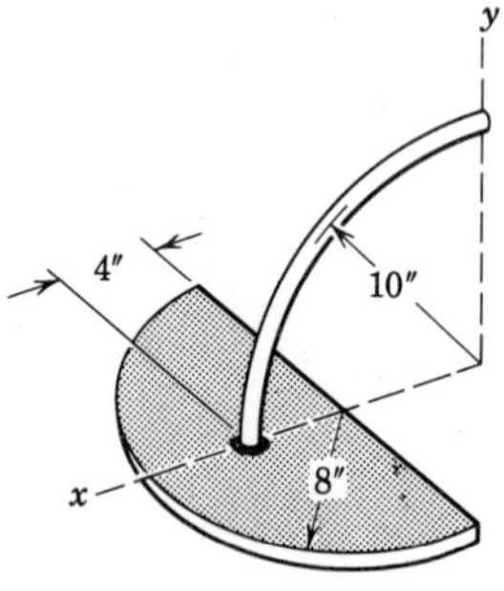

PROB. 372

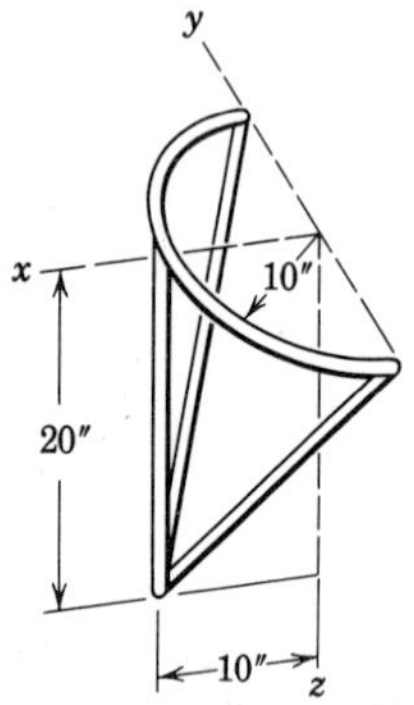

PROB. 373

373. A special purpose bracket is made from 1 in. pipe welded together as shown. Determine the coordinates of its center of gravity.

Ans. $\overline{X} = 6.42$ in., $\overline{Z} = 6.86$ in.

374. Find the radius r_1 which will locate the centroid of the shaded area a distance equal to e above the center of the outer circle.

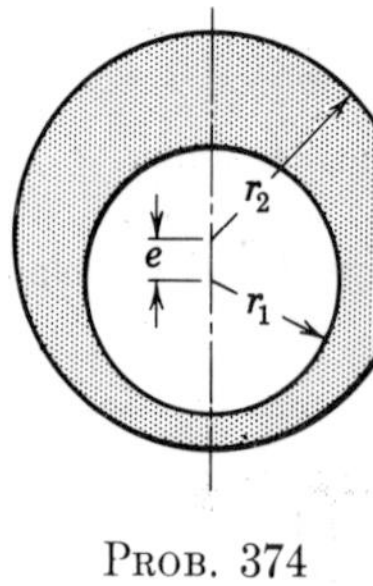

PROB. 374

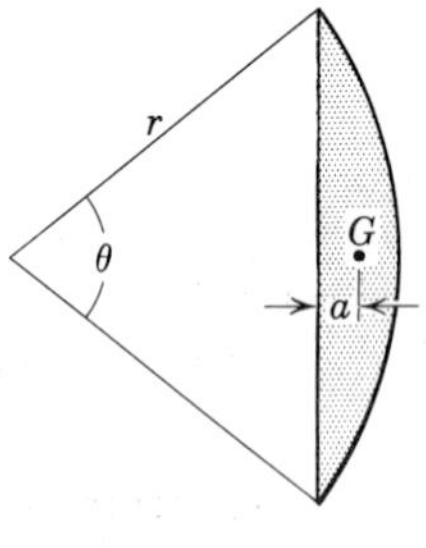

PROB. 375

375. Locate the centroid G of the shaded area by specifying the distance a.

$$Ans. \quad a = r\left(\frac{\frac{4}{3}\sin^3\frac{\theta}{2}}{\theta - \sin\theta} - \cos\frac{\theta}{2}\right)$$

376. A dome is constructed of concrete in the form of a solid of revolution about the vertical z-axis with a cross section closely defined by two parabolas each of the form $z = kr^2$. Note the results of Prob. 348, and specify without calculation the height h of the center of gravity of the dome above its base.

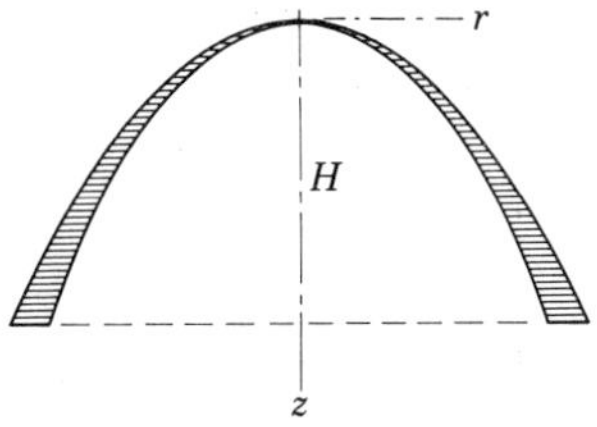

PROB. 376

377. For a given value of R and for $h = R$ determine the value of a which will place the centroid of the shaded area a distance of $0.5R$ above the horizontal diameter. *Ans.* $a = 0.612R$ or $a = 0.388R$

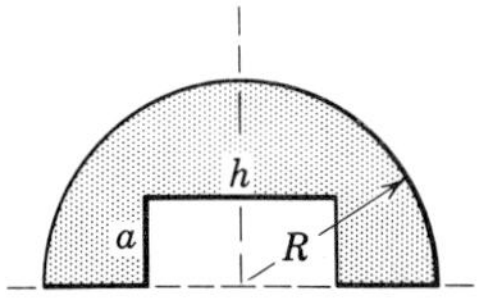

PROB. 377

378. Locate the center of gravity of the solid steel part shown.

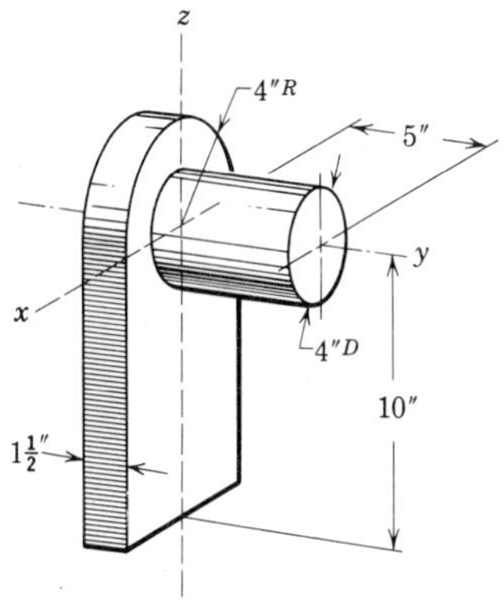

PROB. 378

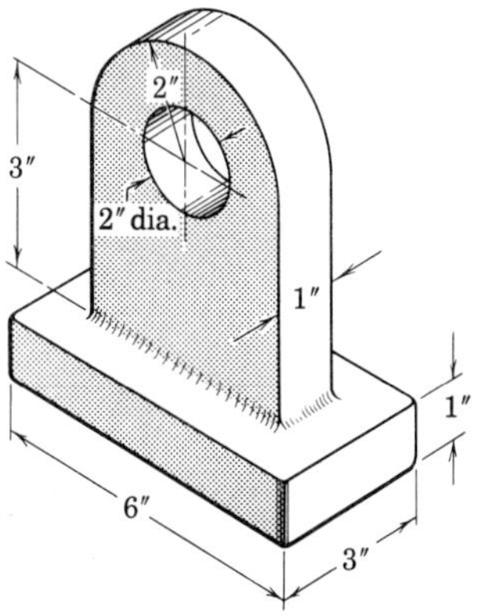

PROB. 379

379. Determine the distance $\bar{H}$ from the bottom of the base to the center of gravity of the bracket casting. *Ans.* $\bar{H} = 1.717$ in.

380. The bracket shown is cut and formed from a single piece of sheet metal. Determine the coordinates of its center of gravity.

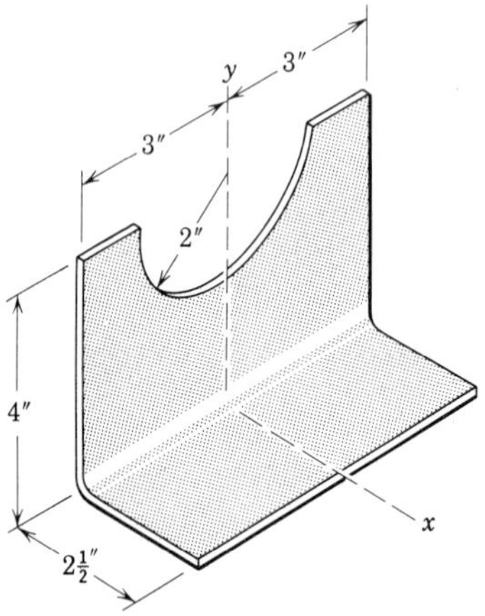

Prob. 380

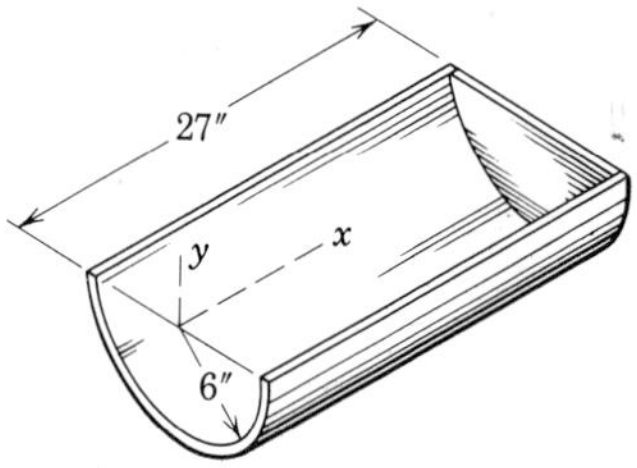

Prob. 381

381. Locate the position of the center of gravity of the half-cylindrical shell with closed end. The shell is made from sheet metal weighing 4.2 lb./ft.^{2} and the material of the end weighs 6.8 lb./ft.^{2} *Ans.* $\overline{X} = 15.5$ in., $\overline{Y} = -3.62$ in.

382. Locate the center of gravity of the sheet-metal form shown. The end A is made from material weighing 5 lb./ft.^{2}, and the remainder is made from material weighing 3 lb./ft.^{2}

Ans. $\overline{X} = 4.96$ in., $\overline{Y} = -0.243$ in., $\overline{Z} = 0.229$ in.

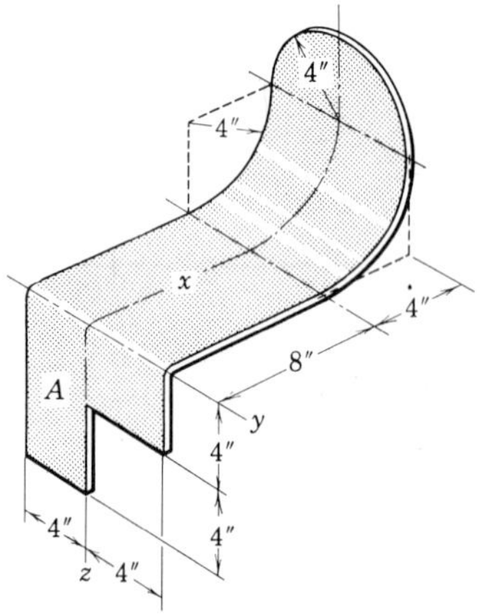

Prob. 382

383. A cylindrical tank with vertical axis and open top has a radius of 2 ft. and a height of 6 ft. The tank is filled with water and the axis is tilted 30 deg.

from the vertical. Find the distance $\bar{h}$ from the level of the water to the center of gravity of the water remaining in the tank. (*Hint:* Use the results of Prob. 362.) *Ans.* $\bar{h} = 2.13$ ft.

384. A flywheel with three radial holes A, B, and C in its rim is to be balanced by drilling one hole D completely through the rim. If the original three holes are ½ in. in diameter and 1 in. deep and the rim is 2 in. wide, determine the necessary diameter d of the balancing hole and the angle θ.

Ans. $d = 0.572$ in., $\theta = 8° 47'$

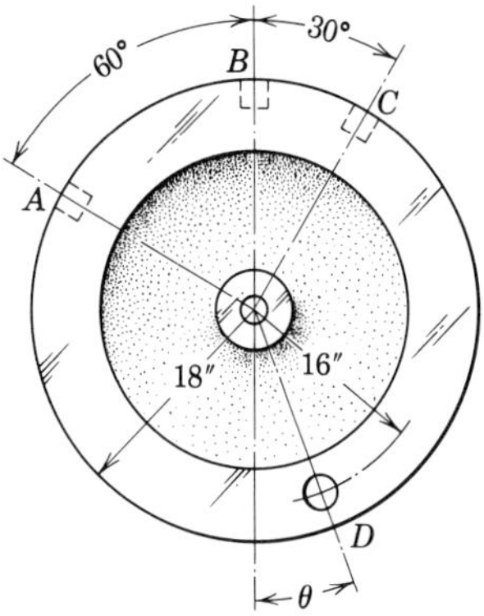

PROB. 384

* **385.** A homogeneous charge of explosive is to be formed as a circular cylinder of length L and diameter d_2 with an axial hole of diameter d_1 and depth h as shown in section. Determine the value of h which will make the center of gravity of the final charge a maximum distance from the open end.

$$Ans.\quad h = \left(\frac{d_2}{d_1}\right)^2 L\left[1 - \sqrt{1 - \left(\frac{d_1}{d_2}\right)^2}\right]$$

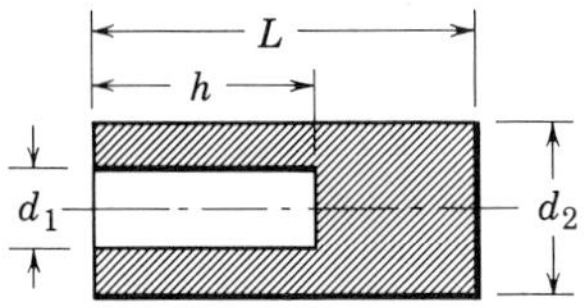

PROB. 385

38. Graphical Approximations. Frequently in practice the boundaries of an area or volume are not expressible in terms of the simple geometrical shapes or in shapes which can be represented mathematically. For such cases it is necessary to resort to a method of approximations.

Consider the problem of locating the centroid of the irregular area shown in Fig. 52. The area may be divided into strips of width Δx and variable height h. The area A of each strip, such as the one cross-hatched, is multiplied by the coordinates x and y to its *centroid* to obtain the moments of the element of area. The sum of the moments for all strips divided by the total area of the strips will give the corresponding centroidal component. A tabulation of the results, similar to that

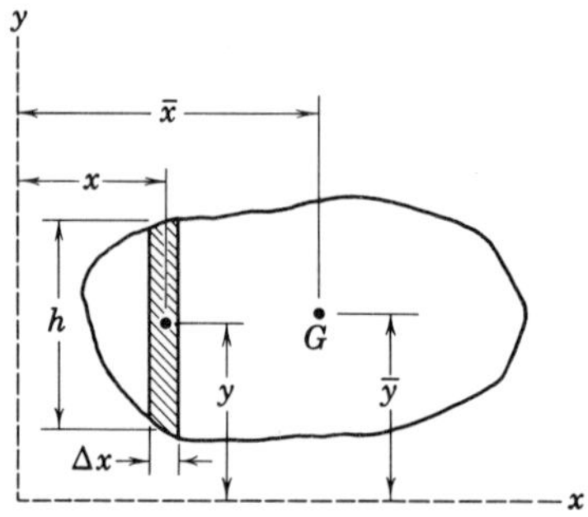

Fig. 52

used in Sample Prob. 367, will permit an orderly evaluation of the total area ΣA, the sums ΣAx and ΣAy, and the results

$$\bar{x} = \frac{\Sigma Ax}{\Sigma A}, \qquad \bar{y} = \frac{\Sigma Ay}{\Sigma A}.$$

The accuracy of the approximation will be increased by decreasing the widths of the strips used. In all cases the average height of the strip should be estimated in approximating the areas. Although it is usually of advantage to use elements of constant width, it is not necessary to do so. In fact elements of any size and shape which approximate the given area to satisfactory accuracy may be used.

In locating the centroid of an irregular volume the problem may be reduced to one of determining the centroid of an area. It is necessary only to plot a curve representing the magnitude of the areas of cross sections of the volume normal to a desired axis. The position along the axis of the centroid of the figure defined by this curve of areas will be the corresponding position of the volume centroid.

PROBLEMS

386. As an example of the accuracy involved in graphical approximations calculate the percentage error e in determining the x-coordinate of the centroid of the triangular area by using the four approximating rectangles of width $a/4$ in place of the triangle. *Ans.* $e = 1.56$ per cent low

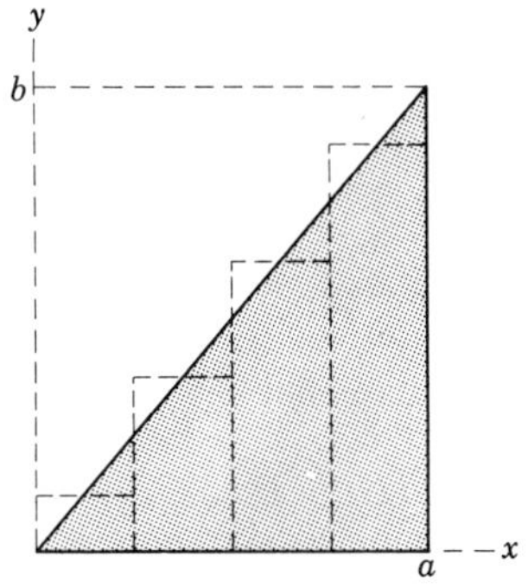

PROB. 386

387. The cross-sectional area of a concrete culvert is determined every 5 ft. along its length. These measurements in square feet are 4.1, 5.7, 7.3, 8.2, 7.5, 5.7, 4.7, where the first and last numbers represent the cross-sectional areas of the two ends. Approximate the distance from the first end (area 4.1 ft.^{2}) to the center of gravity of the culvert.

388. The center of lateral resistance for a ship's hull is the centroid of the projection of the underwater portion of the hull on the vertical central plane. Find the distance $\bar{x}$ of this point aft of point A for the scale drawing of the sailboat hull shown.

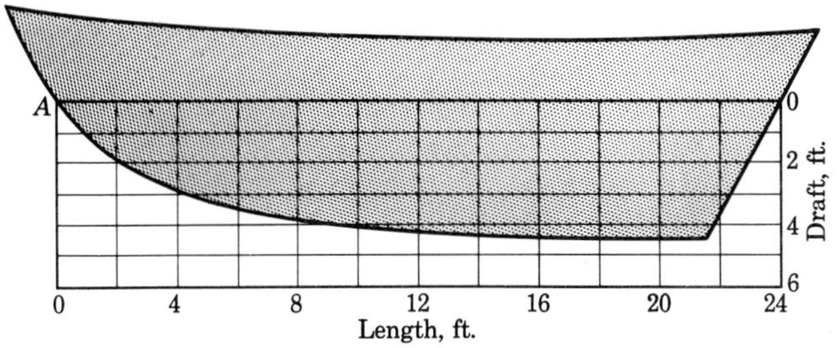

PROB. 388

389. The center of buoyancy of a ship's hull is the centroid of the displaced volume. Find the distance aft of point A to the center of buoyancy for the sailboat hull of Prob. 388 if the longitudinal distribution of the transverse underwater cross-sectional areas (curve of areas) is as plotted here.

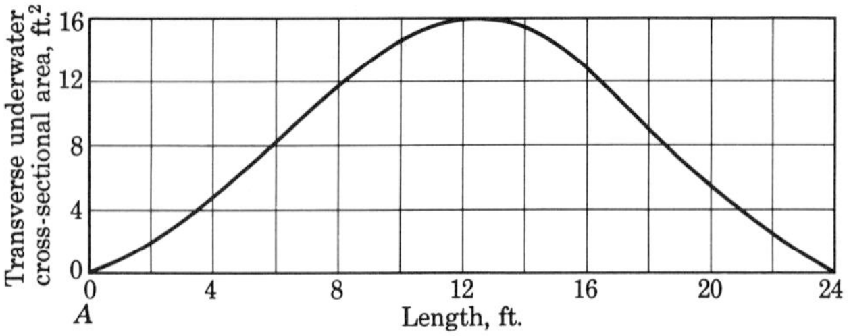

PROB. 389

390. Locate the horizontal position of the centroid of the area shown in Prob. 389 by graphical means in place of a tabular computation. (*Hint:* Consider the area as a sheet-metal figure and represent the weight of each strip by a vertical vector through the centroid of each strip. The centroid of the area will lie on the resultant of the parallel force vectors which is obtained by a funicular polygon.)

391. A beam supports 82 sandbags weighing 100 lb. each and stacked as shown. Approximate the reactions at A and B due to the weight of the bags.

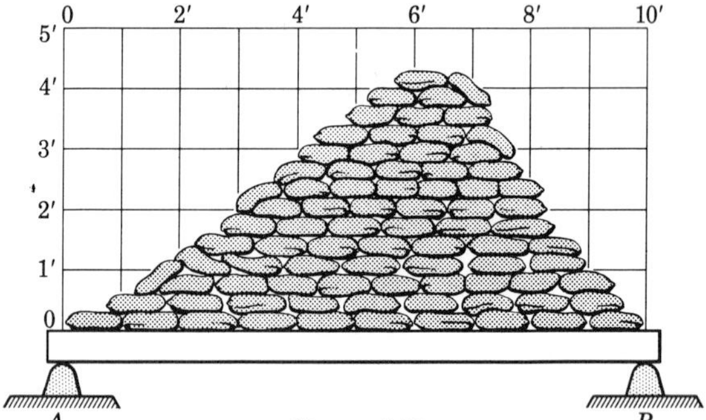

PROB. 391

392. The storage tank in the form of a surface of revolution is to be sprayed with two coats of paint. The surface area of the tank is unknown, but a scale

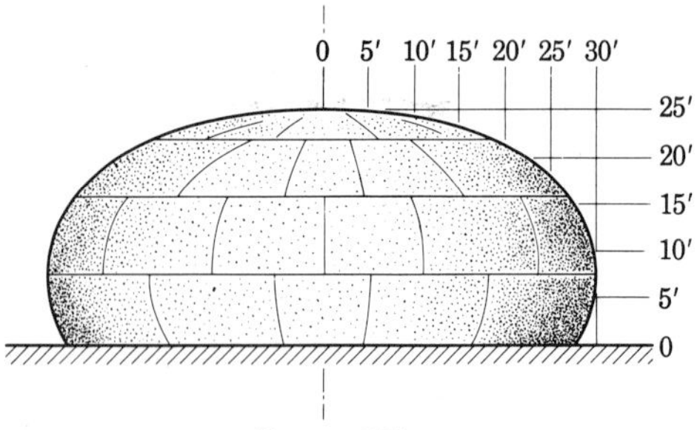

PROB. 392

drawing of the tank, reproduced here, is available. Determine the number of whole gallons of paint which must be purchased if each gallon will cover 500 ft.[2] with one coat. *Ans.* 24 gal.

39. Theorems of Pappus.* A very simple method exists for calculating the surface area generated by revolving a plane curve about a nonintersecting axis in the plane of the curve. In Fig. 53 the line seg-

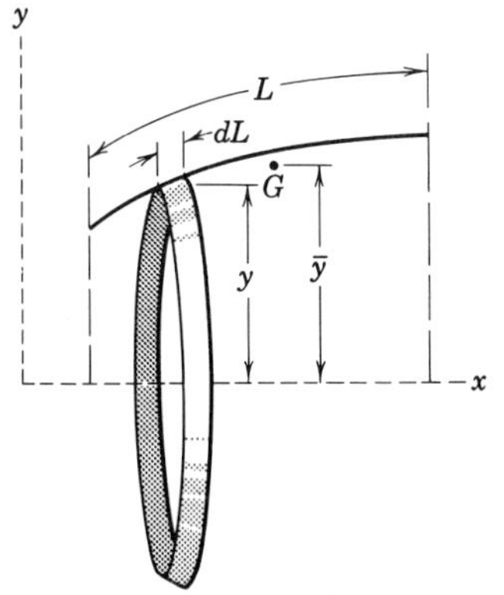

FIG. 53

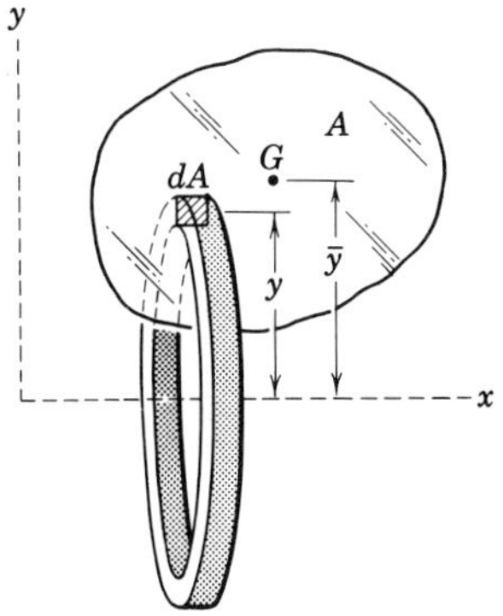

FIG. 54

ment of length L in the x–y plane generates a surface when revolved about the x-axis. An element of this surface is the ring generated by dL. The area of this ring is

$$dA = 2\pi y \, dL,$$

and the total area is then

$$A = 2\pi \int y \, dL.$$

But since $\bar{y}L = \int y \, dL$ the area becomes

$$A = 2\pi \bar{y} L, \tag{22}$$

where $\bar{y}$ is the y-coordinate of the centroid for the line of length L. Thus the generated area is the same as the lateral area of a right circular cylinder of length L and radius $\bar{y}$.

* Attributed to Pappus of Alexandria, a Greek geometer, who lived in the third century A.D. The theorems often bear the name of Guldinus (Paul Guldin, 1577–1643), who claimed original authorship, although the works of Pappus were apparently known to him.

In the case of a volume generated by revolving an area about a nonintersecting line in its plane an equally simple relation exists for finding the volume. An element of the volume generated by revolving the area A about the x-axis, Fig. 54, is the elemental ring of cross section dA and radius y. The volume of the element is $dV = 2\pi y\, dA$, and the total volume is

$$V = 2\pi \int y\, dA.$$

But since $\bar{y}A = \int y\, dA$ the volume becomes

$$V = 2\pi \bar{y} A, \tag{23}$$

where $\bar{y}$ is the y-coordinate of the centroid of the revolved area A. Thus the generated volume is obtained by multiplying the generating area by the circumference of the circular path described by its centroid.

The two theorems of Pappus, expressed by Eqs. 22 and 23, not only are useful in determining areas and volumes of generation, but they are also employed to find the centroids of plane curves and plane areas when the corresponding areas and volumes due to revolution of these figures about a nonintersecting axis are known. Dividing the area or volume by 2π times the corresponding line segment length or plane area will give the distance from the centroid to the axis of revolution.

In the event that a line or an area is revolved through an angle θ less than 2π, the generated surface or volume may be found by replacing 2π by θ in Eqs. 22 and 23. Thus

$$A = \theta \bar{y} L \qquad \text{and} \qquad V = \theta \bar{y} A,$$

where θ is expressed in radians.

PROBLEMS

393. Determine the volume of a sphere from the semicircular area used to generate the sphere.

394. Determine the volume of a right circular cone from the right triangle used to generate the cone.

395. Use the notation of the half torus of Prob. 366 and determine the volume V and the surface area A of a complete torus.

396. Find the volume of the spherical wedge of Prob. 361 by the method of this article.

397. Find the volume of the conical wedge of Prob. 358 by the method of this article.

398. Obtain the answer to Prob. 337 for a semicircular arc by the method of this article.

399. Use the results of Prob. 353 to determine the volume V of the solid of revolution shown with Prob. 365. *Ans.* $V = \pi a^3/12$

400. A hand-control wheel made of steel has the proportions shown in the sectional view. The shaded section has an area of 18.4 in.^{2}, and the wheel weighs 195 lb. Find the distance $\bar{r}$ from the axis of the wheel to the centroid of the shaded section. Steel weighs 0.283 lb./in.^{3}

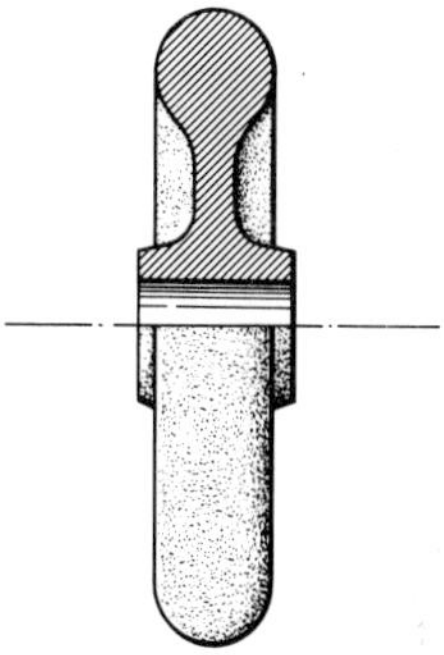

PROB. 400

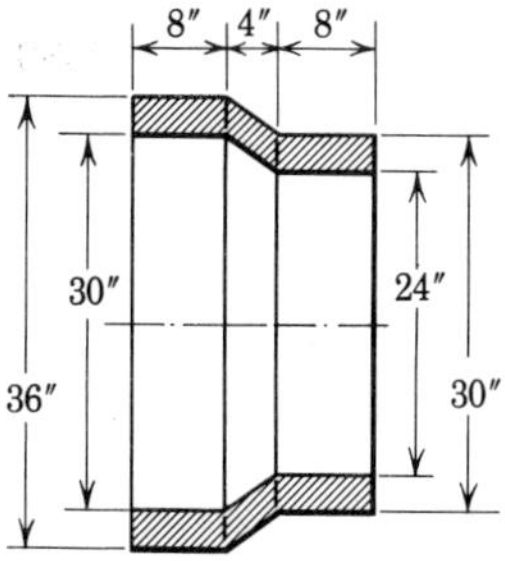

PROB. 401

401. A reducing section for a concrete water main has the dimensions shown on the sectional view. Calculate the total surface area A and the volume V of the reducer. *Ans.* $A = 4524$ in.^{2}, $V = 5655$ in.^{3}

402. In order to provide sufficient support for the stone-masonry arch it is necessary to know the weight W of the arch. Find W if the stone weighs 165 lb./ft.^{3} *Ans.* $W = 54.9$ tons

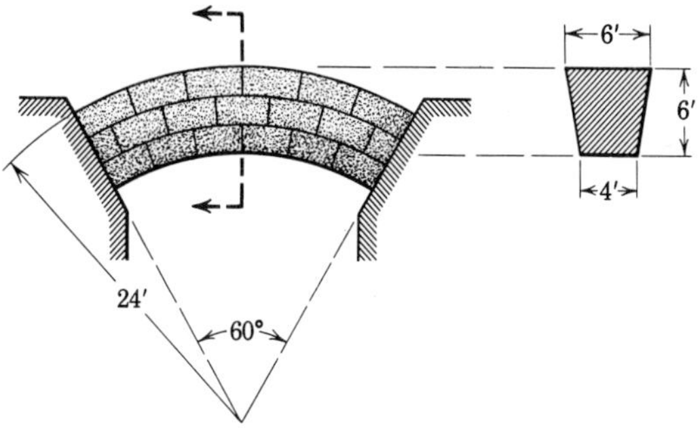

PROB. 402

403. The curved concrete dam has a cross section as shown. Determine the total weight W of the dam assuming that the end sections are vertical. Concrete weighs 150 lb./ft.^{3} *Ans.* $W = 141.4 \times 10^6$ lb.

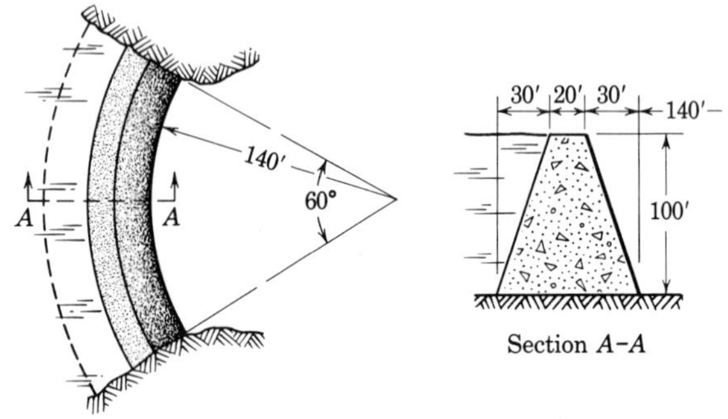

PROB. 403

40. Flexible Cables. One important type of structural member is the flexible cable which is used in suspension bridges, transmission lines, messenger cables for supporting heavy trolley or telephone lines, and in many other applications. In the design of these structures it is necessary to know the relations between the tension, span, sag, and length of the cables. These quantities are determined by examining the cable as a body in equilibrium. In the analysis of flexible cables it is assumed that any resistance offered to bending is negligible. This assumption means that the force in the cable is always in the direction of the cable.

Flexible cables may support a series of distinct concentrated loads, as shown in Fig. 55*a*, or they may support loads which are continuously

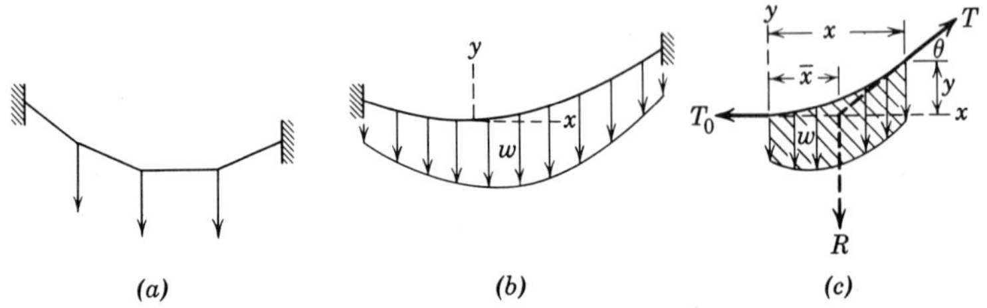

FIG. 55

distributed over the length of the cable, as indicated by the variable intensity loading w in Fig. 55*b*. In some instances the weight of the cable is negligible compared with the loads it supports, and in other cases the weight of the cable may be an appreciable load or the sole load, in which case it cannot be neglected. Regardless of which of these conditions is present the equilibrium requirements of the cable may be formulated in the same manner.

Consider the isolation of a finite length of the loaded cable of Fig. 55*b* as a free body in the *c*-part of the figure. The mathematical description is simplified by choosing one end of the isolated section at the position of maximum sag at which the origin of coordinates is placed. The horizontal tension at the origin is some particular value labeled T_0, and at a position in the cable whose coordinates are x and y the tension is T. In addition to these two forces there is the applied loading which acts on the section isolated. The resultant of this applied loading is shown as the vector R. If the cable supports concentrated loads, the force R is the resultant of those loads supported by the portion of the cable isolated. For the present example if the cable supports a distributed vertical load expressed as a function of x, the resultant R of this distribution would be

$$R = \int dR, \qquad R = \int w\,dx$$

where w is the load per horizontal length of cable. The position of R may be determined by the principle of moments, so that

$$R\bar{x} = \int x\,dR, \qquad \bar{x} = \frac{\int x\,dR}{R}.$$

It follows from these expressions that R is represented by the shaded area in Fig. 55*c* and that the horizontal position of R is defined by the horizontal coordinate $\bar{x}$ to the centroid of this area.

The two force equations of equilibrium may now be applied to the free body of Fig. 55*c*, and they require

$$[\Sigma F_y = 0] \qquad T \sin\theta = R$$

$$[\Sigma F_x = 0] \qquad T \cos\theta = T_0.$$

Eliminating T by division gives

$$\tan\theta = \frac{R}{T_0} \quad \text{or} \quad \frac{dy}{dx} = \frac{R}{T_0}. \tag{24}$$

Equation 24 is the differential equation of the cable, and upon being integrated for a particular problem where R is a known function of x

the solution of the equation gives the shape $y = f(x)$ assumed by the cable. Eliminating θ rather than T by squaring and adding gives

$$(T \sin \theta)^2 + (T \cos \theta)^2 = R^2 + T_0^2 \qquad \text{or} \qquad T^2 = R^2 + T_0^2. \tag{25}$$

It should be noted that the three forces T_0, T, and R are in equilibrium and are therefore concurrent. This requirement may be used to advantage in a graphical solution to the cable problem.

Equations 24 and 25 are applicable to any cable which supports vertical loads. This application will now be made for two important and extreme cases. In the first the weight of the cable is negligible compared with the load it supports, such as in most suspension bridges, and if the load is uniformly distributed along the horizontal, the cable is found to assume the shape of a parabola. In the second case the cable hangs under the action of its own weight only, as in a transmission line. For this condition the cable is found to take the shape of the catenary.

Case I. Parabola. Figure 56 shows a suspension bridge of span L and sag h. Let that portion of the uniform road bed supported by

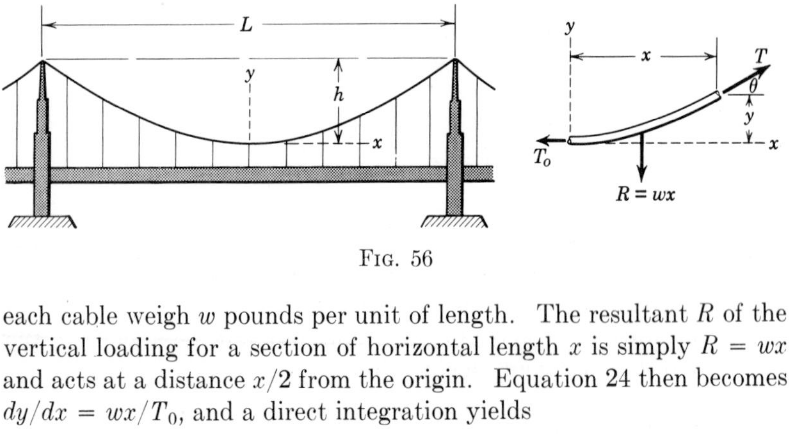

FIG. 56

each cable weigh w pounds per unit of length. The resultant R of the vertical loading for a section of horizontal length x is simply $R = wx$ and acts at a distance $x/2$ from the origin. Equation 24 then becomes $dy/dx = wx/T_0$, and a direct integration yields

$$\int_0^y dy = \frac{w}{T_0}\int_0^x x\,dx \qquad \text{or} \qquad y = \frac{wx^2}{2T_0}. \tag{26}$$

Equation 26 describes a parabola and gives the shape of the cable in terms of the constants w and T_0. Substitution of the boundary conditions $x = L/2$ and $y = h$ gives

$$T_0 = \frac{wL^2}{8h} \qquad \text{and} \qquad y = \frac{4hx^2}{L^2}.$$

The tension T is found from Eq. 25 and is $T = \sqrt{T_0^2 + w^2x^2}$. Eliminating T_0 gives

$$T = w\sqrt{x^2 + \frac{L^4}{64h^2}}. \tag{27}$$

The maximum tension occurs when $x = L/2$ and is

$$T_{\text{max.}} = \frac{wL}{2}\sqrt{1 + \frac{L^2}{16h^2}}.$$

The length S of the complete cable is obtained from the differential relation $dS = \sqrt{(dx)^2 + (dy)^2}$. Thus

$$\frac{S}{2} = \int_0^{L/2} \sqrt{1 + \left(\frac{dy}{dx}\right)^2}\, dx = \int_0^{L/2} \sqrt{1 + \left(\frac{wx}{T_0}\right)^2}\, dx.$$

For convenience in computation this expression is changed to a convergent series and then integrated term by term. From the expansion

$$(1 + x)^n = 1 + nx + \frac{n(n-1)}{2!}x^2 + \frac{n(n-1)(n-2)}{3!}x^3 + \cdots$$

the integral may be written as

$$S = 2\int_0^{L/2}\left[1 + \frac{w^2x^2}{2T_0^2} - \frac{w^4x^4}{8T_0^4} + \cdots\right]dx$$

$$= L\left(1 + \frac{w^2L^2}{24T_0^2} - \frac{w^4L^4}{640T_0^4} + \cdots\right).$$

Substitution of $w/T_0 = 8h/L^2$ yields

$$S = L\left(1 + \frac{8}{3}\left[\frac{h}{L}\right]^2 - \frac{32}{5}\left[\frac{h}{L}\right]^4 + \cdots\right). \tag{28}$$

When the properties of this series are examined, it is found that it converges for all values of $h/L \leqq 1/4$. In most cases h is much smaller than $L/4$ so that the three terms of Eq. 28 give a sufficiently accurate approximation.

Case II. Catenary. Consider now a uniform cable, Fig. 57, suspended at two points in the same horizontal plane and hanging under the action of its own weight only. The free-body diagram of a finite portion of the cable of length s is shown in the right-hand part of the figure. This free-body diagram differs from that in Fig. 56 in that the total vertical force supported is equal to the weight of the section

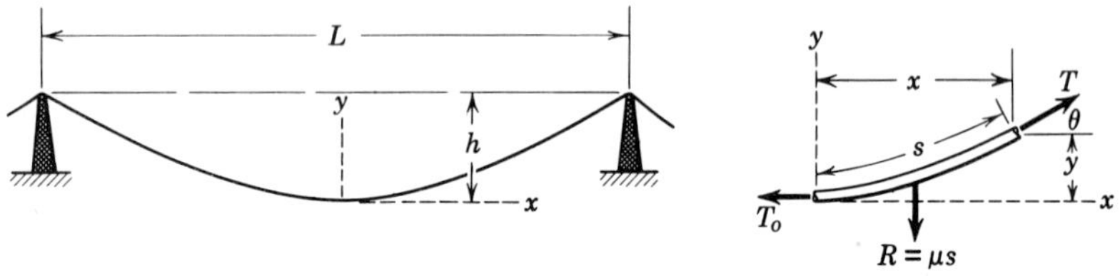

FIG. 57

of cable of length s in place of the uniform horizontal load. If the cable weighs μ pounds per foot of its own length, the resultant R of the load is $R = \mu s$ and Eq. 24 becomes

$$\frac{dy}{dx} = \frac{\mu}{T_0} s.$$

Since $s = f(x,y)$, it is necessary to change this equation to one containing only the two variables. Differentiating gives

$$\frac{d^2y}{dx^2} = \frac{\mu}{T_0} \frac{ds}{dx}.$$

Substituting the identity $(ds)^2 = (dx)^2 + (dy)^2$ yields

$$\frac{d^2y}{dx^2} = \frac{\mu}{T_0} \sqrt{1 + \left(\frac{dy}{dx}\right)^2} \tag{29}$$

Equation 29 is the differential equation of the curve (catenary) assumed by the cable. Solution of this equation is facilitated by the substitution $p = dy/dx$, which gives

$$\frac{dp}{\sqrt{1 + p^2}} = \frac{\mu}{T_0} dx.$$

Integrating this equation produces

$$\log (p + \sqrt{1 + p^2}) = \frac{\mu}{T_0} x + C.$$

The constant C is zero since $dy/dx = p = 0$ when $x = 0$. Substituting $p = dy/dx = (\mu/T_0)s$, changing to exponential form, and clearing the equation of the radical give

$$s = \frac{T_0}{\mu} \frac{e^{\mu x/T_0} - e^{-\mu x/T_0}}{2}.$$

At this point the hyperbolic functions * are introduced for convenience. Thus the arc length s may be written as

$$s = \frac{T_0}{\mu} \sinh \frac{\mu x}{T_0}. \tag{30}$$

Since $\mu s/T_0 = dy/dx$, Eq. 30 may be integrated to obtain

$$y = \frac{T_0}{\mu} \cosh \frac{\mu x}{T_0} + K.$$

The integration constant K is evaluated from the boundary condition $x = 0$ when $y = 0$. This substitution requires that $K = -T_0/\mu$, and hence

$$y = \frac{T_0}{\mu}\left(\cosh \frac{\mu x}{T_0} - 1\right). \tag{31}$$

Equation 31 is the equation of the curve (catenary) assumed by the cable hanging under the action of its weight only.

The tension T in the cable is obtained from Eq. 25. Thus

$$T^2 = \mu^2 s^2 + T_0^2,$$

which, upon combination with Eq. 30, becomes

$$T^2 = T_0^2\left(1 + \sinh^2 \frac{\mu x}{T_0}\right) = T_0^2 \cosh^2 \frac{\mu x}{T_0},$$

or

$$T = T_0 \cosh \frac{\mu x}{T_0}. \tag{32}$$

The tension may also be expressed in terms of y with the aid of Eq. 31, which, when substituted into Eq. 32, gives

$$T = T_0 + \mu y. \tag{33}$$

* See Table D3, Appendix D.

Equation 33 shows that the increment in cable tension from that at the lowest position depends only on y.

Most problems dealing with the catenary involve solutions of Eqs. 30 through 33 which are best handled graphically. This procedure is illustrated in the sample problem following this article.

The solution of catenary problems where the sag-to-span ratio is small may be approximated by the relations developed for the parabolic cable. A small sag-to-span ratio means a tight cable, and the uniform distribution of weight along the cable is not much different from the same load intensity distributed uniformly along the horizontal.

Many problems dealing with both the catenary and parabolic cable involve suspension points which are not on the same level. In such cases the relations may be applied to each part of the cable on either side of the lowest point.

SAMPLE PROBLEM

404. A cable weighing 8 lb./ft. is suspended between two points on the same level and 1000 ft. apart. If the sag is 200 ft., find the length of the cable and the maximum tension.

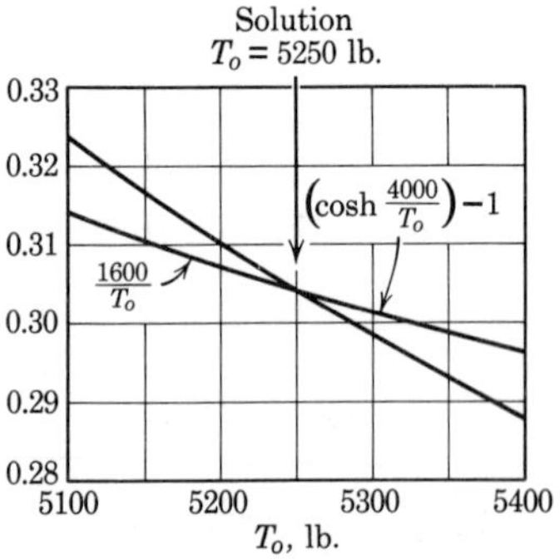

PROB. 404

Solution. Equations 30 and 32 for the cable length and tension both involve the minimum tension T_0 which must be found from Eq. 31. Thus, for x = 500 ft., y = 200 ft., and μ = 8 lb./ft.,

$$200 = \frac{T_0}{8}\left(\cosh \frac{8 \times 500}{T_0} - 1\right) \qquad \text{or} \qquad \frac{1600}{T_0} = \cosh \frac{4000}{T_0} - 1.$$

This equation is most easily solved graphically. The expression on each side of the equal sign is computed and plotted as a function of various values of T_0.

The intersection of the two curves establishes the equality and determines the correct value of T_0. This plot is shown in the figure accompanying this problem and yields the solution

$$T_0 = 5250 \text{ lb.}$$

The maximum tension occurs for maximum y and from Eq. 33 is

$$T = 5250 + 8 \times 200 = 6850 \text{ lb.} \qquad \textit{Ans.}$$

From Eq. 30 the total length of the cable becomes

$$2s = 2\,\frac{5250}{8}\sinh\frac{8 \times 500}{5250} = 1100 \text{ ft.} \qquad \textit{Ans.}$$

PROBLEMS

405. The Golden Gate Bridge has a main span of 4200 ft., a sag of 470 ft., and a total static loading of 21,300 lb. per lineal foot of horizontal measurement. The weight of both cables is included in this figure and is assumed uniformly distributed along the horizontal. Each of the two towers weighs 44,400,000 lb. The angle made by the cables with the horizontal at the top of the towers is θ. Calculate the tension T_0 in each of the two main cables at the center of the span and determine θ.

Ans. $T_0 = 50.0 \times 10^6$ lb., $\theta = 24° 7'$

406. A cable with a span of 500 ft. and a sag of 50 ft. supports a uniformly distributed load of 800 lb. per horizontal foot. Determine the length S of the cable and the maximum tension T. *Ans.* $S = 513$ ft., $T = 539{,}000$ lb.

407. Expand Eq. 31 in a power series for cosh $(\mu x/T_0)$ and show that the equation for the parabola, Eq. 26, is obtained by taking only the first two terms in the series. (See Table D3, Appendix D, for the series expansion of the hyperbolic function.)

408. A cable of negligible weight supports a load of 50 lb./ft. uniformly distributed along the horizontal. The cable hangs between two points on the same horizontal line 100 ft. apart and has a sag of 25 ft. Determine graphically the tension T at the support and the angle θ made by T with the horizontal. Also determine graphically the height b above the center of the cable of a point on the cable 30 ft. from the center of the span measured horizontally.
Ans. $T = 3540$ lb., $\theta = 45°$, $b = 9$ ft.

409. A cable of negligible weight is suspended from the fixed points shown and has a zero slope at its lower end. If

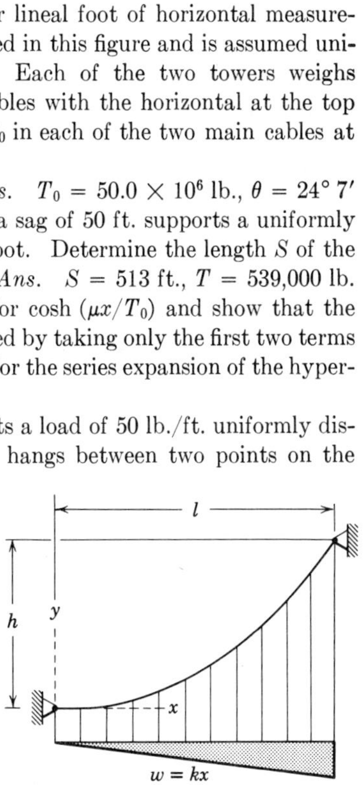

PROB. 409

the cable supports a unit load w which increases uniformly with x as indicated, determine the equation of the curve assumed by the cable.

410. In Prob. 409 determine by graphical means the tension T_0 in the cable at the origin and the angle θ made by the cable with the horizontal at its upper support if $k = 1.20$ lb./ft.^{2}, $h = 30$ ft., and $l = 90$ ft.

411. A cable of negligible weight is suspended from the fixed points shown and has a zero slope at its lower end. If the cable supports a unit load w which decreases uniformly with x from w_0 to zero as indicated, determine the equation of the curve assumed by the cable.

Ans. $y = \frac{3h}{2}\left(\frac{x}{l}\right)^2\left(1 - \frac{x}{3l}\right)$

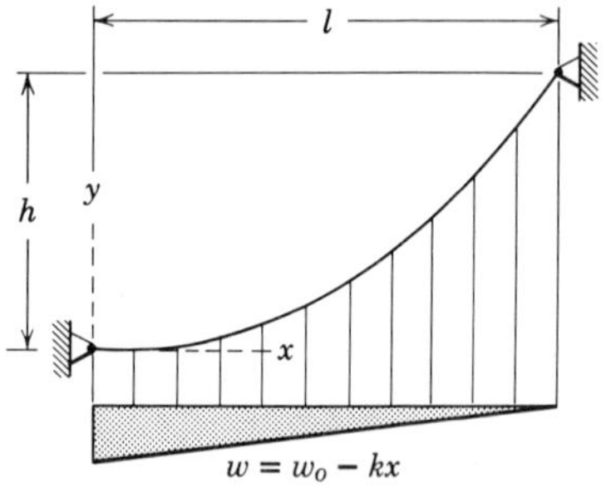

Prob. 411

412. A cable 200 ft. long is suspended between two points on the same level 180 ft. apart. If the cable supports a large load uniformly distributed in the horizontal direction, find the sag h in the cable. (*Hint:* Solve Eq. 28 by successive approximations.)

413. A ship is anchored with 200 ft. of chain from the bow to the anchor. The chain weighs 10 lb./ft. and makes an angle of 45 deg. with the horizontal at the bow. In addition the tension in the chain at the bow winch which secures it is 2500 lb. Determine the length a of chain which is lying flat on the bottom and the depth D of the water. Neglect the buoyancy of the chain in the water.

Ans. $a = 23.2$ ft., $D = 53.2$ ft.

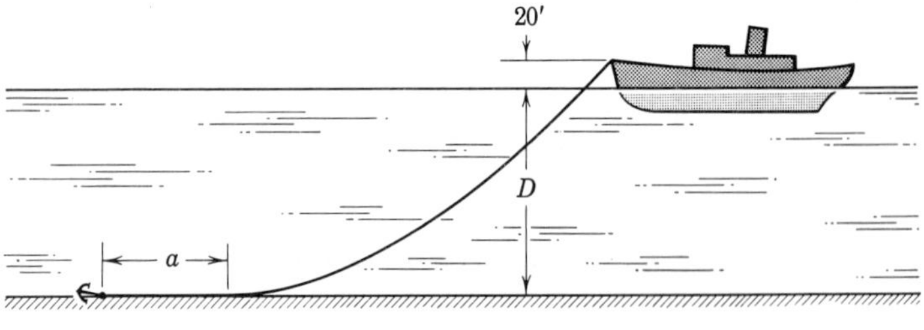

Prob. 413

414. A cable hanging under the action of its own weight is suspended between two points on the same level and 400 ft. apart. If the sag is 100 ft., determine the total length S of the cable. What error is involved if the length is computed from the expression for the parabolic cable?

415. A telephone cable which weighs 5.20 lb. per foot of its length is 500 ft. long and is suspended between two points 400 ft. apart and on the same level. If the maximum safe tension which this cable can support is 2500 lb., determine the total weight W of ice which could form uniformly along the cable without exceeding the safe tension. *Ans.* $W = 1540$ lb.

416. A cable supports a load of 100 lb./ft. uniformly distributed along the horizontal and is suspended from the two fixed points located as shown. Determine the maximum and minimum tensions T and T_0 in the cable.

Ans. $T = 4560$ lb., $T_0 = 2980$ lb.

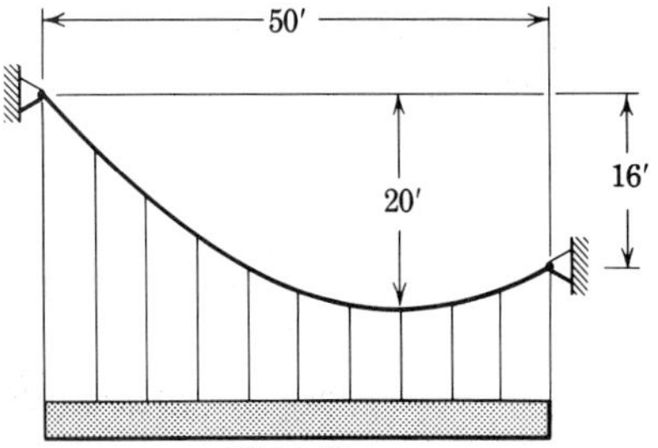

PROB. 416

417. A cable supports a uniform horizontal load of 400 lb./ft. and is suspended from two points which differ in elevation by 20 ft. If the supports are separated by 200 ft. measured along the horizontal and the sag of the cable below the upper support is 40 ft., determine the maximum cable tension T and the total length S of cable.

418. The bridge shown has a road structure whose weight per unit length in the horizontal direction is $w = w_0 + kx^2$. Find the equation of the curve assumed by the cable and the expression for the constant horizontal component T_0 of the cable tension.

Ans. $y = \dfrac{w_0 x^2}{2T_0} + \dfrac{kx^4}{12T_0}$, $T_0 = \dfrac{L^2}{8h}\left(w_0 + k\dfrac{L^2}{24}\right)$

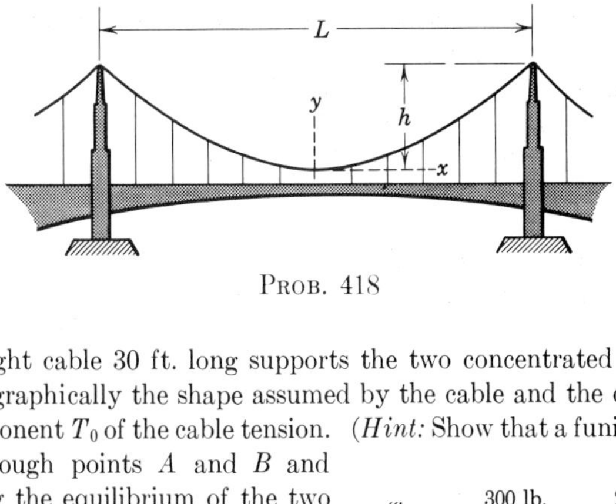

PROB. 418

419. A light cable 30 ft. long supports the two concentrated loads shown. Determine graphically the shape assumed by the cable and the constant horizontal component T_0 of the cable tension. (*Hint:* Show that a funicular polygon passing through points A and B and representing the equilibrium of the two given loads and the vertical components of the support reactions also represents to some scale the correct shape of the cable. By adjusting the horizontal position of the pole O a funicular polygon representing the proper cable length may be drawn.) *Ans.* $T_0 = 286$ lb.

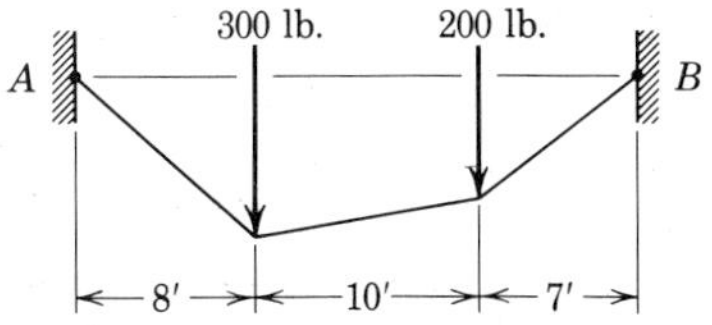

PROB. 419

420. In the suspension bridge shown the total weight of the roadway between towers is 20,000 lb. carried equally by two cables. Without the aid of equations determine graphically the shape of the cable, the constant horizontal component

T_0 of cable tension, and the length S of the cable. (*Hint:* Divide the span into, say, 10 equal parts as indicated and form the funicular polygon for the equal vertical loads. By trying various horizontal positions of the pole O a funicular polygon representing the proper sag and shape can be drawn. Read the hint for Prob. 419.)

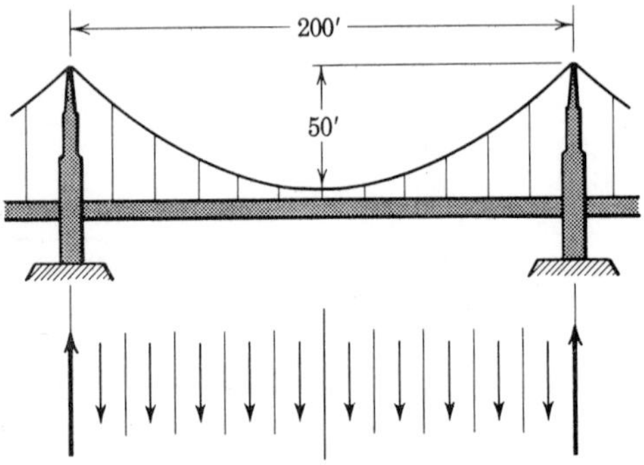

PROB. 420

* **421.** A balloon exerts an upward force of 80 lb. on its 100 ft. ground cable at the attachment point of the cable on the balloon. A horizontal wind causes a shift to the position shown, and the angle made by the cable with the vertical at the ground is observed to be 30 deg. If the cable weighs 0.5 lb./ft., determine the altitude H and the horizontal wind force P on the balloon.

Ans. $H = 94.4$ ft., $P = 17.3$ lb.

* **422.** A cable hanging under the action of its own weight is suspended from the same two supports as in Prob. 417 and has the same sag. Without solving, outline a procedure for determining the maximum tension T in the cable and the total length S of the cable, using the exact relations.

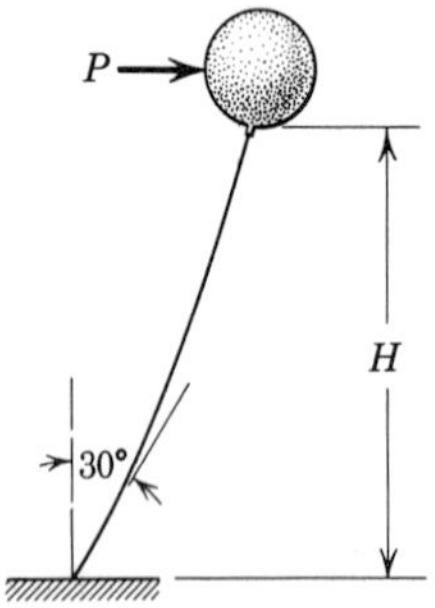

PROB. 421

41. Beams with Distributed Loads. Analysis of the shear forces and bending moments in beams under concentrated loads was developed in Art. 33. This development will now be extended to the case of beams subjected to distributed loads. The conventions used for shear Q and moment M and the same basic equilibrium method of analysis developed in Art. 33 will also be used for distributed forces. Additionally, there are several relations involving Q and M which may be established for any beam with distributed loads and which will aid greatly in the construction of the shear and moment distributions. Figure 58 represents a portion of a loaded beam, and an element dx

of the beam is isolated. The loading p represents the force per unit length of beam. At the location x the shear Q and moment M acting on the element are drawn in their positive directions. On the opposite side of the element where the coordinate is $x + dx$ these quantities are also shown in their positive directions but must be labeled $Q + dQ$ and $M + dM$ since the change in Q and M with x is required.

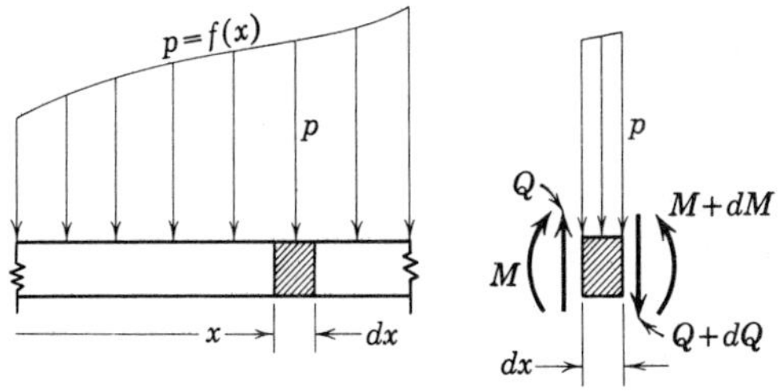

FIG. 58

The applied loading p may be considered constant over the length of the element since this length is a differential quantity. Equilibrium of the element requires that the sum of the vertical forces be zero. Thus

$$Q = p\,dx + (Q + dQ),$$

or

$$p = -\frac{dQ}{dx}. \tag{34}$$

It is clear from Eq. 34 that the slope of the shear diagram must everywhere be equal to the negative of the applied loading. Equation 34 holds on either side of a concentrated load but not at the concentrated load by reason of the discontinuity due to the abrupt change in shear.

Equilibrium of the element in Fig. 58 also requires that the moment sum must be zero. Taking moments about the left end gives

$$M + p\,dx\frac{dx}{2} + (Q + dQ)\,dx = M + dM.$$

The two M's cancel, and the terms $p\frac{(dx)^2}{2}$ and $dQ\,dx$ may be dropped since they are differentials of higher order than those that remain. This leaves merely

$$Q = \frac{dM}{dx} \tag{35}$$

which expresses the fact that the shear everywhere is equal to the slope of the moment curve. Or the moment M may be considered as being equal to the integral of the shear curve. In integral form Eq. 35 may be written

$$\int_{M_0}^{M} dM = \int_{x_0}^{x} Q\,dx,$$

or

$$M = M_0 + \text{(area under shear diagram from } x_0 \text{ to } x\text{)}.$$

In this expression M_0 is the bending moment at x_0 and M is the bending moment at x. For beams where there is no externally applied moment M_0 at $x_0 = 0$, the total moment at any section equals the area under the shear diagram up to that section. Summing up the area under the shear diagram is usually the simplest way to construct the moment diagram.

From Eq. 35 it is now clear why the maximum bending moment M occurs where the shear Q is zero. Mathematically $dM/dx = 0$ is the condition for a maximum or minimum value of M. Thus the critical locations for bending moments may be spotted from the shear diagram wherever $Q = 0$.

It should be noted from Eqs. 34 and 35 that the degree of Q in x is one higher than that of p. Also M is of one higher degree in x than is Q. Furthermore M is two degrees in x higher than p. Thus for a beam loaded by $p = kx$ which is of the first degree in x, the shear Q is of the second degree in x and the bending moment M is of the third degree in x.

Equations 34 and 35 may be combined to yield

$$\frac{d^2M}{dx^2} = -p.$$

Thus, if p is a known function of x, the moment M may be obtained by two integrations, provided the limits of integration are properly evaluated each time. This method is usable only if p is a continuous function of x. It is usually simpler to construct the variation of M directly from the areas under the shear diagram.

SAMPLE PROBLEM

423. Draw the shear-force and bending-moment diagrams for the loaded beam shown at the top of the figure and determine the maximum moment M and its location x from the left end.

Solution. The support reactions are most easily obtained by considering the resultants of the distributed loads as shown on the free-body diagram of the

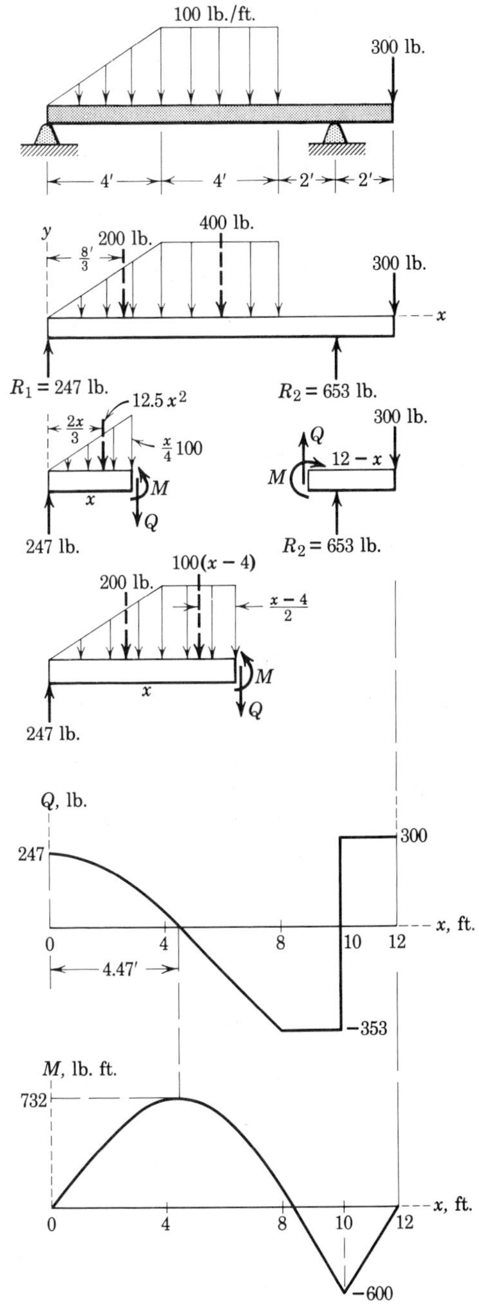
100 lb./ft.
300 lb.
4′
4′
2′
2′
y
200 lb.
8′/3
400 lb.
300 lb.
x
R1 = 247 lb.
R2 = 653 lb.
12.5 x2
2x/3
x/4 100
M
x
Q
247 lb.
Q
300 lb.
12 − x
M
R2 = 653 lb.
100(x − 4)
200 lb.
(x − 4)/2
M
x
Q
247 lb.
Q, lb.
247
300
x, ft.
0
4
8
10
12
4.47′
−353
M, lb. ft.
732
x, ft.
0
4
8
10
12
−600

Prob. 423

beam as a whole. The first interval of the beam is analyzed from the free-body diagram of the section for $x < 4$ ft. A vertical summation of forces for this section gives

$$[\Sigma F_y = 0] \qquad Q = 247 - 12.5x^2,$$

and a moment summation about the cut section yields

$$[\Sigma M = 0] \qquad M + (12.5x^2)\frac{x}{3} - 247x = 0,$$

$$M = 247x - 4.167x^3.$$

These values of Q and M hold for $0<x<4$ ft. and are plotted for that interval in the shear and moment diagrams shown.

From the free-body diagram covering the section for which $4 < x < 8$ ft., equilibrium in the vertical direction requires

$$[\Sigma F_y = 0] \qquad Q + 100(x - 4) + 200 - 247 = 0,$$

$$Q = 447 - 100x.$$

A moment sum about the cut section gives

$$[\Sigma M = 0] \qquad M + 100(x - 4)\frac{x - 4}{2} + 200\left(x - \frac{2}{3} \times 4\right) - 247x = 0,$$

$$M = -266.7 + 447x - 50x^2.$$

These values of Q and M are plotted on the shear and moment diagrams for the interval $4 < x < 8$ ft.

The analysis of the remainder of the beam is continued from the free-body diagram of the portion of the beam to the right of a section in the next interval. It should be noted that Q and M are represented in their positive directions. A vertical force summation requires

$$[\Sigma F_y = 0] \qquad Q + 653 - 300 = 0, \qquad Q = -353 \text{ lb.},$$

and a moment summation about the section yields

$$[\Sigma M = 0] \qquad M + 300(12 - x) - 653(12 - x - 2) = 0,$$

$$M = 2930 - 353x.$$

These values of Q and M are plotted on the shear and moment diagrams for the interval $8 < x < 10$ ft.

The last interval may be analyzed by inspection. The shear is constant at +300 lb., and the moment follows a straight line relation beginning with zero at the right end of the beam.

The maximum moment occurs at $x = 4.47$ ft., where the shear curve crosses the zero axis, and the magnitude of M is obtained for this value of x by substitution into the expression for M for the second interval. The maximum moment is

$$M = 732 \text{ lb. ft.} \qquad \textit{Ans.}$$

The derivative $dM/dx = 0$ for this second interval will check the value $x = 4.47$ ft. Although the shear crosses the zero axis again at $x = 10$ ft., the magnitude of the bending moment is less than that at $x = 4.47$ ft.

Although in this sample solution the moment M was determined by a direct application of the moment equilibrium equation, M may be obtained from the shear diagram as explained in the statements following Eq. 35. Thus, the moment M at any section x equals the net positive area under the shear diagram to the left of x. For $x < 4$ ft., for instance, the moment is

$$\left[\Delta M = \int Q\,dx\right] \qquad M - 0 = \int_0^x (247 - 12.5x^2)\,dx, \qquad M = 247x - 4.167x^3$$

which agrees with the results already computed.

PROBLEMS

424. Draw the shear and moment diagrams for the uniform cantilever beam of weight W.

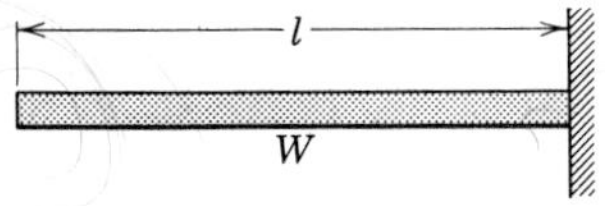

PROB. 424

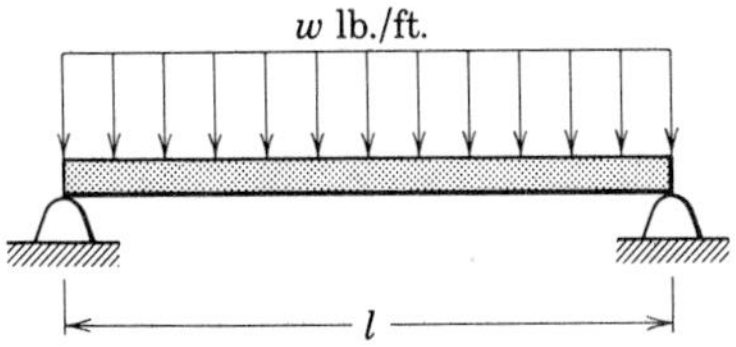

PROB. 425

425. Draw the shear and moment diagrams for the uniformly loaded beam and find the maximum bending moment M. *Ans.* $M = \frac{wl^2}{8}$

426. For the beam of Prob. 425 let the length l be 20 ft. and the unit load w be 100 lb./ft. Approximate the shear and moment diagrams by dividing the beam into, say, five equal parts and replacing the distributed load on each part by an equivalent concentrated load.

427. Find the maximum magnitude M of the bending moment. *Ans.* $M = 900$ lb. ft.

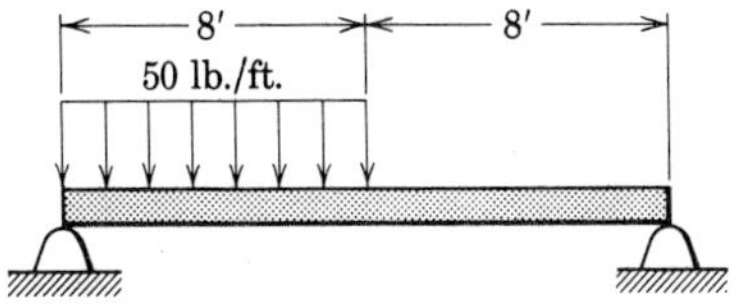

PROB. 427

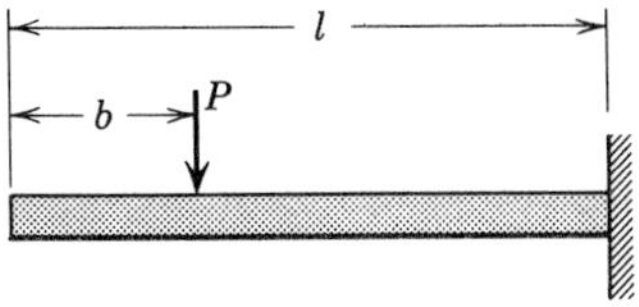

PROB. 428

428. The force P is applied to the uniform cantilever beam of weight W. Draw the shear and moment diagrams.

429. Draw the shear and moment diagrams for the cantilever beam with the linear loading and find the maximum magnitude M of the bending moment.

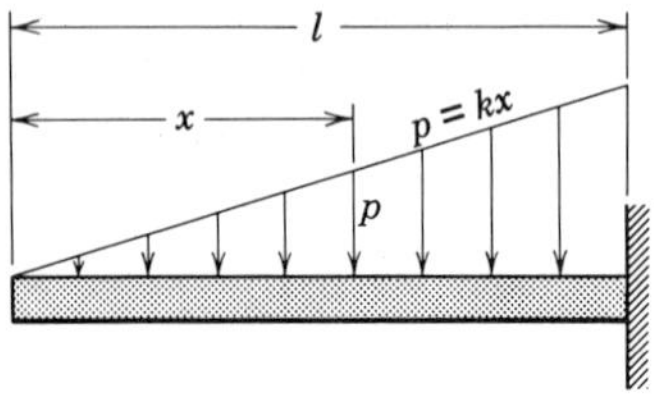

PROB. 429

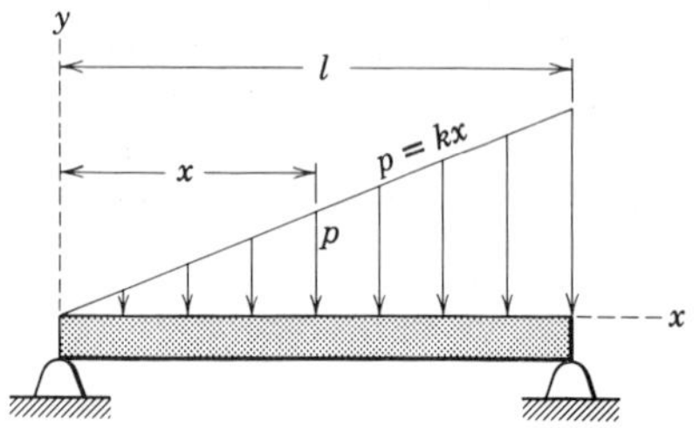

PROB. 430

430. Determine the shear and moment relationships for the loaded beam shown.

431. Draw the shear and moment diagrams for the cantilever beam with the reversed linear loading and find the maximum magnitude M of the bending moment. *Ans.* $M = \frac{1}{3}kl^3$

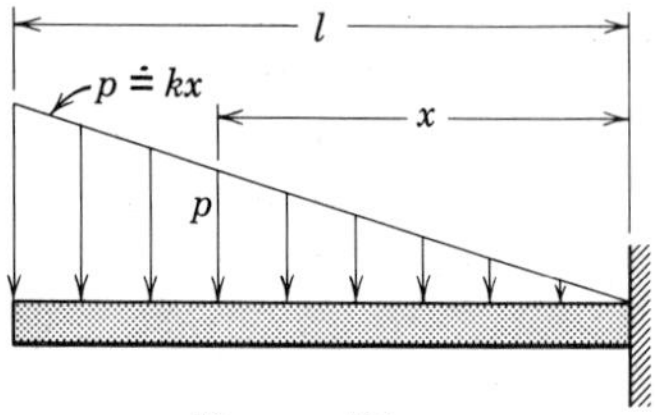

PROB. 431

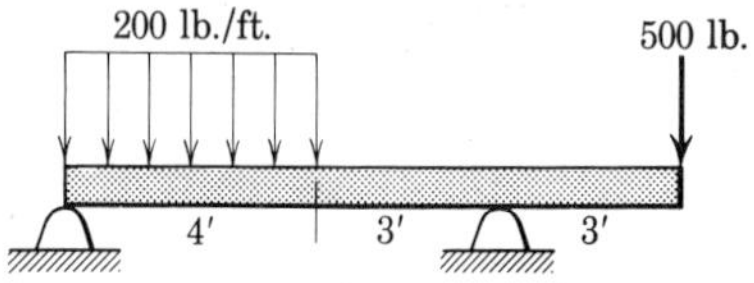

PROB. 432

432. Draw the shear and moment diagrams for the loaded beam and determine the maximum magnitude M of the bending moment.

Ans. $M = 1500$ lb. ft.

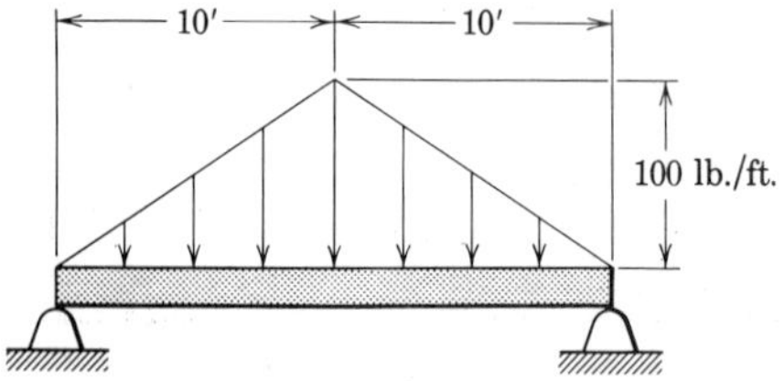

PROB. 433

433. Draw the shear and moment diagrams for the beam and find the maximum bending moment M. *Ans.* $M = 3333$ lb. ft.

434. Draw the shear and moment diagrams for the beam with the linearly varying loads and find the maximum bending moment M.

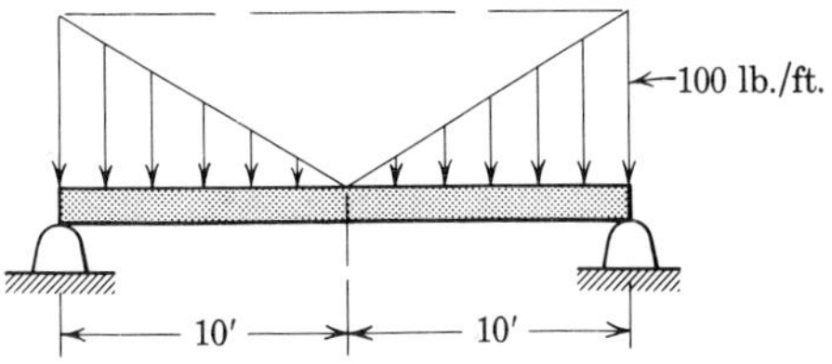

PROB. 434

435. Determine the shear Q and moment M as functions of x for the prismatic cantilever beam loaded by its own weight. The beam is made from homogeneous material with a weight density μ.

Ans. $Q = \dfrac{\mu bh}{2l}x^2$, $M = -\dfrac{\mu bh}{6l}x^3$

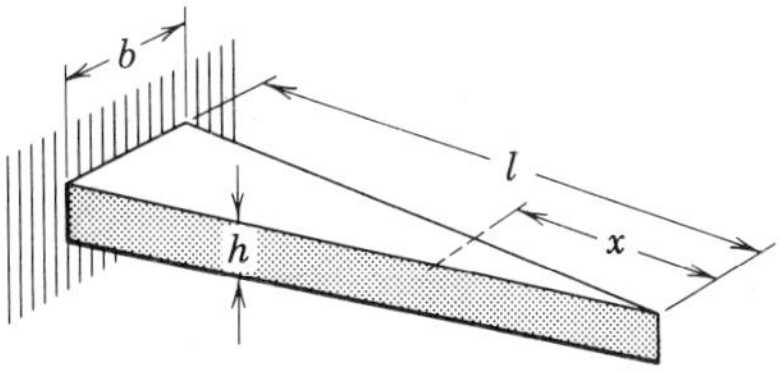

PROB. 435

436. Determine the expression for the shear Q as a function of x, and obtain the moment M by the integration of this function.

Ans. $Q = \dfrac{k}{12}(l^3 - 4x^3)$, $M = \dfrac{k}{12}(l^3x - x^4)$

PROB. 436

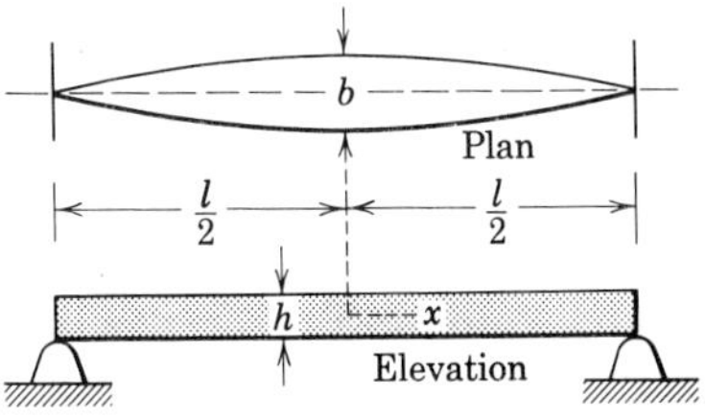

PROB. 437

* **437.** The end-supported beam has a constant depth h and a variable width y so that the two symmetrical contours in the plan view are defined by two parabolas with vertices at the center of the span. Determine the shear Q and moment M, induced by the weight of the beam, as functions of the distance x from the center of the span. The weight density of the beam material is μ.

Ans. $Q = \mu hbx\left(\dfrac{4x^2}{3l^2} - 1\right)$, $M = \mu hb\left(\dfrac{5}{48}l^2 - \dfrac{x^2}{2} + \dfrac{x^4}{3l^2}\right)$

* **438.** Determine the shear Q and moment M as functions of x for the beam whose loading is described by the sine function. Find the maximum magnitude of M.

Ans. $Q = \frac{p_0 l}{\pi} \cos \frac{\pi x}{l}$, $M = \frac{p_0 l^2}{\pi^2} \sin \frac{\pi x}{l}$

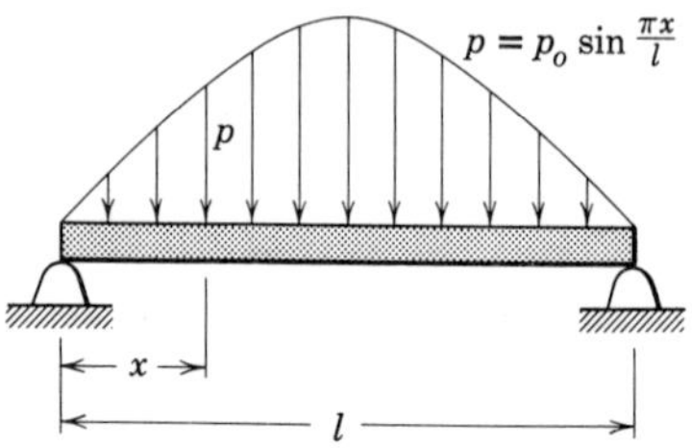

PROB. 438

42. Fluid Statics. The equilibrium of bodies subjected to the forces of fluid pressure is an important problem in statics. A fluid is any continuous substance which, when at rest, can transmit compressive forces but not tensile or shear forces. A shear force is one tangent to the surface upon which it acts. Thus a fluid at rest can exert only normal forces on a bounding surface. Fluids may be either gaseous or liquid.

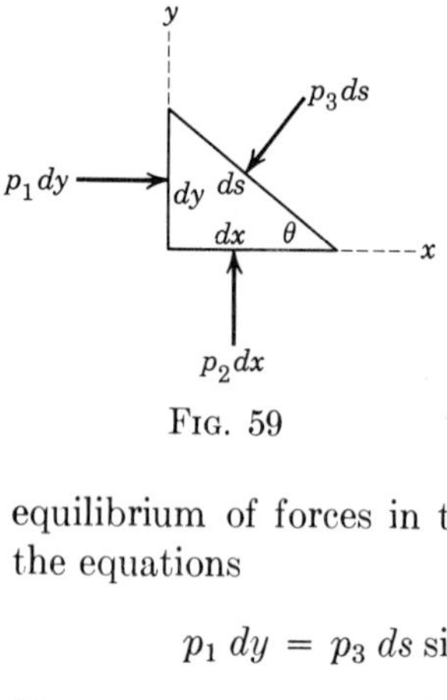

FIG. 59

The pressure in a fluid is the same in all directions (Pascal's law). This fact may be shown by considering the equilibrium of an infinitesimal triangular element of a fluid as shown in Fig. 59. By taking the z-dimension to be unity and the pressures on the three sides to be p_1, p_2, and p_3, the equilibrium of forces in the x- and y-directions may be expressed by the equations

$$p_1\, dy = p_3\, ds \sin \theta \qquad \text{and} \qquad p_2\, dx = p_3\, ds \cos \theta.$$

Since $ds \sin \theta = dy$ and $ds \cos \theta = dx$, these equations require that

$$p_1 = p_2 = p_3 = p.$$

Thus the pressure p is the same in all directions. In this analysis it is unnecessary to account for the weight of the fluid element, since when multiplying the fluid density by the volume of the element, a differential quantity of second order results which may be neglected compared with the first-order pressure force terms.

In all fluids at rest the pressure is a function of the vertical dimension. To determine this function a change in the vertical dimension must be considered and account of the weight of the fluid must be taken. Figure 60 shows a differential element of fluid in the form of a cylinder with vertical axis and cross-sectional area dA. The positive direction of vertical measurement z is taken down. The pressure on the upper face is p, and that on the lower face is p plus the change in p, or $p + dp$. The weight of the element equals its weight density μ multiplied by the volume. The normal forces on the lateral surface have nothing to do with the balance of forces in the vertical direction and are not shown. Equilibrium of the fluid element in the z-direction requires

$$p\,dA + \mu\,dA\,dz - (p + dp)\,dA = 0, \qquad dp = \mu\,dz. \tag{36}$$

This differential relation shows that the pressure in a fluid increases with depth or decreases with increased elevation. Equation 36 holds for both liquids and gases and is in accord with common knowledge of air and water pressures.

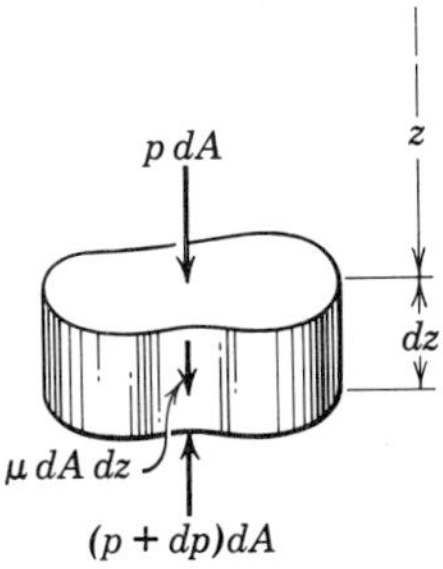

FIG. 60

Fluids which are essentially incompressible are called liquids, and it follows that for most practical purposes the density may be considered constant for every part of the liquid.* With μ a constant Eq. 36 may be integrated as it stands, and the result is

$$p = p_0 + \mu z. \tag{37}$$

The pressure p_0 is the pressure on the surface of the liquid where $z = 0$. If p_0 is due to atmospheric pressure and the measuring instrument records only the increment above atmospheric pressure,† the measurement gives what is known as "gage pressure" and is $p = \mu z$.

Gases, on the other hand, are compressible, and here the density varies with vertical distance. For most engineering problems this variation is negligible when considering gas pressures on a structure, since the height of the structure usually represents only a small change in altitude. If the gas temperature is constant (isothermal), the gas law $p = \mu K$, where K is a constant, may be used to determine the variation of pressure with altitude. Substitution of this value of μ into Eq. 36 and replacement of the downward measurement z by the upward measurement h, $(dz = -dh)$, give $K\,dp = -p\,dh$. Integration

* See Table of Densities, Table D1, Appendix D.

† Atmospheric pressure at sea level may be taken to be 14.7 lb./in.^{2}

from the conditions of pressure p_0 at zero altitude to pressure p at altitude h yields

$$h = K \log \frac{p_0}{p}.$$

When the temperature of a gas is not constant with altitude, such as with the earth's atmosphere, the effect of changing temperature must be accounted for.

43. Pressure on Submerged Surfaces. A surface submerged in a liquid, such as a gate valve in a dam or the walls of a tank, is subjected to fluid pressure normal to its surface and distributed over its area. In problems where fluid forces are appreciable it is necessary to account for the resultant force due to the distribution of pressure on the surface and the position at which this resultant acts. Consider a flat plate of any shape, Fig. 61*a*, submerged in a liquid. The horizontal surface of the liquid is the plane x–y', and the plane of the plate makes an angle θ with the vertical. The effect of atmospheric pressure p_0 need not be considered since it acts over all surfaces and yields a zero resultant. The fluid pressure (gage pressure) is linear with depth according to Eq. 37 and is $p = \mu h$. The force acting on a differential strip of area dA parallel to the surface of the liquid is $dR = p\,dA = \mu h\,dA$. The pressure p has the same magnitude throughout the length of the strip since there is no change of depth along the horizontal strip. The total force acting on the exposed area A is obtained by integration and is

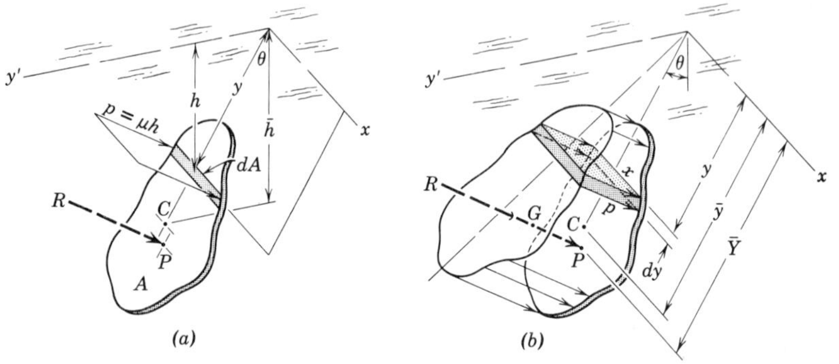

FIG. 61

$$R = \int dR = \int p\,dA = \mu \int h\,dA.$$

Substituting the centroidal relation $\bar{h}A = \int h\,dA$ gives

$$R = \mu\bar{h}A. \tag{38}$$

The quantity $\mu\bar{h}$ represents the pressure which exists at the depth of the centroid C of the area and is the average pressure over the area.

The resultant R may also be represented geometrically by a volume as shown in Fig. 61*b*. Here the pressure vector p is represented as an altitude to the plate considered as a base. The resulting volume is a truncated right cylinder. The force dR acting on the differential area $dA = x\,dy$ yields the elemental volume $dV = p\,dA$ represented by the shaded slice, and the total force is, then, the total volume of the cylinder. Thus

$$R = \int dR = \int dV = V.$$

It is seen from Eq. 38 that the average altitude of the truncated cylinder is the average pressure $\mu\bar{h}$ which exists at a depth corresponding to the centroid C of the area exposed to pressure. For problems where the centroid C or the volume V is not readily apparent a direct integration may be performed to obtain R. Thus

$$R = \int dR = \int p\,dA = \int \mu hx\,dy$$

where the depth h and the length x of the horizontal strip of differential area must be expressed in terms of y to carry out the integration.

The second requirement of the analysis of fluid pressure is the determination of the position of the resultant force in order to account for the moments of the pressure forces. Using the principle of moments with the x-axis of Fig. 61*b* as the moment axis gives

$$R\overline{Y} = \int y\,dR \qquad \text{or} \qquad \overline{Y} = \frac{\int y\,dV}{V}. \tag{39}$$

This second relation satisfies the definition of the coordinate $\overline{Y}$ to the centroid of the volume V, and it is concluded, therefore, that the resultant R passes through the centroid of the volume described by the plate area as base and the linearly varying pressure as altitude. The point P at which R is applied to the plate is known as the *center of pressure*. It should be noted carefully that the center of pressure P and the centroid C of the plate area are *not* the same.

An alternate expression for $\overline{Y}$ involving the so-called *moment of inertia* * of the area may be written. Substitution of $R = \mu\bar{h}A$, $dR = \mu h\, dA$, $\bar{h} = \bar{y} \cos \theta$, and $h = y \cos \theta$ into the principle of moments $R\overline{Y} = \int y\, dR$ gives

$$\overline{Y} = \frac{\int y^2\, dA}{\bar{y}A} \qquad \text{or} \qquad \overline{Y} = \frac{I_x}{\bar{y}A} \tag{40}$$

where I_x is the moment of inertia $\int y^2\, dA$ of the area about the parallel x-axis at the surface of the liquid.

In accounting for the resulting moment of the pressure forces on the plate about some axis parallel to the plate a direct integration is often just as straightforward as is the application of Eqs. 39 or 40. Thus the total moment M of the pressure forces about, say, the x-axis is

$$M = \int y\, dR = \int y\mu hx\, dy$$

and, again, the depth h and the length x of the horizontal strip of differential area must be expressed in terms of y to carry out the integration.

Consider now as a special case of the foregoing general relationships the frequently encountered situation of pressure on a rectangular plate with horizontal top edge and submerged in a liquid. Figure 62*a* shows such a plate 1–2–3–4 with the horizontal surface of the liquid represented by the x–y' plane. This figure corresponds to Fig. 61*b* for the general irregular plate. The volume of the pressure-area figure is clearly a truncated right prism. The centroid C of the plate at which depth the average pressure $\mu\bar{h}$ is determined is clearly the center of the rectangle 1–2–3–4. The center of pressure P is somewhat below C because R passes through the prisim's centroid G which has a greater y-coordinate than does C. Since the faces 1–2–6–5 and 4–3–7–8 and all intermediate sections are identical trapezoids, the analysis of pressure forces on such rectangular plates may proceed from a two-dimensional picture, Fig. 62*b*, which shows a representative section in the vertical plane perpendicular to the plate. The pressure distribution along the section is trapezoidal, and, hence, R may be located through the centroid G of the trapezoid. The distance $\bar{y}$ from the surface measured along the section to the centroid C of the rectangular plate

* See Appendix C.

is the average value $y_{av.}$ to the points 1 and 2. Likewise the average pressure $p_{av.} = \mu\bar{h}$ is the average of the pressures indicated by the vectors 5–1 and 6–2. If the upper surface of the plate coincides with the surface of the liquid, the pressure distribution becomes triangular instead of trapezoidal, and R is easily located through the centroid

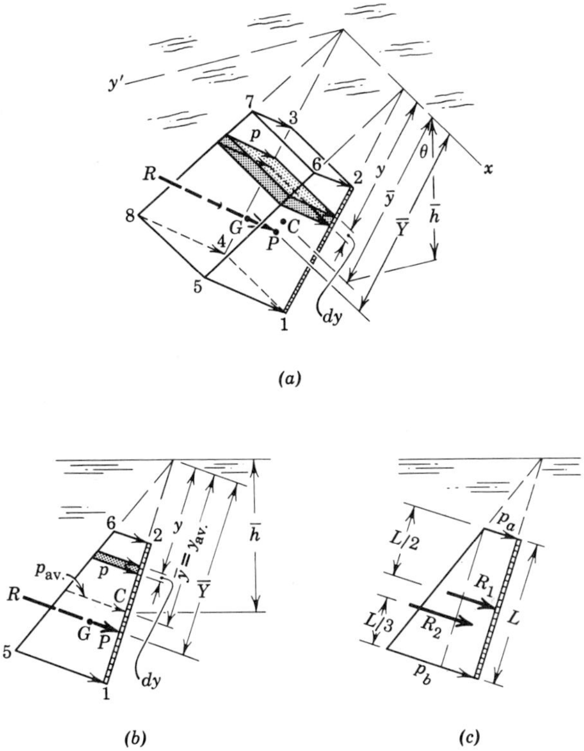

(a) (b) (c)

FIG. 62

of the triangular figure. In dealing with a trapezoidal distribution of pressure it is usually simpler to consider the resultant in two components, Fig. 62*c*. The trapezoid is divided into a rectangle and a triangle, and the force due to each part is considered separately. The force due to the rectangular portion acts at the center of the plate and is $R_1 = p_a A$ where A is the area of the submerged rectangular surface. The force due to the triangular portion acts through the centroid of the triangle and is $R_2 = \frac{1}{2}(p_b - p_a)A$.

For a submerged curved surface the resultant R caused by distributed pressure involves more calculation than for a flat surface.

As an example consider the submerged cylindrical surface shown in Fig. 63*a* where the elements of the curved surface are parallel to the horizontal surface x–y' of the liquid. Vertical sections perpendicular to the surface all disclose the same curve AB and the same pressure distribution. Thus the two-dimensional representation in Fig. 63*b* may be used. To find R by a direct integration it is necessary to integrate

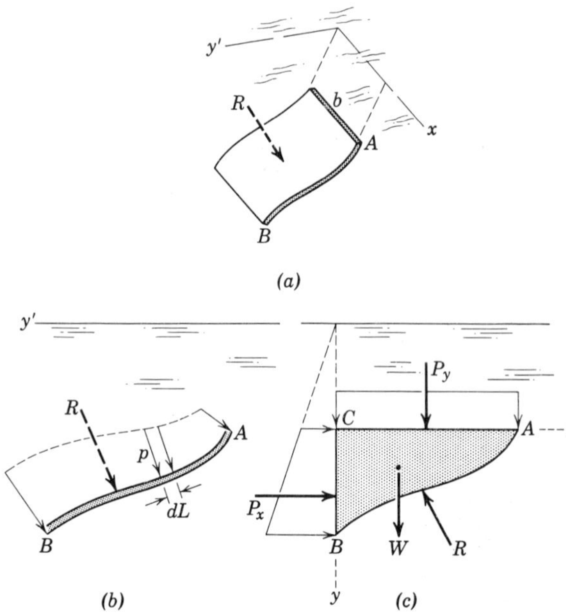

FIG. 63

the x- and y-components of dR along the curve AB since the pressure continuously changes direction. Thus

$$R_x = b\int p_x\,dL = b\int p\,dy \qquad \text{and} \qquad R_y = b\int p_y\,dL = b\int p\,dx.$$

A moment equation would next be required to establish the position of R.

A second method for finding R is often much simpler. The equilibrium of the block of liquid ABC directly above the surface, shown in Fig. 63*c*, is established. The resultant R is, then, disclosed as the equal and opposite reaction of the surface upon the block of liquid. The resultants of the pressures along AC and CB are P_y and P_x, respectively, and are easily obtained. The weight W of the liquid block is calculated from the area ABC of its section multiplied by the constant dimension b and the density. The weight W passes through the centroid of this area. The equilibrant R is then determined completely from the equilibrium equations applied to the free-body diagram of the fluid block.

SAMPLE PROBLEMS

439. Determine the resultant force R exerted on the semicircular end of the water tank shown in the figure if the tank is filled to capacity. Express the result in terms of the radius r of the circular end and the density μ of water.

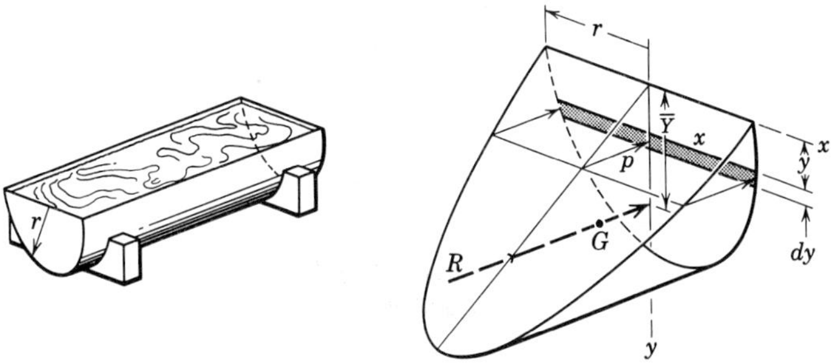

PROB. 439

Solution I. By direct integration R is found from

$$\left[R = \int dR\right] \qquad R = \int p\,dA = \int \mu y(2x\,dy) = 2\mu \int_0^r y\sqrt{r^2 - y^2}\,dy,$$

$$R = \tfrac{2}{3}\mu r^3 \qquad \textit{Ans.}$$

The location of R is determined from the principle of moments which gives

$$\left[R\bar{Y} = \int y\,dR\right] \qquad \tfrac{2}{3}\mu r^3 \bar{Y} = 2\mu \int_0^r y^2\sqrt{r^2 - y^2}\,dy.$$

Upon integrating there results

$$\tfrac{2}{3}\mu r^3 \bar{Y} = \frac{\mu r^4}{4}\frac{\pi}{2} \quad \text{and} \quad \bar{Y} = \frac{3\pi}{16} r. \qquad \textit{Ans.}$$

Solution II. Using Eq. 38 directly to find R gives

$$[R = \mu \bar{h} A] \qquad R = \mu \frac{4r}{3\pi}\frac{\pi r^2}{2} = \tfrac{2}{3}\mu r^3. \qquad \textit{Ans.}$$

Application of Eq. 39 for determining the centroid G amounts to the identical integration of *Solution I.* As an alternative Eq. 40 may be used. With the expression $I_x = \frac{1}{8}\pi r^4$ for the moment of inertia * of the semicircular area

* See Appendix C.

about the x-axis, there results

$$\left[\bar{Y} = \frac{I_x}{\bar{y}A}\right] \qquad \bar{Y} = \frac{\pi r^4/8}{\frac{4r}{3\pi}\frac{\pi r^2}{2}} = \frac{3\pi}{16} r. \qquad \textit{Ans.}$$

440. Determine completely the resultant force R exerted on the cylindrical dam surface by the water. The density of fresh water is 62.4 lb./ft.³, and the dam has a length, normal to the paper, of $b = 100$ ft.

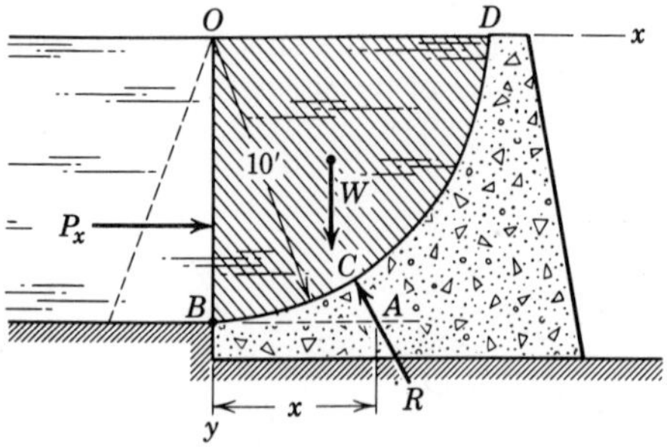

PROB. 440

Solution. The circular block of water $BCDO$ is isolated and its free-body diagram is drawn. The force P_x is

$$P_x = \mu\bar{h}A = \frac{\mu r}{2} br = \frac{62.4 \times 10}{2} \times 100 \times 10 = 312{,}000 \text{ lb.}$$

The weight W of the water is

$$W = \mu V = 62.4 \times \frac{\pi(10)^2}{4} \times 100 = 490{,}000 \text{ lb.}$$

Equilibrium of the section of water requires

$$[\Sigma F_x = 0] \qquad R_x = P_x = 312{,}000 \text{ lb.},$$

$$[\Sigma F_y = 0] \qquad R_y = W = 490{,}000 \text{ lb.}$$

The resultant force R exerted by the fluid on the dam is equal and opposite to that shown acting on the fluid and is

$$[R = \sqrt{R_x^2 + R_y^2}] \qquad R = 581{,}000 \text{ lb.} \qquad \textit{Ans.}$$

The x-coordinate of the point A through which R passes may be located graphically if desired. Algebraically x is found from the principle of moments. Using B as a moment center gives

$$P_x \frac{r}{3} + W\frac{4r}{3\pi} - R_y x = 0, \qquad x = \frac{312{,}000 \times \frac{10}{3} + 490{,}000 \times \frac{40}{3\pi}}{490{,}000} = 6.37 \text{ ft.}$$

Ans.

If the point C on the curved surface is desired, it will be necessary to combine the moment relation with the equation of the circle for solution.

PROBLEMS

441. The cover plate for an access opening in a fresh-water tank is bolted in place with negligible initial tensions in the bolts, and the tank is filled to the level shown. Find the tension in each bolt at A and at B due to the water pressure. *Ans.* $A = 790$ lb., $B = 896$ lb.

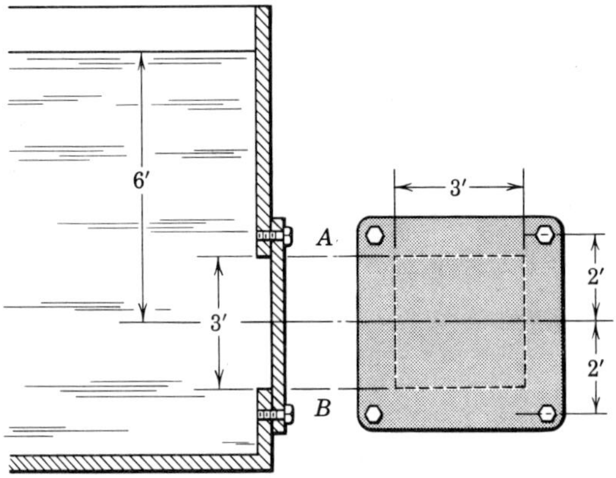

Prob. 441

442. The cylindrical caisson of radius r and wall thickness t is lowered in place, and the water (density μ) is then pumped out. At any particular depth the water pressure causes a compressive stress σ in the cylinder wall which is proportional to the pressure at that particular depth. Determine σ for any depth h.

Ans. $\sigma = \dfrac{\mu h r}{t}$

Prob. 442

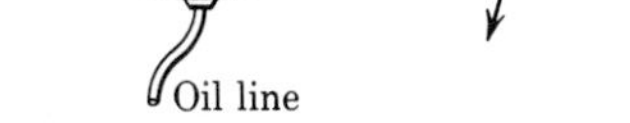

Prob. 443

443. The spherical aluminum shell has an inside diameter of 12 in. and a wall thickness of ¼ in. Oil under pressure is pumped into the shell, causing every element of the shell, such as the one illustrated, to be subjected to equal tensile forces on each side. The force per unit area of shell section is the *stress*. If the aluminum used can withstand a stress of 40,000 lb./in.^{2} before fracture occurs, determine the oil pressure required to burst the shell.

Ans. $p = 3400$ lb./in.^{2} gage

444. The triangular and rectangular sections are being considered for a small fresh-water concrete dam. From the standpoint of resistance to overturning about C, which section will require less concrete, and how much less per foot of dam length? Concrete weighs 150 lb./ft.^{3}

Ans. A, 7010 lb. per foot of section

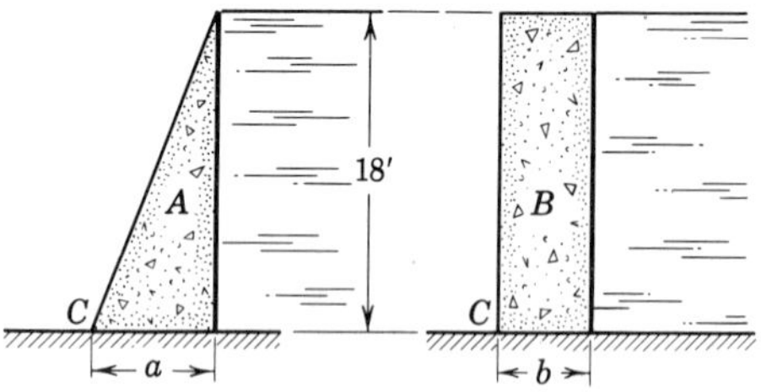

PROB. 444

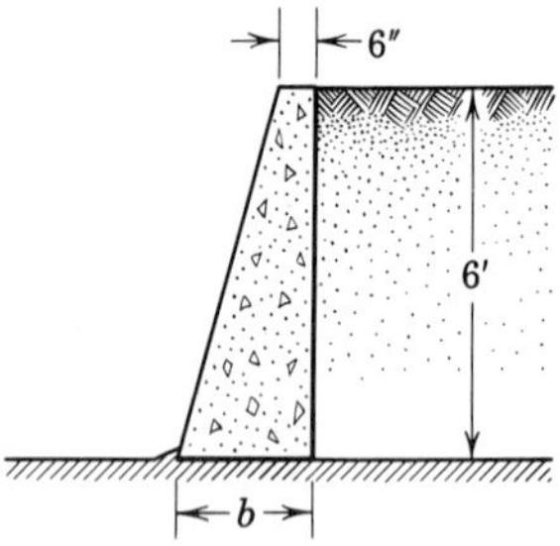

PROB. 445

445. Determine the minimum width b of the footing for the concrete retaining wall shown to prevent tipping of the wall. Concrete weighs 150 lb./ft.^{3}, and the soil above the foundation level may be assumed to be a fluid whose density is 110 lb./ft.^{3}

446. The slanted gate AB is a uniform plate weighing 2000 lb. which separates two bodies of fresh water in a channel 8 ft. wide. As the water is drained

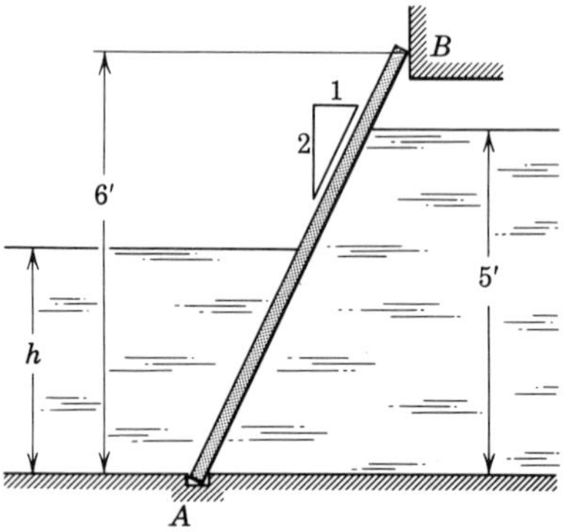

PROB. 446

from the left side of the gate, the reaction against the support at B is changed. Determine the depth h at which this reaction is zero. Assume that the gate is hinged at its lower end.

447. The form for a concrete footing is hinged to its lower edge A and held in place every 4 ft. by a horizontal brace BC. Neglect the weight of the form and compute the compression C in each brace due to the liquid behavior of wet concrete which has a density of 150 lb./ft.^{3} *Ans.* $C = 1200$ lb.

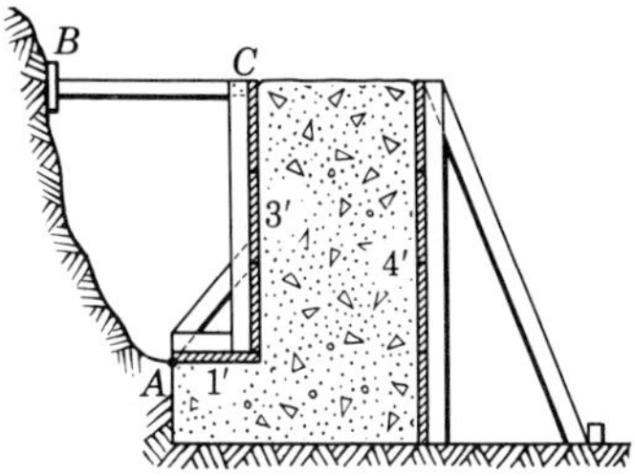

PROB. 447

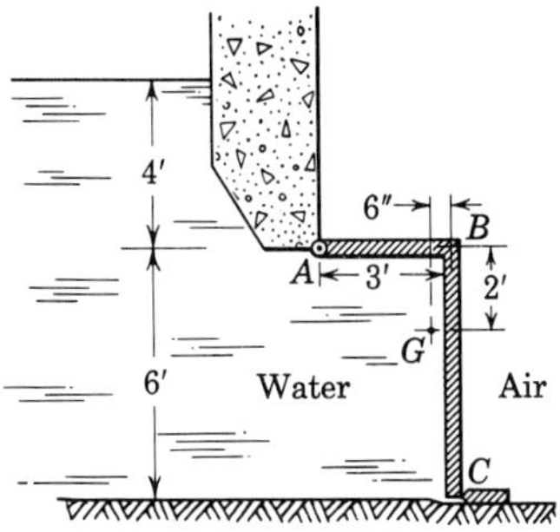

PROB. 448

448. A water-tight gate for a small fresh-water dam weighs 15,000 lb. with center of gravity at G. It has an angular cross section ABC and a length, perpendicular to the paper, of 10 ft. The gate is hinged about its upper edge A and is held in position by the control stop at C which bears horizontally against the gate. Determine the force C exerted against the stop. Neglect the thickness of the gate section compared with the other dimensions involved.

449. The upstream side of an arched dam has the form of a cylindrical surface of 500 ft. radius and subtends an angle of 60 deg. If the water is 100 ft. deep, determine the total force P exerted by the water on the dam.

Ans. $P = 156 \times 10^6$ lb.

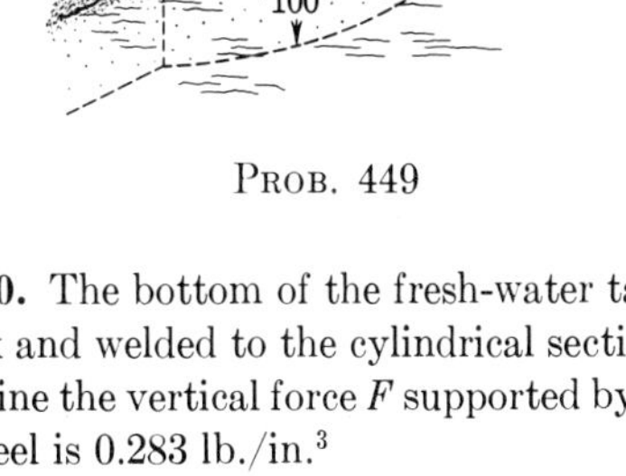

PROB. 449

PROB. 450

450. The bottom of the fresh-water tank is a hemispherical steel shell ½ in. thick and welded to the cylindrical section around the circular periphery. Determine the vertical force F supported by the weld per unit length. The density of steel is 0.283 lb./in.^{3}

451. A rectangular opening in the slanted bottom of a steel tank, shown in section, has the dimensions 3 ft. by 2 ft. and is closed by a self-sealing door of negligible weight which is hinged about its upper edge A. Calculate the tension T in the chain which is required to open the door. The liquid in the tank has a specific gravity of 1.20. *Ans.* $T = 649$ lb.

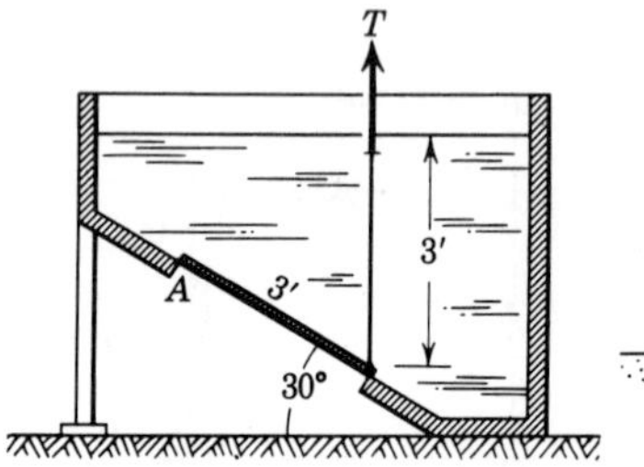

PROB. 451

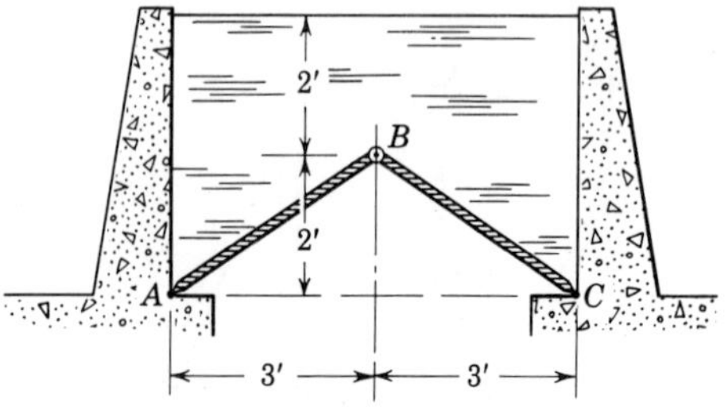

PROB. 452

452. The bottom of a fresh-water channel, shown in section, consists of two uniform rectangular plates AB and BC each weighing 2500 lb. and hinged along their common edge B and hinged also to the base of the fixed channel along their lower edges A and C. The length of the channel is 20 ft., measured perpendicular to the plane of the paper. Determine the force P per foot of channel length exerted by each plate on the connecting hinge at B.

453. Find the resultant force R exerted by the circular concrete dam section A on the foundation B. Also find the coordinate x of the point C through which the resultant acts. Concrete weighs 150 lb./ft.^{3} and the dam is 100 ft. long. *Ans.* $R = 16{,}900$ tons, $x = 19.05$ ft.

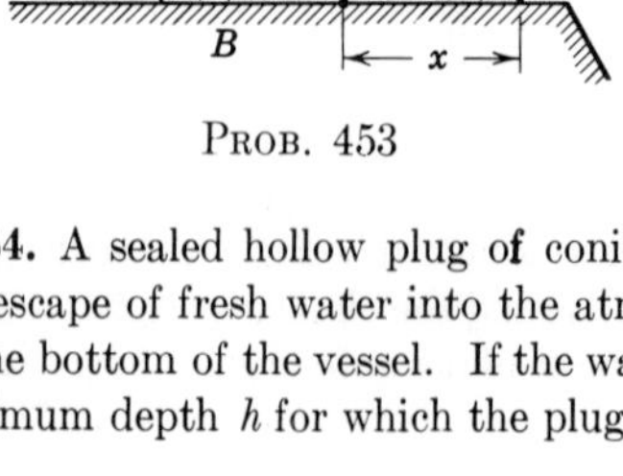

PROB. 453

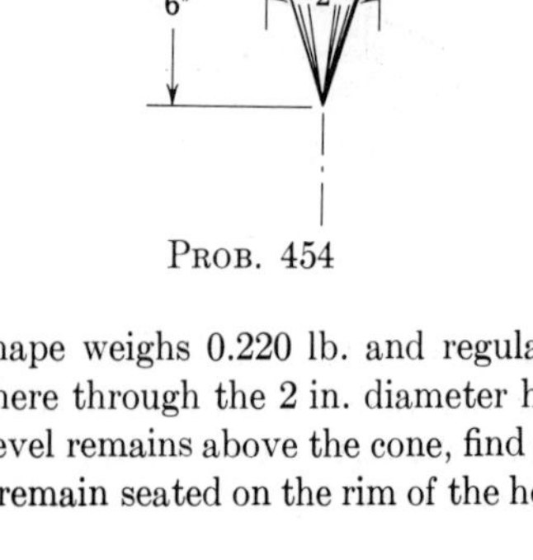

PROB. 454

454. A sealed hollow plug of conical shape weighs 0.220 lb. and regulates the escape of fresh water into the atmosphere through the 2 in. diameter hole in the bottom of the vessel. If the water level remains above the cone, find the minimum depth h for which the plug will remain seated on the rim of the hole.

455. A flat plate seals a triangular opening in the vertical wall of a tank of liquid of density μ. The plate is hinged about the upper edge O of the triangle. Determine the force P required to close the gate against the pressure of the liquid.

Ans. $P = \frac{\mu ab}{6}\left(h + \frac{a}{2}\right)$

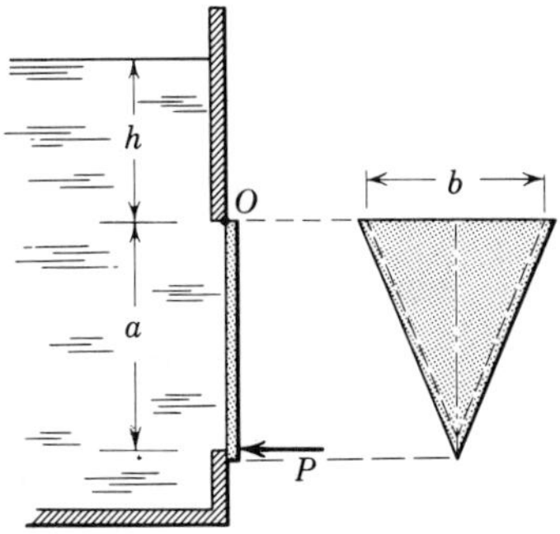

Prob. 455

456. The distribution of pressure due to the action of a wave surging against a sea wall is approximated by the parabolic and linear relations as shown in the figure. The peak pressure of 2000 lb./ft.^{2} occurs at the apex of the parabola. For the instant represented determine the moment M about A of the forces due to wave action per foot of wall length.

Ans. $M = 470{,}000$ lb. ft. per foot

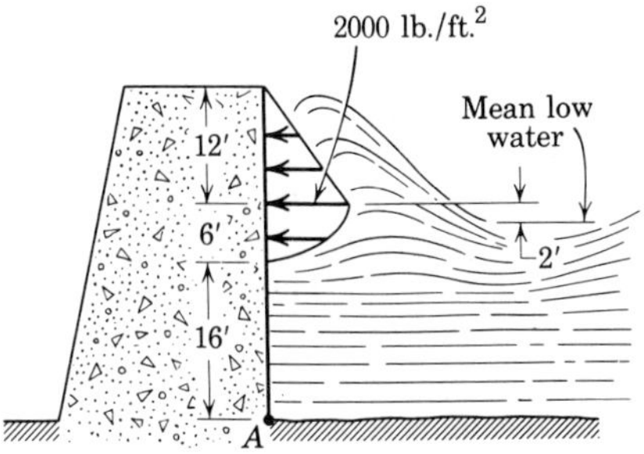

Prob. 456

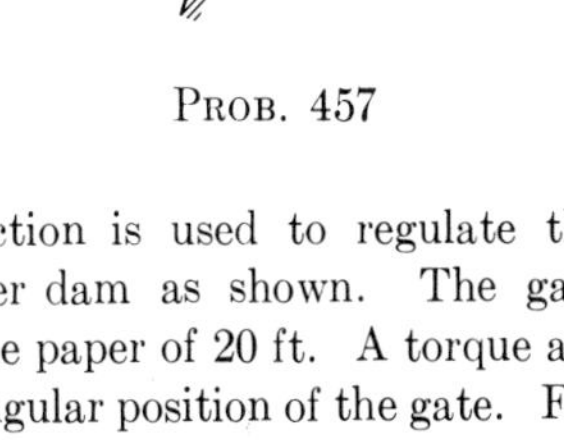

Prob. 457

457. A control gate of cylindrical cross section is used to regulate the flow of water over the spillway of a fresh-water dam as shown. The gate weighs 20,000 lb. and has a length normal to the paper of 20 ft. A torque applied to the shaft of the gate at O controls the angular position of the gate. For the position shown determine the horizontal and vertical components F_x and F_y of the total force exerted by the shaft on its bearings at O. Account for the effect of fluid pressure by a direct integration over the cylindrical surface.

* **458.** A specimen for measuring the breaking strength of metal under combined stresses (stresses acting on any element in more than one direction) is shown in section. The ratio of longitudinal stress σ_l to tangential stress σ_t is controlled by varying both the oil pressure p and the applied tensile load L. If the ratio of σ_l to σ_t is to be maintained at 4:1 for a certain test, find the necessary variation of p in pounds per square inch gage with L in pounds. If the specimen breaks when L = 32,000 lb., what is the breaking stress σ_l? Assume that the specimen is sufficiently long so that the shape of the ends does not affect the test section. *Ans.* $p = 0.0952L$, σ_l = 52,800 lb./in.²

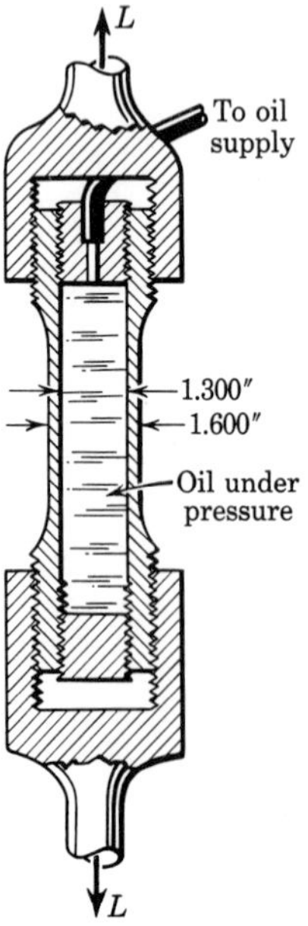

PROB. 458

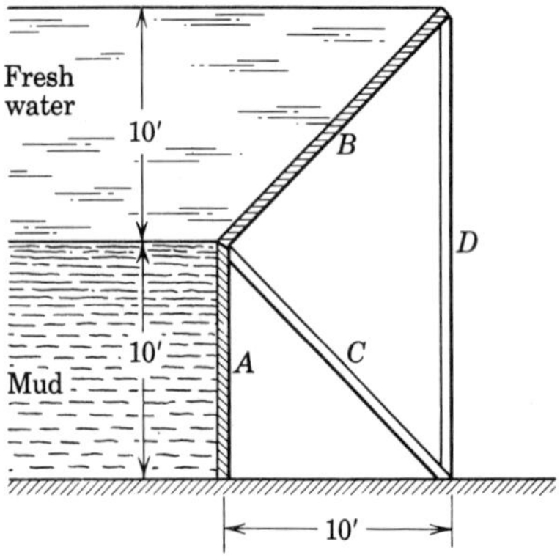

PROB. 459

* **459.** A dam consists of the flat plate barriers A and B whose weights are small. Supporting struts C and D are placed every 10 ft. of dam section. A mud sample drawn up to the surface weighs 100 lb./ft.³ Determine the compression in C and D. All joints may be assumed to be hinged.

Ans. C = 111,900 lb., D = 20,800 lb.

* **460.** The gate A is fixed in the triangular water channel. Determine the magnitude of the resultant force R exerted on A by the water and the height h of the point on the gate through which the resultant acts.

Ans. R = 1665 lb., h = 2 ft.

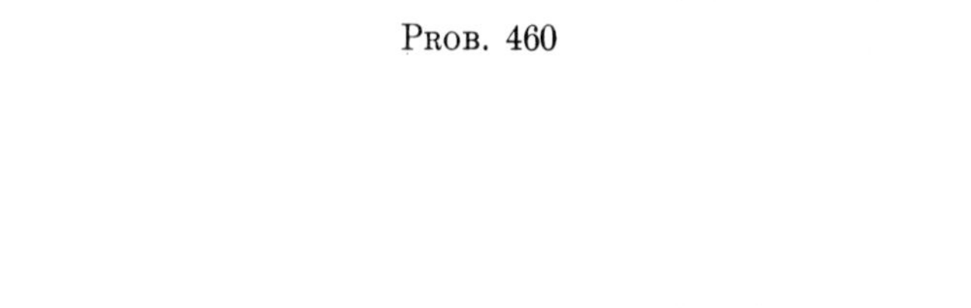

PROB. 460

* **461.** The circular cover plate is bolted to the side of a fresh-water tank to seal the 3 ft. diameter opening. Calculate the increase in the bolt tensions at A, B, and C when the tank is filled to the level shown. Assume negligible initial bolt tensions. *Ans.* $A = 800$ lb., $B = C = 925$ lb.

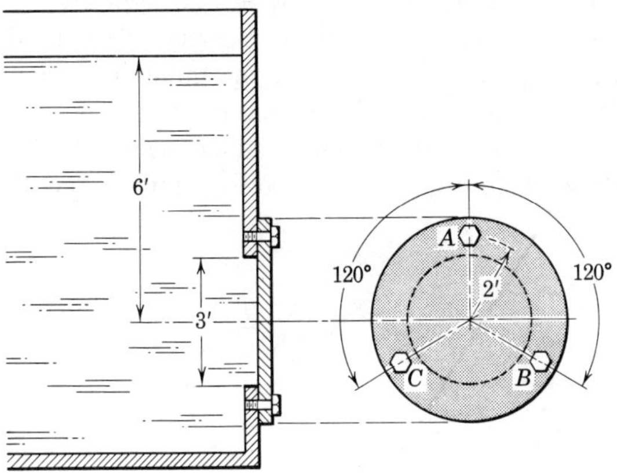

Prob. 461

* **462.** A hollow metal sphere with a diameter of 10 in. and a weight of 8 lb. is used as a valve to close the hole in the fresh-water tank. What force P is required to raise the valve? *Ans.* $P = 14.12$ lb.

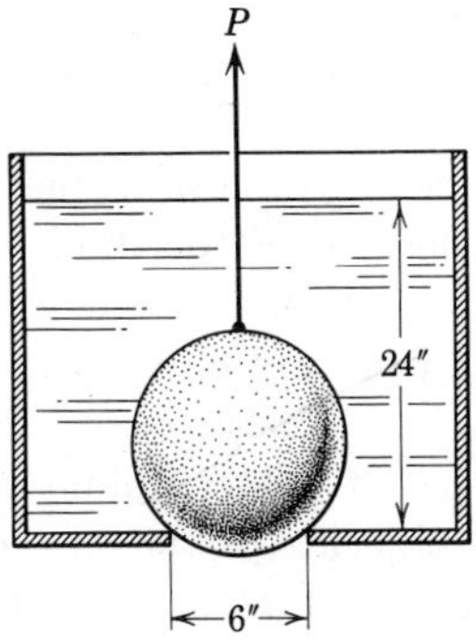

Prob. 462

44. Buoyancy. The principle of buoyancy, the discovery of which is accredited to Archimedes, can be explained in the following manner for any fluid, gaseous or liquid, in equilibrium. Consider a portion of the fluid defined by an imaginary closed surface, as illustrated by the irregular dotted boundary in Fig. 64*a*. If the body of the fluid could be sucked off from within the closed cavity and replaced simultaneously by the forces which it exerted on the boundary of the cavity, Fig. 64*b*, there would be no disturbance of the equilibrium of the surrounding fluid. Furthermore, a free-body diagram of the fluid portion before removal, Fig. 64*c*, shows that the resultant of the pressure forces distributed over its surface must be equal and opposite to its weight W and must pass through the center of gravity of the fluid element. If the element is replaced by a body of the same dimensions, the surface forces acting on the body held in this position will be identical with those acting on the fluid element. Thus the resultant force exerted on the surface of an object immersed in a fluid is equal and opposite

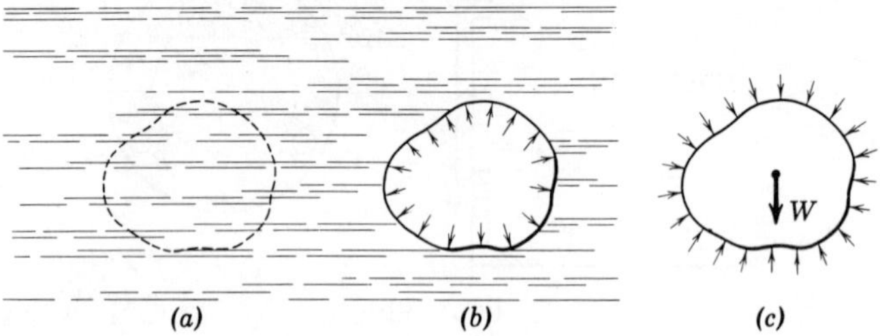

FIG. 64

to the weight of fluid displaced and passes through the center of gravity of the displaced fluid. This resultant force is the force of buoyancy. In the case of a liquid whose density is constant the center of gravity of the displaced liquid coincides with the centroid of the displaced volume.

It follows from the foregoing discussion that, when the density of an object is less than the density of the fluid in which it is immersed, there will be an unbalance of force in the vertical direction, and the object will rise. The object continues to rise until it comes to the surface of the fluid and then comes to rest in an equilibrium position, assuming that the density of the new fluid above the surface is less than the density of the object. In the case of the surface boundary between a liquid and a gas, such as water and air, the effect of the gas pressure on that portion of the floating object above the liquid is balanced by the added pressure in the liquid due to the action of the gas on its surface.

45. Stability of Floating Bodies. The relations between hull shape and weight distribution in a ship are basic design considerations. The ship shown in Fig. 65*a* is floating in an upright position. Point B is the centroid of the displaced volume and is known as the *center of buoyancy*. The resultant of the forces exerted on the hull by the water is the resultant buoyant force F. Force F passes through B and is equal and opposite to the weight W of the ship. If the ship is caused to roll through an angle α, Fig. 65*b*, the shape of the displaced volume changes, and the center of buoyancy will shift to some new position such as B'. The point of intersection of the vertical line through B' with the centerline of the ship is called the *metacenter* M, and the distance h of M above the center of gravity G is known as the *metacentric height.* For most hull shapes it is found that the metacentric height remains practically constant for angles of roll up to about 20 deg. When M is above G, as in Fig. 65*b*, there is clearly a

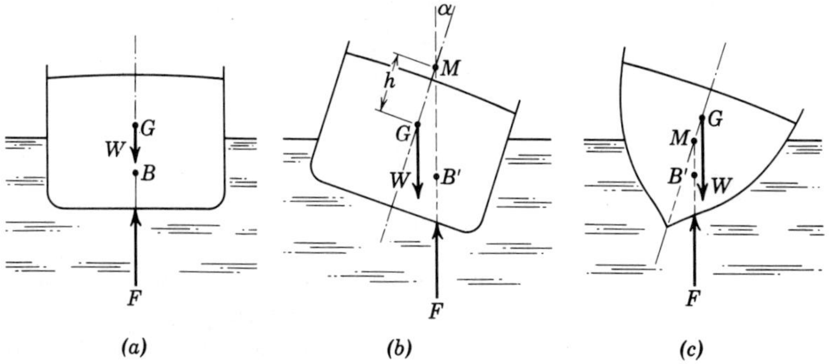

FIG. 65

righting moment which tends to bring the ship back to its original position. The magnitude of this moment for any particular angle of roll is a measure of the stability of the ship. If M is below G, as for the hull shape of Fig. 65*c*, the moment accompanying any roll is in the direction to increase the roll. This is clearly a condition of instability and must be avoided in the design of any ship.

PROBLEMS

463. A spherical steel buoy 4 ft. in diameter and weighing 350 lb. is to be anchored in salt water 50 ft. below the surface. Find the weight W of scrap iron to be sealed inside the buoy in order that the force on its anchor chain will not exceed 1000 lb. For negligible change in water density, does the buoyancy force depend on the depth of submergence? *Ans.* $W = 795$ lb., no

464. A captive balloon weighing 1 lb. empty is inflated with helium to a diameter of 6 ft. and secured at an altitude of 50 ft. by a wire of that length weighing 0.01 lb./ft. Determine the weight W of the helium in the balloon if the tension in the wire at the ground is 5.90 lb. The density of the air is 0.0766 lb./ft.^{3} *Ans.* $W = 1.26$ lb.

465. A marker buoy consisting of a cone and cylinder has the dimensions shown and weighs 625 lb. out of water. Determine the protrusion h when the buoy is floating in salt water. The buoy is weighted so that a low center of gravity insures stability. *Ans.* $h = 3.89$ ft.

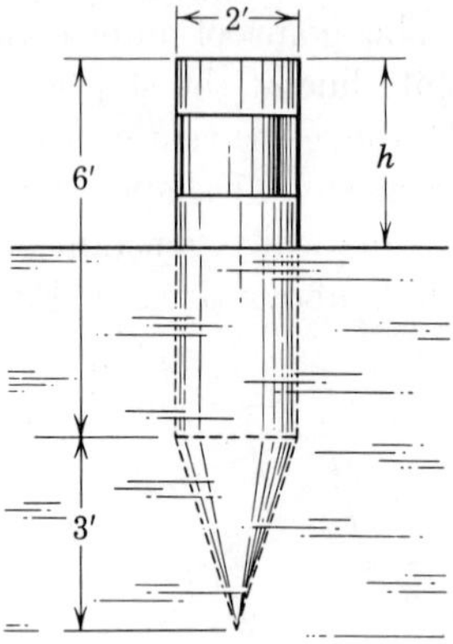

PROB. 465

466. With a spring scale a body weighs 50 lb. in air and when immersed in fresh water "weighs" 25 lb. Find its volume V and density μ.

467. The density of ice is 56 lb./ft.^{3} Determine the ratio n of depth below water to height above water for an iceberg floating in salt water and having rectangular proportions. *Ans.* $n = 7$

468. Show that both the homogeneous solid hemisphere and the hemispherical shell float with stability. If both have the same total weight and radius, which one is the more stable?

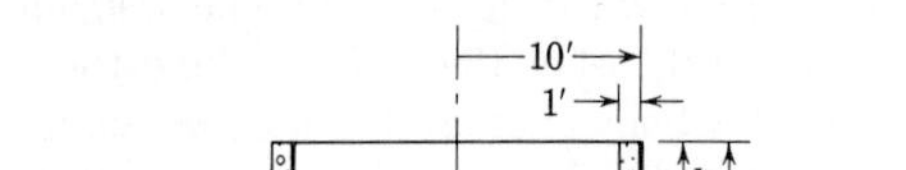

PROB. 468

469. The caisson shown is made of concrete weighing 150 lb./ft.^{3} and is in the form of a cylindrical tank of 20 ft. diameter. Determine the maximum

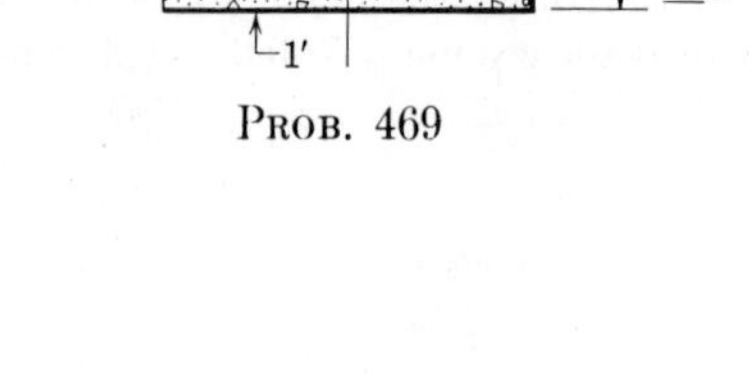

PROB. 469

depth h of salt water which may be left in the caisson without decreasing the freeboard b to less than 5 ft. when floating in salt water. *Ans.* $h = 1.75$ ft.

470. A ship moves from a fresh-water anchorage to a berth in salt water. After the ship takes on 50,000 gal. of fuel oil (specific gravity 0.89), it is noted that the draft marks read the same as previously in fresh water. Determine the displacement W (total weight) of the ship in long tons before fueling.

471. A doughnut barge of net weight W is used to transport sludge or waste oil and consists of a floating ring without a bottom. For the barge shown where the cross section of the ring is rectangular, determine the maximum

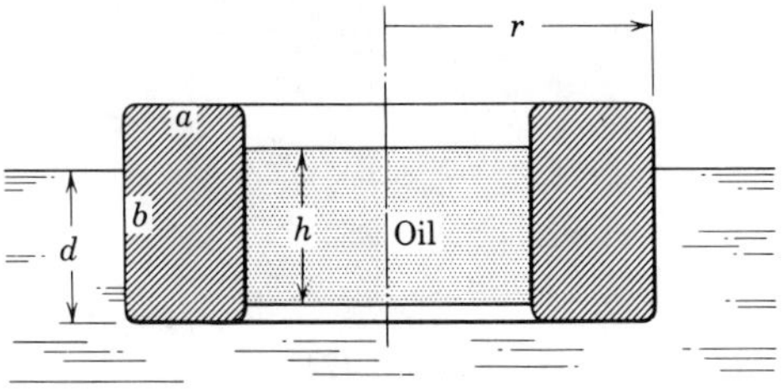

PROB. 471

depth h of oil which can be pumped into the barge without flowing out of the bottom under the barge. Freeboard (height of barge above water) is sufficient to prevent overflow at the top. The specific gravity γ of the oil is less than unity, and the barge is floating in fresh water. Does d depend on h?

Ans. $h = \dfrac{W}{\pi \gamma \mu a (2r - a)}$

472. A steel chain weighs 0.78 lb./ft. and has a breaking strength of 4500 lb. If it is lowered into the ocean, determine the depth h which could be reached before the chain breaks.

473. One end of a uniform pole of length l and density μ' is tied to the bottom of a tank of liquid which has a density μ and depth h. For the conditions $\mu' < \mu$ and $h < l$ find the angle θ assumed by the pole.

Ans. $\theta = \sin^{-1}\left(\dfrac{h}{l}\sqrt{\dfrac{\mu}{\mu'}}\right)$

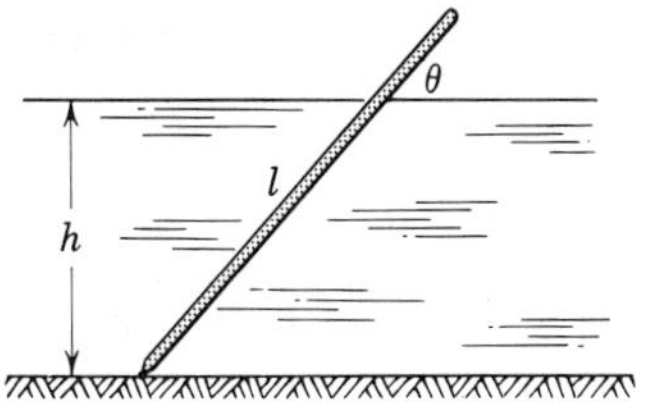

PROB. 473

474. A solid right circular cone of base radius r, altitude h, and density μ_c is mounted on a fixed vertical wire through a small axial hole so that the cone is able to slide freely along the wire. If the cone is allowed to float in a liquid of density μ_l, find its height b above the surface.

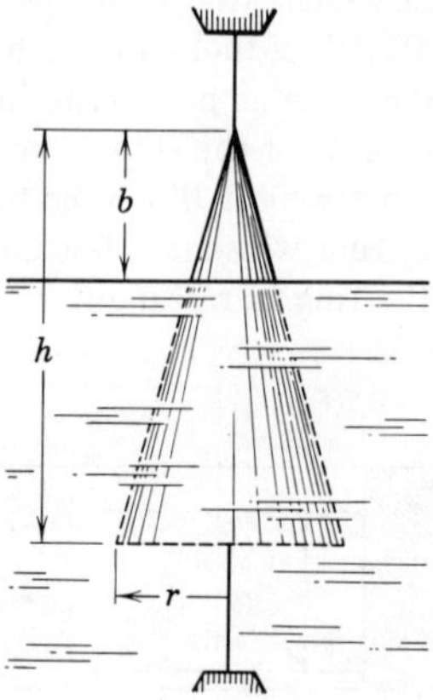

PROB. 474

475. A sphere of radius a and density μ_s floats in a liquid of density μ_l. Find the relation between the radius, the densities, and the height b which the sphere protrudes above the surface.

Ans. $1 - \dfrac{\mu_s}{\mu_l} = \dfrac{3}{4}\dfrac{b^2}{a^2}\left(1 - \dfrac{b}{3a}\right)$

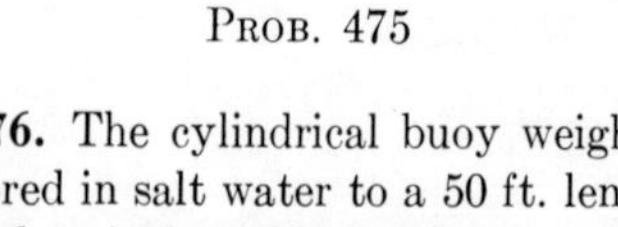

PROB. 475

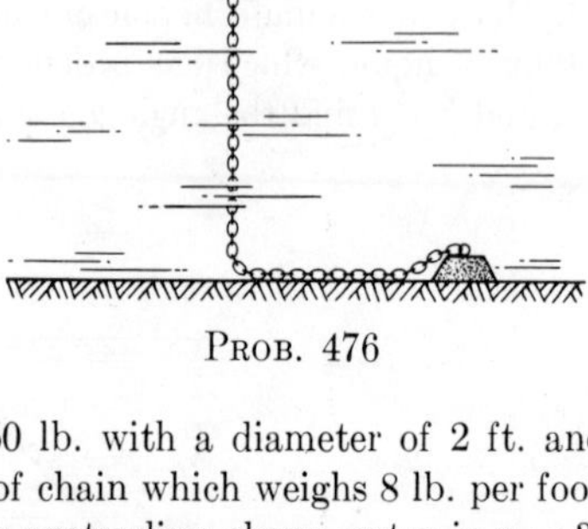

PROB. 476

476. The cylindrical buoy weighs 450 lb. with a diameter of 2 ft. and is moored in salt water to a 50 ft. length of chain which weighs 8 lb. per foot of length. At low tide the height of buoy protruding above water is $x = 3$ ft. Find the value of x after the tide has risen 7 ft. In each condition a part of the chain is lying on the bottom as shown. Steel has a density of 0.281 lb./in.^{3}

Ans. $x = 2.77$ ft.

* **477.** The accurate determination of the vertical position of the center of gravity G of a ship is difficult to achieve by calculation. It is more easily ob-

tained by a simple inclining experiment on the loaded ship. With reference to the figure, a known external weight w is placed a distance d from the center line, and the angle of list θ is measured by means of the deflection of a plumb bob. The displacement of the ship and the location of the metacenter M are known. Calculate the metacentric height GM for a 7500 ton ship (long tons) inclined by a 70,000 lb. weight placed 22 ft. from the center line if a 20 ft. plumb bob is deflected a distance a = 12 in. The weight w is at a distance b = 5 ft. above M.

Ans. $GM = 1.85$ ft.

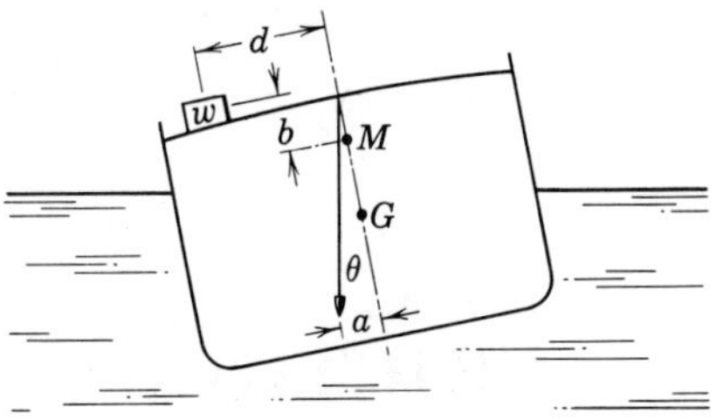

PROB. 477

* **478.** A spherical balloon is made from material which stretches in proportion to the force applied to it. Since the amount of stretch of any element depends directly on the original length and the force acting, the equation $u = Krp$ may be written, where u is the increase in radius of the balloon, r is the radius of the unstretched balloon, p is the internal gas pressure (gage), and K is the constant of proportionality. As the balloon is filled with gas, such as helium, under pressure, the sphere expands and creates greater buoyancy in the air. At the same time the weight of the balloon is increasing as more gas is injected. Find the pressure p for which the balloon has a maximum lift. The density of air is μ_a, and that of the gas is $\mu_g = k(p + p_0)$ for constant temperature, where k is a constant and where p_0 is the atmospheric pressure.

$$\textit{Ans.}\quad p = \frac{1}{4}\left(\frac{3\mu_a}{k} - \frac{1}{K} - 3p_0\right)$$

* **479.** Determine the minimum ratio of a to b for stability of the rectangular block of density μ_b for very small angles of list. The density of the liquid is μ_l.

$$\textit{Ans.}\quad \frac{a}{b} = \sqrt{6\frac{\mu_b}{\mu_l}\left(1 - \frac{\mu_b}{\mu_l}\right)}$$

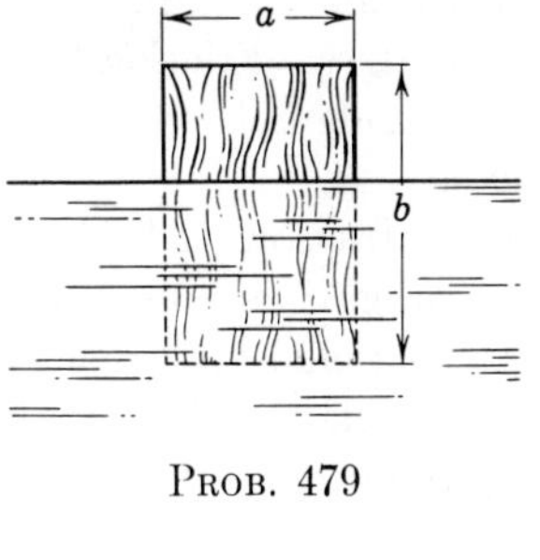

PROB. 479

CHAPTER 6

FRICTION

46. Introduction. In the preceding chapters contacting surfaces were considered as being perfectly smooth so that the forces of interaction were normal to the surface. Although in many instances this ideal assumption involves only a very small error, there are a great many problems wherein the ability of contacting surfaces to support tangential as well as normal forces must be considered. Forces tangent to contacting surfaces are known as friction forces and are present to some degree with the interaction between all actual surfaces. Whenever a tendency exists for the sliding of one contacting surface along another surface, the friction forces developed are always found to be in a direction to oppose this tendency.

In some types of machines and processes it is desirable to minimize the retarding effect of friction forces. Examples are bearings of all types, power screws, gears, and the flow of fluids in pipes. In other machines effort is made to take advantage of friction, as in brakes, clutches, belt drives, and wedges. Friction forces are present throughout nature and exist to a considerable extent in all machines no matter how accurately constructed.

There are several types of friction. *Fluid friction* is developed when layers in a fluid (liquid or gas) are moving at different velocities. This motion gives rise to frictional forces between fluid elements, and these forces depend on the relative velocity between layers. When there is no such velocity there is no friction. Fluid friction depends not only on the velocity gradients but also on the viscosity or resistance to shearing action of the fluid. The analysis of the fluid friction in fully lubricated bearings, centrifugal pumps, ship propulsion, aircraft performance, and projectile flight, to mention only a few examples, is basic to the design of these elements and systems. The investigation of fluid friction is best undertaken in the study of fluid mechanics and will not be developed in this book. It is mentioned, nevertheless, because of the importance of this type of friction in many engineering problems. *Internal friction* in solids is present in all inelastic deformations of solid bodies and results in energy loss through the generation and dissipation of heat. The ability of a body to damp out vibrations generated within it is due to the action of internal friction forces. *External friction* between contacting surfaces of solid bodies in the absence of a separating layer of lubricating fluid is known as *dry friction* or *Coulomb friction.* This type of friction involves the action between solid rigid bodies, and, consequently, is the only type of friction developed in this book.

47. Dry Friction. The theory of dry friction often bears the name of *Coulomb* friction, although the basic relations involved were known before Coulomb's day. The laws governing the behavior of dry friction * can be explained for most practical purposes by means of a very simple experiment. Consider a solid block of weight W resting on a horizontal surface as shown in Fig. 66*a*. The contacting surfaces possess a certain amount of roughness. The experiment will involve the application of a horizontal force P which will vary continuously from zero to a value sufficient to move the block and give it an appreciable velocity. The free-body diagram of the block for any value of P is shown in Fig. 66*b*, and the tangential friction force exerted by the plane on the block is labeled F. This friction force will *always* be in a direction to oppose motion or the tendency toward motion of the body on which it acts. There is also a normal force N which in this case equals W, and the total force R exerted by the supporting surface on the block is the resultant of N and F. A magnified view of the

* The principles of dry friction are based largely on the experiments of Coulomb in 1781 and on the work of Morin from 1831 to 1834. A comprehensive theory of dry friction, not yet available, must go beyond the mechanical explanation given in this chapter. For example, there is some evidence to support the theory that molecular attraction may be an important cause of friction under conditions where the mating surfaces are in very intimate contact. Other important factors in a more comprehensive theory are the deformation and tearing of surface irregularities, generation of high local temperatures and adhesion at contact points, relative hardness of mating surfaces, and the presence of thin surface films of oxide, oil, dirt, or other substances.

irregularities of the mating surfaces, Fig. 66*c*, will aid in visualizing the mechanical action of friction. Support is necessarily intermittent and exists at the mating humps. The direction of each of the reactions on the block R_1, R_2, R_3, etc., may be taken to be along the normal to the contact surface of each respective hump. The total normal force N is merely the sum of the n-components of the R's, and the total frictional force F is the sum of the t-components of the R's. When the surfaces are in relative motion, the contacts are more nearly along

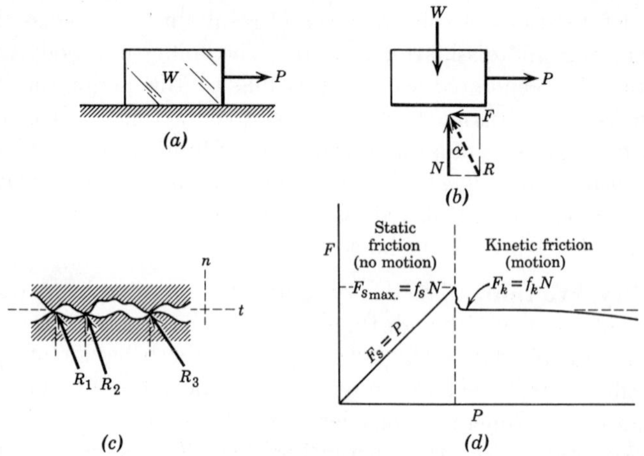

Fig. 66

the tops of the humps, and the t-components of the R's will be smaller than when the surfaces are at rest relative to one another. This consideration will explain the well-known fact that the force P necessary to maintain motion is less than that required to start the block when the irregularities are more nearly in mesh.

Assume now that the experiment indicated is performed and the friction force F is measured as a function of P. The resulting experimental relation is indicated in Fig. 66*d*. When P is zero, equilibrium requires that there be no friction force. As P is increased, the friction force must be of equal magnitude to P as long as the block does not slip. During this period the block is in equilibrium, and all forces acting on the block must satisfy the equilibrium equations. Finally a value of P is reached which causes the block to slip and to move in the direction of the applied force. At this same time the friction force drops slightly and abruptly to a somewhat lesser value. Here it remains essentially constant for a period but then drops off still more with higher velocities.

The region up to the point of slippage or impending motion is known as the range of *static friction*, and the value of the friction force is determined by the *equations of equilibrium.* This force may have any value from zero up to and including, in the limit, the maximum value. For a given pair of mating surfaces this maximum value of static friction $F_{s_{max.}}$ is found to be proportional to the normal force N. Thus

$$F_{s_{max.}} = f_s N,$$

where f_s is the proportionality constant, known as the *coefficient of static friction.* It must be carefully observed that this equation describes only the *limiting* or *maximum* value of the static friction force and not any lesser value. Thus the equation applies *only* to cases where it is known that motion is impending.

After slippage occurs a condition of *kinetic friction* is involved. Kinetic friction force is always somewhat less than the maximum static friction force. The kinetic friction force F_k is also found to be proportional to the normal force. Thus

$$F_k = f_k N,$$

where f_k is the *coefficient of kinetic friction.* It follows that f_k is somewhat less than f_s. As the velocity of the block increases, the kinetic friction coefficient decreases somewhat, and when high velocities are reached, the effect of lubrication by intervening air film may become appreciable. Coefficients of friction depend greatly on the exact condition of the surfaces as well as on the velocity and are subject to a considerable measure of uncertainty.

It is quite customary to write the two friction force equations merely as

$$F = fN. \tag{41}$$

There will be an understanding from the problem whether limiting static friction with its corresponding coefficient of static friction or whether kinetic friction with its corresponding kinetic coefficient is implied. It should be emphasized again that many problems involve a static friction force which is less than the maximum value at impending motion, and therefore the friction equation cannot be used.

From Fig. 66*c* it may be observed that for rough surfaces there is a greater possibility for large angles between the reactions and the n-direction than for smoother surfaces. Thus a friction coefficient measures the roughness of a pair of mating surfaces and incorporates a geometric property of these mating contours. It is meaningless to speak of a coefficient of friction for a single surface.

The direction of the resultant R in Fig. 66b measured from the direction of N is specified by $\tan \alpha = F/N$. When the friction force reaches its limiting static value, the angle α reaches a maximum value ϕ_s. Thus

$$\tan \phi_s = f_s.$$

When slipping occurs, the angle α will have a value ϕ_k corresponding to the kinetic friction force. In like manner

$$\tan \phi_k = f_k.$$

It is customary to write merely

$$\tan \phi = f, \tag{42}$$

where application to the limiting static case or to the kinetic case is inferred from the problem at hand. The angle ϕ_s is known as the *angle of static friction*, and the angle ϕ_k is called the *angle of kinetic friction.* This friction angle ϕ for each case clearly defines the limiting position of the total reaction R between two contacting surfaces. If motion is impending, R must be one element of a right circular cone of vertex angle $2\phi_s$, as shown in Fig. 67. If motion is not impending, R will be within the cone. This cone of vertex angle $2\phi_s$ is known as the *cone of static friction* and represents the locus of possible positions for the reaction R at impending motion. If motion occurs the angle of kinetic friction applies, and the reaction must lie on the surface of a slightly smaller cone of vertex angle $2\phi_k$. This cone is the cone of *kinetic friction.*

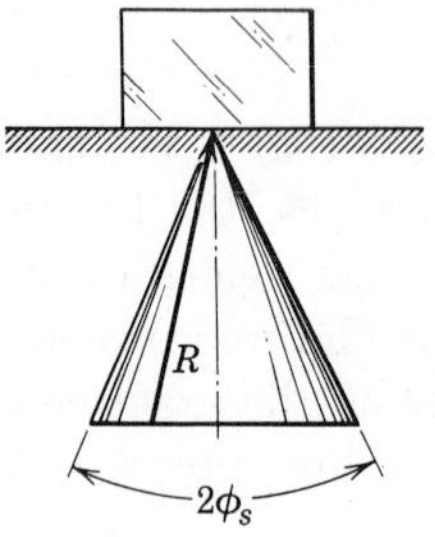

FIG. 67

Further experiment shows that the friction force is independent of the area of contact. This is true as long as the pressure is not great. For high pressures the surface characteristics are changed and the frictional coefficient increases.

There are three types of problems in dry friction commonly encountered in mechanics. In the *first* type the condition of impending motion is to be investigated. It will be clear from the wording of the problem that the requirement of limiting static friction should be used. In the *second* type of problem impending motion need not exist, and therefore the friction force may be smaller than that given by Eq. 41 with the static coefficient. In this event the friction force will be determined only by the equations of equilibrium. In such a problem it may be asked whether or not the existing friction is sufficient to maintain the body at rest. To answer the question equilibrium may be assumed, and the corresponding friction force necessary to maintain this state can be calculated from the equations of equilibrium. This friction force may then be compared with the maximum static friction which the surfaces can support as calculated from Eq. 41 with $f = f_s$. If F is less than that given by Eq. 41, it follows that the assumed friction force can be supported and therefore the body is at rest. If the calculated value of F is greater than the limiting value, it follows that the given surfaces cannot support that much friction force, and therefore motion exists and the friction becomes kinetic. The *third* type of problem involves relative motion between the contacting surfaces, and here the kinetic coefficient of friction applies. For this case Eq. 41 with $f = f_k$ will always give the kinetic friction force directly.

The foregoing discussion applies to all dry contacting surfaces and, to a limited extent, to moving surfaces which are partially lubricated. Some typical values of the coefficients of friction are given in Table D2, Appendix D. These values are only approximate and are subject to considerable variation, depending on the exact conditions prevailing. They may be used, however, as typical examples of the magnitudes of frictional effects. When a reliable calculation involving friction is required, it is often desirable to determine the appropriate friction coefficient by experiment wherein the surface conditions of the problem are duplicated as closely as possible.

SAMPLE PROBLEMS

480. Determine the range of values which the weight W may have so that the 100 lb. block shown in the figure will neither start moving up the plane nor slip down the plane. The coefficient of static friction for the contact surfaces is 0.30.

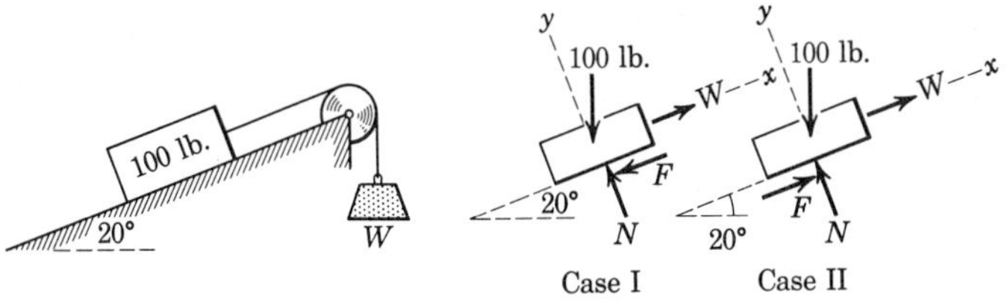

PROB. 480

Solution. The maximum value of W will be given by the requirement for motion impending up the plane. The friction force on the block therefore acts down the plane as shown in the free-body diagram of the block for Case I in the figure. Applying the equations of equilibrium gives

$[\Sigma F_y = 0]$ $\quad N - 100 \cos 20° = 0, \quad N = 94$ lb.,

$[F = fN]$ $\quad F = 0.30 \times 94.0 = 28.2$ lb.,

$[\Sigma F_x = 0]$ $\quad W - 28.2 - 100 \sin 20° = 0, \quad W = 62.4$ lb. *Ans.*

The minimum value of W is determined when motion is impending down the plane. The friction force on the block will act up the plane to oppose the tendency to move as shown in the free-body diagram for Case II. Equilibrium in the x-direction requires

$[\Sigma F_x = 0]$ $\quad W + 28.2 - 100 \sin 20° = 0, \quad W = 6.0$ lb. *Ans.*

Thus W may have any value from 6.0 lb. to 62.4 lb., and the block will remain at rest.

481. Determine the amount and direction of the friction force acting on the 100 lb. block shown if, first, $P = 50$ lb., and, second, $P = 10$ lb. The coefficient of static friction is 0.20, and the coefficient of kinetic friction is 0.17.

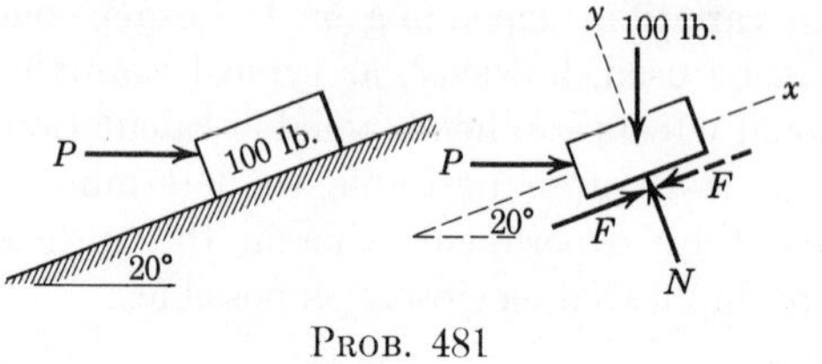

PROB. 481

Solution. There is no way of telling from the statement of the problem whether the block is or is not on the verge of slipping or whether it is in motion at the position shown. It is therefore necessary to make an assumption. Assume the friction force to be up the plane, as shown by the solid arrow, and the block to be in equilibrium. A balance of forces in both x- and y-directions gives

$[\Sigma F_x = 0]$ $\quad P \cos 20° + F - 100 \sin 20° = 0,$

$[\Sigma F_y = 0]$ $\quad N - P \sin 20° - 100 \cos 20° = 0.$

Case I. $P = 50$ lb.

Substitution into the first of the two equations gives

$$F = -12.8 \text{ lb.}$$

The negative sign means that, *if* the block is in equilibrium, the friction force acting on it is in the direction opposite to that assumed and therefore is down the plane as represented by the dotted arrow. Conclusion on the magnitude of F cannot be reached, however, until it is verified that the surfaces are capable of supporting 12.8 lb. of friction force. This may be done by substituting P = 50 lb. into the second equation, which gives

$$N = 111.1 \text{ lb.}$$

The maximum static friction force which the surfaces can support is then

$[F = fN]$ $$F = 0.20 \times 111.1 = 22.2 \text{ lb.}$$

Since this force is greater than that required for equilibrium, it follows that the assumption of equilibrium was correct. The answer is, then,

$$F = 12.8 \text{ lb. down the plane.}$$ *Ans.*

Case II. $P = 10$ lb.

Substitution into the two equilibrium equations gives

$$F = 24.8 \text{ lb.,} \qquad N = 97.4 \text{ lb.}$$

But the maximum possible static friction force is

$[F = fN]$ $$F = 0.20 \times 97.4 = 19.5 \text{ lb.}$$

It follows that 24.8 lb. of friction cannot be supported. Therefore equilibrium cannot exist, and the correct value of the friction force is obtained by using the kinetic coefficient of friction accompanying the motion down the plane. Thus the answer is

$[F = fN]$ $$F = 0.17 \times 97.4 = 16.6 \text{ lb. up the plane.}$$ *Ans.*

It should be noted that, even though ΣF_x is no longer equal to zero, equilibrium does exist in the y-direction so that $\Sigma F_y = 0$.

482. A homogeneous rectangular block of weight W rests on a horizontal plane and is subjected to the horizontal force P as shown. If the coefficient of friction is f, determine the greatest value which h may have so that the block will slide without tipping.

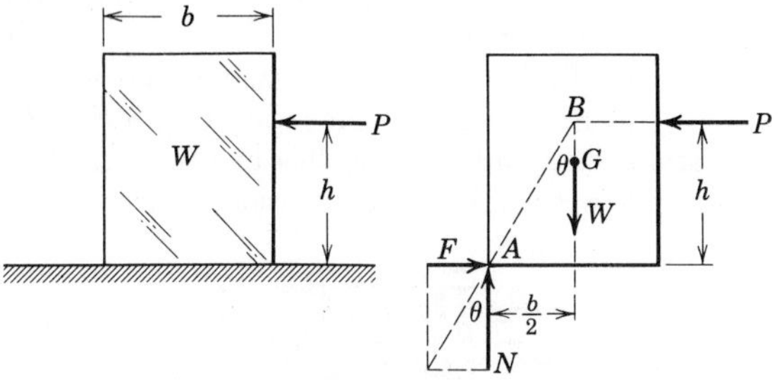

PROB. 482

Solution. If the block is on the verge of tipping, the entire reaction between the plane and the block will be at A. The free-body diagram of the block for this condition is shown in the right side of the figure. If P is sufficient to cause slipping, the friction force is the limiting value fN, and the angle θ becomes $\theta = \tan^{-1} f$. The resultant of F and N passes through a point B through which P must also pass since three coplanar forces in equilibrium are concurrent. Hence from the geometry of the block

$$\tan\theta = f = \frac{b/2}{h}, \qquad h = \frac{b}{2f}. \qquad \textit{Ans.}$$

If h were greater than this value, moment equilibrium about A would not be satisfied. For h less than $b/2f$ the resultant of F and N would be concurrent with P and W at a point below B. Thus this resultant would act not at A but at some point to the right of A.

PROBLEMS

483. Determine the maximum angle θ which an inclined plane may have with the horizontal and not cause a block resting upon it to slide down. The coefficient of static friction is f. (This angle is known as the *angle of repose.*)

Ans. $\theta = \tan^{-1} f$

484. Prove whether the block is in equilibrium or whether it is sliding. Find the friction force F acting on the block. *Ans.* Slides, $F = 2.11$ lb.

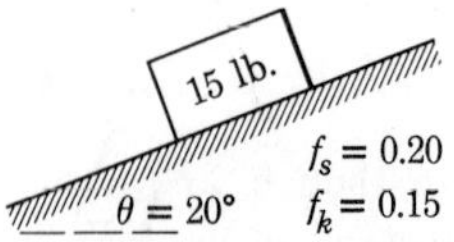

PROB. 484

485. If the angle θ in Prob. 484 is reduced to 10 deg. and the block is released with an initial velocity up the plane, (*a*) determine what it will do and the friction force F acting on it. (*b*) If it is given an initial start down the plane, determine its action and the friction force.

Ans. (*a*) Block will stop and remain at rest with $F = 2.60$ lb., (*b*) Block will continue to move with $F = 2.21$ lb.

486. The steel straps shown are held together by two bolts which have been tightened with a torque wrench so that the tension in each bolt is 2000 lb. If

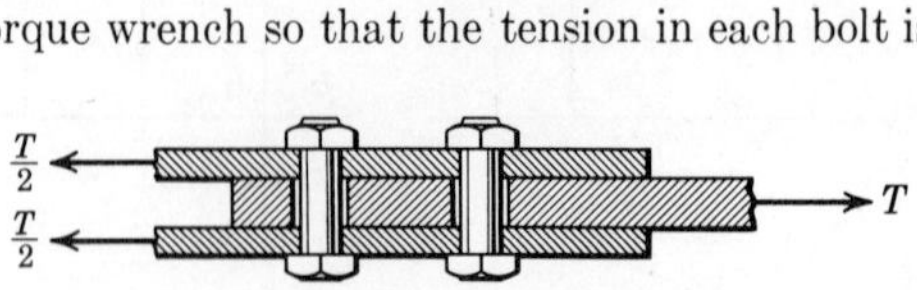

PROB. 486

the holes in the center strap were drilled slightly oversized, find the tension T which can be supported before the joint slips enough to induce shear in the bolts. Take the coefficient of friction to be 0.2. *Ans.* $T = 1600$ lb.

487. Find the total horizontal force S (shear) which the two anchor bolts must exert on the structure to prevent slipping if $f = 0.3$.

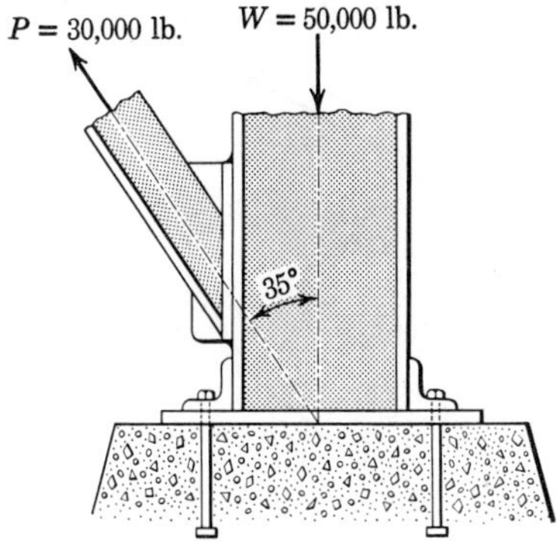

PROB. 487

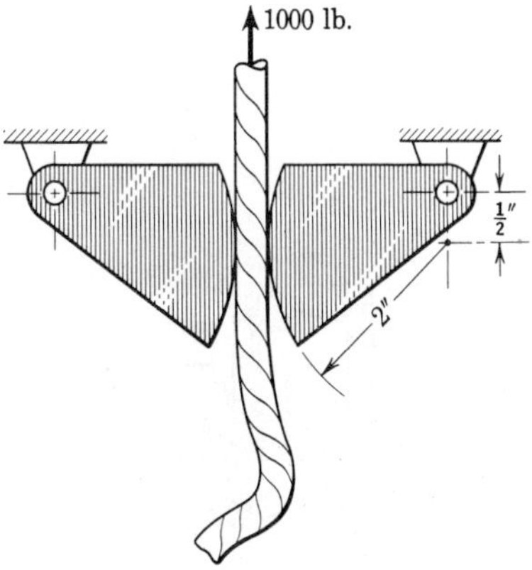

PROB. 488

488. In the figure is shown a device which secures a rope or cable under tension by reason of large friction forces developed. For the position shown determine the total reaction R on the cam bearing. The coefficient of friction is 0.30.

Ans. $R = 2060$ lb.

489. Determine the minimum coefficient of friction f between the wheel and the obstruction that will permit the wheel to roll over the obstruction without slipping if the applied torque M is sufficiently great.

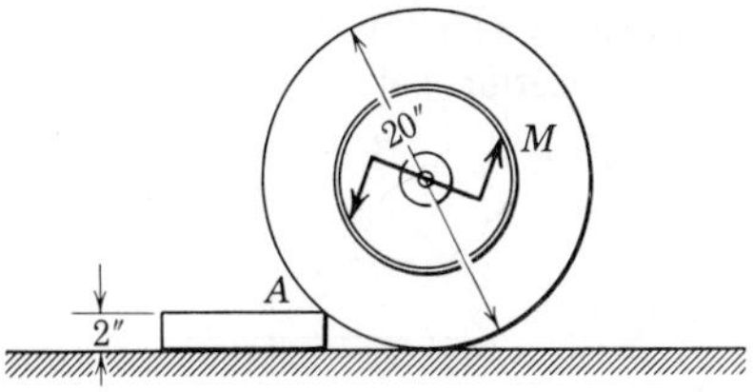

PROB. 489

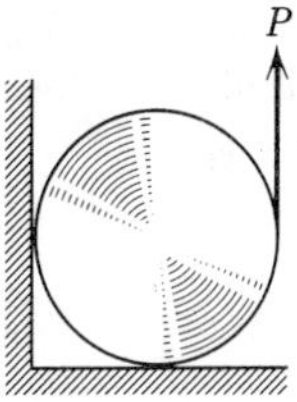

PROB. 490

490. Determine the maximum force P in terms of the weight W of the cylinder that can be applied without causing it to rotate. The coefficient of friction for both pairs of contacting surfaces is 0.5. Solve by using only one equation, a moment equation, which eliminates all forces except P and W. Determine the moment center and moment arms graphically.

Ans. $P = \frac{3}{8}W$

491. Determine the torque M which the cone clutch shown can transmit when the engaging spring exerts a compressive force R and the force P on the disengaging collar is equal to zero. Assume that the forces between the clutch surfaces act at the mean diameter d and that after engagement any friction force in the direction of a cone element is negligible. The coefficient of friction between the cone surfaces is f.

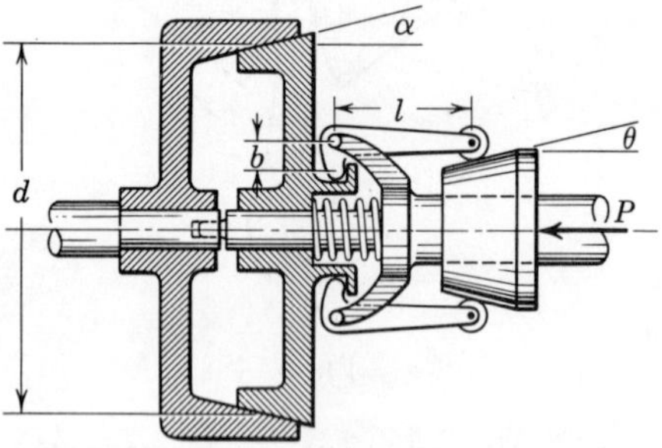

PROB. 491

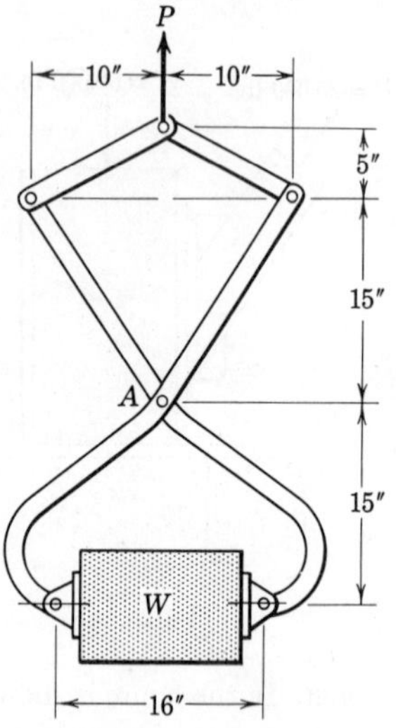

PROB. 492

492. For the friction tongs shown determine the minimum coefficient of friction f which can exist between the block and the tongs without the block slipping. *Ans.* $f = 0.31$

493. A uniform block of weight W is at rest on an incline θ. Determine the maximum force P which can be applied to the block in the direction shown before slipping begins. The coefficient of friction between the block and the incline is f. *Ans.* $P = W\sqrt{f^2 \cos^2 \theta - \sin^2 \theta}$, $f > \tan \theta$

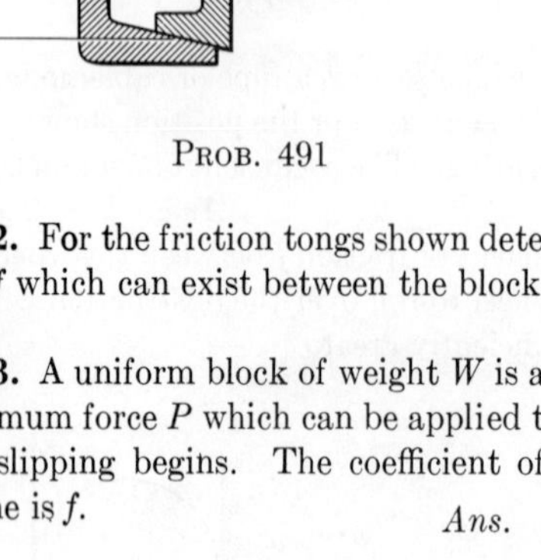

PROB. 493

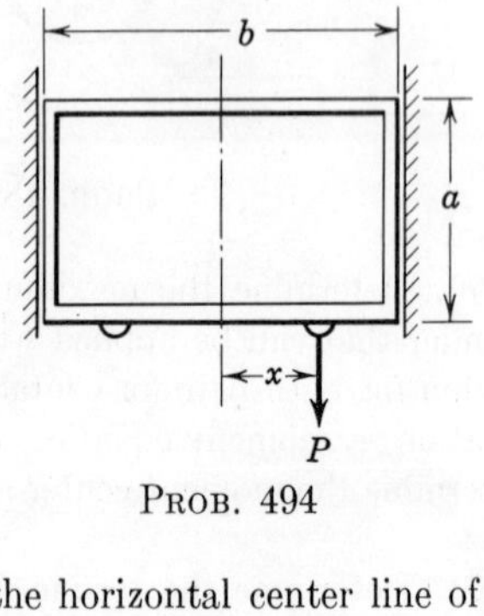

PROB. 494

494. Find the maximum distance x from the horizontal center line of the drawer at which the force P may be applied and still open the drawer without binding at the corners. Neglect friction on the bottom of the drawer and take the coefficient of friction at the corners to be f.

495. The wheel shown will roll to the left when the angle α of the cord is small. When α is large the wheel rolls to the right. Determine by inspection from the geometry of the free-body diagram the angle α for which the wheel will not roll in either direction. If the coefficient of friction is f and the weight of the wheel is W, calculate the value of P for which the wheel will slip for the critical value of α.

$$Ans. \quad \alpha = \cos^{-1}\frac{r_1}{r_2}, \quad P = \frac{fr_2W}{r_1 + f\sqrt{r_2^2 - r_1^2}}$$

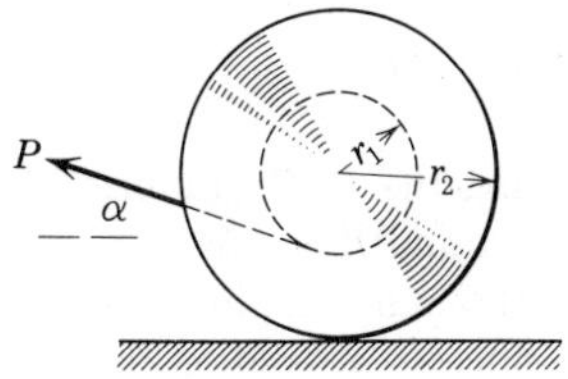

PROB. 495

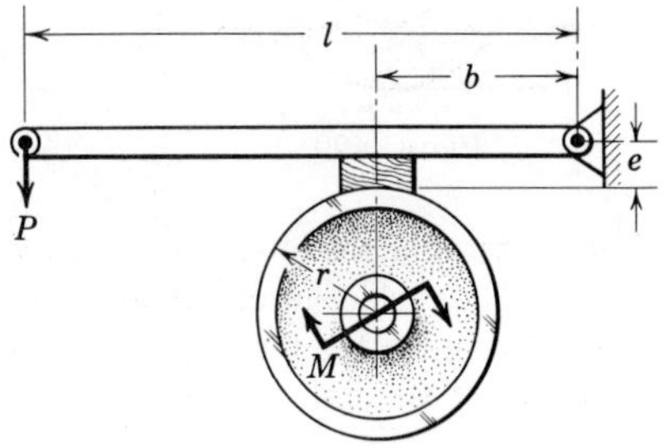

PROB. 496

496. The single-lever block brake shown prevents rotation of the flywheel under an applied clockwise torque M. (a) Find the required force P if the coefficient of friction is f. (b) How much force is required if $b = fe$?

497. The brake block and flywheel of Prob. 496 are replaced by a V-grooved pulley and matching V-shaped brake block of angle α as shown in the figure.

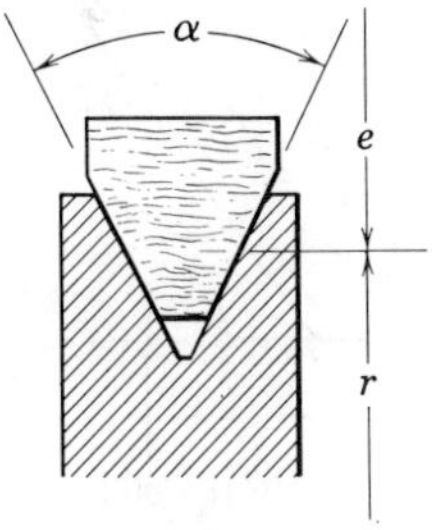

PROB. 497

PROB. 498

The distance e is measured to the mean radius r of the pulley groove. (a) Determine the force P necessary to brake the applied clockwise torque M. (b) For what angle α will the brake be self-locking for given values of b, f, and e?

$$Ans. \quad (a)\ P = \frac{M}{r}\,\frac{b \sin\frac{\alpha}{2} - fe}{fl}, \quad (b)\ \alpha = 2\sin^{-1}\frac{fe}{b}, \quad b > fe$$

498. Determine the torque M required to spin the wheel of weight W in its position against the wall as shown. The coefficient of friction is f.

499. Determine the force P required to rotate the 100 lb. reel of telephone wire which rests on its hubs and bears against a vertical wall. The coefficient of friction for each pair of contacting surfaces is 0.5. *Ans.* $P = 30.8$ lb.

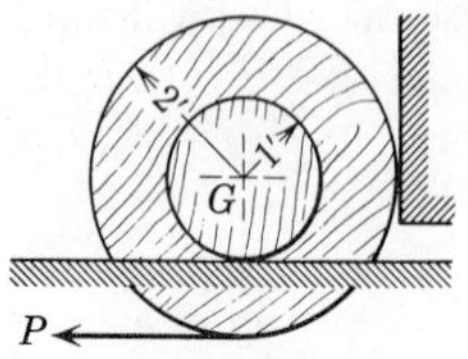

PROB. 499

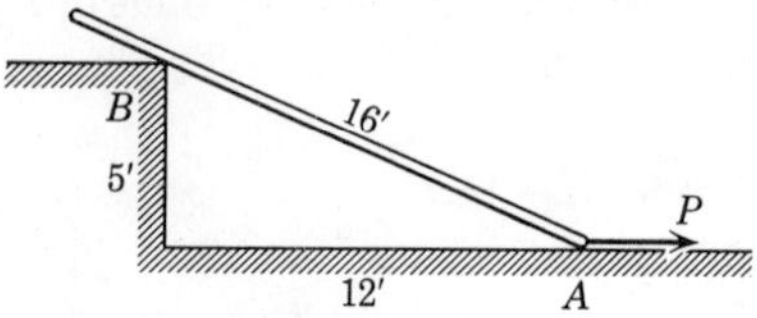

PROB. 500

500. Determine the force P required to start moving the 16 ft. uniform 300 lb. pole. The coefficient of friction at each contact A and B is 0.5.

501. Determine the minimum angle θ at which the uniform plank may be placed against the wall and still not slip. The coefficient of friction for each end is f.

Ans. $\theta = \tan^{-1}\dfrac{1 - f^2}{2f}$

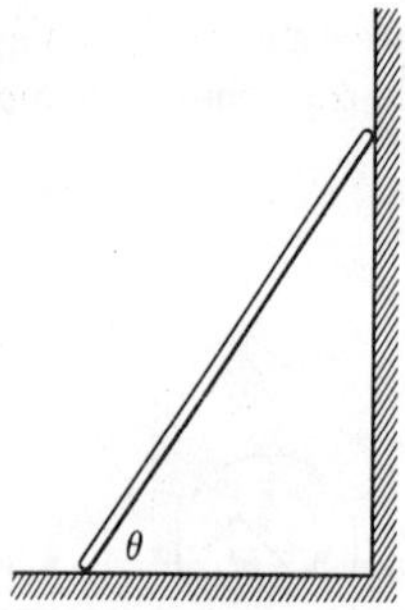

PROB. 501

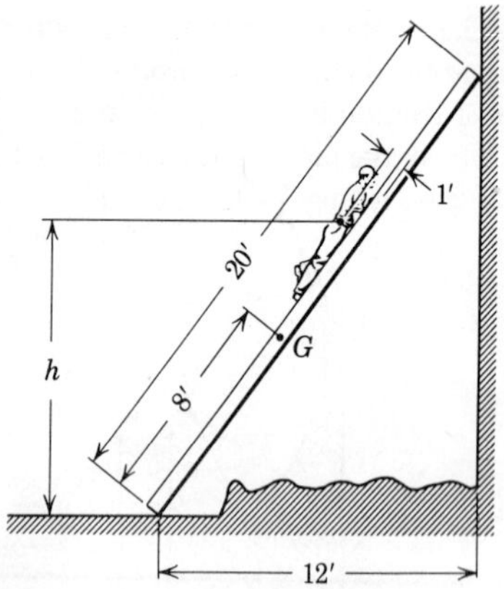

PROB. 502

502. The center of gravity of the 50 lb. ladder which is 20 ft. long is at G. The coefficient of friction for the upper end of the ladder and the wall is 0.3, and that for the bottom and the ground is 0.4. Determine the maximum safe height h which a 150 lb. man may climb.

503. An I-beam of weight W is supported by two fixed horizontal rails as shown. Compute the applied load P which is just sufficient to cause the beam to slip and determine the corresponding friction force at A as slipping begins. The coefficient of friction between the beam and the rails is f.

Ans. $P = \dfrac{fWb}{2(a + b)}$, $F_A = \dfrac{fWa}{2(a + b)}$

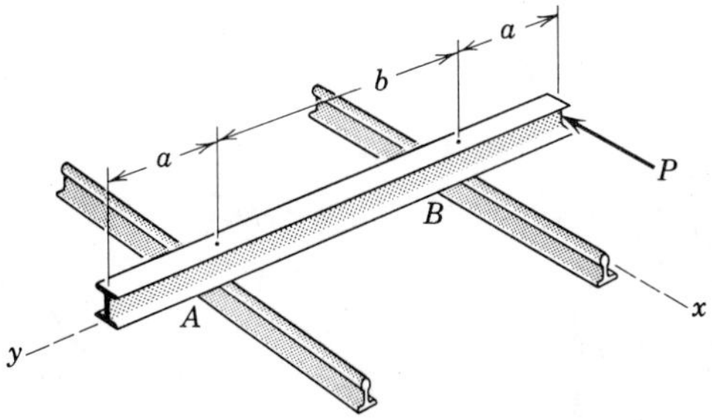

PROB. 503

504. Shaft A drives shaft B at constant speed by means of the attached wheel and friction disk. The center lines of the two shafts intersect at right angles. Constant pressure between the friction surfaces is maintained by the coil spring which bears against the underside of the disk. In assembly the spring is compressed 3/8 in. If the coefficient of friction is 0.6 and a torque of 10 lb. ft. is to be maintained on shaft A, determine the necessary spring constant k to prevent slipping and the total forces on the bearings C and D.

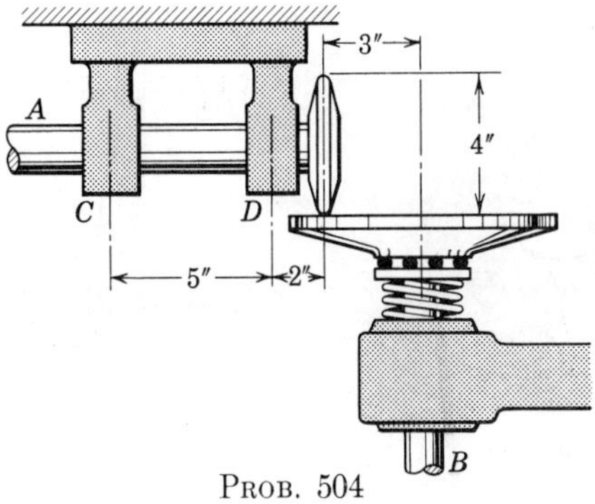

PROB. 504

505. Determine the torque M which the engine must supply to the rear axle of the 3000 lb. car with center of gravity at G to roll it over the curbing from a rest position. What is the necessary coefficient of friction f if the rear wheels do not slip? *Ans.* $M = 22{,}700$ lb. in., $f = 1.034$

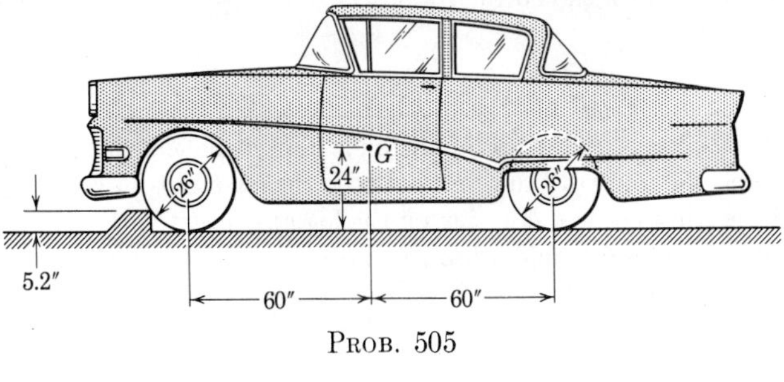

PROB. 505

506. A torque of 9 lb. ft. is required to turn the 80 lb. shaft in the V-block shown. Determine the coefficient of friction between the shaft and the block.

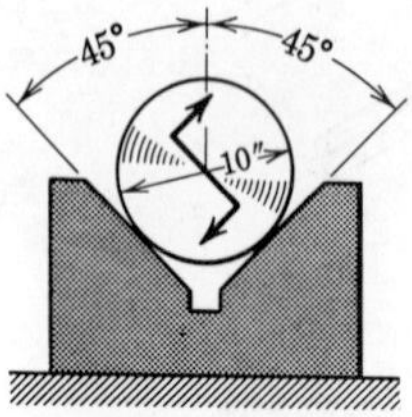

Prob. 506

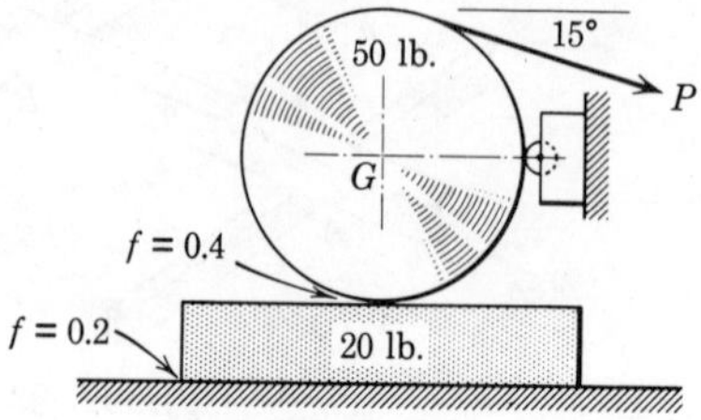

Prob. 507

507. Determine the force P necessary to rotate the 50 lb. cylinder. The coefficient of friction between the cylinder and the 20 lb. block is 0.4 and that between the block and the plane is 0.2. *Ans.* $P = 14.76$ lb.

508. The three identical rollers are stacked as shown. If the friction coefficient is the same for all pairs of surfaces, find the minimum value of f so that the rollers will not slip.

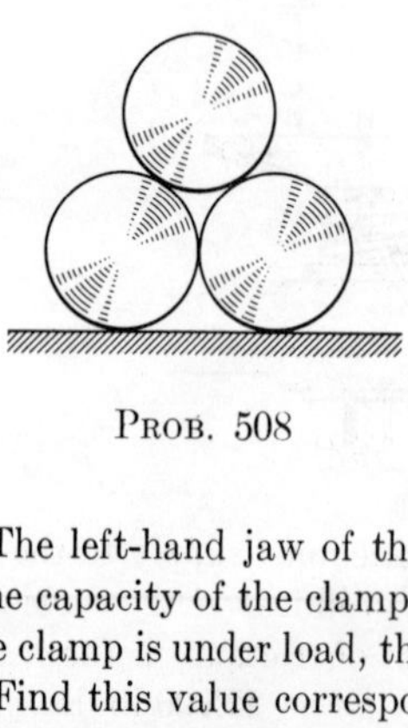

Prob. 508

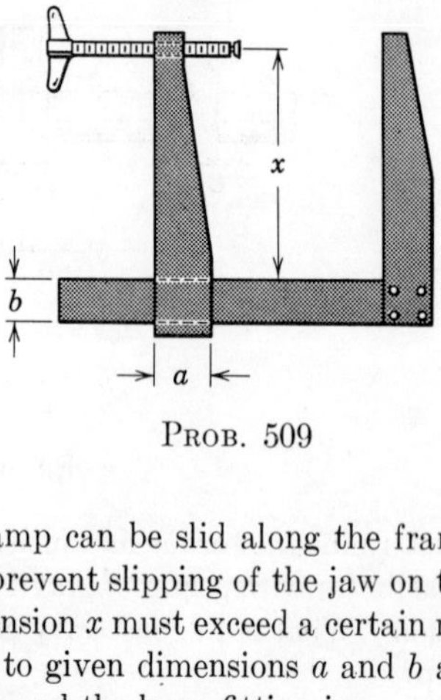

Prob. 509

509. The left-hand jaw of the C-clamp can be slid along the frame to increase the capacity of the clamp. To prevent slipping of the jaw on the frame when the clamp is under load, the dimension x must exceed a certain minimum value. Find this value corresponding to given dimensions a and b and a coefficient of friction f between the frame and the loose-fitting jaw.

$$\textit{Ans.} \quad x = \frac{a - bf}{2f}$$

510. Find the force P normal to the blade which the bulldozer must exert on the 3000 lb. log to roll it up the incline. The coefficient of friction between the blade and the log is 0.4 and that between the log and the ground is also 0.4. Also find the friction force F acting on the log at contact with the ground. At what angle of slope θ would slipping at the blade and at the ground occur simultaneously?

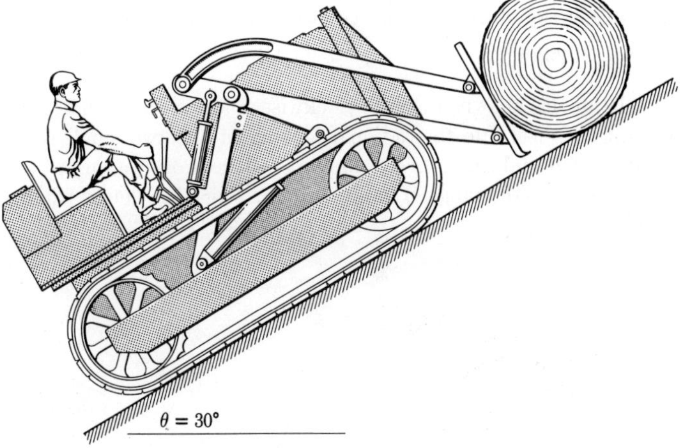

PROB. 510

511. A stepladder with hinge at A is placed with one leg B on a horizontal surface for which $f = 0.20$ and the other leg C on a parallel surface for which $f = 0.60$. Determine the friction force F_B which acts at B as a vertical load P is applied half way up the ladder. The weight of the stepladder is negligible compared with P.

Ans. $F_B = \dfrac{P}{4\sqrt{3}}$

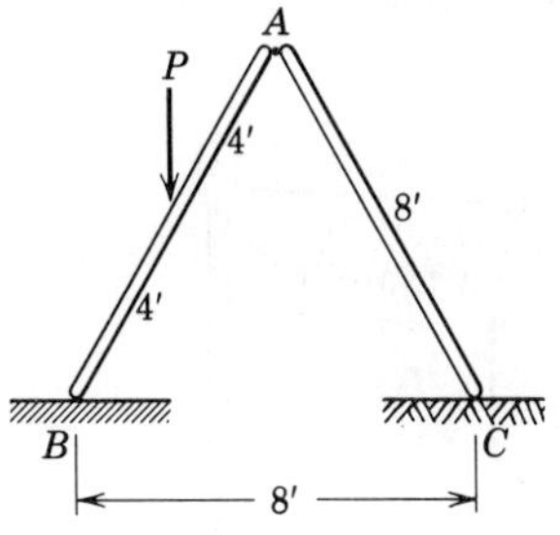

PROB. 511

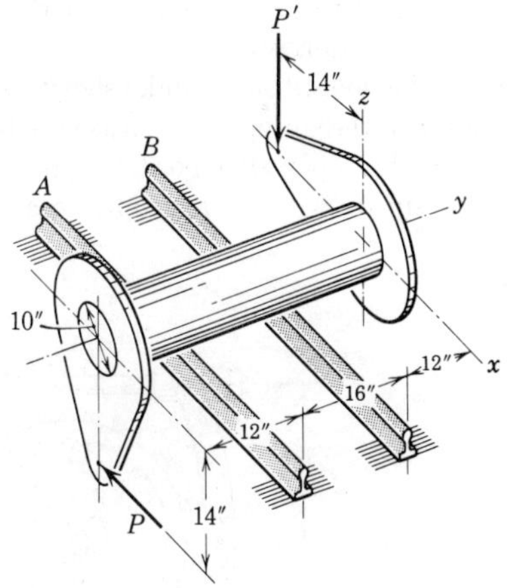

PROB. 512

512. Two forces P and P' are applied gradually to the levers secured to the ends of the shaft as shown. During their application the ratio of P to P' is maintained at the value which prevents rolling of the assembly on the rails.

The assembly weighs 80 lb. with center of gravity midway between the rails. If the coefficient of static friction at both rails is 0.3, determine the value of P at which slipping first occurs. For this condition find the friction force at rail B.

513. The device shown prevents clockwise rotation in the horizontal plane of the central wheel due to frictional locking of the two small rollers. For given values of R and r and for a common coefficient of friction f at all contact surfaces, determine the range of values of d for which the device will operate as described.

Ans. $d_{min.} = \dfrac{2r + (1 - f^2)R}{1 + f^2}$, $d_{max.} = 2r + R$

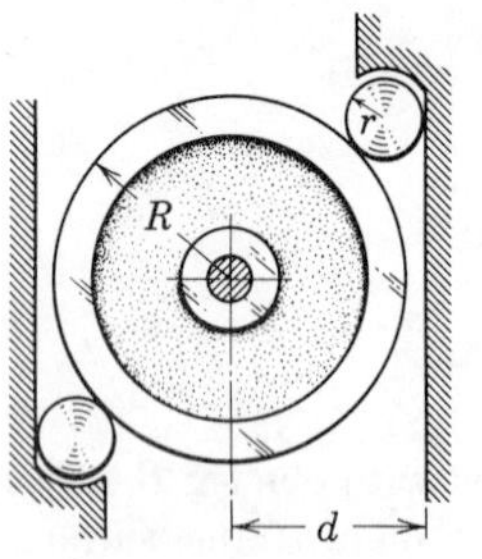

PROB. 513

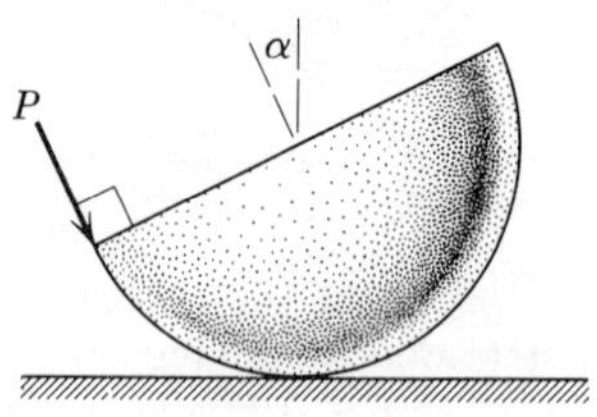

PROB. 514

*** 514.** A hemispherical body of uniform density is subjected to a force P at the rim as shown. If P is increased slowly and is always kept normal to the rim surface, determine the angle of tilt α at which slipping occurs. The coefficient of friction is 0.3. *Ans.* $\alpha = 41°$ (graphical solution)

*** 515.** The double block brake shown is applied to the flywheel by means of the action of the spring. To release the brake a force P is applied to the control lever. In the operating position with $P = 0$ the spring is compressed 1 in. Select a spring with an appropriate constant k which will provide sufficient

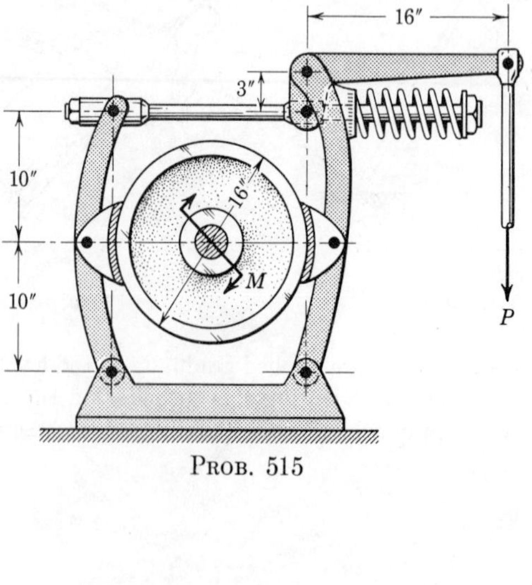

PROB. 515

force to brake the flywheel under the torque $M = 60$ lb. ft. if the coefficient of friction for both brake shoes is $f = 0.2$. Neglect the dimensions of the brake shoes. *Ans.* $k = 113$ lb./in.

* **516.** In the figure are shown the elements of a rolling mill. Determine the maximum thickness b which the slab may have and still enter the rolls by means of the friction between the slab and the rolls. Assume that the coefficient of friction is f and that $b - a$ is small compared with d. *Ans.* $b = a + \dfrac{f^2d}{2}$

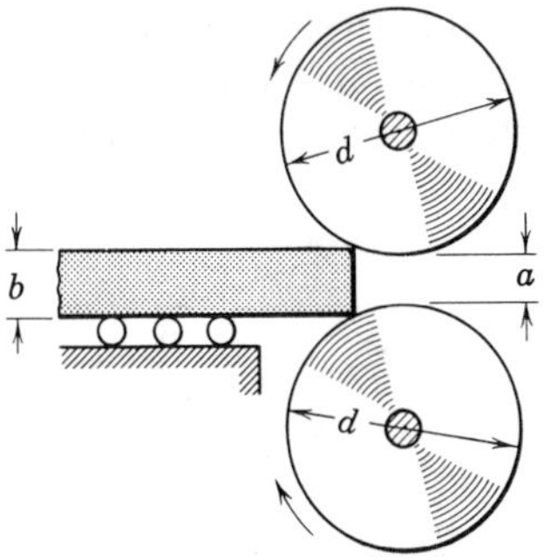

PROB. 516

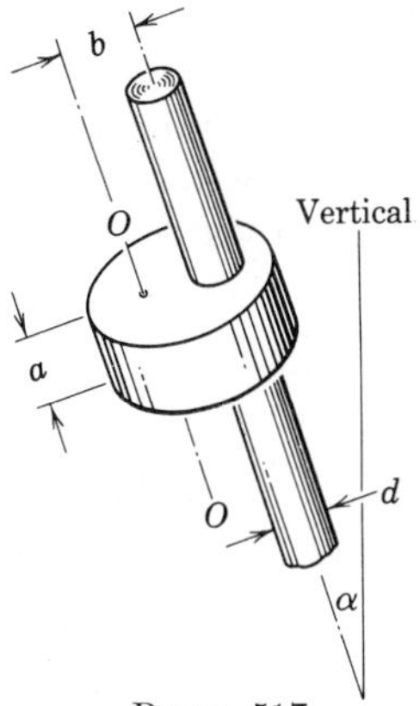

PROB. 517

* **517.** The collar has a center of gravity on line O–O midway between the two parallel surfaces and fits loosely on the shaft. As the angle α is decreased, the collar will begin to slide down the shaft. Find the value of α at which slipping begins for a given coefficient of friction f.

Ans. $\alpha = \tan^{-1} \dfrac{a - 2bf}{f^2d}$ provided $b < \dfrac{a}{2f}$

48. Wedges. A wedge is one of the simplest of machines and is used as a means of producing small adjustments in the position of a body or as a means of applying large forces. Wedges depend upon friction for their action. When the sliding of a wedge is impending, the resultant force on each surface of the wedge will be inclined from the normal to the surface an amount equal to the friction angle. The component of the resultant along the surface is the friction force which is always in the direction to oppose the motion of the wedge.

After drawing the necessary free-body diagram, solution of a wedge problem is usually facilitated by constructing the equilibrium polygon of forces which is normally a triangle. This approach lends itself to a graphical solution, and errors inherent in graphical construction are well within those due to the uncertainty of the friction coefficients. The analysis of wedges is best shown by the solution of a sample problem.

SAMPLE PROBLEM

518. Determine the force P applied to the 10 deg. wedge necessary to start the 1000 lb. block upward. The coefficient of static friction between all surfaces is 0.30, and the weight of the wedge is negligible.

Graphical Solution. The free-body diagrams of the block and wedge are shown in the figure. The reactions R_1, R_2, and R_3 are all inclined with their normals an amount equal to the friction angle ϕ, since slipping occurs simultaneously at both surfaces, and lean in a direction to oppose the impending motion.

The equilibrium of the block is established by first laying off the 1000 lb. force to scale, as shown in the upper right part of the figure. Next the known directions of the reactions R_2 and R_3 are used to determine point A, which then establishes the magnitudes of R_2 and R_3. A similar equilibrium triangle for the

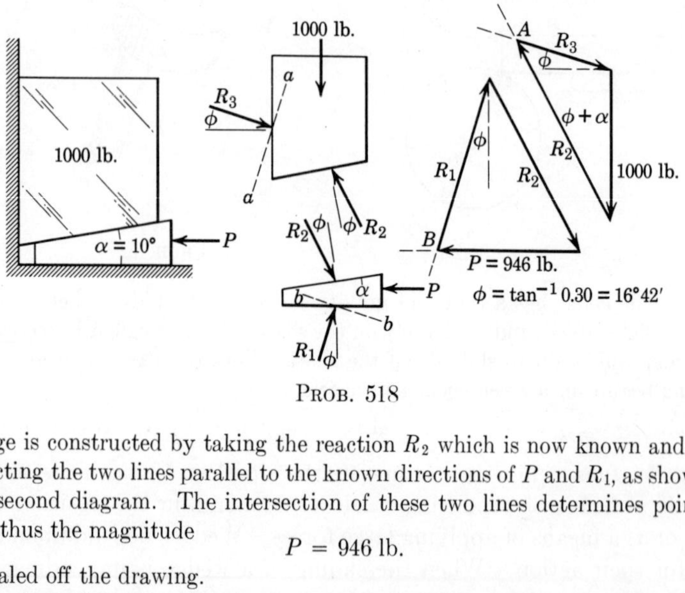

PROB. 518

wedge is constructed by taking the reaction R_2 which is now known and constructing the two lines parallel to the known directions of P and R_1, as shown in the second diagram. The intersection of these two lines determines point B, and thus the magnitude

$$P = 946 \text{ lb.} \qquad \textit{Ans.}$$

is scaled off the drawing.

Algebraic Solution. The simplest choice of axes for the necessary force summations is, in the case of the block, in the direction a–a normal to R_3, and for the wedge in the direction b–b normal to R_1. In this way a simultaneous solution of two equations is avoided. The angle between R_2 and the a-direction amounts to $2\phi + \alpha = 43° 24'$. Thus for the block

$$[\Sigma F_a = 0] \qquad 1000 \cos (16° 42') - R_2 \cos (43° 24') = 0,$$

$$R_2 = 1320 \text{ lb.}$$

For the wedge the angle between R_2 and the b-direction is $\pi/2 - (2\phi + \alpha) = 46° 36'$. Equilibrium then requires that

$$[\Sigma F_b = 0] \qquad 1320 \cos (46° 36') - P \cos (16° 42') = 0,$$

$$P = 946 \text{ lb.} \qquad \textit{Ans.}$$

If the given coefficients of friction between mating surfaces were not all alike, the same procedure would be employed and the modified friction angles would be used.

PROBLEMS

519. A wedge of angle α is used to split wood as shown. If the coefficient of friction between the wedge and the wood is f, determine the maximum angle α for which the wedge will be self-locking. *Ans.* $\alpha = 2 \tan^{-1} f$

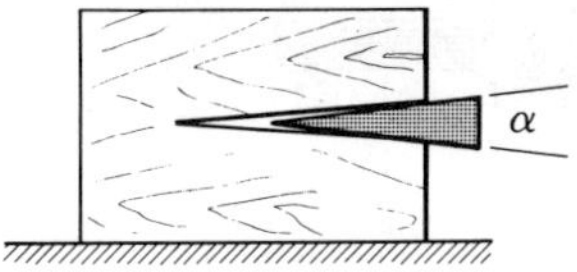

PROB. 519

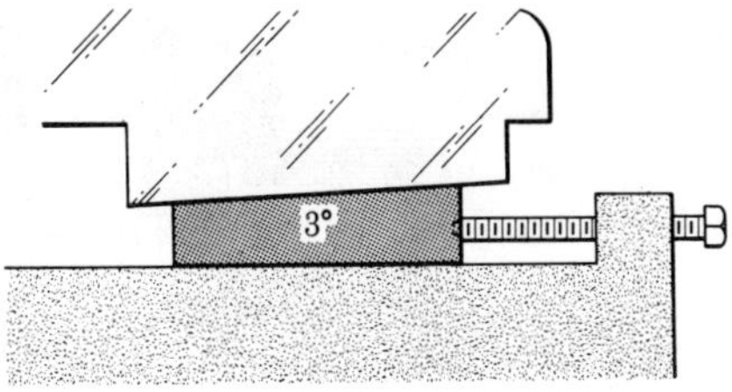

PROB. 520

520. The accurate alignment of a heavy-duty engine on its bed is accomplished by a screw-adjusted wedge with a 3 deg. taper. Determine the horizontal thrust P in the adjusting screw necessary to raise the mounting if the wedge supports ¼ of the total engine weight of 12,000 lb. The coefficient of friction for all surfaces is 0.2. *Ans.* $P = 1365$ lb.

521. In adjusting the position of a vertical column under a load of 5000 lb., two 5 deg. wedges are used as shown. Determine the force P necessary to raise the load if the coefficient of friction for all surfaces is 0.4. *Ans.* $P = 4520$ lb.

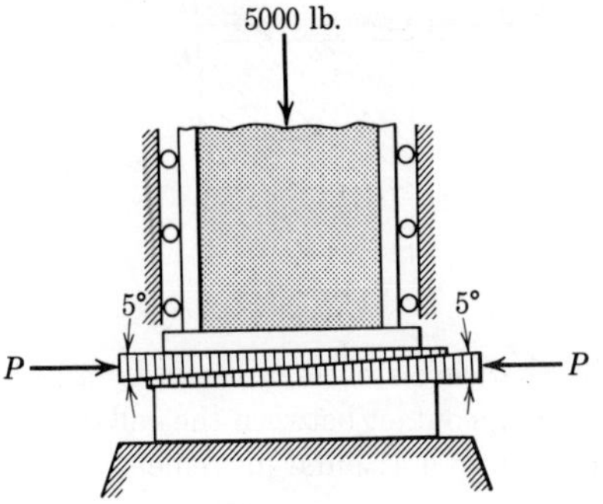

PROB. 521

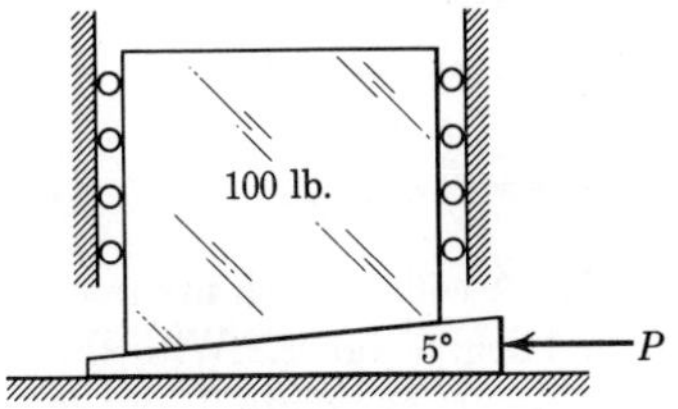

PROB. 522

522. By neglecting friction in the rollers, find (*a*) the force P necessary to start the wedge moving under the weight and (*b*) the horizontal force P' required to pull the wedge from under the block. The coefficient of friction between the wedge and the weight is 0.25, and that between the wedge and the horizontal surface is 0.20.

523. Two shafts connected by a flat 5 deg. tapered cotter, as shown by the two views in the figure, are under a constant tension T of 200 lb. Find the force

P required to move the cotter and take up any slack in the joint. The coefficient of friction is 0.20. Neglect horizontal friction between the shafts.

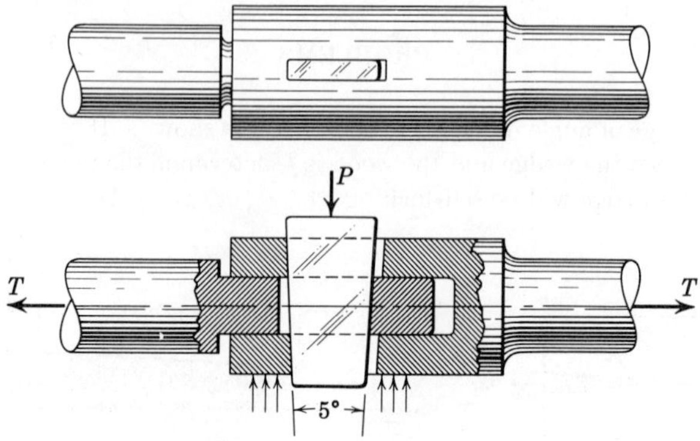

PROB. 523

524. A 5 deg. wedge is used to position the 3500 lb. milling machine shown. If the center of gravity of the machine is at *G* and the coefficient of friction of both wedge surfaces is 0.30, find the force *P* required to withdraw the wedge. The angle through which the machine is tipped is extremely small.

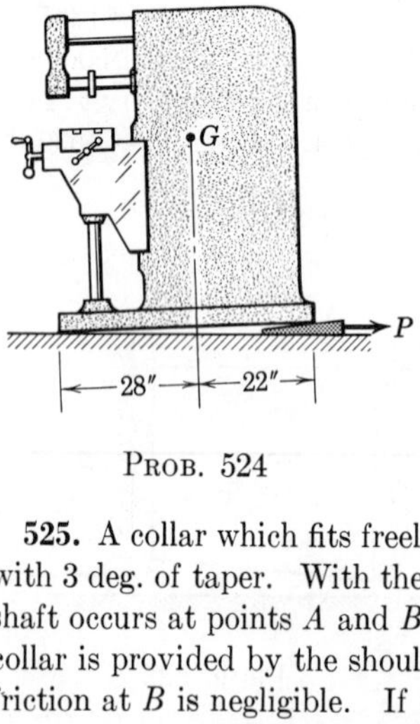

PROB. 524

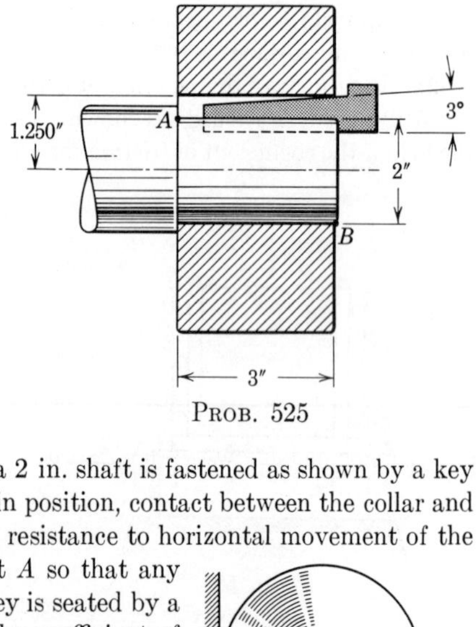

PROB. 525

525. A collar which fits freely on a 2 in. shaft is fastened as shown by a key with 3 deg. of taper. With the key in position, contact between the collar and shaft occurs at points *A* and *B*. All resistance to horizontal movement of the collar is provided by the shoulder at *A* so that any friction at *B* is negligible. If the key is seated by a horizontal force *P* of 400 lb. and the coefficient of friction is 0.3, determine the total reaction *R* at *A* while *P* is applied. *Ans.* $R = 218$ lb.

526. A 5 deg. wedge is used to lift the 1000 lb. cylinder as shown. If the coefficient of friction is ¼ for all surfaces, determine the force *P* required to move the wedge. *Ans.* $P = 378$ lb.

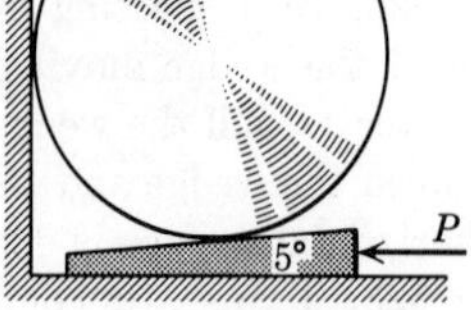

PROB. 526

* **527.** For the cone clutch of Prob. 491 determine the force P on the sliding collar required to disengage the clutch if (*a*) $f < \tan \alpha$ and (*b*) $f > \tan \alpha$. Assume that no torque is being transmitted so that all friction forces are in the direction of cone elements. (*Hint:* When $f > \tan \alpha$ the clutch surfaces are wedged together and a force P greater than that necessary to counterbalance R will be required. It may be assumed that the pressure normal to the cone surface is the same as when the clutch was initially wedged under the action of R alone.)

Ans. (*a*) $P = \frac{Rb}{l} \tan \theta$, (*b*) $P = \frac{Rb}{l}\left[1 + \frac{\sin(\phi - \alpha)}{\sin(\phi + \alpha)}\right] \tan \theta$, $\phi = \tan^{-1} f$

* **528.** The split disk shown has a hole with 2 deg. of taper and is held together by two bolts each of which has a negligible initial tension. A pin with

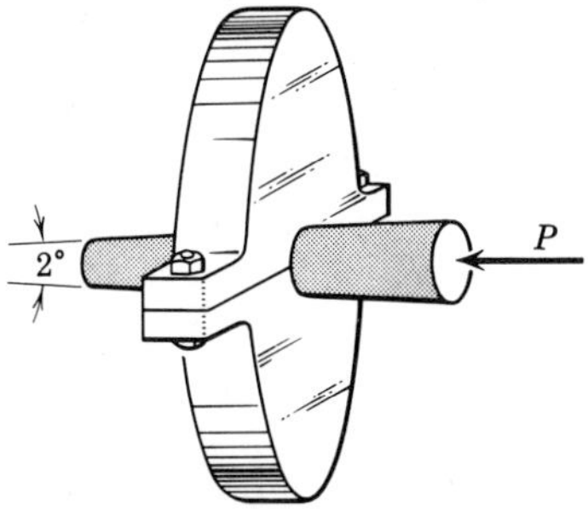

PROB. 528

mating taper is pressed into the hole with a force P of 1000 lb. If the coefficient of friction is 0.20, determine the tension T in each bolt (*a*) while P is acting and (*b*) after P has been removed. Assume that the pressure is constant over the surface of the hole and that its component normal to the surface remains unchanged upon removal of the load.

Ans. (*a*) $T = 728$ lb., (*b*) $T = 732$ lb.

49. Screws. Screws are used for fastenings and for transmitting power or motion, and in each case the friction developed in the threads is important. For transmitting power or motion the square thread is more efficient than the V-thread; the analysis which follows will be confined to the square thread.

Consider the square-threaded jack, Fig. 68, under the action of the axial load W and an applied moment $M = Pa$ about the axis of the screw. The force R exerted by the thread of the jack frame on a small representative portion of the thread of the screw is shown on the free-body diagram of the screw. Similar reactions exist on all segments of the screw thread where contact occurs with the thread of the base. If M is just sufficient to turn the screw, the thread of the screw will slide around and up on the fixed thread of the frame. The angle ϕ made by R with the normal to the thread will be the angle of friction, so that

$\tan \phi = f$. The moment of R about the vertical axis of the screw is $Rr \sin (\alpha + \phi)$, and the total moment due to all reactions on the screw

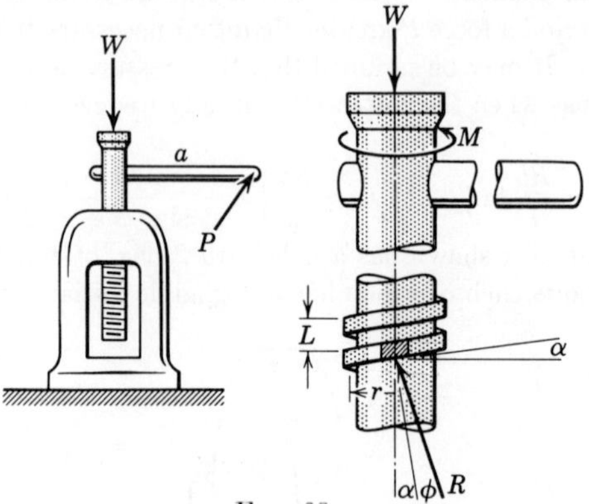

FIG. 68

threads is $\Sigma Rr \sin (\alpha + \phi)$. Since $r \sin (\alpha + \phi)$ appears in each term, it may be factored out. The moment equilibrium equation for the screw becomes

$$M = [r \sin (\alpha + \phi)]\Sigma R.$$

Equilibrium of forces in the axial direction further requires

$$W = \Sigma R \cos (\alpha + \phi) = [\cos (\alpha + \phi)]\Sigma R.$$

Dividing M by W gives

$$M = Wr \tan (\alpha + \phi), \tag{43}$$

where $\phi = \tan^{-1} f$. The angle α is determined from the lead L or advancement per revolution of the screw. Thus $\alpha = \tan^{-1} (L/2\pi r)$. This relation is easily seen by unwrapping the thread for one turn of the screw and forming the right triangle whose base is the mean circumference $2\pi r$ and whose altitude is the lead L.

Equation 43 gives the moment required to start the screw upward or to maintain upward movement, depending on whether the static or kinetic coefficient of friction is used. If the moment M is removed, the friction force changes direction so that ϕ is measured to the other side of the normal. Thus the screw will remain in place and be self-locking providing $\phi > \alpha$ and will be on the verge of unwinding if $\phi = \alpha$. A moment M must be applied in the direction opposite to that shown in Fig. 68 to lower the screw when $\phi > \alpha$ and is given by

$$M = Wr \tan (\phi - \alpha).$$

If $\phi < \alpha$ the screw will unwind by itself and would require a moment to keep it from unwinding equal to

$$M = Wr \tan (\alpha - \phi).$$

PROBLEMS

529. The link A, shown in section, is mounted loosely on the fixed shaft and is clamped between the faces of two ball thrust bearings by the nut B. The nut and shaft have a single square thread with a mean diameter of $1\frac{1}{2}$ in., and there are 4 threads per inch. The coefficient of friction for the threads and for

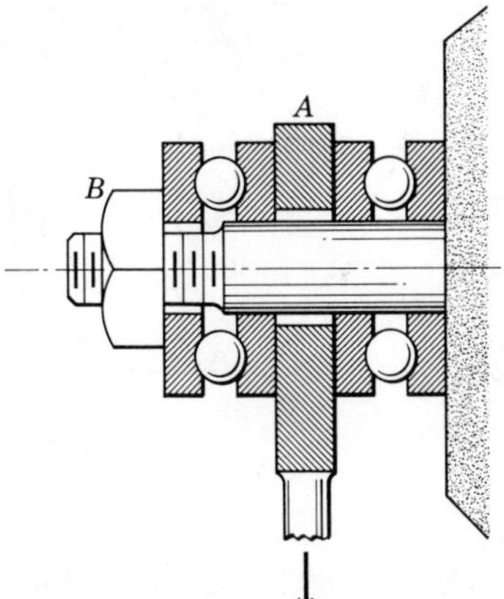

PROB. 529

the surfaces between the link and the bearings is 0.20. Determine the least torque M which must be applied to the nut in order to prevent any slipping between the link and the bearings under the action of the 1000 lb. load on the link. *Ans.* $M = 480$ lb. in.

530. The screw of the small press has a mean diameter of 2 in. and has a double square thread with a lead of 1 in. Determine the coefficient of friction f which exists in the threads if a torque of 50 lb. ft. on the handwheel produces a compressive force of 1200 lb. in the press. Neglect friction between the end of the screw and the clamping head at A. *Ans.* $f = 0.316$

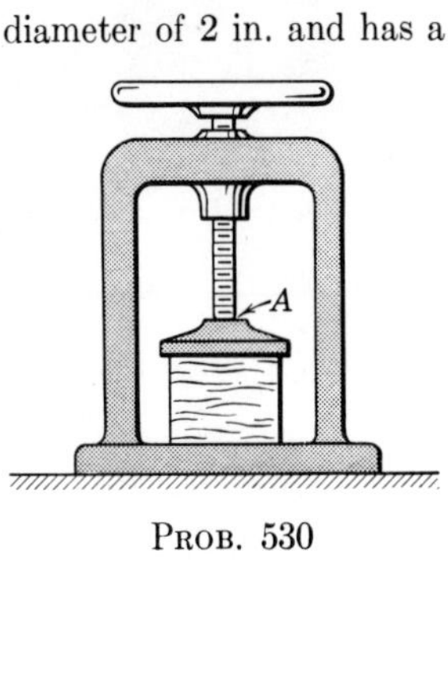

PROB. 530

531. A screw jack, similar to that shown in Fig. 68, has square threads with a mean radius of 1 in. and supports a load of 1000 lb. The lever arm of the jack handle is 12 in. If the coefficient of friction is 0.3, what is the greatest lead L of the screw for which the screw will not unwind by itself? For this condition what force P on the lever will raise the load?

532. A device for removing wheels and collars from shafts is shown in the figure. The screw is single-threaded with a mean diameter of 1 in. and has 4 square threads per inch. If a torque of 20 lb. ft. is required on wheel B to slip the collar off the shaft, determine the average pressure p between the shaft and the collar. The coefficient of friction for the screw is 0.20, and that for the collar and shaft is 0.30. Neglect any friction at A. *Ans.* $p = 449$ lb./in.^{2}

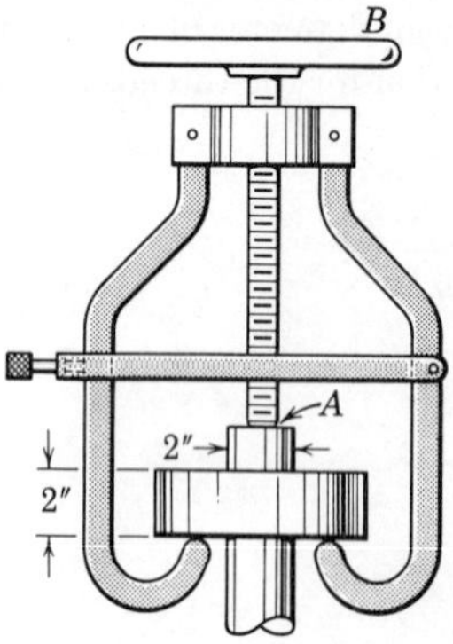

PROB. 532

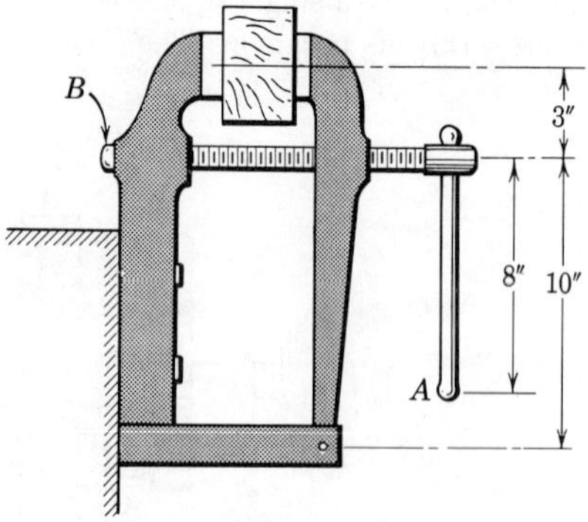

PROB. 533

533. The single-threaded screw of the vise has a mean diameter of 1 in. and has 5 square threads per inch. If a 60 lb. pull applied normal to the handle at A produces a clamping force of 1200 lb. at the jaws of the vise, determine the frictional moment M_f developed at B due to the thrust of the screw against the frame. The coefficient of friction in the threads may be taken to be 0.20.

534. The device shown is used as a jack. The screw has a double square thread with a mean diameter of $1\frac{1}{4}$ in. and a lead of 0.4 in. Section A of the

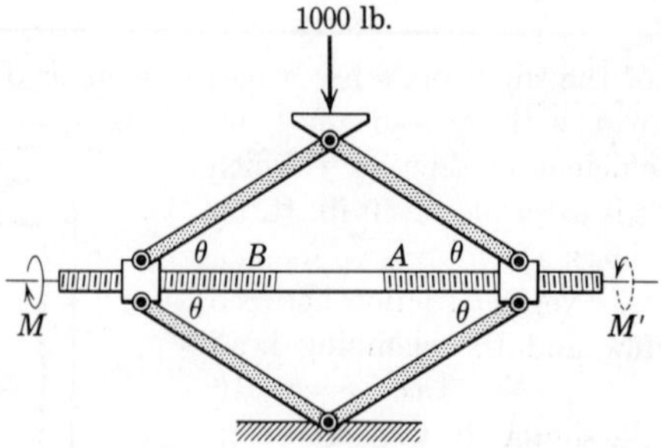

PROB. 534

screw has right-hand threads, and section B has left-hand threads. For $\theta =$ 30 deg. determine (a) the torque M which must be applied to the screw to raise the 1000 lb. load and (*b*) the torque M' needed to lower the load. The coefficient of friction may be taken to be 0.30.

Ans. $M = 897$ lb. in., $M' = 416$ lb. in.

535. The turnbuckle has 10 square threads per inch on each of its two screws and supports a cable tension of 500 lb. The mean diameter of the screws is ½ in. While both screws are prevented from rotating, a force P of 6.7 lb. applied 10 in. from the axis of the screws to the handle of a wrench at A is required to tighten the turnbuckle. If the same wrench is used, determine the force P' required to loosen the turnbuckle. The screws are single-threaded.

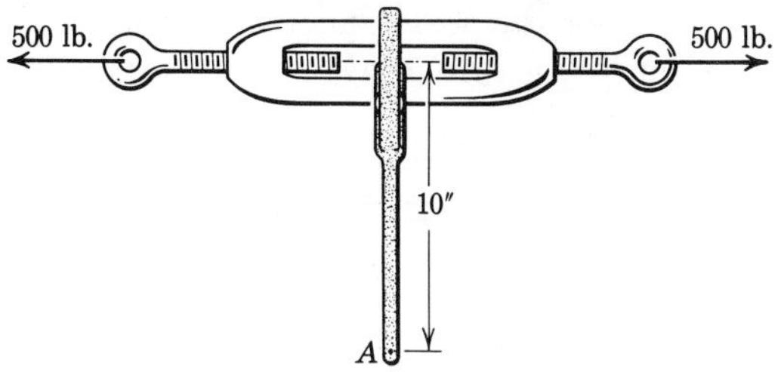

PROB. 535

* **536.** Replace the square thread of the screw jack in Fig. 68 by a V-thread as indicated in the figure accompanying this problem and determine the moment M on the screw required to raise the load W. The force R acting on a representative small section of the thread is shown with its relevant projections. The vector R_1 is the projection of R in the plane of the figure containing the axis of the screw. The analysis is begun with an axial force and a moment summation and includes substitutions for the angles γ and β in terms of θ, α, and the friction angle $\phi = \tan^{-1} f$. The helix angle of the single thread is exaggerated for clarity.

$$\textit{Ans.} \quad M = Wr \frac{\tan\alpha + f\sqrt{1 + \tan^2\dfrac{\theta}{2}\cos^2\alpha}}{1 - f\tan\alpha\sqrt{1 + \tan^2\dfrac{\theta}{2}\cos^2\alpha}}, \quad \tan\alpha = \frac{L}{2\pi r}$$

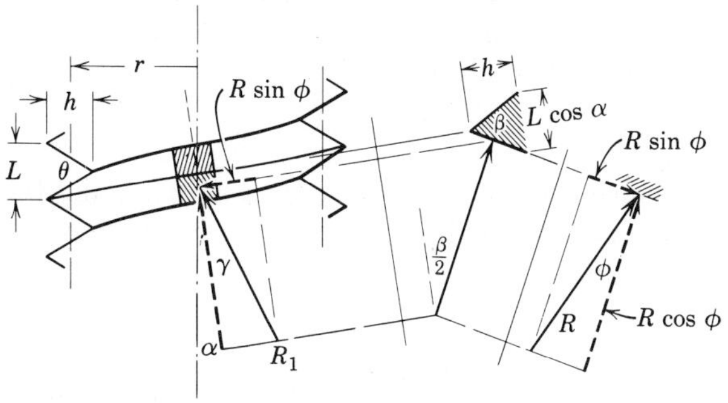

PROB. 536

50. Journal Bearings. A journal bearing is a bearing which gives lateral support to a shaft in contrast to axial or thrust support. For many partially lubricated bearings an analysis by the principles of dry friction gives a good approximation. The behavior of fully lubricated bearings is quite different, however, and analysis of the frictional resistance involves the clearance in the bearing, the speed of rotation, and the viscosity of the lubricant, and is considerably more complicated than the approximation of partially lubricated bearings based on dry friction. A partially lubricated journal bearing with contact or near contact between the shaft and the bearing is shown in Fig. 69, where the clearance is greatly exaggerated. As the shaft begins to

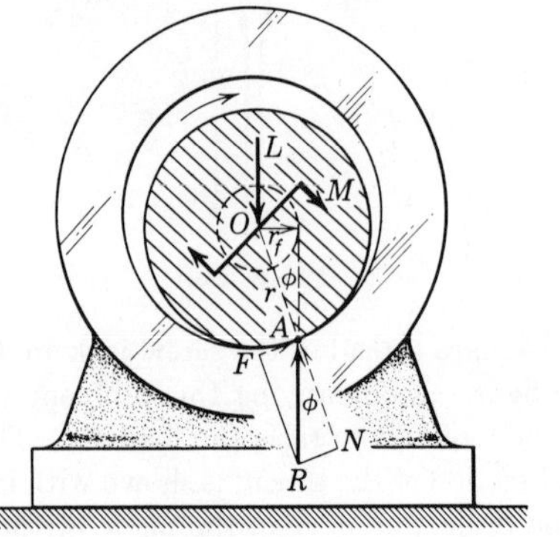

FIG. 69

turn in the direction shown, it rolls up on the bearing until slippage occurs. Here it remains in more or less of a fixed position during rotation. The torque M required to maintain rotation and the radial load L on the shaft will cause a reaction R at the contact point A. For equilibrium in the vertical direction R must equal L but will not be collinear with it. The force R will be tangent to a small circle of radius r_f called the *friction circle.* The angle between R and its normal component N is the friction angle ϕ. Equating the sum of the moments about O to zero gives

$$M = Rr_f = Rr \sin \phi.$$

For a small coefficient of friction the angle ϕ is small, and the sine and tangent may be interchanged with only small error. Since $f = \tan \phi$, a good approximation to the torque is

$$M = fRr.$$

This relation gives the amount of torque or moment applied to the shaft which is necessary to overcome friction for a partially lubricated journal bearing.

PROBLEMS

537. A torque M of 1015 lb. in. is required to hoist the 100 lb. weight at a constant speed. Find the coefficient of friction f for the bearing if the diameter of the shaft is 2 in. and the drum weighs 50 lb. *Ans.* $f = 0.10$

538. If the coefficient of static friction for the bearing of the hoist of Prob. 537 is 0.15, determine the minimum value of the torque M which will prevent the 50 lb. drum from unwinding clockwise. The diameter of the shaft is 2 in. *Ans.* $M = 978$ lb. in.

539. A freight car with 33 in. diameter wheels and 6 in. diameter journals is on the verge of rolling when on a track with a 1 per cent grade. With the assumption that all the resistance to rolling is due to journal friction and that the weight of the wheels and axles may be neglected compared with the total weight of the car, determine the coefficient of static friction f for the bearings. *Ans.* $f = 0.055$

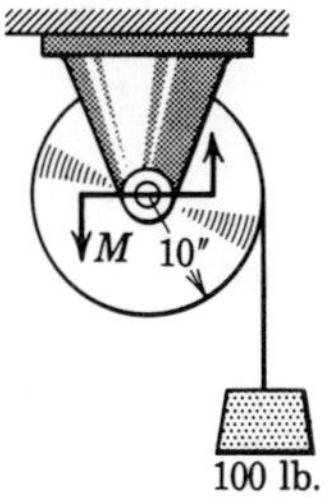

PROB. 537

540. The shaft A fits loosely in the wrist-pin bearing of the connecting rod with center of gravity at G as shown. With the rod initially in the vertical position the shaft is rotated slowly until the rod slips at the angle α. Determine the coefficient of friction, assuming α to be small.

541. A single-cylinder reciprocating engine starts from rest in the position shown when the cylinder pressure p reaches a certain value. Determine the angle α which the resultant compressive force in the rod makes with the axis of the rod if the coefficient of friction is 0.05 for both rod bearings. The diameters of the wrist pin A and crank pin B are 2 in. and 3 in., respectively, and the rod is 24 in. between bearing centers. Neglect the weight of the rod. *Ans.* $\alpha = 0° 18'$

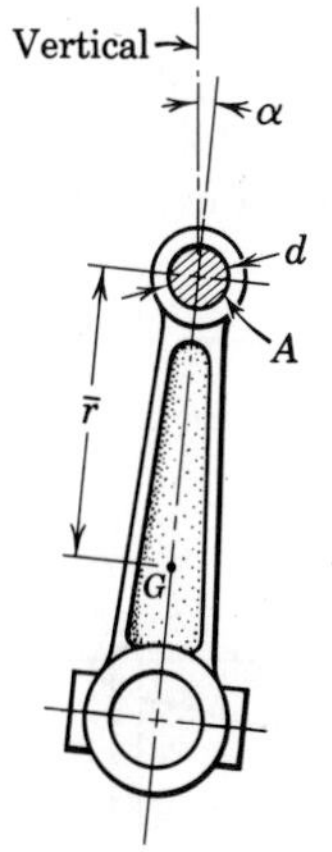

PROB. 540

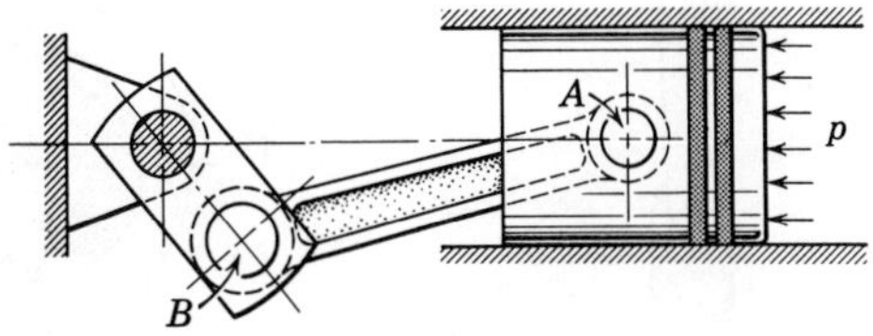

PROB. 541

542. For the hoisting rig shown a force of $P = 104$ lb. is required to overcome friction in the bearings A and B and lift the 200 lb. load. If the shaft is 2 in. in diameter, determine the coefficient of friction for the bearings. *Ans.* $f = 0.227$

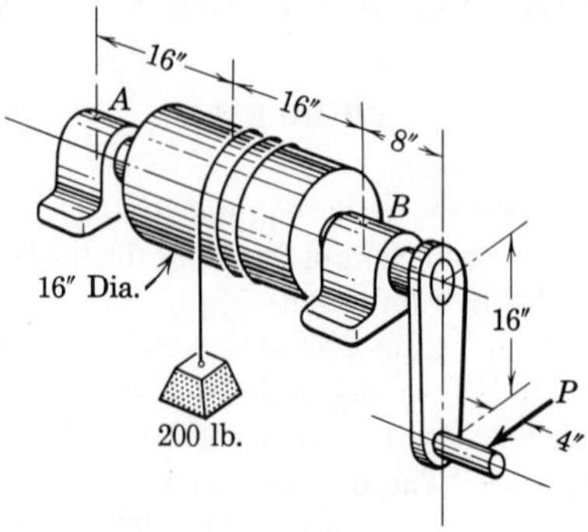

Prob. 542

543. During the application of a thrust of 2000 lb. the compression link shows a lateral deflection δ at its center of 0.110 in. measured from the vertical line through the center of its bearings. The ends also undergo a slight rotation. If the bending moment at the center of the link in the deflected condition is 150 lb. in. and if the coefficient of friction at the ½ in. diameter pins is known to be 0.20, determine whether the ends of the link roll slightly on the pins with or without slipping. The pins are fixed to the rigid heads and cannot rotate.

* **544.** The bell crank fits loosely on its shaft and is operated by the two right-angle links, one supporting a constant compression of 100 lb. and the other a tension T. The fixed shaft over which the crank fits has a diameter of 2 in., and the coefficient of friction between the crank and the shaft is ¼. Determine the range of values which T may have without allowing the crank to turn in either direction.

Ans. $73.4 < T < 94.4$ lb.

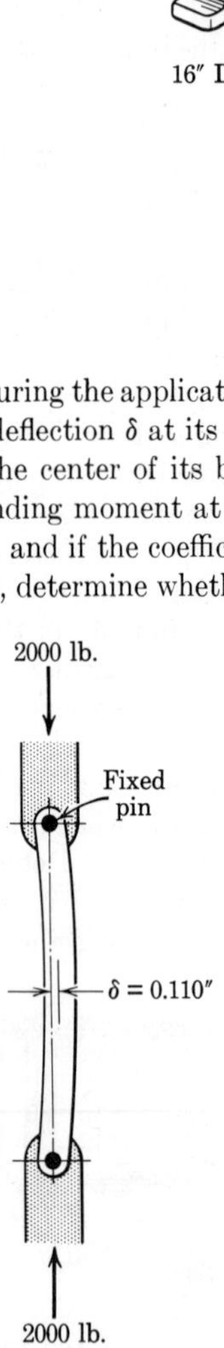

Prob. 543

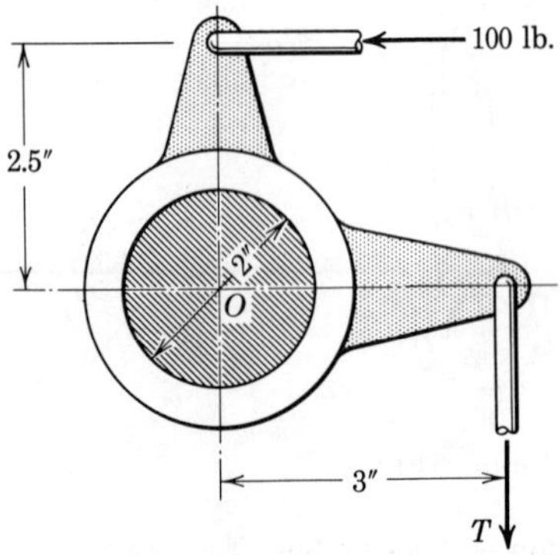

Prob. 544

51. Disk and Pivot Friction. Friction between circular surfaces under normal pressure is encountered in pivot bearings, clutch plates, and disk brakes. Consider the two flat circular disks of Fig. 70 whose shafts are mounted in bearings (not shown) so that they can be brought in contact under the axial force P. The maximum torque that this clutch can transmit will be equal to the torque M required to slip one disk against the other. If p is the normal pressure at any location between the plates, the frictional force acting on an elemental

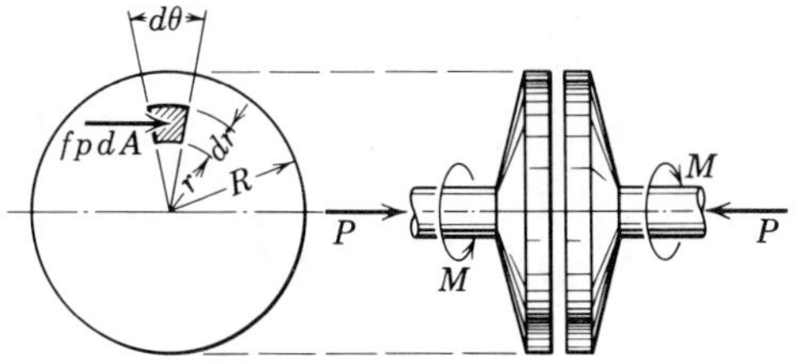

FIG. 70

area is $fp\ dA$, where f is the friction coefficient and dA is the area $r\,dr\,d\theta$ of the element. The moment of this elemental friction force about the shaft axis is $fpr\ dA$, and the total moment is

$$M = \int fpr\ dA,$$

where the integral is evaluated over the area of the disk. To carry out this integral the variation of f and p with r must be known.

In the following examples f is assumed to be constant. Furthermore, if the surfaces are new, flat, and well supported, it is reasonable to assume that the pressure p is constant and uniformly distributed so that $\pi R^2 p = P$. Substituting this constant value of p in the expression for M gives

$$M = \frac{fP}{\pi R^2} \int_0^{2\pi} \int_0^R r^2\,dr\,d\theta = \tfrac{2}{3} fPR.$$

This result may be interpreted as being equivalent to the moment due to a friction force fP acting at a distance $2R/3$ from the center of the shaft.

If the friction disks are rings, the limits of integration are the inside and outside radii R_i and R_o, respectively, and the frictional torque becomes

$$M = \tfrac{2}{3} fP \frac{R_o^{\,3} - R_i^{\,3}}{R_o^{\,2} - R_i^{\,2}}.$$

After some wear of the surfaces has taken place, it is found that the frictional moment decreases somewhat. When the wearing-in period is over, the surfaces retain their new relative shape and further wear is therefore constant over the surface. This wear depends on the circumferential distance traveled and the pressure p. Since the distance traveled is proportional to r, the expression $rp = K$ may be written, where K is a constant. The value of K is determined by equating the axial forces to zero, or

$$P = \int p\, dA = K \int_0^{2\pi} \int_0^R dr\, d\theta = 2\pi K R.$$

The expression for M may now be integrated, and it becomes

$$M = \int f \frac{P}{2\pi R}\, dA = \frac{fP}{2\pi R} \int_0^{2\pi} \int_0^R r\, dr\, d\theta,$$

or, since $pr = K = \dfrac{P}{2\pi R}$,

$$M = \tfrac{1}{2} fPR.$$

The frictional moment for worn-in plates is, therefore, only $(\tfrac{1}{2})/(\tfrac{2}{3})$, or $\tfrac{3}{4}$ as much as for new surfaces.

If the friction disks are rings of inside radius R_i and outside radius R_o, substitution of these limits in the integrations shows that the frictional torque for worn-in surfaces is

$$M = \tfrac{1}{2} fP(R_o + R_i).$$

PROBLEMS

545. The collar bearing shown supports a shaft thrust of 1200 lb. If a torque of 45 lb. ft. is required to overcome friction in the bearing, what is the coefficient of friction f? Assume the bearing to be worn-in.

Ans. $f = 0.18$

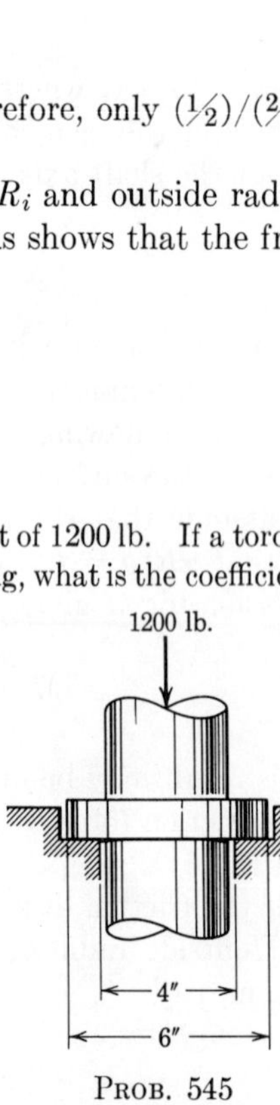

Prob. 545

546. A disk brake used on the landing wheels of an airplane contains three floating metal rings keyed to the wheel and three metal rings keyed to a flange which is attached to the axle. There are five pairs of friction surfaces, and the action is identical with that of the multiplate clutch shown in the figure for Prob. 549 which follows. The contact surface of each ring has outside and inside diameters of 12 in. and 10 in., respectively. If the friction coefficient is 0.15 and the maximum normal pressure between rings is 80 lb./in.², what is the frictional braking torque M for each wheel? Is it necessary in this problem to use a moment equation obtained by integration? *Ans.* $M = 11{,}400$ lb. in., no

547. A new and flat collar bearing supports the thrust P on the shaft. If a constant moment M of 60 lb. in. is applied to the shaft, (*a*) what value of P is required to maintain a constant speed of rotation? The coefficient of friction is known to be 0.15. (*b*) After the bearing has worn in, compute the increase in thrust ΔP which is necessary in order to maintain constant speed.

Ans. (*a*) $P = 56.1$ lb., (*b*) $\Delta P = 5.4$ lb.

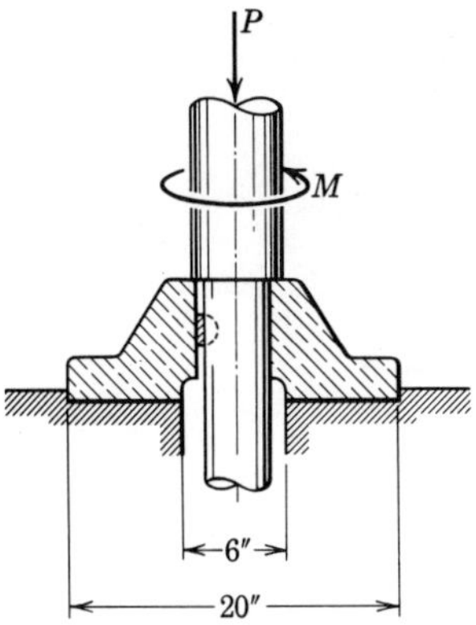

PROB. 547

548. Plot the radial distribution of pressure for the worn-in bearing of Prob. 545. What is the maximum pressure p?

549. In the figure is shown a multiple-disk clutch for marine use. The driving disks A are splined to the driving shaft B so that they are free to slip along

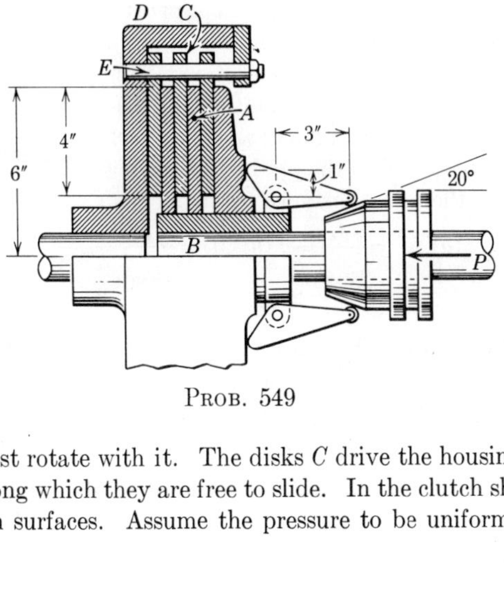

PROB. 549

the shaft but must rotate with it. The disks C drive the housing D by means of the bolts E along which they are free to slide. In the clutch shown there are 5 pairs of friction surfaces. Assume the pressure to be uniformly distributed over the area of the disks and determine the maximum torque M which can be transmitted if the coefficient of friction is 0.15 and $P = 100$ lb.

Ans. $M = 2680$ lb. in.

550. The increase of flexibility with increase in radius for the friction disks shown results in a pressure which decreases parabolically from p_0 at the center to essentially zero at the rim as indicated in the sketch. Determine the expression for the moment M required to turn one disk against the other under an axial load L. The coefficient of friction f is a constant.

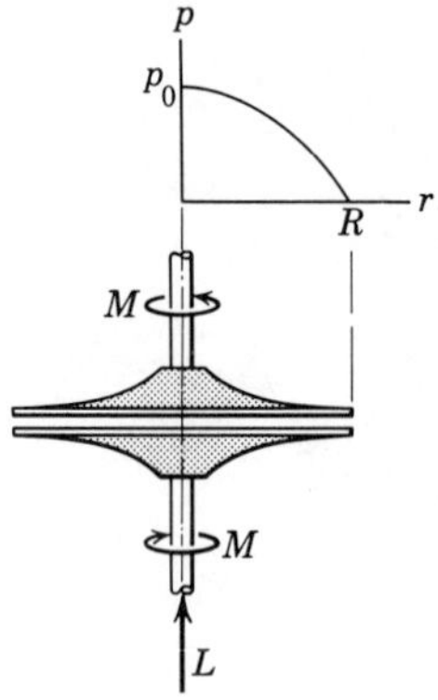

PROB. 550

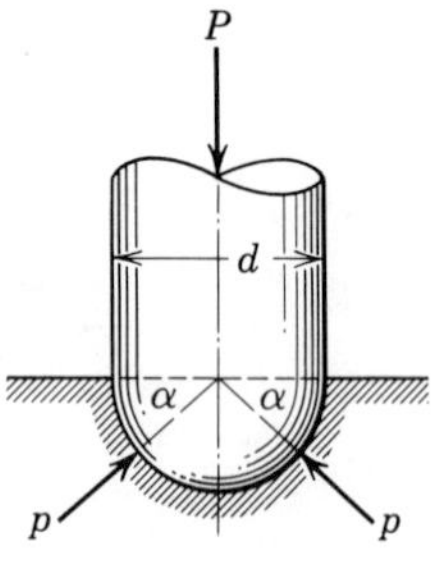

PROB. 551

* **551.** The spherical thrust bearing on the end of the shaft supports an axial load P. Determine the expression for the moment M required to turn the shaft against friction in the bearing. Assume that the pressure p is directly proportional to $\sin \alpha$ and that the coefficient of friction is f.

Ans. $M = \frac{1}{2}fPD$

* **552.** The conical pivot bearing shown supports a shaft thrust P. Derive an expression for the torque M required on the shaft to overcome friction, assuming (*a*) new bearing surfaces with uniform pressure distribution and (*b*) worn-in surfaces where the constant wear is proportional to the product of the normal pressure and the radial distance from the shaft axis.

Ans. (*a*) $M = \dfrac{fPd}{3 \sin \dfrac{\alpha}{2}}$, (*b*) $M = \dfrac{fPd}{4 \sin \dfrac{\alpha}{2}}$

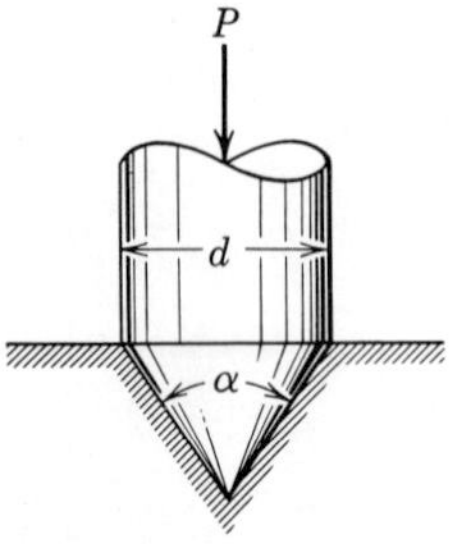

PROB. 552

52. Belt Friction. The impending slippage of flexible members such as belts and ropes over sheaves and drums is of importance in the design of belt drives of all types, band brakes, and hoisting rigs. In Fig. 71 is shown a drum subjected to the two belt tensions T_1 and T_2 and the moment M necessary to prevent rotation. With M in the direction shown T_2 is greater than T_1. The free-body diagram of an element of the belt of length $r\,d\theta$ is also shown in the figure. The tension increases from T at the angle θ to $T + dT$ at the angle $\theta + d\theta$. The normal force is a differential dN since it acts on a differential element of area. Likewise the friction force, which must act on the

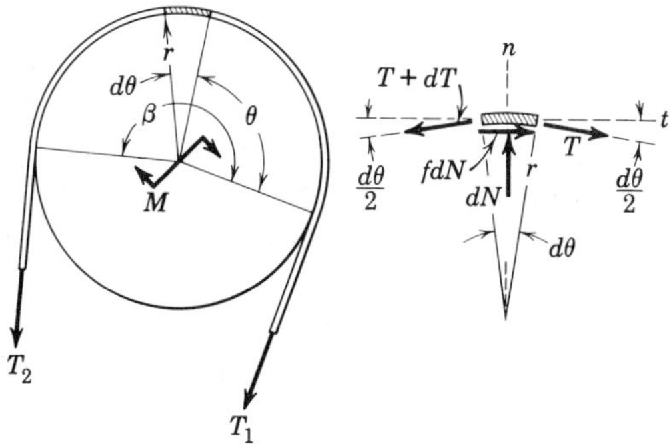

FIG. 71

belt in a direction to oppose slipping, is a differential and is $f\,dN$ for impending motion. Equilibrium in the t-direction gives

$$T \cos \frac{d\theta}{2} + f\,dN = (T + dT) \cos \frac{d\theta}{2},$$

or

$$f\,dN = dT,$$

since the cosine of a differential quantity is unity. Equilibrium in the n-direction requires that

$$dN = (T + dT) \sin \frac{d\theta}{2} + T \sin \frac{d\theta}{2},$$

or

$$dN = T\,d\theta.$$

In this reduction it must be remembered that the sine of a differential angle equals the angle and that the product of two differentials must be neglected in the limit compared with the first-order differentials remaining. Combining the two equilibrium relations gives

$$\frac{dT}{T} = f\,d\theta.$$

Integrating between corresponding limits yields

$$\int_{T_1}^{T_2} \frac{dT}{T} = \int_0^{\beta} f\,d\theta,$$

or

$$\log \frac{T_2}{T_1} = f\beta,$$

where the log (T_2/T_1) is a natural logarithm to the base e. Solving for T_2 gives

$$T_2 = T_1 e^{f\beta}. \tag{44}$$

It should be noted that β is the total angle of belt contact and is expressed in radians. If a rope were wrapped around a drum n times, the angle β would be $2\pi n$ radians. Equation 44 holds equally well for a noncircular section where the total angle of contact is β. This conclusion is evident from the fact that the radius r of the circular drum of Fig. 71 does not enter into the equations for the equilibrium of a differential element of the belt.

The relation expressed by Eq. 44 also applies to belt drives where both the belt and the pulley are rotating at constant speed. In this case the equation describes the ratio of belt tensions for slipping or impending slipping. When the speed of rotation becomes large, there is a tendency for the belt to leave the rim, so that Eq. 44 will involve some error.

SAMPLE PROBLEM

553. Determine the torque M required to maintain rotation of the pulley if $P = 50$ lb. for the simple band brake shown. The band is steel and the drum is cast iron.

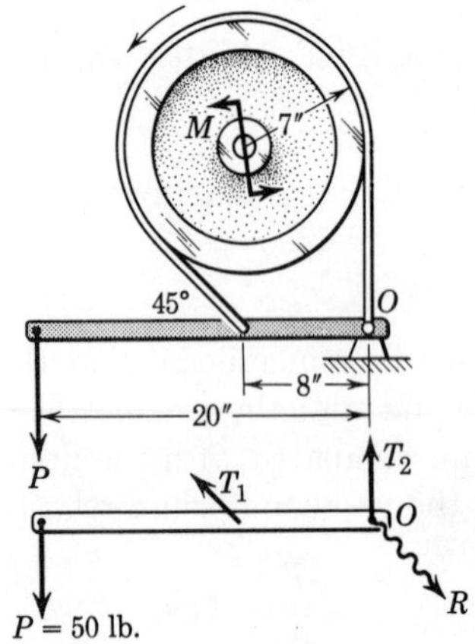

PROB. 553

Solution. From the free-body diagram of the brake lever the moment equation gives

$[\Sigma M_O = 0]$ $$50 \times 20 - 8T_1 \cos 45° = 0,$$

$$T_1 = 177 \text{ lb.}$$

For counterclockwise rotation the tension T_2 will be greater than T_1. The angle of belt contact is $\beta = \frac{225}{360} \times 2\pi = 3.93$ radians, and a suitable coefficient of kinetic friction for steel on cast iron is $f = 0.10$, assuming a dry surface. Substituting these values into Eq. 44 gives

$$[T_2 = T_1 e^{f\beta}] \qquad T_2 = 177e^{0.393}, \qquad T_2 = 262 \text{ lb.}$$

The equilibrium of moments about the axle of the pulley requires

$$[\Sigma M = 0] \qquad (262 - 177) \times 7 - M = 0, \qquad M = 595 \text{ lb. in.} \qquad \textit{Ans.}$$

PROBLEMS

554. Determine the required force P on the rope which will support a 2000 lb. tension if the rope is wrapped four complete turns around the fixed capstan. The coefficient of friction is 0.30. *Ans.* $P = 1.06$ lb.

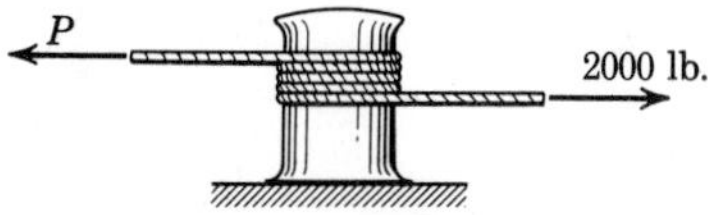

PROB. 554

555. A flexible steel band passes around the three fixed pins, leading vertically from two of them and horizontally from the third as shown. Determine the maximum and minimum values of the horizontal tension T_2 which will insure that the band will not slip. The vertical tension T_1 is constant at 40 lb., and the coefficient of friction is 0.25. *Ans.* $5.61 < T_2 < 285$ lb.

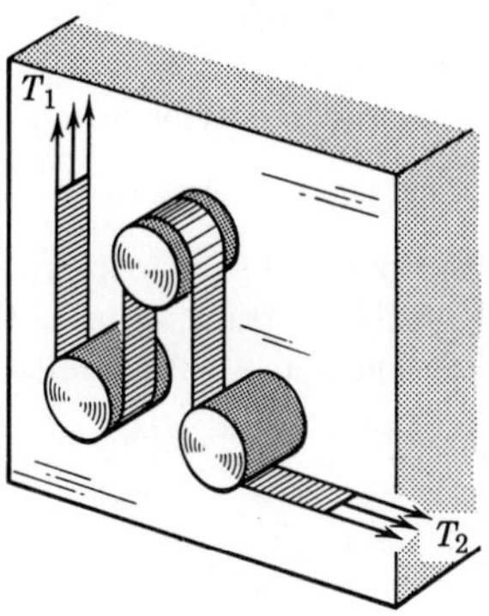

PROB. 555

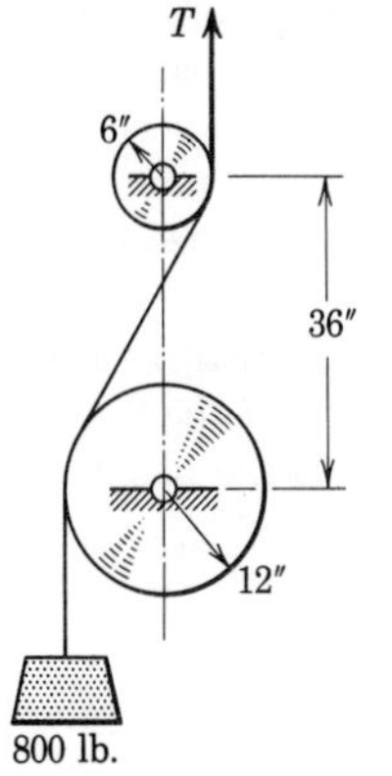

PROB. 556

556. Determine the coefficient of friction f, common to both contact surfaces, if a tension T of 1000 lb. is required to slip the cable around the fixed cylinders and lift the 800 lb. weight.

557. The painter and bosun's chair together weigh 180 lb., and the coefficient of friction between the rope and the fixed bar is 0.40. Determine the pull P which he must exert on the rope with his hands in order to lower himself with a constant velocity. *Ans.* $P = 39.9$ lb.

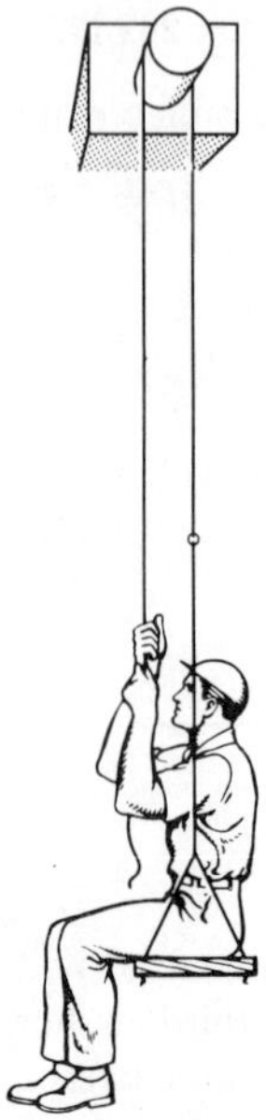

PROB. 557

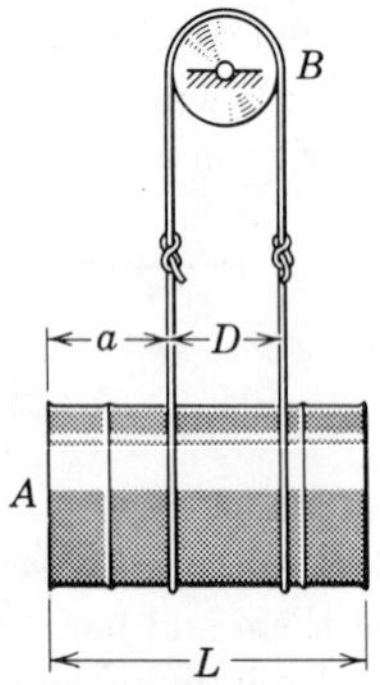

PROB. 558

558. The uniform drum A with center of gravity at midlength is suspended by a rope which passes over the fixed cylindrical surface B. The coefficient of static friction between the rope and the surface over which it passes is f. Determine the maximum value which the dimension a may have before the drum tips out of its horizontal position.

Ans. $a = \dfrac{L}{2} - \dfrac{D}{1 + e^{f\pi}}$

559. By adjusting the position of the idler pulley A so as to increase the angular contact β of the flat belt shown it is possible to transmit more torque from the motor to the pulley B. If the safe tension in the belt is limited to 120 lb.

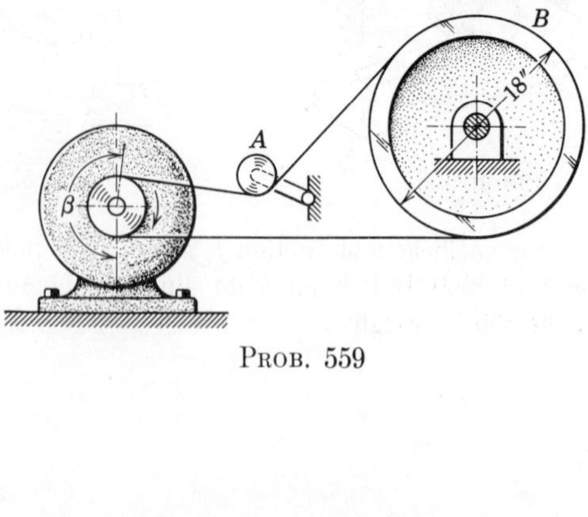

PROB. 559

and the pulley B must supply a torque of 60 lb. ft. to its shaft, determine the minimum angular contact β. The coefficient of friction is 0.3 for both pulleys, and the motor rotates clockwise as shown.

560. A band brake for use with rotation in either direction is shown in the figure. If the coefficient of friction is f and the braking force is P, determine the torque M required to turn the wheel.

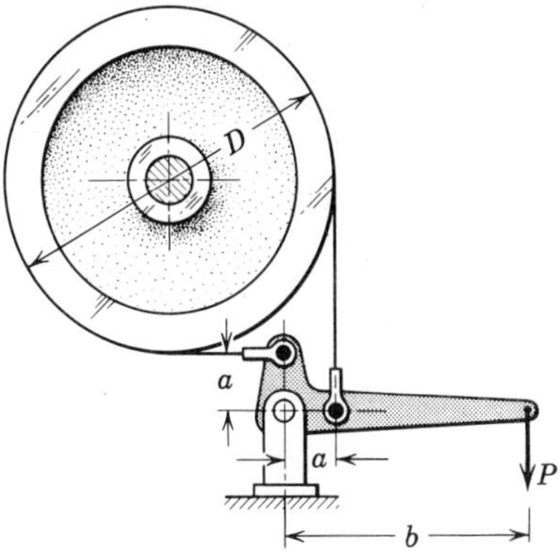

PROB. 560

561. In the figure is shown a differential band brake. Determine the force P required to brake the wheel under a clockwise torque M if the coefficient of friction is f. What happens if $a_1/a_2 \leq e^{f\beta}$?

$$Ans.\quad P = \frac{2M}{Db}\,\frac{a_1 - a_2 e^{f\beta}}{e^{f\beta} - 1}$$

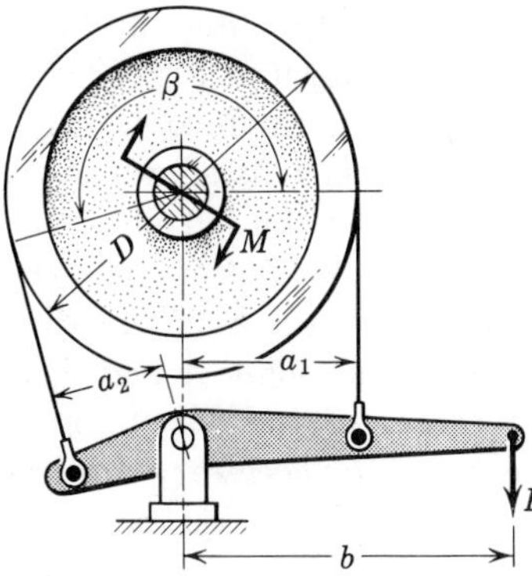

PROB. 561

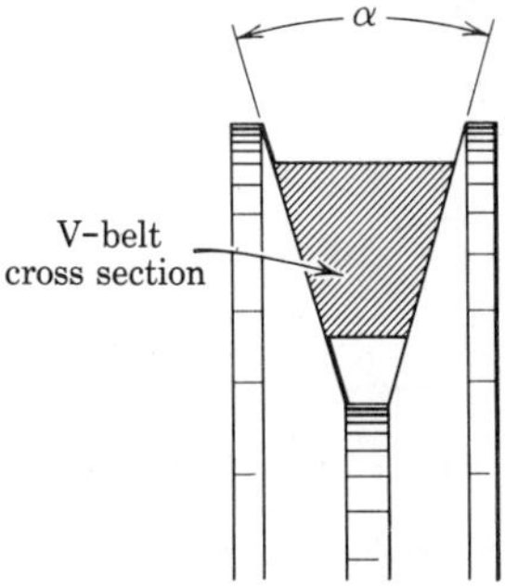

PROB. 562

* **562.** Replace the flat belt and pulley of Fig. 71 by a V-belt and matching grooved pulley as indicated by the cross-sectional view accompanying this problem. Derive the relation between the belt tensions, the angular contact, and the coefficient of friction for the V-belt when slipping impends.

$$Ans.\quad T_2 = T_1 e^{\frac{f\beta}{\sin(\alpha/2)}}$$

* **563.** The V-belt angle most commonly used is $\alpha = 35$ deg. (see the figure for Prob. 562). With the results of Prob. 562 show that using a V-belt of this angle in place of a flat belt is equivalent to increasing the coefficient of friction for the flat belt by a factor of 3.33. By what factor F is the limiting ratio of belt tensions increased?

$$\textit{Ans.}\quad F = \left(\frac{T_2}{T_1}\right)^{2.33}_{\text{Flat belt}}$$

* **564.** A chain with a weight μ per unit length is to be pulled over the circular form shown. The coefficient of friction is f. Determine the pull P which must be applied to start the chain moving. (*Hint:* The resulting differential

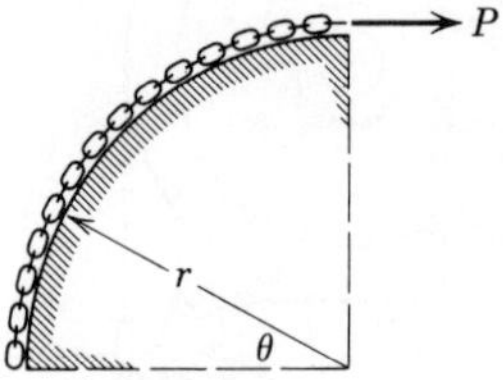

PROB. 564

equation involving the variable chain tension T at the corresponding angle θ is of the form $\frac{dT}{d\theta} + KT = f(\theta)$, a first-order, linear, nonhomogeneous equation with constant coefficient. The solution is $T = Ce^{-K\theta} + e^{-K\theta}\int e^{K\theta} f(\theta)\, d\theta$ where C and K are constants.)

$$\textit{Ans.}\quad P = \frac{\mu r}{1 + f^2}\left[1 - f^2 + 2fe^{\pi f/2}\right]$$

53. Rolling Resistance. Another type of resistance to motion is encountered in a rolling object. The wheel shown in Fig. 72 carries a load L on the axle, and a force P is applied to produce rolling. The deformation of the wheel and supporting surface as shown is greatly exaggerated. The distribution of pressure p over the area of contact is similar to that indicated, and the resultant R of this distribution will act at some point A and will pass through the center of the wheel for equilibrium. The force P necessary to produce rolling may be found by equating the moments of all forces about A to zero. This gives

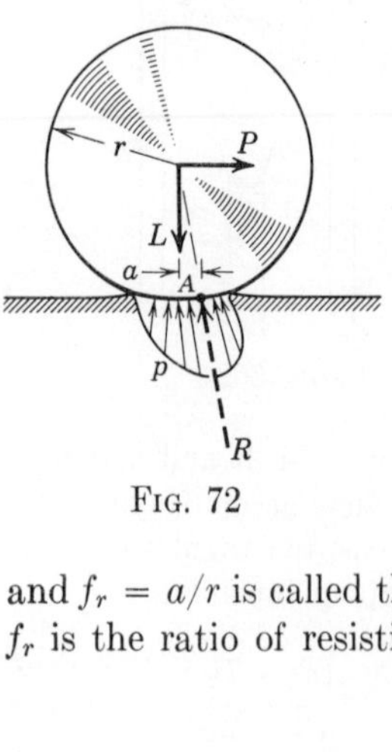

FIG. 72

$$P = \frac{a}{r} L = f_r L,$$

where the moment arm of P is taken to be r, and $f_r = a/r$ is called the coefficient of rolling friction. The coefficient f_r is the ratio of resisting force to normal load and in this respect is similar to the coefficients of static and kinetic friction. On the other hand there is no slipping involved in the interpretation of f_r.

The quantity a depends on many factors which are not completely understood, so that a comprehensive theory of rolling resistance is not available. This distance a is a function of the elastic (and in some cases plastic) properties of the mating materials, the radius of the wheel, the speed of travel, and the roughness of the surfaces. Some tests indicate only a small variation with wheel radius, and a is often taken to be independent of the rolling radius. The quantity a is frequently referred to as the "coefficient of rolling resistance." It is not a dimensionless coefficient since it has the dimension of length and is usually expressed in inches.

Two typical values of f_r are listed in Table D2, Appendix D. These values are only approximate and may be used merely for rough calculations.

CHAPTER 7

VIRTUAL WORK

54. Work. In this chapter a method involving the concept of work will be developed for solving the equilibrium problem. For certain types of equilibrium problems this method will be found greatly superior to the method based on the summation of forces and moments. The term *work* is used in an exact sense as contrasted to its common nontechnical usage. The work done by a force F during a displacement ds of its point of application O, Fig. 73, is by definition

$$dU = F\,ds\cos\alpha,$$

where α is the angle between F and ds. This expression may be interpreted either as the displacement multiplied by the force component $F\cos\alpha$ in the direction of the displacement or as the force multiplied by the displacement component $ds\cos\alpha$ in the direction of the force. With this definition it should be noted that the component $F\sin\alpha$ normal to the displacement does no work. Work is positive if the working component $F\cos\alpha$ is in the direction of the displacement and negative if in the opposite direction. Work is a scalar quantity with the dimensions of (distance) × (force) and is usually expressed in foot-pound units. Dimensionally, work and moment are the same. In order to distinguish between the two quantities it is recommended that work be expressed as foot pounds (ft. lb.) and moment as pound

FIG. 73

feet (lb. ft.). It should be noted that work is a scalar and involves the product of a force and a distance, both measured along the same line, whereas moment is a vector and involves the product of force and distance measured at right angles to the force.

During a finite displacement s of the point of application of a force the force does an amount of work equal to

$$U = \int F \cos \alpha \, ds.$$

In order to carry out this integration, it is necessary to know the relationships between F and s and between $\cos \alpha$ and s. The path s need not be restricted to a straight line. The work done by the force of gravity equals the weight multiplied by the vertical component of the displacement of the center of gravity of the body. If this movement is down, the weight does positive work. If the movement is up, the weight does negative work. The force of gravity does no work during a horizontal movement of the center of gravity.

In the case of concurrent forces acting on a body the work done by their resultant equals the total work done by the several forces. This may be seen from the fact that the component of the resultant in the direction of the displacement equals the sum of the components of the several forces in the same direction.

The work done by a couple M acting on a body during a rotation $d\theta$ of the body in the plane of the couple is $dU = M\, d\theta$, and the total work done during a finite angular displacement is

$$U = \int M \, d\theta.$$

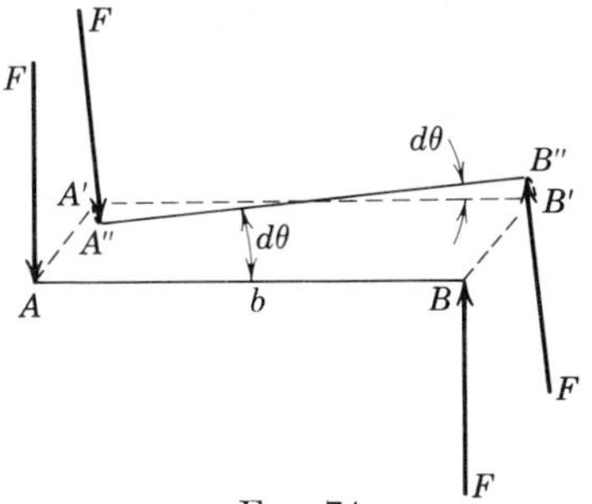

FIG. 74

This result may be seen from Fig. 74, where the couple consists of the two forces F separated by a distance b. Consider any displacement of the body which moves line AB to $A''B''$ in the plane of the paper. This movement may be represented as taking place in two parts. The first is a linear movement to a parallel position $A'B'$, during which time the work done by one force F is equal and opposite to that done by the other force F. Second, the line rotates an amount $d\theta$ to the final position $A''B''$, during which time each force does an amount of work equal to $Fb\, d\theta/2$ so that the total work done is $Fb\, d\theta$ or $M\, d\theta$. The angle θ is expressed in radian measure. Positive work is done when the rotation is in the direction of the couple, and negative work is done when the rotation is in the direction opposite to the couple.

55. Virtual Work. Consider a particle whose position is determined by the forces which act upon it. Any assumed and arbitrary small displacement δs away from this natural position is called a *virtual displacement.* The term *virtual* is used to indicate that the displacement does not exist in reality but is only assumed. The virtual movement is used in order that various possible equilibrium positions may be compared in the process of selecting the correct one. The work done by any force F acting on the particle during the virtual displacement is called *virtual work* and is

$$\delta U = F\,\delta s \cos \alpha,$$

where α is the angle between F and δs. The difference between ds and δs is that ds refers to an infinitesimal change in an actual movement, whereas δs refers to an infinitesimal virtual or assumed movement. Mathematically both quantities are differentials of the first order.

A virtual displacement may also be measured by a rotation. The angular rotation $\delta\theta$ of a line could be a virtual angular displacement. The virtual work done by a couple M during a virtual angular displacement $\delta\theta$ is, then, $\delta U = M\,\delta\theta$.

The magnitude of the force F or couple M may be considered as remaining constant during any corresponding infinitesimal virtual displacement δs or $\delta\theta$. If account of the change in F or M during the movement is made, higher-order terms will result which disappear in the limit. This consideration is identical with that which permits the writing of an element of area under the curve $y = f(x)$ as $dA = y\,dx$.

56. Equilibrium of a Particle. If a particle is in equilibrium, the virtual work done by all forces acting on it during any arbitrary virtual displacement δs away from the equilibrium position is

$$\begin{aligned}\delta U &= (F_1 \cos \alpha_1)\delta s + (F_2 \cos \alpha_2)\delta s + (F_3 \cos \alpha_3)\delta s + \cdots,\\ &= \delta s \Sigma(F \cos \alpha) = 0,\end{aligned}$$

where $\Sigma(F \cos \alpha)$ represents the sum of the components of all forces in the δs direction. This sum is zero since the component of the resultant force in that same direction is zero for equilibrium. The equation $\delta U = 0$ is, then, an alternate way of stating the equilibrium conditions for a particle. This condition is both necessary and sufficient since it may be applied to movements, one at a time, in all three mutually perpendicular directions and is therefore equivalent to the equilibrium requirements $\Sigma F_x = 0$, $\Sigma F_y = 0$, and $\Sigma F_z = 0$.

The principle of zero virtual work for the equilibrium of a single particle usually does not simplify this already simple problem since δs appears in every term and hence cancels. The concept of virtual work for a particle is introduced so that it may be applied to systems of particles in the discussion which follows.

57. Equilibrium of a Rigid Body. For a "rigid" body the distances between particles remain constant, and no part of the work done by forces external to the body can be absorbed by internal friction or by elastic elongations or compressions which are assumed absent in a rigid body. Since the virtual work done on each particle of the body in equilibrium is zero, it follows that the virtual work done on the entire rigid body is zero. Only the virtual work done by external forces appears in the evaluation of $\delta U = 0$ for the entire body, since the internal forces occur in pairs of equal and opposite forces and the net work done by these forces during any movement is necessarily zero.

Again, as in the case of a particle, the principle of virtual work offers no real advantage to the solution for a single rigid body in equilibrium. Any assumed virtual displacement defined by a linear or angular movement will appear in each term in $\delta U = 0$ and when canceled will leave the same expression as would have been obtained by using one of the force or moment equations of equilibrium directly. This condition is illustrated in Fig. 75, where it is required to determine the reaction R under the roller for the hinged plate of negligible weight under the action of a given force P. A small assumed rotation $\delta\theta$ of the plate about O is consistent with the constraining hinge at O and is taken as the virtual displacement. The work done by P is $-Pa\,\delta\theta$, and the work done by R is $+Rb\,\delta\theta$. Therefore the principle $\delta U = 0$ gives

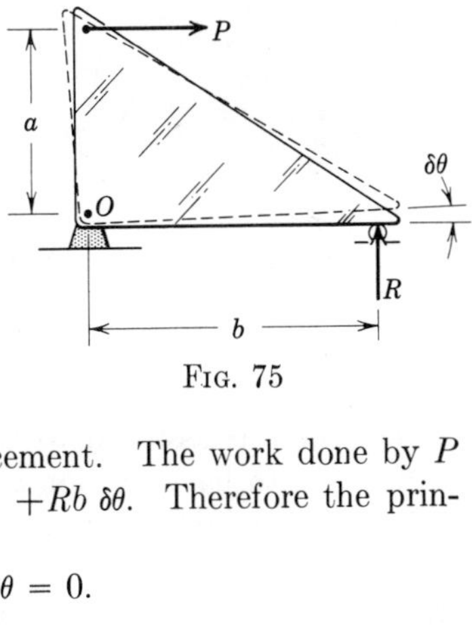

FIG. 75

$$-Pa\,\delta\theta + Rb\,\delta\theta = 0.$$

Canceling out $\delta\theta$ leaves

$$Pa - Rb = 0,$$

which is simply the moment equilibrium equation about O. Therefore nothing is gained by the use of the virtual work principle for a single rigid body. Use of the principle will be a decided advantage for interconnected bodies as described in the next two articles.

58. Ideal Systems. Two or more rigid bodies fastened together by mechanical connections which are frictionless and which cannot absorb energy by elongation or compression constitute an ideal mechanical system. Examples of ideal systems are shown in Fig. 76. In each

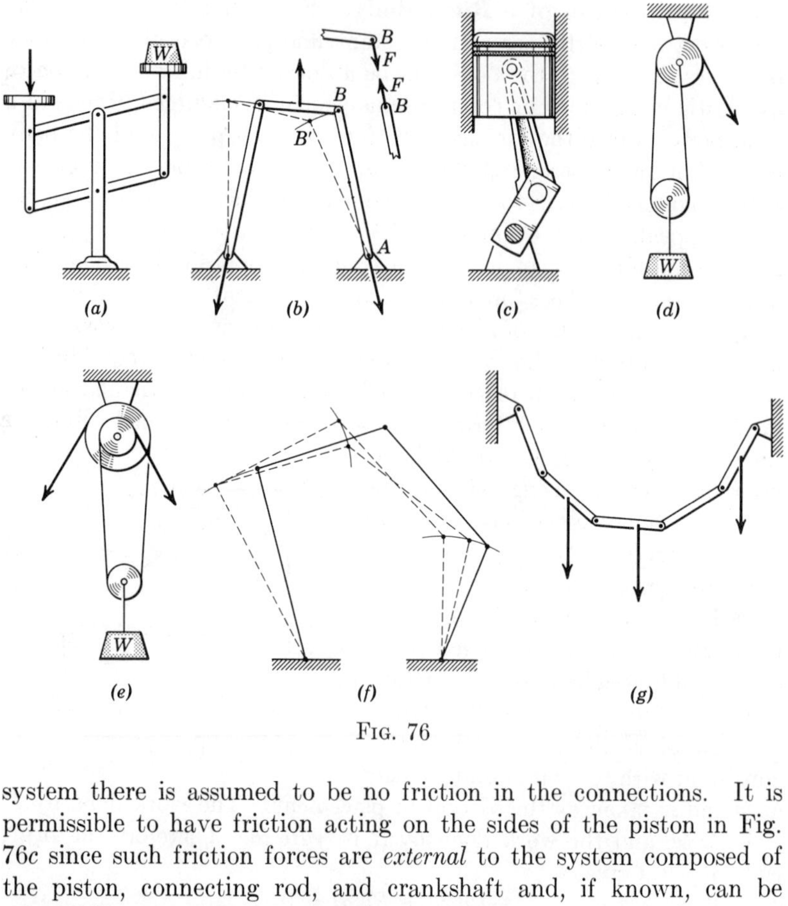

FIG. 76

system there is assumed to be no friction in the connections. It is permissible to have friction acting on the sides of the piston in Fig. 76*c* since such friction forces are *external* to the system composed of the piston, connecting rod, and crankshaft and, if known, can be treated like any other external force. The rope and pulley arrangements in Figs. 76*d* and *e* are ideal systems as long as the stretch in the rope is negligible and as long as the rope does not slip on the pulleys, thereby inducing kinetic friction and heat loss. By isolating an ideal system with a free-body diagram showing all forces external to the system, such as indicated in Fig. 76*b*, it is seen that during any and all possible movements of the system or its parts the *net work done by the internal forces at the connections is zero.* This is so because the internal forces exist in pairs of equal and opposite forces, as illustrated for joint B in Fig. 76*b*, and any reaction will do work equal and opposite to that done by its corresponding action. Hence the principle of virtual work applies to such a connected system. The principle may now be restated as follows: *For any ideally connected system in equilibrium the net work done by all forces external to the system is zero for any and all possible virtual displacements consistent with the connections.*

For the slider-crank mechanism shown in Fig. 76*c*, where the piston is confined to move in the vertical cylinder and the crankshaft is restrained in its bearing, only one coordinate is needed to specify the virtual displacements of the three parts. Thus a small movement δs of the piston will uniquely define the corresponding consistent movements of the connecting rod and crankshaft. With the existing constraints provided by the cylinder sleeve and crankshaft bearing this system is said to have *one degree of freedom.* The pulley device of Fig. 76*d* is also a system of one degree of freedom since the position of each of its parts is determined uniquely by the movement of the free end of the rope. In the four-link mechanism in the *b*-part of the figure (one link is the ground) a small rotation of one of the members such as AB to AB' completely determines the positions of the other movable ones. Thus it has a single degree of freedom, as does the balance in Fig. 76*a*. In the pulley device in Fig. 76*e* the two independent movements of the free ends of the rope must be known to determine the position of W. Therefore this device has two degrees of freedom. The five-link mechanism in Fig. 76*f* will require two separate specified rotations before the configuration of each part is uniquely determined, and hence it has two degrees of freedom. The connection of links in Fig. 76*g* has three degrees of freedom. A rigid body free to move in space has six degrees of freedom, three components of translation and three components of rotation. The *number of degrees of freedom*, then, equals the *number of independent coordinates* required to determine the unique configuration of the system. The number of possible virtual displacements of a system will equal the number of degrees of freedom.

All external forces at fixed reactions do no work during any virtual displacement consistent with the constraints at these reactions. Such external forces are called *reactive forces* as distinguished from the externally applied or *active forces.* Weight or any other body force must be treated in the same way as any applied or active force.

The principle of virtual work is now restated in a restricted form for ideal systems with constraints. *The virtual work done by all external active forces on an ideal system in equilibrium is zero for any and all virtual displacements consistent with the constraints.* It is in this form that the principle is most useful for ideal systems. This principle may be stated symbolically by the equation

$$\delta U = 0, \tag{45}$$

where δU stands for the total work done by all external active forces during a virtual displacement.

The real advantages of the method of virtual work can only now be seen. There are essentially two. First, it is not necessary to dismember ideal systems to establish the relations between the active forces, as is generally the case with the equilibrium method based on force and moment summations. Second, the relations between the active forces may be determined directly without reference to the reactive forces. These advantages make the method of virtual work particularly useful in determining the position of equilibrium of a system under known loads. This type of problem is in contrast with the problem of determining the forces acting on a body whose equilibrium position is fixed.

In the method of virtual work a diagram which isolates the system under consideration must be drawn. Unlike the free-body diagram, where all forces are shown, the diagram for the method of work need show only the *active* forces since the reactive forces do not enter into the application of $\delta U = 0$ in the restricted sense for constrained systems. Such a drawing may be termed an *active-force diagram.*

Most problems involve a single degree of freedom, and, since the number of possible virtual displacements equals the number of degrees of freedom, such problems will require one application of Eq. 45 for the one virtual displacement. For systems of n degrees of freedom it is necessary to solve n equations, each expressing zero virtual work of all active forces due to each of the n possible virtual displacements considered separately while the remaining ones are held zero.

SAMPLE PROBLEMS

565. Each of the two uniform hinged bars has a weight W and a length l, and is supported and loaded as shown. For a given force P determine the angle θ for equilibrium.

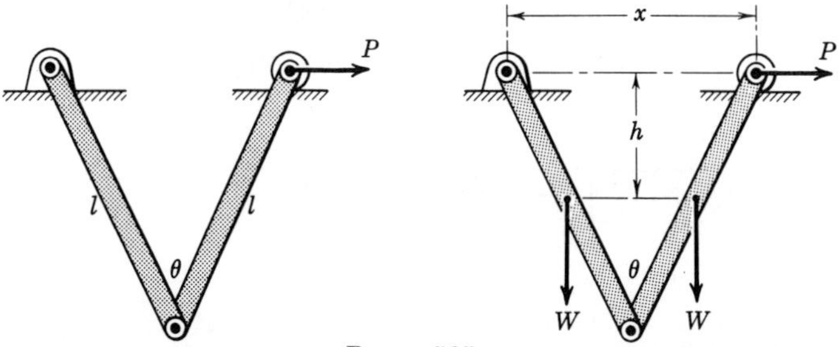

PROB. 565

Solution. The active-force diagram for the system composed of the two members is shown separately and includes the two weights in addition to the force P. All other forces acting externally on the system are reactive forces which do no work during a virtual movement δx and are not shown.

The principle of virtual work requires that the total work of all external active forces is zero for any virtual displacement consistent with the constraints. Thus for a movement δx

$$[\delta U = 0] \qquad P\,\delta x + 2W\,\delta h = 0.$$

It should be evident from the geometry that δh will be negative for a positive δx. Each of these virtual displacements will now be expressed in terms of the variable θ, the required quantity. Thus

$$h = \frac{l}{2}\cos\frac{\theta}{2} \qquad \text{and} \qquad \delta h = -\frac{l}{4}\sin\frac{\theta}{2}\,\delta\theta.$$

Similarly,

$$x = 2l\sin\frac{\theta}{2} \qquad \text{and} \qquad \delta x = l\cos\frac{\theta}{2}\,\delta\theta.$$

Substitution into the equation of virtual work gives

$$Pl\cos\frac{\theta}{2}\,\delta\theta - 2W\frac{l}{4}\sin\frac{\theta}{2}\,\delta\theta = 0$$

from which

$$\tan\frac{\theta}{2} = \frac{2P}{W} \qquad \text{or} \qquad \theta = 2\tan^{-1}\frac{2P}{W}. \qquad \textit{Ans.}$$

In order to obtain this result by the principles of force and moment summation, it would be necessary to dismember the frame and take into account all forces acting on each member. Solution by the method of virtual work involves a simpler operation.

566. A couple M is applied to the shaft fixed to the lever OA. Determine the force P on the smooth slider block required to keep OA in the horizontal position. The length of the link AB is b.

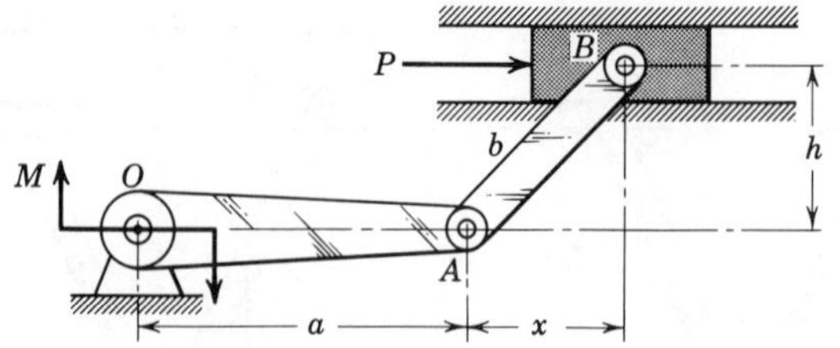

PROB. 566

Solution. The active-force diagram includes only the force P and the couple M as shown. A small rotation of the arm OA is accompanied by a small horizontal movement of the slider block at B. The total work done by P and M during these consistent movements is zero. The relation between these movements is obtained from the right triangle of which b is the hypotenuse. Differentiating the relation $x^2 + h^2 = b^2$ and noting that the change δb in the length of the link is zero give

$$2x\,\delta x + 2h\,\delta h = 2b\,\delta b = 0, \qquad x\,\delta x = -h\,\delta h.$$

If δh is arbitrarily taken as positive, δx is negative, and the rotation $\delta\theta$ of the arm OA is clockwise with the value $\delta\theta = \delta h/a$.

The work done by P during the virtual displacement is

$$P\,\delta x = -P\frac{h}{x}\,\delta h,$$

and the work done by the couple M is

$$M\,\delta\theta = M\frac{\delta h}{a}.$$

Applying the principle of virtual work requires

$$[\delta U = 0] \qquad P\,\delta x + M\,\delta\theta = 0, \qquad -P\frac{h}{x}\,\delta h + M\frac{\delta h}{a} = 0,$$

$$P = \frac{x}{h}\frac{M}{a} = \frac{\sqrt{b^2 - h^2}}{h}\frac{M}{a}. \qquad \textit{Ans.}$$

567. A horizontal force P is applied to the end of one of three identical hinged links each of which has a weight W and a length l. Determine the equilibrium configuration.

Solution. The equilibrium configuration may be specified by determining the angles θ_1, θ_2, and θ_3. Thus three independent coordinates or measurements are required to describe uniquely the positions of the bars. The problem, consequently, is one of *three degrees of freedom*. It will be necessary to apply the principle $\delta U = 0$ three times, where each application is made by varying *one* of the coordinates at a time with the remaining two held constant.

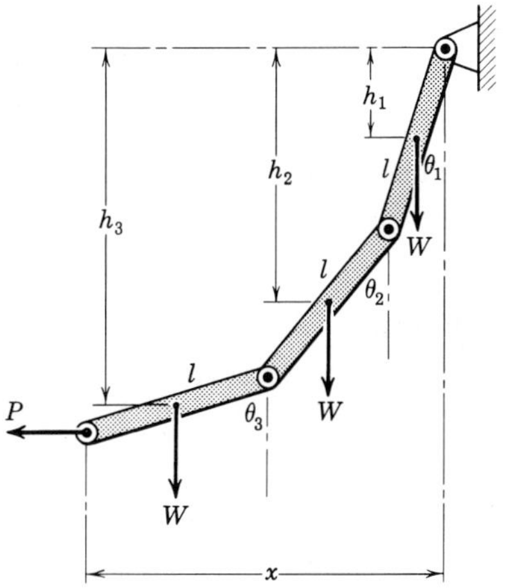

PROB. 567

The active-force diagram shows the three weights and the applied load P. The geometry of the figure gives

$$h_1 = \frac{l}{2}\cos\theta_1, \qquad h_2 = l\,(\cos\theta_1 + \tfrac{1}{2}\cos\theta_2),$$

$$h_3 = l\,(\cos\theta_1 + \cos\theta_2 + \tfrac{1}{2}\cos\theta_3),$$

$$x = l\,(\sin\theta_1 + \sin\theta_2 + \sin\theta_3).$$

If θ_3 is allowed to vary first and θ_1 and θ_2 are held constant, the principle of virtual work requires

$[\delta U = 0]_{\theta_3}$ $\qquad P\,\delta x + W\,\delta h_3 = 0, \qquad Pl\cos\theta_3\,\delta\theta_3 - W\frac{l}{2}\sin\theta_3\,\delta\theta_3 = 0,$

$$\tan\theta_3 = \frac{2P}{W}. \qquad \textit{Ans.}$$

Next, θ_2 is allowed to vary and θ_1 and θ_3 are held constant, so that

$[\delta U = 0]_{\theta_2}$ $\qquad P\,\delta x + W\,\delta h_3 + W\,\delta h_2 = 0,$

$$Pl\cos\theta_2\,\delta\theta_2 - Wl\sin\theta_2\,\delta\theta_2 - W\frac{l}{2}\sin\theta_2\,\delta\theta_2 = 0,$$

$$\tan\theta_2 = \frac{2P}{3W}. \qquad \textit{Ans.}$$

Lastly, θ_1 is allowed to vary while θ_2 and θ_3 are held constant. Thus

$[\delta U = 0]_{\theta_1}$ $\quad P\,\delta x + W\,\delta h_3 + W\,\delta h_2 + W\,\delta h_1 = 0,$

$$Pl\cos\theta_1\,\delta\theta_1 - Wl\sin\theta_1\,\delta\theta_1 - Wl\sin\theta_1\,\delta\theta_1 - W\frac{l}{2}\sin\theta_1\,\delta\theta_1 = 0,$$

$$\tan\theta_1 = \frac{2P}{5W}. \qquad \textit{Ans.}$$

The order in which the coordinates are allowed to vary makes no difference. In this problem the three angles were independently determined by each of the three applications of $\delta U = 0$. In other problems of multiple degrees of freedom it may be necessary to effect a simultaneous solution of the equations arising from each application of $\delta U = 0$ in order to separate the unknowns.

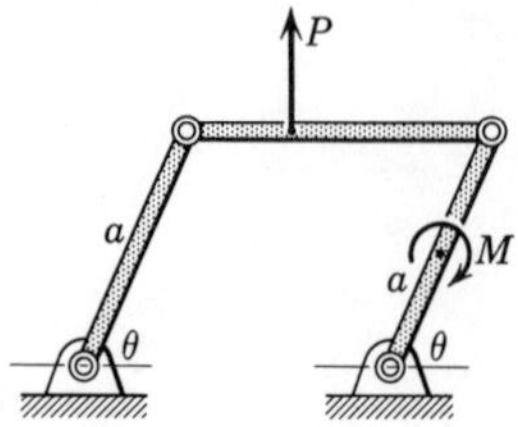

PROB. 568

PROBLEMS

Solve the following problems by the method of virtual work.

568. For the parallel linkage shown determine the angle θ for equilibrium under the action of the vertical load P and the couple M.

Ans. $\theta = \cos^{-1}\dfrac{M}{Pa}$

569. The compound snips of Prob. 294 are shown again here. Find the cutting force P at a distance of 1 in. along the blade from A.

Ans. $P = 1125$ lb.

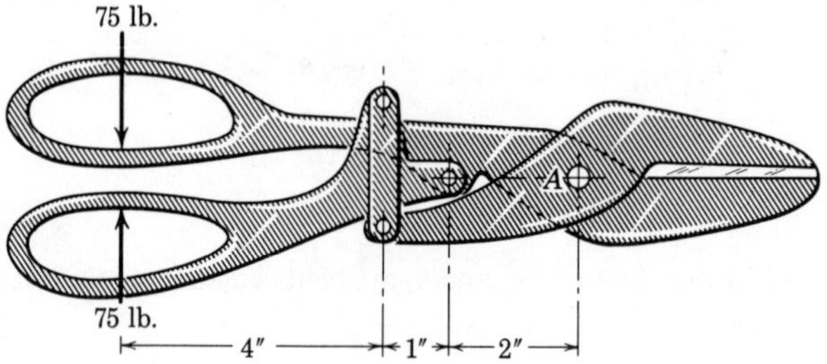

PROB. 569

570. Find the shear Q for the paper punch of Prob. 303 repeated here.

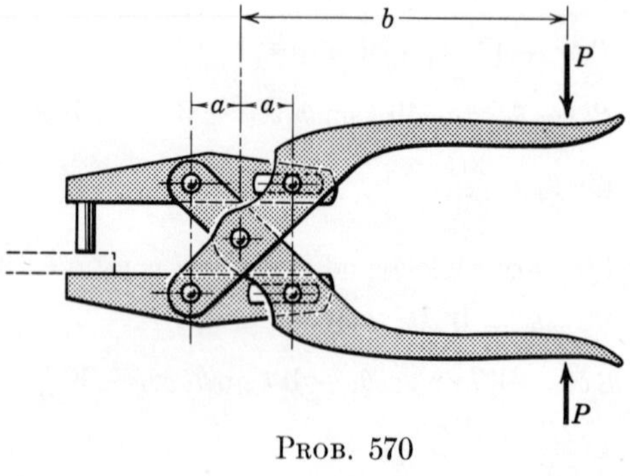

PROB. 570

571. The foot-operated truck lock shown is used to jack up a small hand truck a short distance above the floor. Stepping on the lever at A with a force P causes the link CD to raise the upper frame. Find the weight W which can be lifted from the position shown by a force P of 100 lb. *Ans.* $W = 179$ lb.

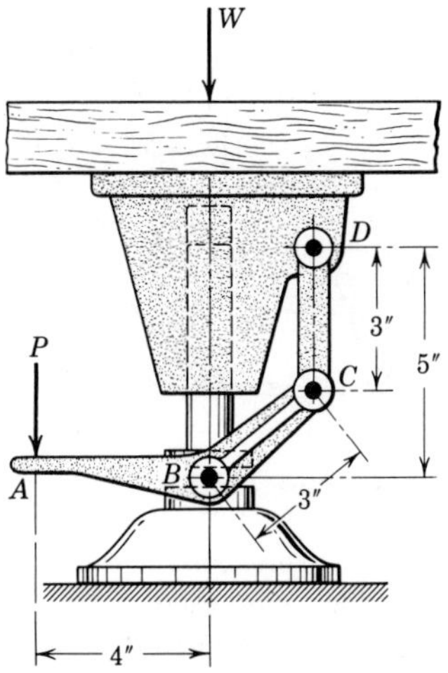

Prob. 571

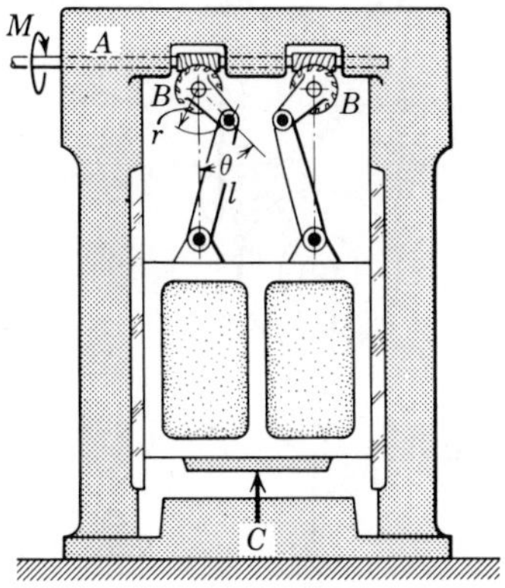

Prob. 572

572. In the toggle press shown, n turns of the worm shaft A are required to produce one turn of the worm wheels B. Determine the torque M on the worm shaft required to generate a force C in the press for the position $\theta = 90$ deg. Neglect the weight of the ram.

573. Determine the weight W of the uniform roadway of the balanced bascule bridge of Prob. 286 repeated here. *Ans.* $W = 667$ tons

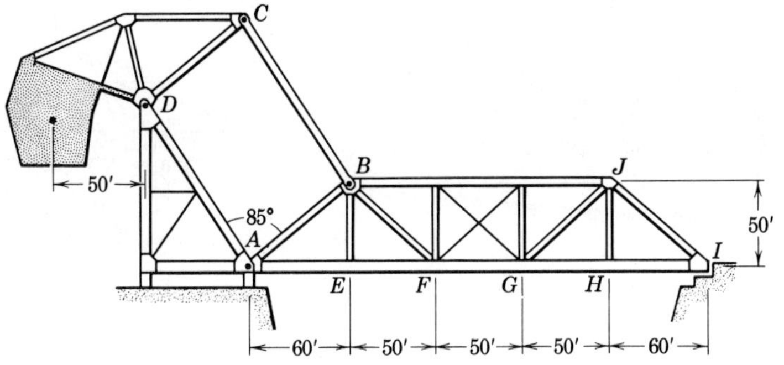

Prob. 573

574. Find the force P required to lift the load W for the differential chain hoist.

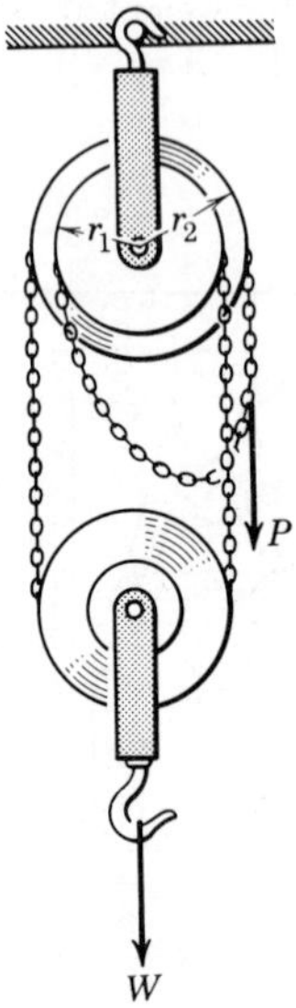

PROB. 574

575. A small railway work car of weight W is propelled by its motor which supplies a torque M to the pinion of radius r_1. The pinion, in turn, drives a gear of radius r_2 which is integral with the wheel. Determine the torque M required to maintain a constant velocity up the incline.

Ans. $M = \frac{r_1}{r_2} WR \sin \theta$

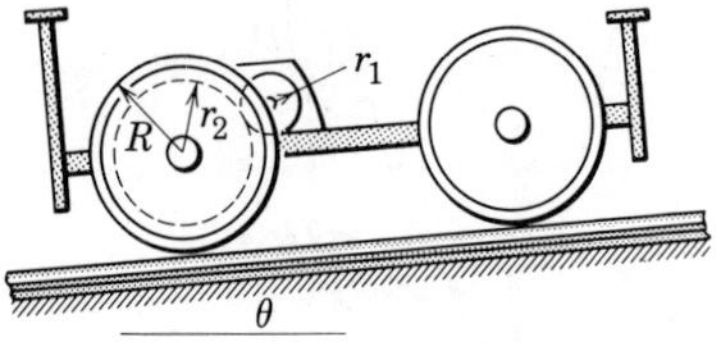

PROB. 575

576. Determine the expression for the downward force F which the rider must exert on the pedal in the position shown in order to maintain equilibrium of the bicycle on the incline. The bicycle and rider together have a weight W. The diameter ratio of pedal sprocket to wheel sprocket is n. (Note that the friction force exerted on the wheel by the ground does no work as long as the wheel does not slip.)

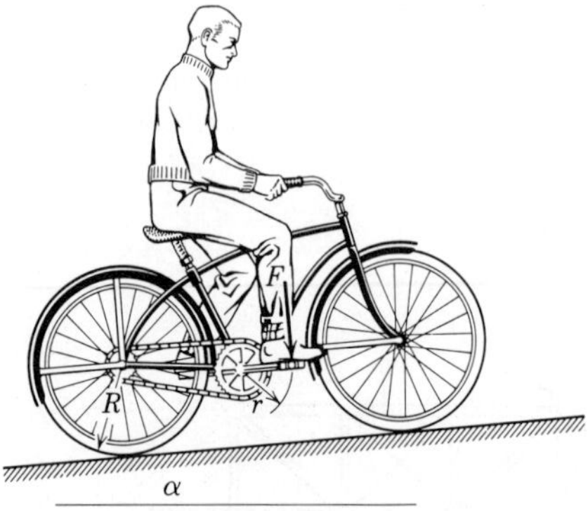

PROB. 576

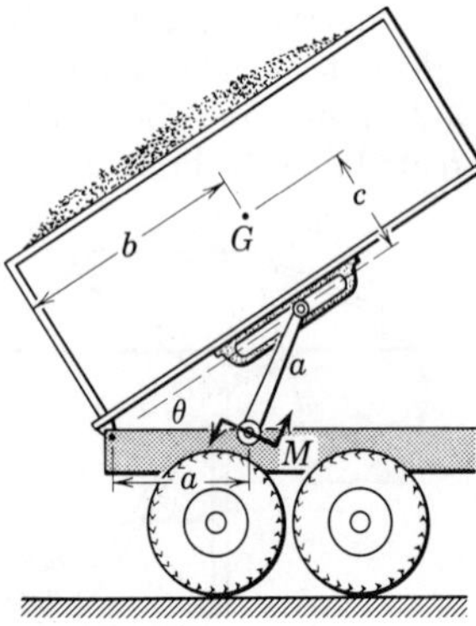

PROB. 577

577. A moment M is applied to the shaft of the elevating lever of the dump truck in order to raise a total load W with center of gravity at G. Determine M as a function of θ.

Ans. $M = \frac{W}{2} (b \cos \theta - c \sin \theta)$

578. Replace the force P acting on the right-hand member in Sample Prob.

565 by a clockwise couple M applied to the same member at any point and determine the angle θ for equilibrium.

579. A power-operated loading platform for the back of a truck is shown in the figure. The position of the platform is controlled by the hydraulic cylinder which applies force at C. The links are pivoted to the truck frame at A, B, and F. Determine the force P supplied by the cylinder in order to support the platform in the position shown. The weight of the platform and links may be neglected compared with that of the 400 lb. crate with center of gravity at G which it supports. *Ans.* $P = 514$ lb.

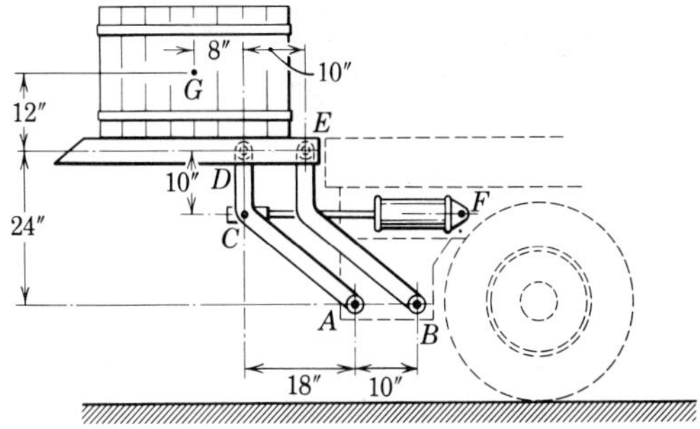

PROB. 579

580. Determine the compression C in the strut AB. (*Hint:* Replace the strut by the forces it exerts on the cables.)

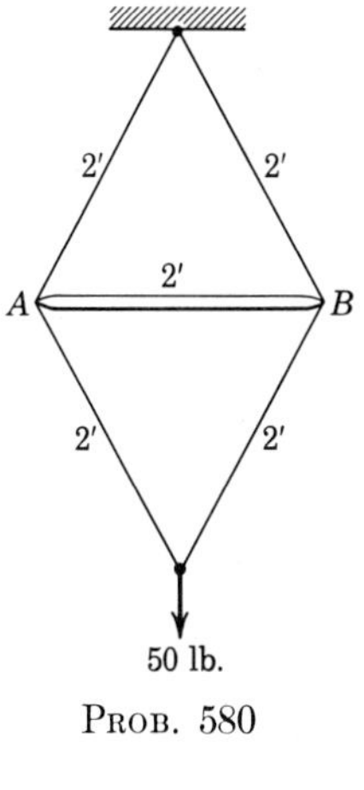

PROB. 580

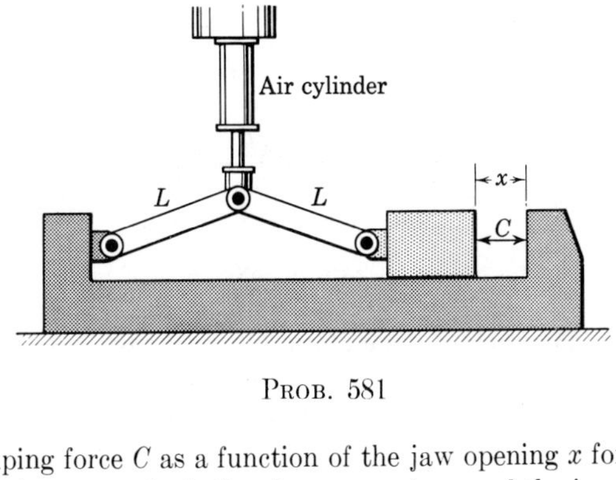

PROB. 581

581. Determine the clamping force C as a function of the jaw opening x for the quick-acting vise. The piston area is A, the air pressure is p, and the jaws are just closed when the toggle links are horizontal. The air cylinder remains in a vertical position.

Ans. $C = pA \dfrac{L - x/2}{\sqrt{4Lx - x^2}}$

582. For the linkage shown determine the horizontal force F applied at A which will support the sliding weight W in any position θ. The weights of the links are negligible. Could W be supported by a downward force at A?

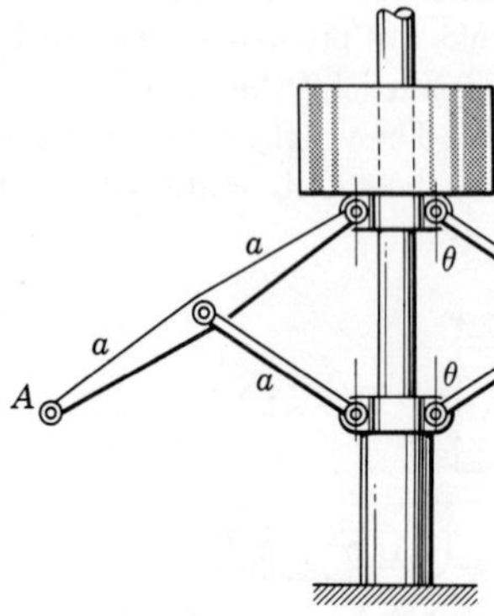

PROB. 582

583. In Prob. 582 if, in place of the force F, a counterclockwise couple M were applied at point A to support the sliding weight, determine its value.

584. For the position of the clamping device shown determine the reaction C in terms of the applied load P.

$$Ans.\quad C = \frac{b(e-c)}{ac} P$$

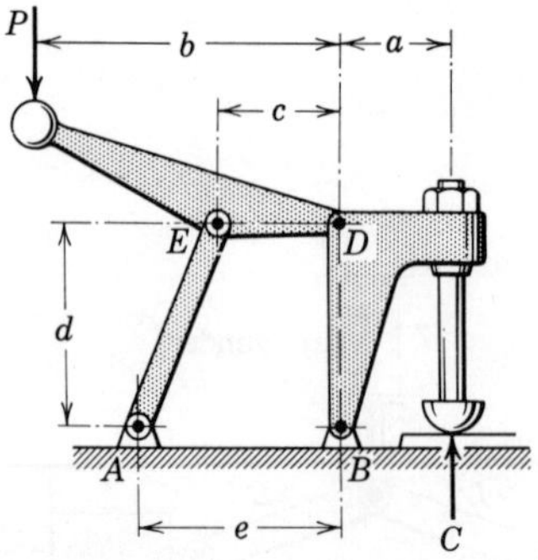

PROB. 584

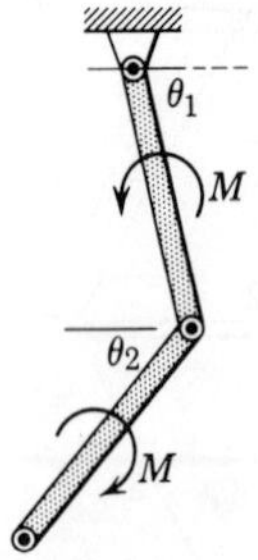

PROB. 585

585. Each of the uniform identical links has a length l and a weight W and is subjected to a couple M as shown. Determine the angle which each link makes with the horizontal in the equilibrium condition.

586. The doors of the ash dumping pit of Prob. 306 are shown again here in cross section. If the weight of each uniform door is W, determine the force P on the piston of the hydraulic cylinder necessary to support the doors in the position θ.

$$Ans.\quad P = \frac{W \cos\theta \sqrt{22 + 12(\sin\theta - \cos\theta)}}{\sin\theta + \cos\theta}$$

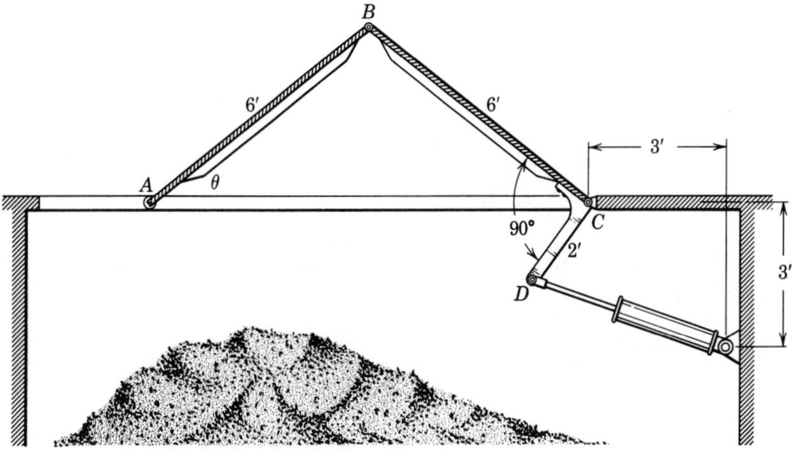

PROB. 586

587. If the lead of the screw for the clamp is L, determine the torque M which must be applied to the handle of the screw in order to develop a compression C at the jaws. Neglect friction in the screw. (*Hint:* Take the horizontal line through point E to be the fixed reference.) *Ans.* $M = \frac{CL}{2\pi}\left(\frac{a}{b} + \tan\theta\right)$

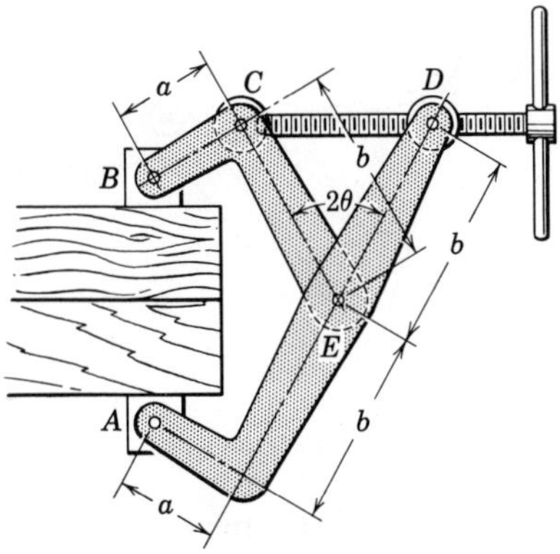

PROB. 587

588. The rivet squeezer of Prob. 311 is shown here with symbol dimensions. Determine the punching force P. *Ans.* $P = \frac{2ebF}{c(b - a)}$

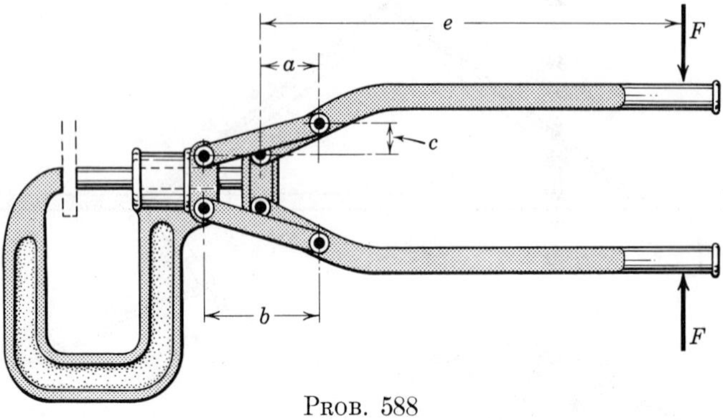

Prob. 588

* **589.** Each of the uniform hinged bars A and B has a weight W and a length l. The weight of the supporting bar C is negligible. For any given value P for which $0 < x < L$ determine the equilibrium configuration by specifying x and θ.

Ans. $x = \dfrac{4PL}{3W}$, $\theta = \tan^{-1} \dfrac{PL}{\sqrt{(3Wl)^2 - (2PL)^2}}$

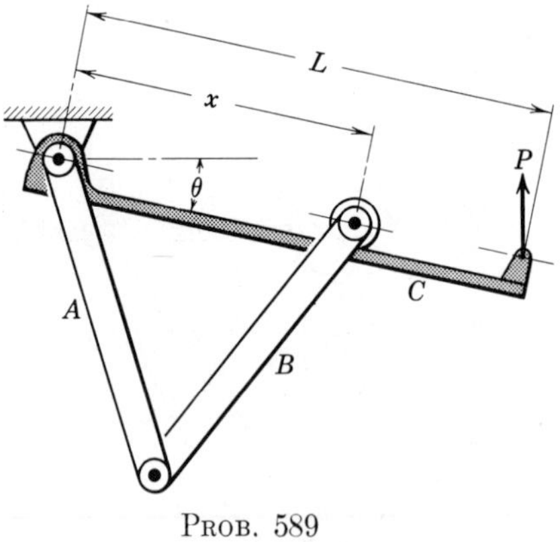

Prob. 589

59. Systems with Elastic Members. When a system of bodies containing elastic members is in equilibrium, some of the work done on the system by the active forces is absorbed in the elastic members during their compressions or extensions. The principle of virtual work as stated for ideal systems without elastic members must be extended to cover the effect of work done on or by the elastic members. Before extending the principle, the work of deformation of an elastic body by a force will be discussed.

The work done on an elastic member is stored in the member and is called *elastic potential energy* V_e. This energy is potentially usable and may be recovered by allowing the member to do work on some body during the relief of its compression or extension. Consider a spring, Fig. 77, which is being compressed by a force F. The spring is assumed to be elastic or linear, i.e., the force F is found to be directly proportional to the deflection x. This relation is written as $F = kx$, where k is the *spring constant* and is a measure of the stiffness of the spring. The work done by F during a movement dx is $dU = F\,dx$, so that the elastic potential energy of the spring for a compression x is

$$V_e = \int_0^x F\,dx = \tfrac{1}{2}kx^2.$$

Thus the potential energy of the spring equals the triangular area on the diagram of F versus x. The virtual work done by F during a displacement δx is the virtual change in potential energy of the spring and is

$$\delta V_e = F\,\delta x = kx\,\delta x.$$

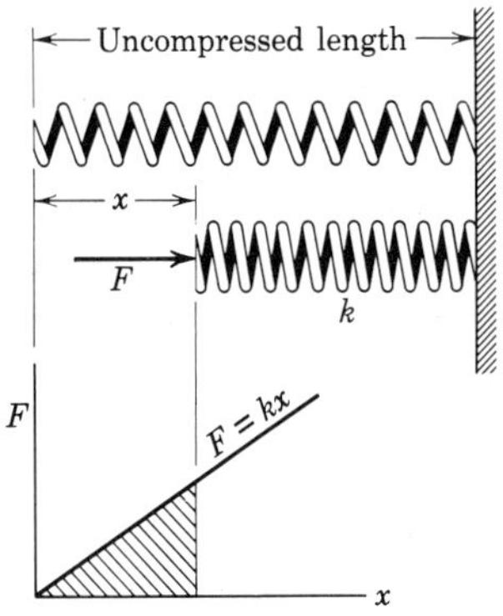

FIG. 77

If the spring is stretched instead of compressed, a tensile force is required which also does positive work on the spring since the movement would likewise be in the direction of the force. Any body which exhibits a linear relation between applied force and resulting deformation is said to be elastic and may be analyzed in this same manner.

The principle of conservation of energy requires that the work done on a mechanical system by external forces must equal its change in energy. This principle must hold for infinitesimal virtual displacements as well as for finite real displacements. Thus the principle of virtual work may now be extended as follows: *when a system of bodies with elastic members is in equilibrium, the net work done by all active forces external to the system during any virtual displacement consistent with the constraints equals the change in the elastic energy of the system.* This principle may be stated symbolically by the equation

$$\delta U = \delta V_e \tag{46}$$

where δU is the total virtual work of all external active forces including the weights of the members and where δV_e is the net change in the total elastic energy of the system during the virtual displacement. If δU is positive, δV_e will be positive, or if δU is negative, δV_e will also be a negative quantity.

For problems with a single degree of freedom Eq. 46 need be applied only once. If there are n degrees of freedom, it will be necessary to apply the principle n times. For each application the movements of the system due to one virtual displacement at a time are considered while the remaining $n - 1$ coordinates are held constant.

Equation 46 finds important use in the analysis of both statically determinate and indeterminate systems. The elasticity of the system may come from the inclusion of manufactured springs, such as the coiled spring of Fig. 77, or may be due to the natural elastic deformation of the loaded structural members. A variation of the principle of virtual work as presented in Eq. 46 is called the unit-load method and is commonly used in structural analysis for finding the deflection of any part of a loaded structure. The work done by a fictitious or virtual unit load during the application of the real loads is equated to the increase of elastic energy which results when the internal forces due to the fictitious load act over the displacements caused by the real loads. The deflection Δ of any point on a structure may be found by placing the unit load at that point and in the direction of Δ, so that the work of the virtual unit load is $1 \times \Delta$. The work-energy equation is then solved for Δ.

SAMPLE PROBLEMS

590. The unstretched length of the spring is h and its stiffness is k. Find the deflection x for equilibrium if each of the identical uniform bars has a weight W.

PROB. 590

Solution. From the active-force diagram it is seen that the work done by the weights of the two bars during a virtual movement δx is

$$\delta U = 2W\frac{\delta x}{2},$$

and the change in the elastic energy of the spring during the same movement is

$$\delta V_e = \delta(\tfrac{1}{2}kx^2) = kx\,\delta x.$$

Equilibrium is specified by

$$[\delta U = \delta V_e] \qquad W\,\delta x = kx\,\delta x, \qquad x = \frac{W}{k}. \qquad \textit{Ans.}$$

The method illustrated in this simple problem is the same as used with more complex problems. The results here, of course, could have been obtained by inspection.

591. The collar is free to slide on the fixed vertical shaft and compresses the spring under the action of the two weights W. If the spring is uncompressed when $\theta = 60$ deg., determine the angle θ for equilibrium. The spring constant is k, there is negligible friction in the joints, and the weights of the arms and spring are negligible.

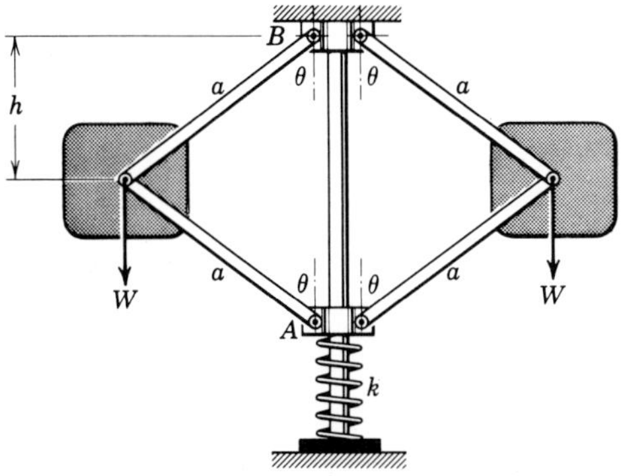

PROB. 591

Solution. The spring compression is

$$x = 2a\cos\theta - 2a\cos 60° = 2a(\cos\theta - \tfrac{1}{2}).$$

The variation in elastic potential energy due to a small increase in θ becomes

$$\delta V_e = kx\,\delta x = 2ka(\cos\theta - \tfrac{1}{2})(-2a\sin\theta\,\delta\theta).$$

The work done by the weights is

$$\delta U = 2W\,\delta h = 2W\,\delta(a\cos\theta) = -2Wa\sin\theta\,\delta\theta.$$

The equilibrium position requires

$$[\delta U = \delta V_e] \qquad -2Wa\sin\theta\,\delta\theta = -4ka^2(\cos\theta - \tfrac{1}{2})\sin\theta\,\delta\theta,$$

$$\cos\theta = \frac{W + ka}{2ka}, \qquad \theta = \cos^{-1}\left(\frac{W + ka}{2ka}\right). \qquad \textit{Ans.}$$

A second solution is given by $\sin\theta = 0$ which would require absence from mechanical interference.

PROBLEMS

592. The figure shows the cross section of a uniform 200 lb. ventilator door hinged about its upper horizontal edge at O. The door is controlled by the spring-loaded cable which passes over the small pulley at A. The spring has a stiffness of 15 lb. per foot of stretch and is undeformed when $\theta = 0$. Determine the angle θ for equilibrium. *Ans.* $\theta = 53°8'$

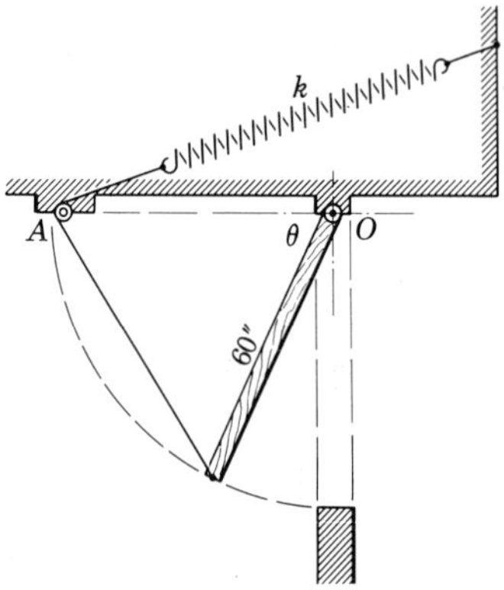

PROB. 592

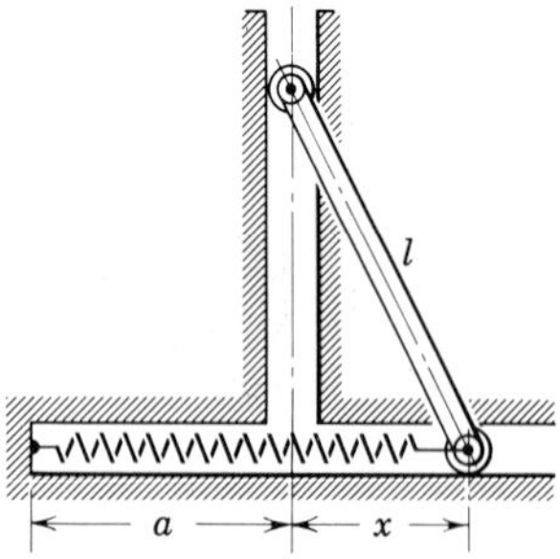

PROB. 593

593. The spring has an unstretched length a, and the uniform bar has a weight W. If the stiffness of the spring is k, determine the stretch x of the spring in the equilibrium position shown.

$$\textit{Ans.} \quad x = \sqrt{l^2 - \frac{W^2}{4k^2}}, \quad k > \frac{W}{2l}$$

594. When θ is equal to 180 deg., the spring of stiffness k is uncompressed. Neglect the weight of the rods and determine the equilibrium position θ other than the one at $\theta = 180$ deg. The collar A slides on the vertical shaft with negligible friction.

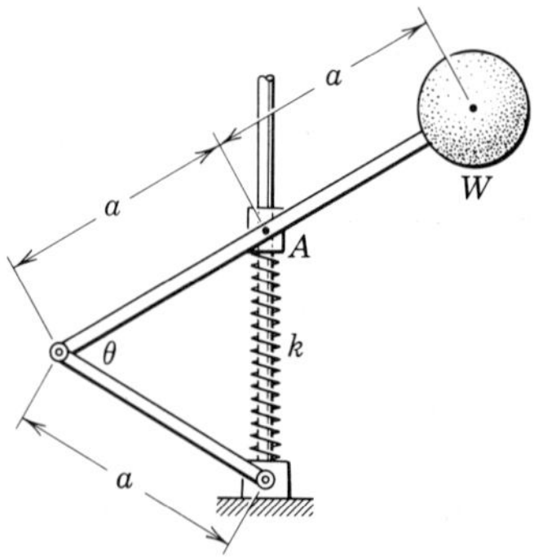

PROB. 594

595. The heavy bar of weight W is held in an equilibrium position by the action of a moment M applied by a torsion spring to the lower end of one of the links. The moment is proportional to the angle θ of twist starting from $\theta = 0$ and is M_0 when the twist is 1 radian. Neglect the weights of the links and find the angle θ for equilibrium. (*Hint:* Approximate the solution for θ small by replacing the sine of θ by the first two terms in its power series expansion.)

Ans. $\theta = \sqrt{6\left(1 - \frac{M_0}{Wa}\right)}$, $M_0 < Wa$

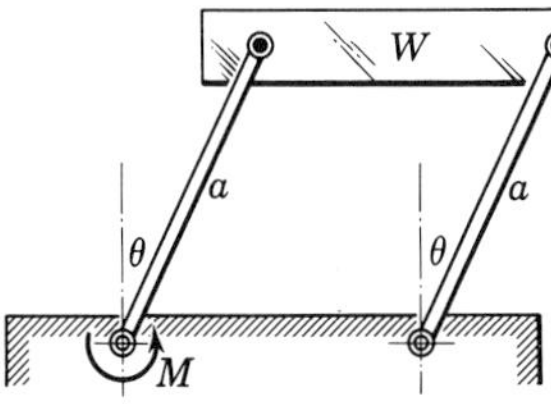

PROB. 595

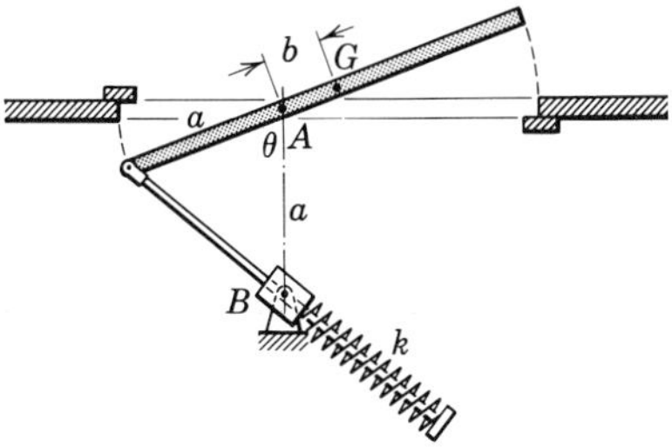

PROB. 596

596. The cross section of a ventilating door hinged at A and with weight W and center of gravity at G is shown in the figure. The spring is compressed by the rod which is pinned to the lower end of the door and which passes through the swivel block at B. When $\theta = 0$, the spring is undeformed. Show that with the proper stiffness k of the spring, the door will be in equilibrium for any angle θ.

597. Determine the angle θ for the equilibrium positions of the mechanism shown. The force in the spring is zero when $\theta = 180$ deg., and the weights of the links are negligible.

Ans. $\theta = \pi$, or $\theta = 2\sin^{-1}\frac{2W}{ka}$

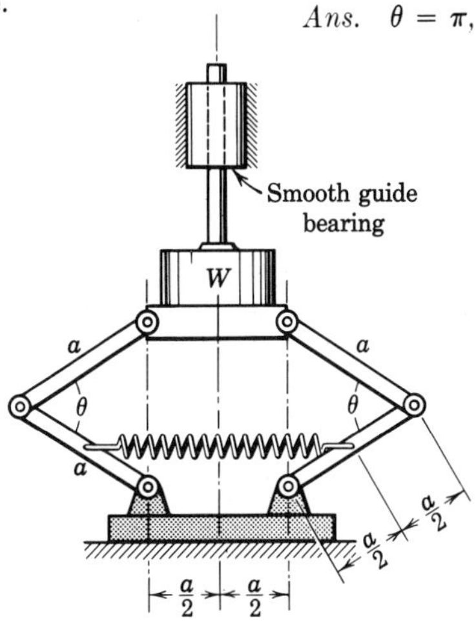

PROB. 597

598. A simplified desk-typewriter lift is shown in the figure. The spring has a stiffness k and has an unstretched length of $a/2$. If the weight of the typewriter and shelf is W, determine the stiffness k of the spring required to maintain equilibrium for a specified angle θ.

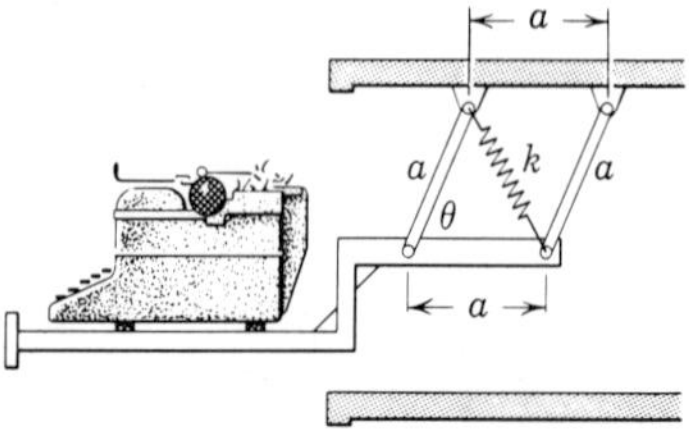

PROB. 598

599. The sketch of the automobile front-end suspension of Prob. 309 is repeated here. If the frame F must be jacked up so that $x = 14.5$ in. in order to relieve the compression in the coil springs, determine the value of x for equilibrium when the jack is removed. Assume that the line through AC remains vertical and that the weight of the frame is included in the vertical loading of 1500 lb. The constant of each spring is 409 lb./in. *Ans.* $x = 9.6$ in.

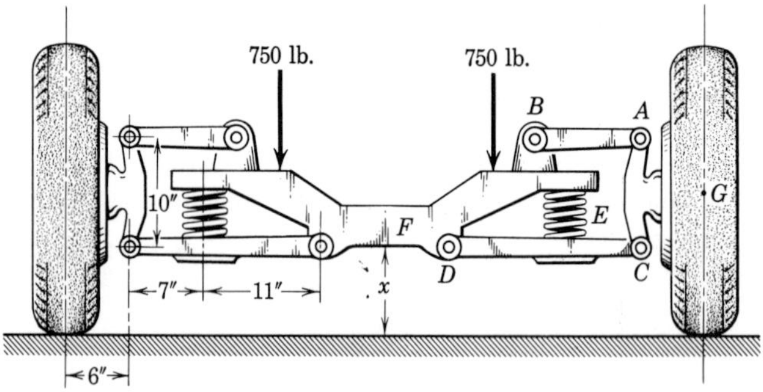

PROB. 599

600. The figure shows a tilting desk chair together with a detail of the spring-loaded tilting mechanism. The frame of the seat is pivoted about the fixed point O on the base. The increase in distance between A and B as the chair tilts back about O is the increase in compression of the spring. The spring, which has a stiffness of 500 lb./in., is uncompressed when $\theta = 0$. For small angles of tilt it may be assumed with negligible error that the axis of the spring remains parallel to the seat. The center of gravity of a 160 lb. person who sits in the chair is at G on a line through O perpendicular to the seat. Determine the angle of tilt θ for equilibrium. (*Hint:* The deformation of the spring may be visualized by allowing the base to tilt through the required angle θ about O while the seat is held in a fixed position.) *Ans.* $\theta = 16° 15'$

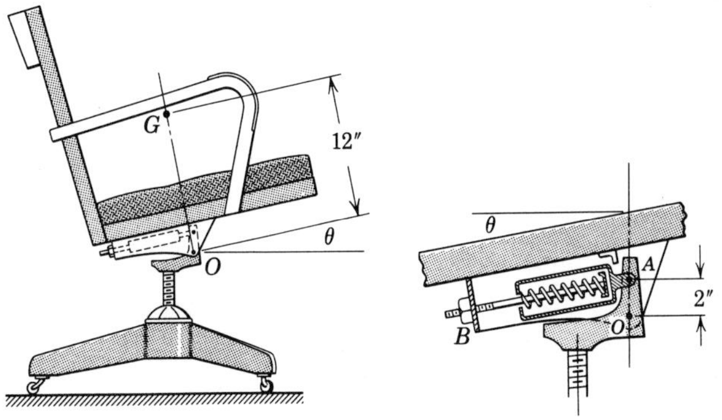

Prob. 600

* **601.** The two rollers of unequal weight are connected by a light spring of stiffness k and unstretched length l. Determine the value of x and the corresponding elongation Δ of the spring at equilibrium.

$$Ans.\quad x = W_1\left(\frac{l}{\sqrt{W_1^2 + W_2^2}} + \frac{1}{k\sqrt{2}}\right),\ \Delta = \frac{1}{k}\sqrt{\frac{W_1^2 + W_2^2}{2}}$$

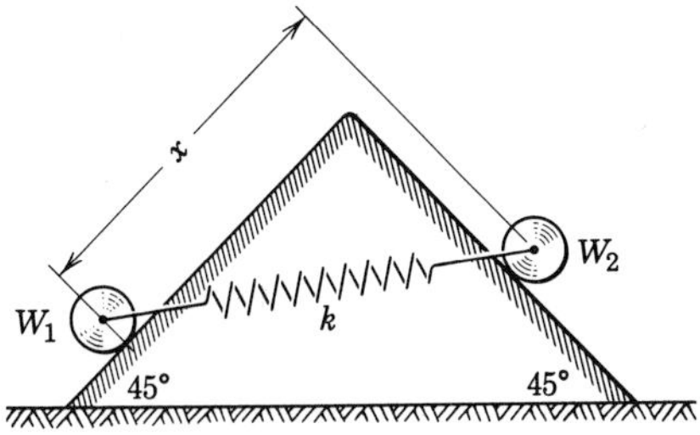

Prob. 601

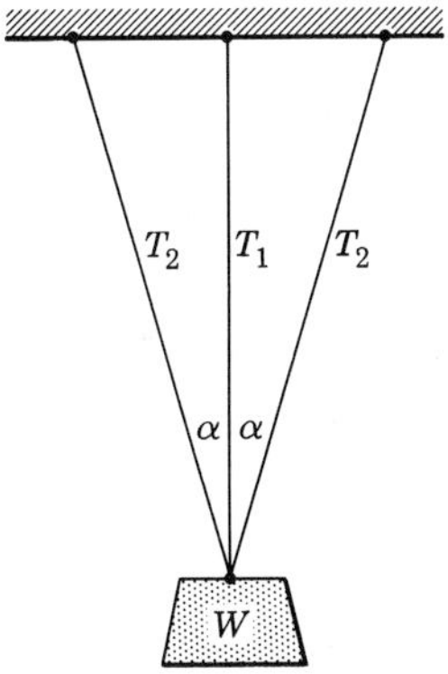

Prob. 602

* **602.** A load W is suspended by the three elastic wires which differ only in length. When the load is removed, the wires are straight and meet at a point. It is known that the central wire alone requires a force K to stretch it a unit amount. Determine the vertical deflection x of W when suspended by the three wires and calculate the tensions in the wires. (*Hint:* Assume the deflection to be so small that the angle α remains essentially unchanged. Treat each wire as a stiff spring with the appropriate stiffness.)

$$Ans.\quad x = \frac{W}{K(1 + 2\cos^3\alpha)},\ T_1 = \frac{W}{1 + 2\cos^3\alpha},\ T_2 = \frac{W\cos^2\alpha}{1 + 2\cos^3\alpha}$$

60. Systems with Friction: Mechanical Efficiency. When sliding friction is present to any appreciable degree in a system of bodies some of the work done on the system by the external active forces is dissipated in the form of heat generated by the negative work of the friction forces during movement of the system. In every case when there is sliding of one contact surface relative to another the friction force present will do negative work. The work is negative since the direction of the force is always opposite to the direction of the movement of the body on which it acts. Thus the friction force fW for the sliding block in Fig. 78*a* does work on the block during the displacement x by an amount equal to $-fWx$. During a virtual displacement

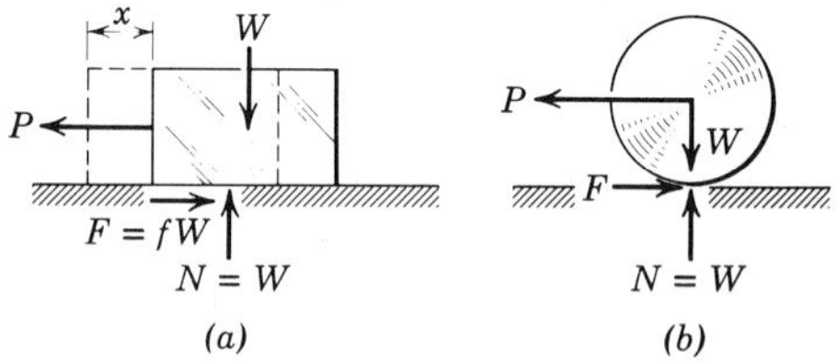

FIG. 78

δx the friction force does work equal to $-fW\ \delta x$. The friction force acting on the rolling wheel in Fig. 78*b*, on the other hand, does no work if the wheel does not slip as it rolls. The negative work done by kinetic friction forces cannot be regained, as all of it is dissipated in the form of heat. Negative frictional work may be due to kinetic friction forces which are both external and internal to the system.

The principle of virtual work as expressed by Eq. 46 for frictionless systems must be modified to account for energy loss by friction. The principle of conservation of energy requires that the work done on the system during any movement must equal the energy stored in the elastic members of the system plus that lost by friction. Thus, if δQ stands for the total negative work done on a system in equilibrium by all kinetic friction forces during a virtual displacement consistent with the constraints, then

$$\delta U = \delta V_e + \delta Q. \tag{47}$$

It has been seen in the previous two articles that a major advantage of the method of virtual work is the analysis of an entire system of connected members without taking them apart. If there is appreciable friction internal to a mechanical system, however, it is usually necessary to dismember the system in order to compute the friction forces. In such cases a prime advantage of the virtual-work method is lost. Consequently the method finds little use for determining the equilibrium configuration for systems with friction.

Because of energy loss by friction the ratio of useful work derived from a machine to the work done on the machine during the same interval is always less than unity. This ratio is a measure of the mechanical efficiency e of a machine. Thus

$$e = \frac{\text{useful work done by machine}}{\text{work done on machine}}.$$

The mechanical efficiency of simple machines which have one degree of freedom and which operate in a uniform manner may be determined by the principle of virtual work by evaluating the numerator and denominator of the expression for e during a virtual displacement. If a machine operates in a uniform manner with time, any elastic changes due to elongations or compressions which occurred during the initial application of the loads will remain constant during the continuous operation and will not be involved in the expressions.

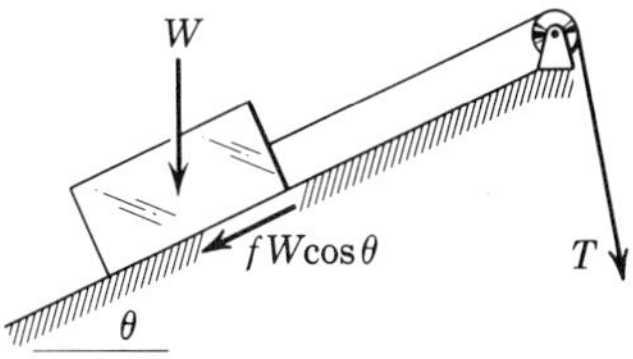

Fig. 79

As an example consider the work done by the tension T in the cable, Fig. 79, in causing the body to slide up the inclined plane at constant speed. The active-force diagram discloses only three forces which do work on the system composed of the body and cable. During a virtual movement δs up the plane the work done on the body is

$$T\,\delta s = (W \sin\theta + fW\cos\theta)\,\delta s.$$

The useful work done by the machine consists of the work in raising the weight W the vertical distance $\delta s \sin\theta$ and is

$$W\,\delta s \sin\theta.$$

The efficiency of the inclined plane is then

$$e = \frac{W\,\delta s \sin\theta}{(W\sin\theta + fW\cos\theta)\,\delta s} = \frac{1}{1 + f/\tan\theta}.$$

As a second example of mechanical efficiency consider the screw jack described in Art. 49 and shown in Fig. 68. Equation 43 gives the moment M applied to the screw necessary to raise the weight W, where the screw has a mean radius r and a helix angle α, and where the friction angle is ϕ. This relation is

$$M = Wr \tan (\alpha + \phi).$$

During a small rotation $\delta\theta$ of the screw in a direction to raise the load the moment M does work in the amount of

$$M\ \delta\theta = Wr\ \delta\theta \tan (\alpha + \phi).$$

The work done by the machine is the work done in raising the load through the vertical distance $(\delta\theta/2\pi)L = r\ \delta\theta \tan \alpha$, where L is the lead or advancement per revolution of the screw. Thus the efficiency of the screw is

$$e = \frac{Wr\ \delta\theta \tan \alpha}{Wr\ \delta\theta \tan (\alpha + \phi)} = \frac{\tan \alpha}{\tan (\alpha + \phi)}.$$

As the friction in the threads is decreased, the friction angle ϕ becomes smaller, and the efficiency approaches unity.

61. Potential Energy. Energy represents the capacity to do work. A body or system of bodies is said to have *potential energy* when, by virtue of its elastic state or position, it is capable of doing work on some other body. There are these two types of mechanical potential energy. Potential energy V_e associated with the elastic state has been discussed in Art. 59 and is $V_e = \frac{1}{2}kx^2$, where k is the constant ratio of applied force to resulting deformation x. This expression represents recoverable energy provided the limit of the elasticity of the spring material has not been exceeded. The second type of potential energy V_g is that associated with the position of a body in a field of force. More exactly it is the work done on a body in changing its position in the force field to which it is subjected. The most common force field is, of course, the earth's gravitational field, and for experiments near the surface of the earth the intensity may be assumed to be constant. Thus for the body of weight W, shown in Fig. 80, the work done by a force (not shown) in raising the body a height h above some arbitrary datum plane is Wh, which is its potential energy of position V_g relative to this datum plane. When the body is a distance h below the plane,

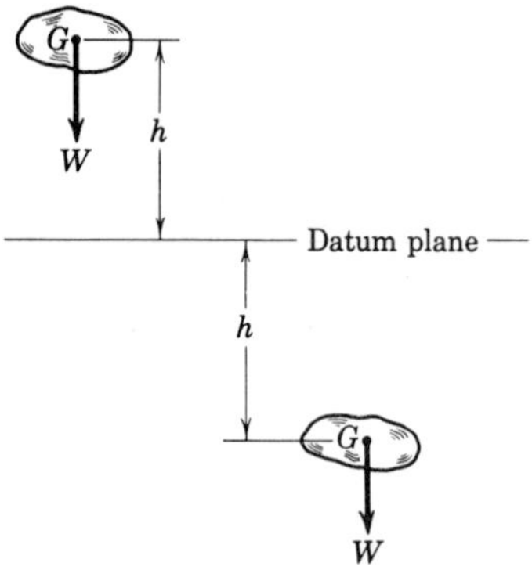

FIG. 80

its potential energy is $-Wh$. Inasmuch as it is always the *change* in potential energy which is involved, the reference plane may be chosen at any convenient altitude. This potential energy of position for a given body is determined only by the resulting change in height h and not by the path followed in arriving at the altitude h. The energy of position is potentially available since, in allowing the body to be lowered the height h, it will do Wh units of work on the body which lowers it.

The total mechanical potential energy V of a body or system of bodies is the sum of the recoverable elastic energy and the energy of position and is

$$V = V_e + V_g.$$

62. Energy Criterion for Equilibrium. A well-known principle of mechanics states that the natural position of equilibrium for any system of bodies without friction is that position which makes the total potential energy a minimum. Water seeks its lowest position, a marble in a bowl will come to rest when its potential energy is a minimum, a hanging coil spring will come to rest in the position where the sum of its potential energies of position and extension is the lowest possible value. The validity of this principle will now be shown and demonstrated by example.

As shown in Art. 61, the work done by gravity forces may be accounted for by the term V_g representing potential energy of position. The work done by externally applied active forces may also be accounted for in the potential energy term V_g. In Fig. 81 the force F

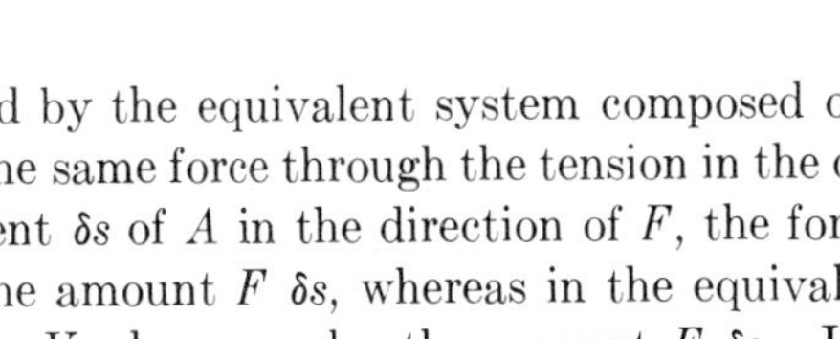

FIG. 81

may be replaced by the equivalent system composed of the weight F which applies the same force through the tension in the cord. During a virtual movement δs of A in the direction of F, the force F does positive work by the amount $F\ \delta s$, whereas in the equivalent system the potential energy V_g decreases by the amount $F\ \delta s$. Hence the work done by an external active force may be accounted for in the potential energy term if the algebraic sign is reversed.

For a system without friction where the effect of all external active forces is expressed by the potential energy term, the equilibrium requirement, Eq. 46, may now be written as

$$\delta V = 0. \tag{48}$$

Thus the variation of the total potential energy V evaluated for a virtual displacement must be zero for equilibrium. Equation 48 is another way of expressing the equilibrium requirement for frictionless systems.

As an example of the foregoing concept consider the simple system in equilibrium shown in Fig. 82, consisting of the spring which is deflected

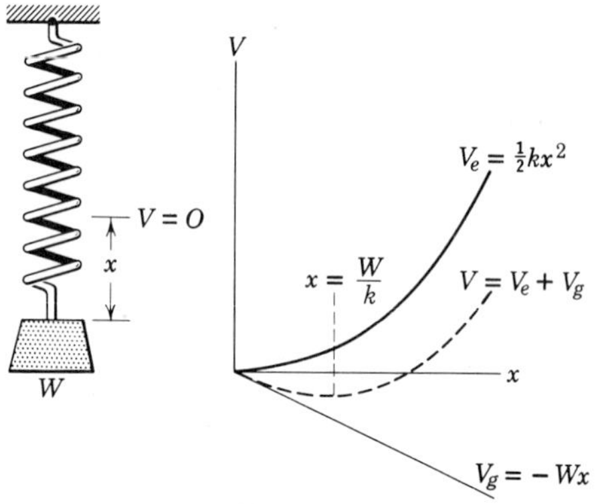

FIG. 82

an amount x due to the attached weight W. By taking $x = 0$ arbitrarily as the position for which $V = 0$, the potential energy for the displacement x is

$$V = V_e + V_g = \tfrac{1}{2}kx^2 - Wx.$$

The condition for equilibrium given by Eq. 48 requires

$$\delta V = kx\,\delta x - W\,\delta x = 0, \qquad x = \frac{W}{k}\cdot$$

This value agrees with the result which can be obtained by inspection. The contribution of V_e and V_g to the total potential energy V for various possible values of x is also shown in Fig. 82, and the value $x = W/k$ is seen to give a minimum value for V.

For systems with n degrees of freedom the variation of V with respect to each of the n coordinates separately, the remaining ones held constant, must be evaluated and set equal to zero. This procedure will give n equations in the n unknown coordinate values. If x_n represents one of the n coordinates, the partial derivative

$$\frac{\partial V}{\partial x_n} = 0$$

must be evaluated for each of the n coordinates.

The principle of zero variation in potential energy for equilibrium may be applied to *conservative systems* only, i.e., systems free from kinetic friction forces which do negative work. A system with kinetic friction will approach the position of minimum potential energy but will not reach it.

63. Stability of Equilibrium. The requirement of zero variation of the potential energy for equilibrium, as stated by Eq. 48, is equivalent to the requirement

$$\frac{dV}{dx} = 0 \tag{48a}$$

for a system with a single degree of freedom, where x is the coordinate defining the position of the system. Mathematically this equation defines the condition for a stationary value of V, a maximum, a minimum, or a point of inflection in the curve of V versus x. Although the natural equilibrium configuration usually represents a minimum value of V, there are the other two possibilities for stationary values which also represent equilibrium positions. Figure 83 shows an example of

FIG. 83

each type of equilibrium for the simple case of a sphere supported by surfaces of three different curvatures. The equilibrium is said to be *stable*, *unstable*, or *neutral* according to whether the potential energy is a *minimum* or a *maximum* or exhibits a *point of inflection*. Equilibrium is stable if a slight displacement from the equilibrium position results in an *increase* of potential energy and a corresponding tendency to reduce this energy by returning to the former position. Equilibrium is unstable if a slight displacement results in a *decrease* of potential energy and a corresponding tendency to reduce this energy still further by additional movement away from the equilibrium position. In the case of neutral equilibrium a slight displacement causes neither a tendency to return to nor a tendency to move away from the equilibrium position.

The potential energy criteria for the three types of equilibrium are represented in Fig. 84 for the case of a single degree of freedom where the coordinate defining the configuration is x. Once the total potential energy V is expressed as a function of the defining coordinate, the

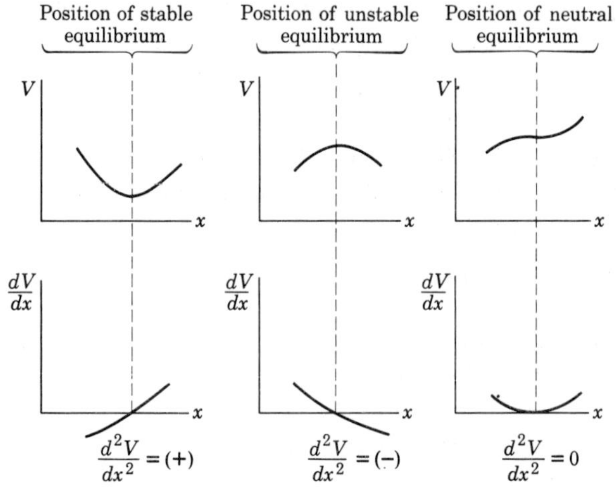

FIG. 84

equilibrium position is determined by Eq. 48*a*. The type of equilibrium is determined by the second derivative of V and is stable, unstable, or neutral according to whether d^2V/dx^2 is positive, negative, or zero at the equilibrium position.

SAMPLE PROBLEMS

603. The total potential energy V of a conservative mechanical system with a single degree of freedom in the coordinate x is given by

$$V = 4x^3 - 6x^2 + 3.$$

Determine the equilibrium positions and indicate the stability.

Solution. Equilibrium requires

$$\left[\delta V = 0 \quad \text{or} \quad \frac{dV}{dx} = 0\right] \qquad \frac{dV}{dx} = 12x^2 - 12x = 0,$$

$$x = 0, \qquad x = 1.$$

The stability is found from the second derivative. Thus,

$$\frac{d^2V}{dx^2} = 24x - 12.$$

For $x = 0$, $d^2V/dx^2 = -12$, and, since the sign is negative, this position is unstable. For $x = 1$, $d^2V/dx^2 = +12$, and this position is stable since the second derivative is positive.

604. Solve Prob. 591 by considering the total potential energy of the system.

Solution. An arbitrary datum plane for zero potential energy of position V_g must first be selected. Let this plane pass through B so that the potential energy of the two weights is

$$V_g = -2Wa \cos \theta.$$

The elastic potential energy due to the extension of the spring is

$$V_e = \tfrac{1}{2}kx^2 = \tfrac{1}{2}k(2a \cos \theta - a)^2.$$

The total potential energy of the system is then

$$V = V_g + V_e = -2Wa \cos \theta + \tfrac{1}{2}k(2a \cos \theta - a)^2.$$

The derivatives of V are

$$\frac{dV}{d\theta} = 2a(W + ka) \sin \theta - 4ka^2 \sin \theta \cos \theta$$

and

$$\frac{d^2V}{d\theta^2} = 2a(W + ka) \cos \theta - 4ka^2(2 \cos^2 \theta - 1).$$

For equilibrium $dV/d\theta = 0$, so that

$$(\sin \theta)\,[2a(W + ka) - 4ka^2 \cos \theta] = 0,$$

and the two solutions to this equation give the two equilibrium positions

$$\theta = 0 \qquad \text{and} \qquad \cos \theta = \frac{W + ka}{2ka}.$$

Since the cosine of an angle greater than zero must be less than unity, the second solution requires that $k > W/a$. At the position specified by the second solution the second derivative of V becomes

$$\frac{d^2V}{d\theta^2} = 2a(W + ka)\frac{W + ka}{2ka} - 4ka^2\left[2\left(\frac{W + ka}{2ka}\right)^2 - 1\right]$$

which reduces to

$$\frac{d^2V}{d\theta^2} = \frac{1}{k}(ka - W)(3ka + W).$$

Since $k > W/a$, the second derivative is positive, and $\theta = \cos^{-1} \dfrac{W + ka}{2ka}$ is a stable position.

The second derivative for the position $\theta = 0$ becomes

$$\frac{d^2V}{d\theta^2} = 2a(W + ka) - 4ka^2 = 2a(W - ka).$$

Thus when $k > W/a$, the second derivative of V for $\theta = 0$ is negative which means instability. If $k < W/a$, the only solution is $\theta = 0$ for which the second derivative of V is positive and indicates stability.

PROBLEMS

Solve the following problems by considering the total potential energy of each system.

605. The uniform beam AB has a weight W and is supported by the light-hinged link OA at one end and by the roller at B. Prove that the bar is in unstable equilibrium when OA is in the vertical position shown.

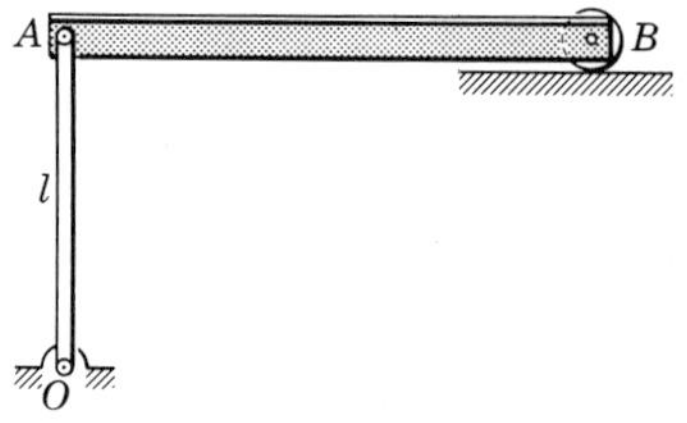

PROB. 605

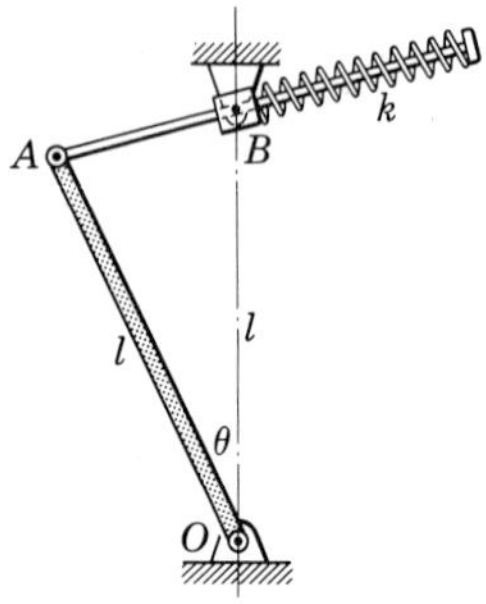

PROB. 608

606. A conservative mechanical system has a total potential energy of $V = x^4 - 8x^2 + 5$, where x is the coordinate which specifies the position of the system. Find the equilibrium positions and the type of stability.

Ans. $x = 0$ unstable, $x = \pm 2$ stable

607. The potential energy V of a conservative system is given by $V = ax^2/2 + bx^3/3$, where x is the coordinate specifying the position of the system. Determine the equilibrium positions and the stability if a and b are positive.

Ans. $x = -a/b$ unstable, $x = 0$ stable

608. The figure shows a cross section of a uniform door of weight W hinged about its horizontal bottom edge at O. When $\theta = 0$, the spring of stiffness k is undeformed by the supporting rod which slides through the swivel block B. Show that with the proper spring stiffness k the door will be in neutral equilibrium for any position.

Ans. $k = \dfrac{W}{2l}$

609. Check the stability for the equilibrium position $\theta = \pi$ for the mechanism of Prob. 597.

610. A uniform rectangular block of height h and weight W is centered in a horizontal position on the fixed circular surface of radius r. Show that this position is one of stable equilibrium if $h < 2r$.

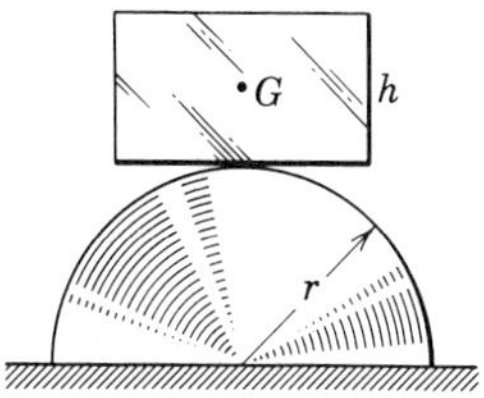

PROB. 610

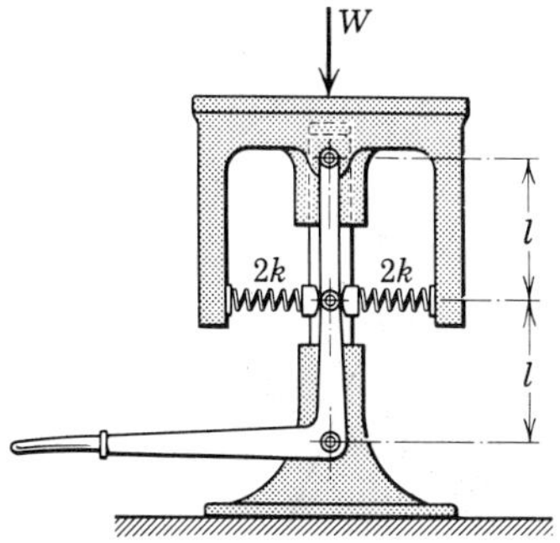

PROB. 611

611. In the figure is shown a small industrial foot lift. There are four identical springs, two on each side of the central shaft. The stiffness of each pair of springs is $2k$. Specify the values of k which will insure stable equilibrium when the lift supports a load W in the position shown with no force on the pedal. The springs have an equal initial precompression and may be assumed to act in the horizontal direction at all times.

Ans. $k > \dfrac{W}{2l}$

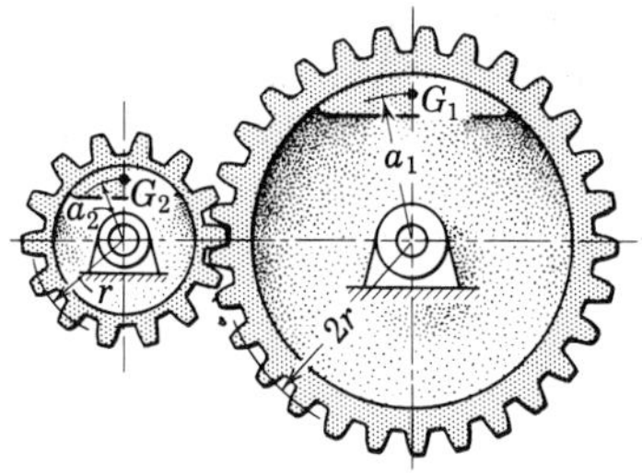

PROB. 612

* **612.** The two gears carry equal eccentric weights W with centers of gravity at G_1 and G_2 and turn freely on their bearings until they find their stable equilibrium position. Find the angle θ measured from the vertical through which the larger gear rotates from the position shown to the equilibrium position. Discuss the stability.

Ans. $\theta = \cos^{-1}\left(\dfrac{-a_1}{4a_2}\right)$ for $a_1 < 4a_2$, $\theta = \pi$ for $a_1 > 4a_2$

* **613.** In the mechanism shown gear B is fixed and cannot rotate. Gears A and C, together with the attached arm, are free to rotate about B. Gear C carries an eccentric weight whose center of gravity is at G. The center of gravity of the remainder of the system is at O. When $\theta = 0$, the point G is

on the vertical center line through O. Determine the angle θ for equilibrium under the action of the unbalanced weight for $b > a/2$. What will happen if $b < a/2$?

Ans. $\theta = \cos^{-1} \dfrac{a}{2b}$

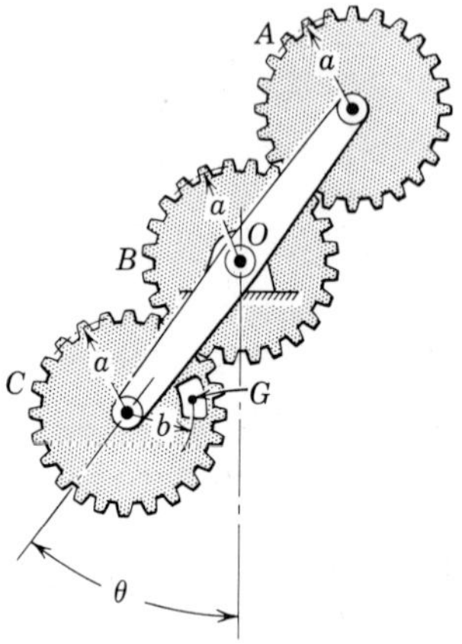

Prob. 613

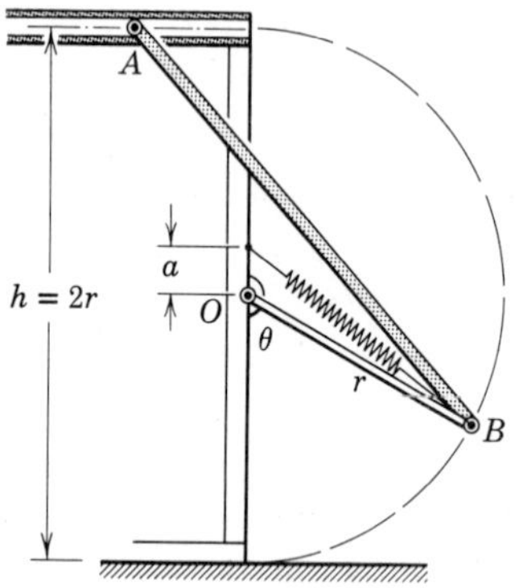

Prob. 614

* **614.** The uniform garage door AB shown in section has a weight W and is equipped with two of the spring-loaded mechanisms shown, one on each side of the door. The arm OB has negligible weight, and the upper corner A of the door is free to move horizontally on a roller. The unstretched length of the spring is $r - a$, so that in the top position with $\theta = \pi$ the spring force is zero. In order to insure smooth action of the door as it reaches the vertical closed position $\theta = 0$, it is desirable that this position be one of neutral equilibrium. Determine the required spring stiffness k.

Ans. $k = \dfrac{W(r + a)}{8a^2}$

APPENDIX

A

REVIEW PROBLEMS

In the preceding chapters the problems which are included with the various articles illustrate application of the particular topic involved. Thus the problem category and method of solution for these problems are to a great extent indicated automatically by their association with the article. The student of mechanics should develop ability to classify a new problem by recognizing the topic or topics involved and by selecting the appropriate method or methods of solution. The following review problems in Appendix A are included to help the student develop this ability. The problems are arranged without regard for topic or method of solution, although they are arranged approximately in order of increasing difficulty. Some problems include more than one topic or may be worked by more than one method. It is suggested that the student use his time to outline the solution to as many of the problems as possible rather than to concentrate on the complete solution of only a limited few of them. In this way considerably more ground can be covered. The answers to all of the problems are included for those who wish them.

A1. A steel plate ¾ in. thick in the form of a circular sector is supported by the three legs shown. Determine the force in each leg.

Ans. $A = 152$ lb., $B = C = 212$ lb.

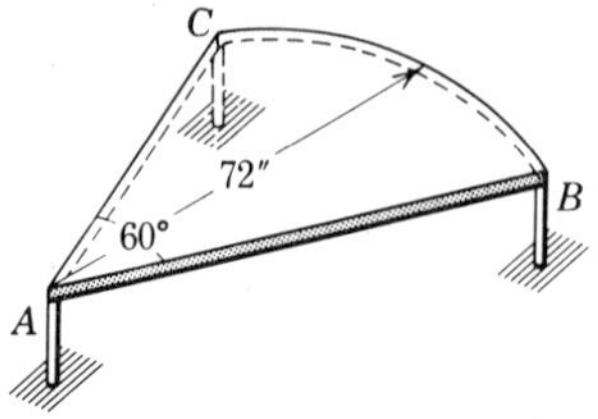

Prob. A1

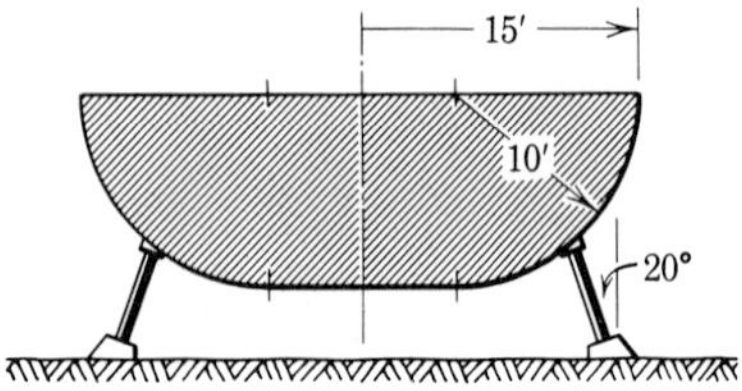

Prob. A2

A2. A circular fresh-water tank 30 ft. in diameter has the cross section shown. Determine the compression C in each of the six equally spaced struts supporting the tank when full. (Only two struts are shown.) Neglect the weight of the empty tank and treat each strut as if it were pin-connected at its ends.

Ans. $C = 59{,}200$ lb.

A3. A semicircular section of a concrete culvert is resting on a horizontal surface as shown. Determine the maximum bending moment M in the section. The culvert has a weight W and a thickness which is small compared with its radius r.

Ans. $M = \dfrac{Wr}{\pi}$

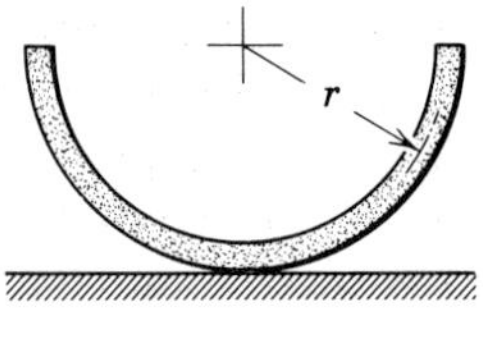

Prob. A3

A4. Each of the main legs of the derrick is divided into equal panels as shown. Determine the compression in AB in terms of the load W.

Ans. $AB = 2.23W$

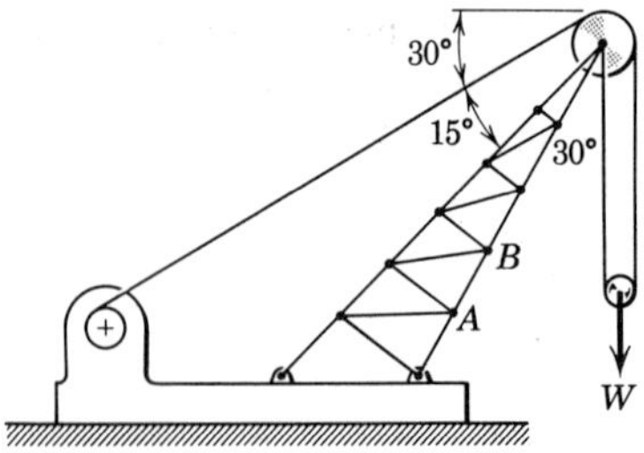

Prob. A4

A5. The weight of the bar is W, and the pressure between it and the horizontal surface upon which it rests is uniformly distributed. If the coefficient of friction between the surfaces is f, determine the couple M required to rotate the bar. The dimension a is negligible. *Ans.* $M = fWl/4$

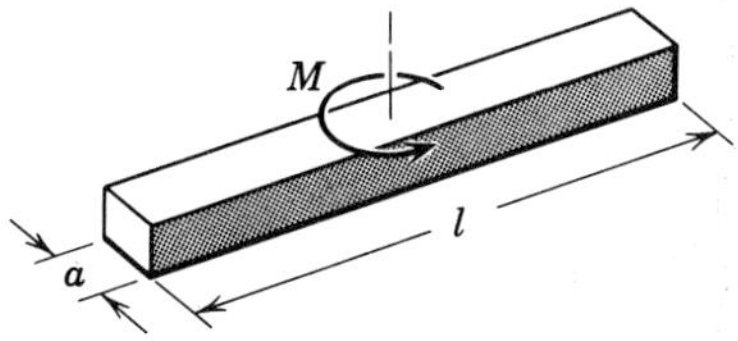

PROB. A5

A6. The cylindrical fresh-water tank shown in section has a removable bottom in the form of an inverted conical shell. The shell has a flange which seats itself under the action of fluid pressure on a rubber-ring gasket with an outside diameter of 40 in. and an inside diameter of 36 in. Calculate the mechanical pressure p (above atmospheric) which acts on the gasket when the tank is filled to the level indicated. The weight of the shell is negligible compared with the other forces involved. *Ans.* p = 6.76 lb./in.^{2}

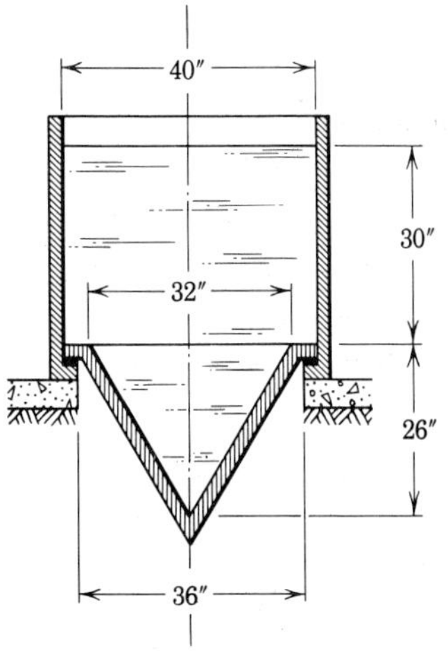

PROB. A6

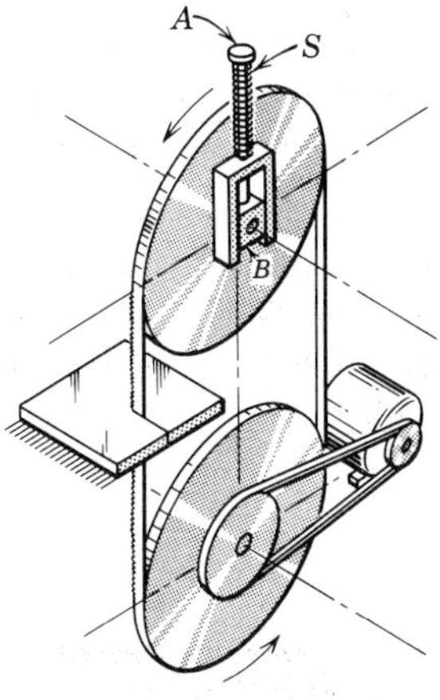

PROB. A7

A7. A tension is maintained in the band-saw blade by the spring S which pushes up on the rod A which, in turn, is connected to the bearing block B of the idler pulley. If a 50 lb. force is required to shear off a tooth on the blade, determine the spring force F which can be allowed and still insure that the blade slips on its pulley before a tooth is sheared. Assume that force is applied to only one tooth at a time. The coefficient of friction between the band and the pulley may be taken to be 0.40. Neglect the weight of the upper pulley.

Ans. F = 39.8 lb.

A8. The foundry ladle contains molten metal which has a density of 0.392 lb./in.³ The empty ladle weighs 7200 lb. with center of gravity at G. Determine the tension T in the vertical control cable required to begin the pour in the position shown. (Refer to Prob. 362.) *Ans.* $T = 493$ lb.

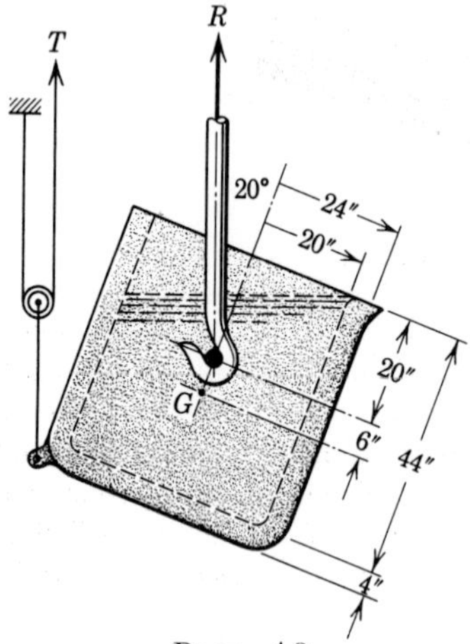

PROB. A8

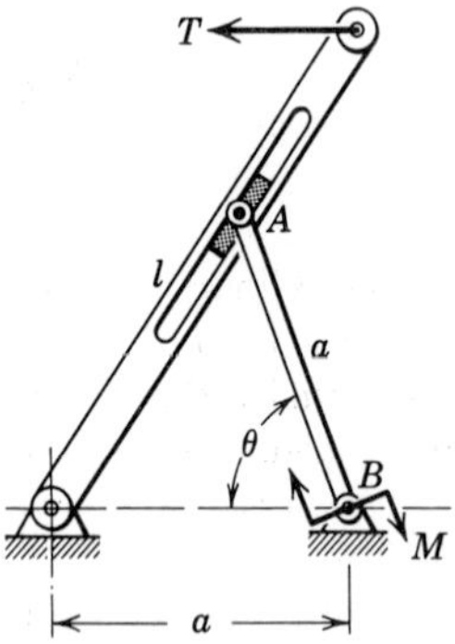

PROB. A9

A9. Determine the torque M applied to the lever AB required to support the horizontal tension T for any possible equilibrium angle θ. End A is pinned to the slider block which is free to move in the smooth slot.

Ans. $M = \dfrac{Tl}{2} \cos \dfrac{\theta}{2}$

A10. A chain with a weight μ per unit length is pulled around the pulley. The pulley is free to rotate about O. Determine the tension T required to support the chain in the position shown if friction on the horizontal surface A is negligible. *Ans.* $T = \mu r$

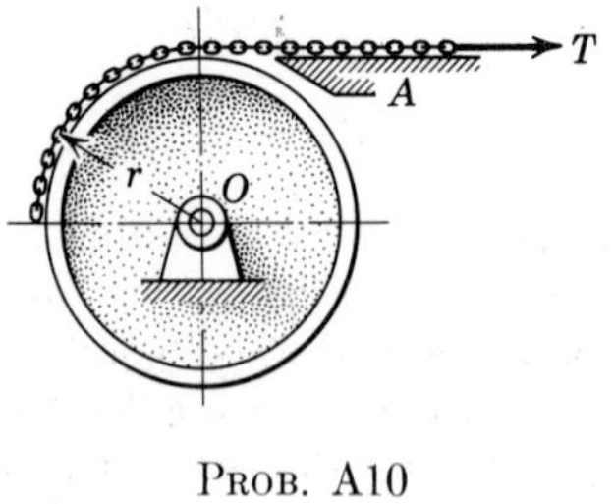

PROB. A10

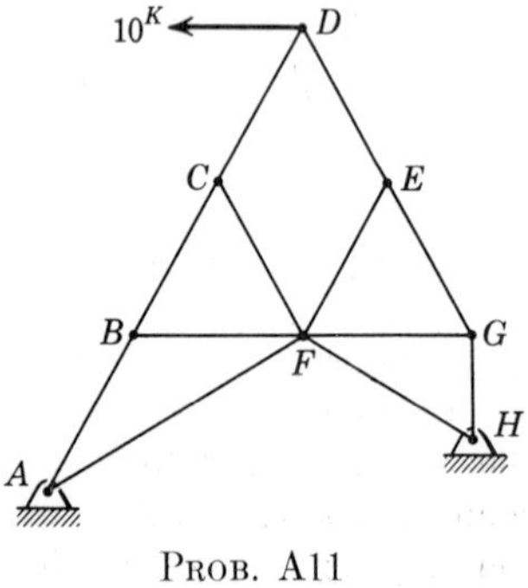

PROB. A11

A11. Determine the force in members BF and GF for the truss. All angles are 30, 60, 90, or 120 deg. *Ans.* $BF = 0$, $GF = 5$ kips C

A12. Find the x- and y-components of all forces acting on each member of the frame. Neglect the weights of the pulley and members.

Ans. $A_x = 160$ lb., $A_y = 120$ lb., $C_x = 840$ lb., $C_y = 1120$ lb.

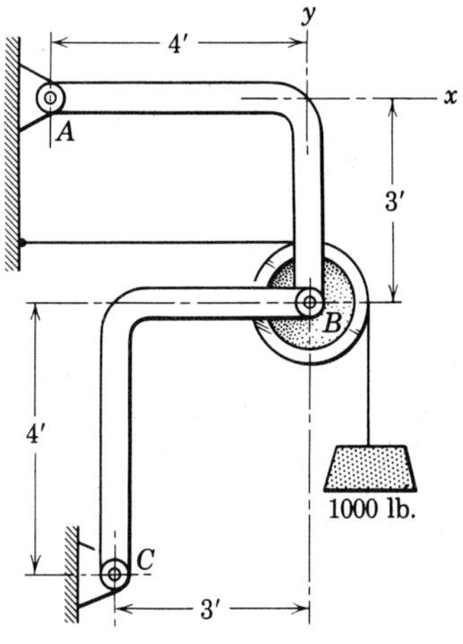

PROB. A12

A13. Determine the forces F required to lift the weight W in terms of the angle θ. The slider blocks which support the links are free to move in the horizontal guide.

$$Ans.\quad F = \frac{W(a + 2b)}{2a} \text{ ctn } \theta$$

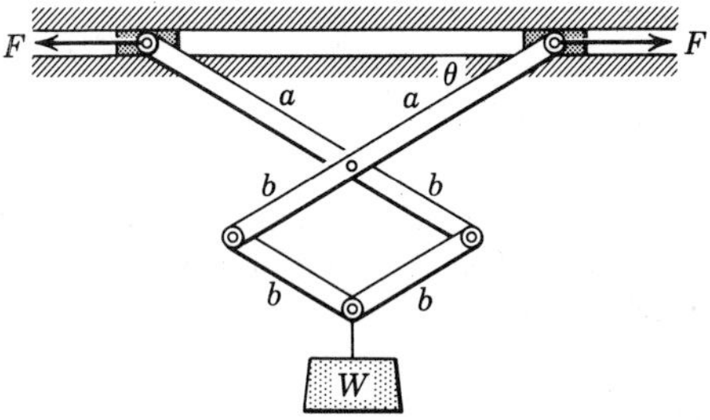

PROB. A13

A14. The figure shows a booster unit for a hydraulic brake system. The force F on the small piston rod is applied by foot pressure. The increased force T is used to activate the brake mechanism. If the piston diameters are 4 in. and $1\frac{1}{2}$ in., and the remaining dimensions are as shown, calculate T in terms of F and find the force on the pin A in terms of F.

Ans. $T = 3.56F$, $A = 11.38F$

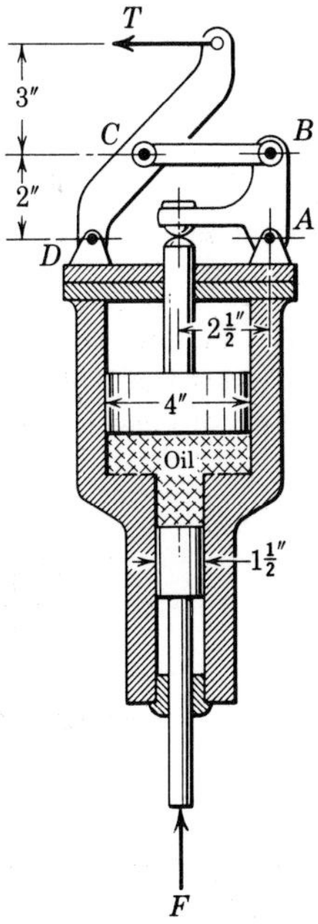

PROB. A14

A15. Determine the force in member *GD* of the truss loaded as shown. All angles are either 45, 60, or 90 deg. *Ans.* $GD = 0.789L$, *C*

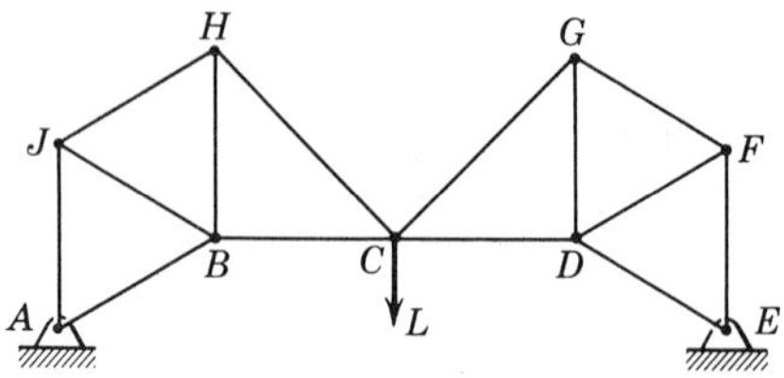

Prob. A15

A16. A 15 ft. section of concrete culvert weighing 15,000 lb. is rolled up the 15 deg. slope into the dotted position preparatory to being lowered into the trench. Determine the tension T in the cable wrapped around the culvert required to roll the culvert up the incline. Also find the friction force F acting on the culvert if the coefficient of friction is 0.4 and the cable tension T is vertical. *Ans.* $T = 3080$ lb., $F = 3080$ lb.

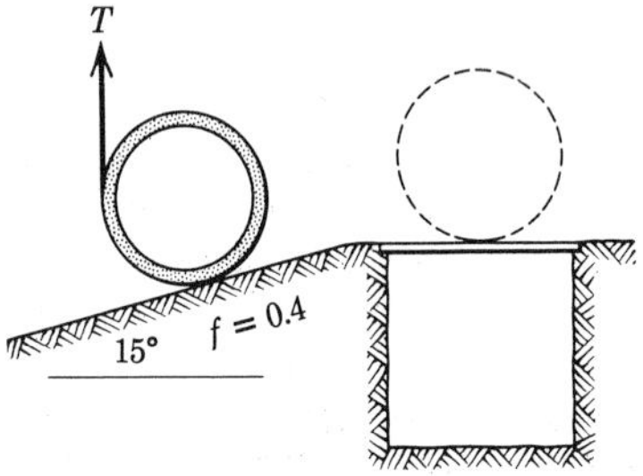

Prob. A16

A17. Compute the torque M on the handle of the screw required for the wedge to lift the 1000 lb. weight. The coefficient of friction between all pairs of sliding surfaces is 0.4. The single-threaded screw has a mean diameter of

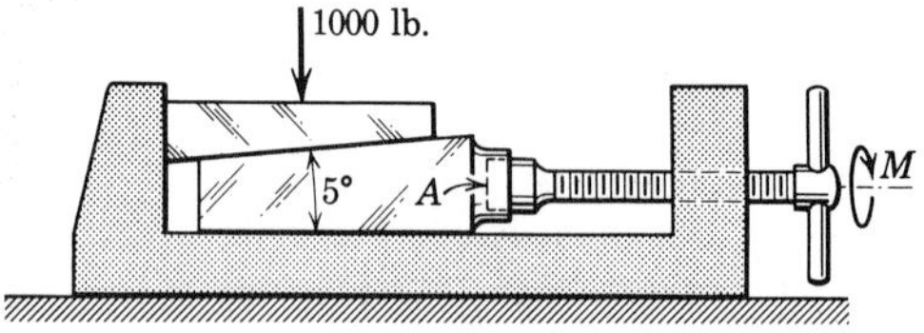

Prob. A17

1 in. and has 5 square threads per inch. The thrust bearing at A has a diameter of 1.5 in., and the pressure on its surface is uniform over the area.

Ans. $M = 497$ lb. in.

A18. The electric motor weighs 80 lb. with center of gravity at G. It is hinged about the horizontal axis AB so as to maintain tension in the V-belt. If the motor is turning clockwise and delivering a torque of 120 lb. in., determine the resultant force on each of the supports A and B and the tensions T_1 and T_2 in the belt.

Ans. $A = 107.8$ lb., $B = 46.7$ lb., $T_1 = 54$ lb., $T_2 = 14$ lb.

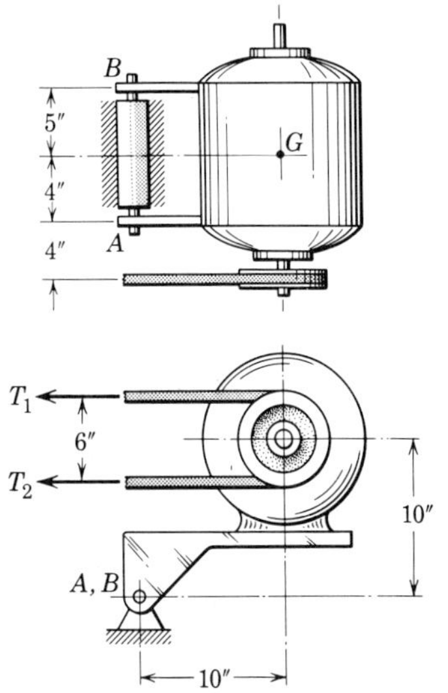

Prob. A18

A19. The figure shows a beam ABC to which is assembled a framework of light pin-jointed links. Determine the force in BD, and find the bending moment M in the beam half way between B and C due to the 5 kip load. Neglect the weight of the beam. *Ans.* $BD = 14.43$ kips C, $M = 25{,}000$ lb. ft.

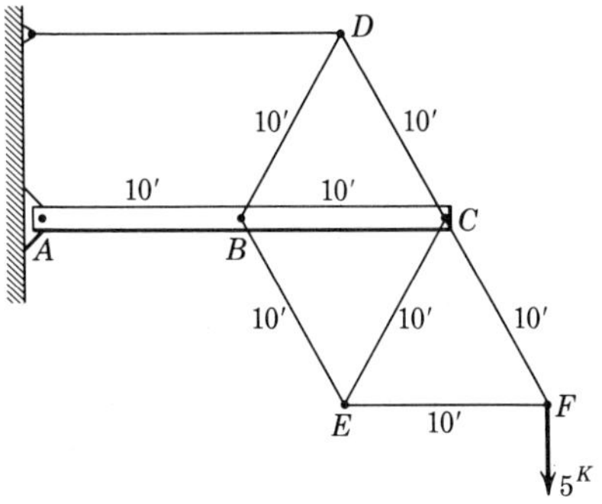

Prob. A19

A20. A bridge consists of three sections hinged at A, B, D, and E. The end sections are prevented from rocking by horizontal support either at C or at F but not at both simultaneously. The midsection is uniform and weighs 50 tons, and each end section weighs 100 tons with center of gravity at G. Determine the reaction at C or F and the total force on the hinge at D.

Ans. $C_x = 17.2$ tons, $D = 91.2$ tons

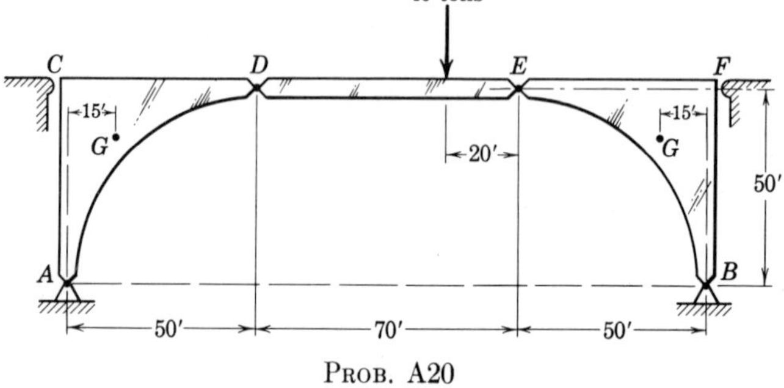

PROB. A20

A21. If the coefficient of friction between the hemispherical shell and the plane is f, show that the maximum angle θ which the plane may be tilted before slipping occurs is equal to $\tan^{-1} f$. Also specify the angle β made by the diametral plane with the horizontal for any equilibrium angle θ.

Ans. $\sin \beta = 2 \sin \theta$

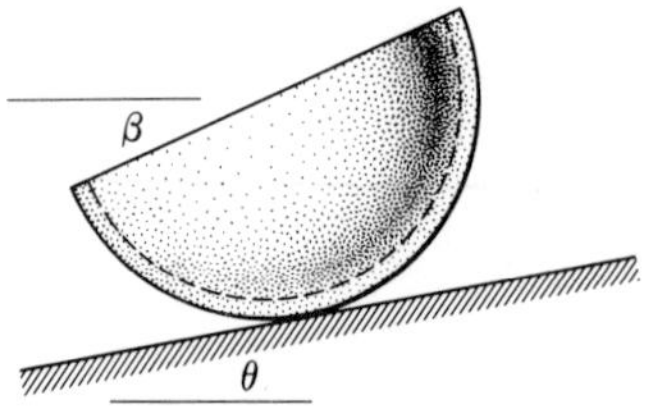

PROB. A21

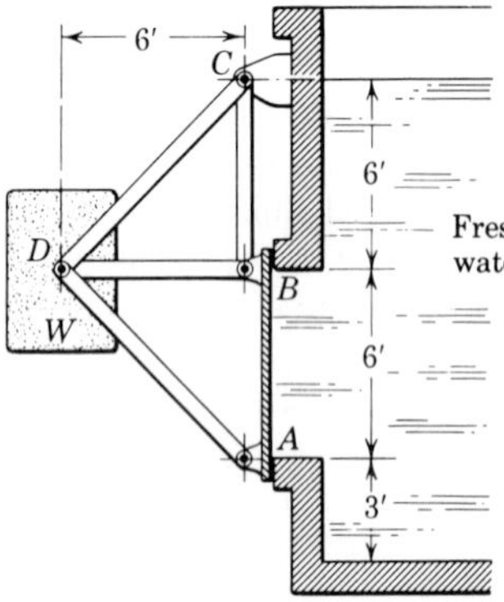

PROB. A22

A22. A gate for limiting the depth of water in a small reservoir consists of a flat plate which seals a rectangular opening 6 ft. high and 4 ft. wide. The plate and attached frame have negligible weight and are hinged at C and counterweighted as shown. Determine the counterweight W which will limit the depth of water to the level shown. Also find the force in strut DB.

Ans. $W = 21{,}000$ lb., $DB = 5990$ lb. C

A23. The figure shows an overhead industrial door with a total weight of 300 lb. and made of hinged segments so that it will pass over the rollers on the cylindrical guide. When the door is closed, the end A is at position B. On each side of the door there is a control cable which is fastened to the bottom of

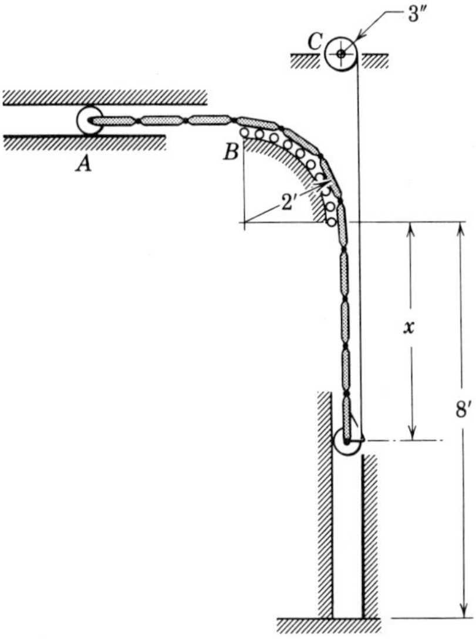

PROB. A23

the door and which is wound around a drum C. Each of the two drums is connected to its own torsion spring which offers a torsional resistance of 85 lb. in. per revolution of the drum starting from an unwound position when $x = 0$. Determine the equilibrium position x and prove that this position is stable.

Ans. $x = 5.88$ ft.

A24. The truss of Prob. 266 is repeated here. Determine the force in member DE by an algebraic solution. *Ans.* $DE = 1578$ lb. C

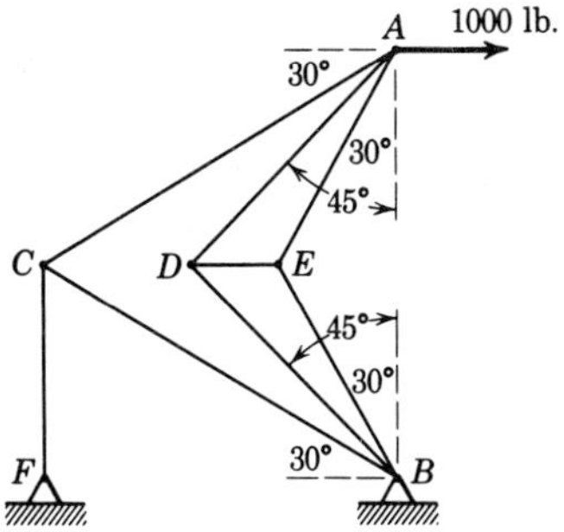

PROB. A24

A25. The figure shows the cross section of a cofferdam with the bracing repeated every 12 ft. of dam length. Determine the force in braces BE and BF. The weights of the members are small, and they may be treated as two-force members. The panels AB and BC may be considered as separate members hinged at their ends to the respective joints. Panels FE and ED are considered in a similar way. The density of the mud is 80 lb./ft.^{3} and that of the salt water is 64 lb./ft.^{3} *Ans.* BE = 2590 lb. C, BF = 69,500 lb. C

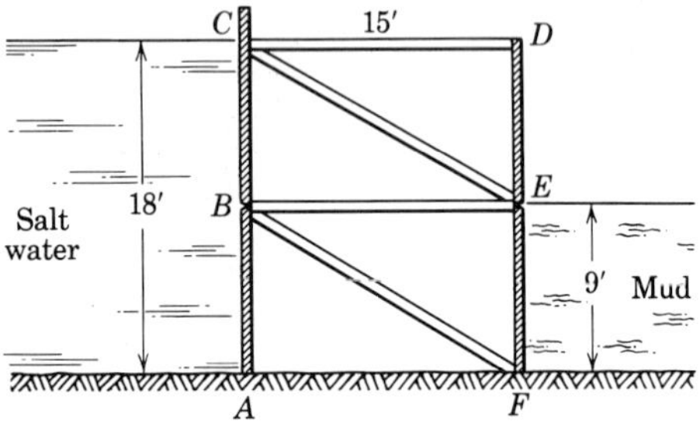

PROB. A25

A26. Each of the two springs has a stiffness k and is precompressed a distance Δ when the arm AB is horizontal. Determine the maximum height b at which the weight W may be set on the rod in order to insure that the weighted arm will return to the upright position shown after being displaced from it.

Ans. $b_{max.} = \dfrac{2ka^2}{W}$

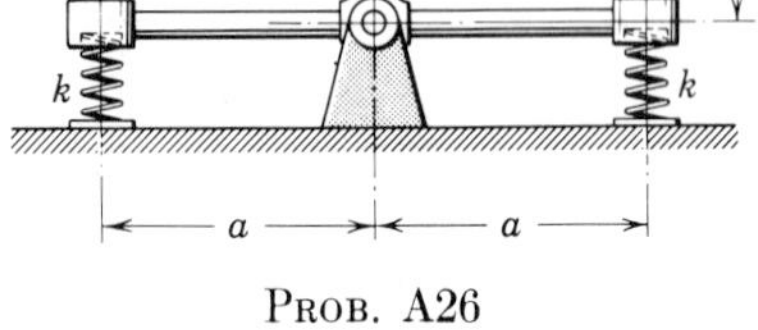

PROB. A26

A27. A force of 20 lb. applied to the knob perpendicular to the plane of the door is required to hold it open against the action of the spring-loaded door check in the position shown. Determine the torque M applied to the link CD at D by the torsion spring in the door-check mechanism, and compute the horizontal component H of the force supported by the hinge at B. At this particular position CD is parallel to the plane of the door, and CE is perpendicular to the plane of the wall. The combined weight of the door and door check is 80 lb., and the center of gravity G may be taken to be in the center of the door. *Ans.* $M = 447$ lb. in., $H = 28.6$ lb.

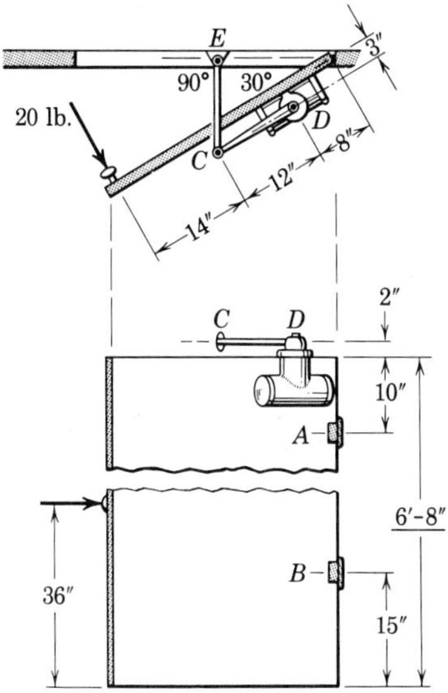

PROB. A27

APPENDIX

B

VECTOR METHODS

B1. Introduction. Mechanics is inherently a subject which depends on vector quantities. The basic concepts of a vector are set forth in Art. 3 of Chapter 1 and will not be repeated again here. Force, moment, displacement, velocity, acceleration, momentum, and impulse are the common vector quantities found in mechanics. Statics involves, primarily, the first three of these vectors. In the preceding chapters the addition and subtraction of vectors is denoted by the respective symbols $+\!\!\!\!\rightarrow$ and $\rightarrow$ to call attention to the distinction between vector and scalar operations. Where the multiplication of vector quantities occurs, such as in the calculation of a moment, the magnitude of the product is specified with its scalar value, and the direction of the product, if a vector, is indicated or described separately.

An alternate system of notation may be used which incorporates the magnitude and directional aspects of a vector in a single symbol. This system, which permits the use of ordinary plus and minus signs, which distinguishes between the vector or scalar aspects of the multiplication of vectors, and which permits the representation of vector operations in three dimensions with a simplicity comparable to that in two dimensions, is contained in the dot- and cross-product notation invented by Josiah Willard Gibbs (1839–1903). This notation is widely used by physicists, mathematicians, and some engineers and is often referred to as *Gibbs' Notation.* In mechanics this vector notation finds its most important use in three-dimensional problems of dynamics where time derivatives of space vectors are encountered. It should be emphasized that the vector notation is of assistance in formulating certain general relations, primarily three dimensional, but in the end must give way to scalar computation when engineering results in the form of numerical answers are required.

It is the purpose of the following treatment to provide an introduction to the vector notation as it applies to statics. This notation may be used where applicable as an alternative to the scalar symbols employed in the preceding chapters. A full development of vector algebra and vector calculus may be found in numerous references devoted to this subject and is not the purpose of the following abbreviated treatment.

B2. Notation. In the notation of vector algebra it is necessary to distinguish between scalars and vectors by the appearance of the symbol used. The most common designation is the use of boldface type for vectors and lightface type for scalars. This designation is used hereafter in Appendix B. Thus $\boldsymbol{V}$ represents some vector quantity with the scalar magnitude $V = |\boldsymbol{V}|$. The vector equation $\boldsymbol{P} = \boldsymbol{Q}$ signifies the equality of two vectors and means not only equality of magnitudes $|\boldsymbol{P}| = |\boldsymbol{Q}|$, but also that the direction and sense of the two vectors are the same. A vector $\boldsymbol{V}$ when multiplied by a scalar a is the vector $a\boldsymbol{V}$ or $\boldsymbol{V}a$ which has the magnitude aV and the direction of $\boldsymbol{V}$.

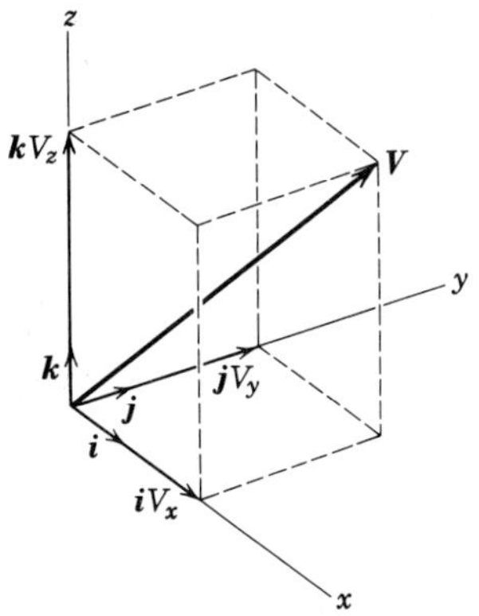

FIG. B1

A vector $\boldsymbol{V}$ may be resolved into three mutually perpendicular components in, say, the x-, y-, and z-directions, Fig. B1. These components are actually vectors with magnitudes equal to V_x, V_y, and V_z, respectively. To represent these components as vectors it is necessary to introduce the vectors $\boldsymbol{i}$, $\boldsymbol{j}$, $\boldsymbol{k}$ of unit magnitude and directed along the x-, y-, and z-axes, respectively. Thus the component vectors of $\boldsymbol{V}$ are $\boldsymbol{i}V_x$, $\boldsymbol{j}V_y$, and $\boldsymbol{k}V_z$, and their vector sum is

$$\boldsymbol{V} = \boldsymbol{i}V_x + \boldsymbol{j}V_y + \boldsymbol{k}V_z \tag{B1}$$

where the plus signs denote vector addition. The quantities V_x, V_y, and V_z are known as the scalar components of $\boldsymbol{V}$, and they must satisfy the relation

$$V = \sqrt{V_x^2 + V_y^2 + V_z^2}. \tag{B2}$$

B3. Addition. From the basic concept of vector addition it follows that the sum of two vectors $\boldsymbol{P}$ and $\boldsymbol{Q}$ may be written in terms of the sums of their components,

$$\boldsymbol{P} + \boldsymbol{Q} = \boldsymbol{i}(P_x + Q_x) + \boldsymbol{j}(P_y + Q_y) + \boldsymbol{k}(P_z + Q_z).$$

This expression may be extended to cover the sum $\boldsymbol{R}$ of any number of vectors $\boldsymbol{F}$. Thus

$$\boldsymbol{R} = \Sigma \boldsymbol{F} = \boldsymbol{i}\Sigma F_x + \boldsymbol{j}\Sigma F_y + \boldsymbol{k}\Sigma F_z,$$

and

$$R_x = \Sigma F_x, \qquad R_y = \Sigma F_y, \qquad R_z = \Sigma F_z.$$

If the vectors represented by $\Sigma \boldsymbol{F}$ constitute a system of forces, then $\boldsymbol{R}$ is merely the resultant of the system, and R_x, R_y, and R_z are the scalar components of the resultant. For a system of forces in equilibrium the resultant is zero, and $\Sigma \boldsymbol{F} = 0$ gives $\Sigma F_x = 0$, $\Sigma F_y = 0$, $\Sigma F_z = 0$ which are the familiar force equations of equilibrium.

It has already been established that the sum of two vectors is independent of the order in which they are added. Thus

$$\boldsymbol{P} + \boldsymbol{Q} = \boldsymbol{Q} + \boldsymbol{P}$$

which is the commutative law for vector addition. Further, it is clear from the elementary concepts of vector addition that the associative law

$$\boldsymbol{P} + (\boldsymbol{Q} + \boldsymbol{R}) = (\boldsymbol{P} + \boldsymbol{Q}) + \boldsymbol{R}$$

also holds.

The subtraction of vectors may be considered as a special case of addition by using the fact that the negative of a vector $\boldsymbol{Q}$ is a vector $-\boldsymbol{Q}$ of the same magnitude but opposite in direction. Thus $\boldsymbol{P} - \boldsymbol{Q} = \boldsymbol{P} + (-\boldsymbol{Q})$.

B4. Dot or Scalar Product. One type of product involving two vectors is formed by multiplying the product of their magnitudes by the cosine of the angle between them. Thus, for the vectors in Fig. B2, this product is defined as

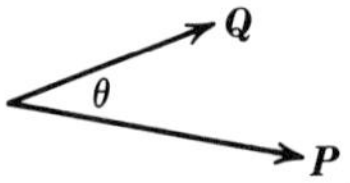

FIG. B2

$$\boldsymbol{P}\cdot\boldsymbol{Q} = PQ \cos \theta \tag{B3}$$

and is known as the *dot* or *scalar product*. This product may be viewed as the magnitude of $\boldsymbol{P}$ multiplied by the component of $\boldsymbol{Q}$ in the direction of $\boldsymbol{P}$ or as the magnitude of $\boldsymbol{Q}$ multiplied by the component of $\boldsymbol{P}$ in the direction of $\boldsymbol{Q}$. The scalar result does not depend upon the order of the multiplication. Thus

$$\boldsymbol{P}\cdot\boldsymbol{Q} = \boldsymbol{Q}\cdot\boldsymbol{P}$$

which means that the commutative law holds for scalar products.

The most common example of the dot product in mechanics is the expression for work. It is seen that the foregoing definition of the dot product is identical to the definition of the work of a force $\boldsymbol{F}$ whose point of application moves through a vector displacement $\boldsymbol{s}$. The

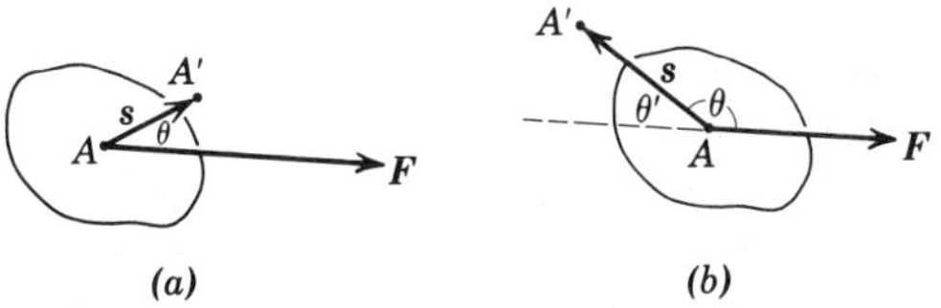

FIG. B3

work done by the force $\boldsymbol{F}$ in Fig. B3a during a displacement $\boldsymbol{s}$ of its point of application from A to A' is

$$U = \boldsymbol{F}\cdot\boldsymbol{s} = Fs\cos\theta$$

and is positive if θ is less than 90 deg. For θ greater than 90 deg., Fig. B3b, the work done by $\boldsymbol{F}$ is $U = Fs\cos\theta = Fs\cos(\pi - \theta') = -Fs\cos\theta'$ which shows that the work is negative.

For an infinitesimal virtual displacement $\delta\boldsymbol{s}$ the virtual work done by $\boldsymbol{F}$ is $U = \boldsymbol{F}\cdot\delta\boldsymbol{s}$. The principle of virtual work, $\delta U = 0$, is, then, equivalent to forming the sum of the dot products of each active force with the corresponding virtual displacement of its point of application and setting the sum equal to zero.

With the definition of the dot product of two vectors it is at once apparent that the following relations hold for unit vectors:

$$\boldsymbol{i}\cdot\boldsymbol{i} = \boldsymbol{j}\cdot\boldsymbol{j} = \boldsymbol{k}\cdot\boldsymbol{k} = 1,$$

$$\boldsymbol{i}\cdot\boldsymbol{j} = \boldsymbol{j}\cdot\boldsymbol{i} = \boldsymbol{i}\cdot\boldsymbol{k} = \boldsymbol{k}\cdot\boldsymbol{i} = \boldsymbol{j}\cdot\boldsymbol{k} = \boldsymbol{k}\cdot\boldsymbol{j} = 0.$$

With the aid of these identities the dot product of $\boldsymbol{P}$ and $\boldsymbol{Q}$ may be written in component form as

$$\begin{aligned}\boldsymbol{P}\cdot\boldsymbol{Q} &= (\boldsymbol{i}P_x + \boldsymbol{j}P_y + \boldsymbol{k}P_z)\cdot(\boldsymbol{i}Q_x + \boldsymbol{j}Q_y + \boldsymbol{k}Q_z)\\ &= P_xQ_x + P_yQ_y + P_zQ_z.\end{aligned}$$

The dot product of a vector by itself becomes

$$P\cdot P = P_x^2 + P_y^2 + P_z^2 = P^2.$$

The distributive law holds for the dot product as may be seen by regrouping the terms. Thus

$$\begin{aligned} \boldsymbol{P}\cdot(\boldsymbol{Q}+\boldsymbol{R}) &= P_x(Q_x+R_x)+P_y(Q_y+R_y)+P_z(Q_z+R_z) \\ &= \boldsymbol{P}\cdot\boldsymbol{Q}+\boldsymbol{P}\cdot\boldsymbol{R}. \end{aligned}$$

B5. Cross or Vector Product. A second product involving two vectors is known as the *cross product* or *vector product*. The cross product of the vectors **P** and **Q** in Fig. B4*a* is defined as the vector **R** whose magnitude equals the product of the magnitudes of **P** and **Q** multiplied by the sine of the angle (less than 180 deg.) between **P** and

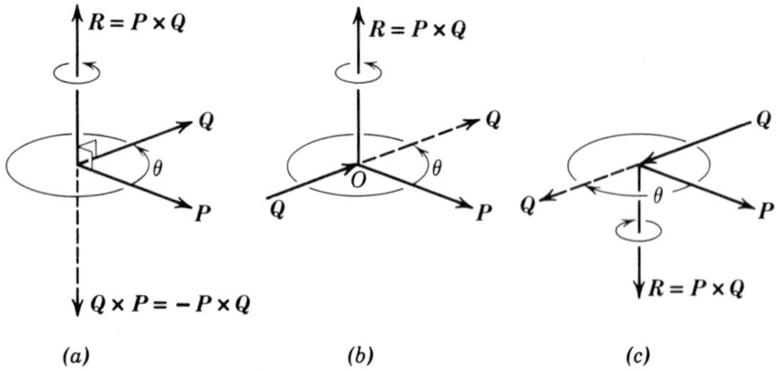

FIG. B4

Q. Further, the direction of **R** is the direction of advancement of a right-hand screw when revolved from **P** to **Q** through an angle θ less than 180 deg. This cross product is written as

$$\boldsymbol{R}=\boldsymbol{P}\times\boldsymbol{Q} \qquad \text{where } R = PQ\sin\theta. \tag{B4}$$

By using the right-hand rule it is seen that $\boldsymbol{P}\times\boldsymbol{Q}=-\boldsymbol{Q}\times\boldsymbol{P}$, and, hence, the commutative law does not hold for the cross product. The cross product $\boldsymbol{Q}\times\boldsymbol{P}$ is a vector in the opposite direction to $\boldsymbol{P}\times\boldsymbol{Q}$ as shown in Fig. B4*a*. The validity of the distributive law for the cross product may be shown by a relatively simple geometrical proof. It is stated here without proof and is

$$\boldsymbol{P}\times(\boldsymbol{Q}+\boldsymbol{R})=\boldsymbol{P}\times\boldsymbol{Q}+\boldsymbol{P}\times\boldsymbol{R}.$$

In forming the vector product it is well to consider the vectors according to the definition given. Thus in Fig. B4*b* the product $\boldsymbol{P}\times\boldsymbol{Q}$ is correctly formed by moving **Q** so that both **Q** and **P** stem from *O*. For the configuration of Fig. B4*c* the angle θ (less than 180 deg.) between **P** and **Q** extended must be used. Advancement from

$\boldsymbol{P}$ to $\boldsymbol{Q}$ by the right-hand rule through the angle θ requires that the cross product be down.

With the definition of the cross product the following relations between the unit vectors are apparent:

$$\boldsymbol{i} \times \boldsymbol{j} = \boldsymbol{k} \qquad \boldsymbol{j} \times \boldsymbol{k} = \boldsymbol{i} \qquad \boldsymbol{k} \times \boldsymbol{i} = \boldsymbol{j}$$

$$\boldsymbol{j} \times \boldsymbol{i} = -\boldsymbol{k} \qquad \boldsymbol{k} \times \boldsymbol{j} = -\boldsymbol{i} \qquad \boldsymbol{i} \times \boldsymbol{k} = -\boldsymbol{j}$$

$$\boldsymbol{i} \times \boldsymbol{i} = \boldsymbol{j} \times \boldsymbol{j} = \boldsymbol{k} \times \boldsymbol{k} = 0.$$

With the aid of these identities and the distributive law the vector product may be written

$$\boldsymbol{P} \times \boldsymbol{Q} = (\boldsymbol{i}P_x + \boldsymbol{j}P_y + \boldsymbol{k}P_z) \times (\boldsymbol{i}Q_x + \boldsymbol{j}Q_y + \boldsymbol{k}Q_z)$$
$$= \boldsymbol{i}(P_yQ_z - P_zQ_y) + \boldsymbol{j}(P_zQ_x - P_xQ_z) + \boldsymbol{k}(P_xQ_y - P_yQ_x)$$

upon rearrangement of terms. This expression may be written compactly as the determinant

$$\boldsymbol{P} \times \boldsymbol{Q} = \begin{vmatrix} \boldsymbol{i} & \boldsymbol{j} & \boldsymbol{k} \\ P_x & P_y & P_z \\ Q_x & Q_y & Q_z \end{vmatrix}.$$

It is readily seen that the cross product as defined fits the requirement for the description of the moment of a force. In Fig. B5 consider the moment $\boldsymbol{M}$ produced by the force $\boldsymbol{F}$ about an axis through O normal to the plane of the figure. The force acts at a point A whose vector position with respect to O as origin is $\boldsymbol{r} = \boldsymbol{i}x + \boldsymbol{j}y + \boldsymbol{k}z$. The moment has a magnitude of $Fd = Fr \sin \theta$. The direction of $\boldsymbol{M}$ is out from the paper which is the direction of the advancement of a right-hand screw when rotated from $\boldsymbol{r}$ to $\boldsymbol{F}$ through the smaller of the two angles θ between them. Thus

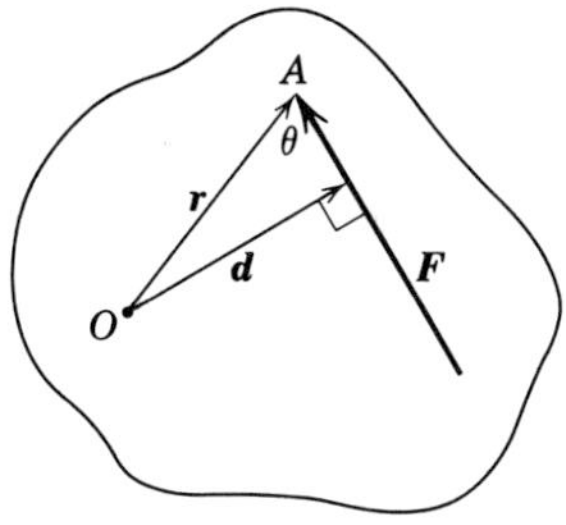

FIG. B5

$$\boldsymbol{M} = \boldsymbol{r} \times \boldsymbol{F}. \tag{B5}$$

It is important to observe that $\boldsymbol{M} \neq \boldsymbol{F} \times \boldsymbol{r}$ which expression would be a vector in the opposite sense to the moment.

In component form Eq. B5 may be written as

$$\boldsymbol{M} = (\boldsymbol{i}x + \boldsymbol{j}y + \boldsymbol{k}z) \times (\boldsymbol{i}F_x + \boldsymbol{j}F_y + \boldsymbol{k}F_z)$$
$$= \boldsymbol{i}(yF_z - zF_y) + \boldsymbol{j}(zF_x - xF_z) + \boldsymbol{k}(xF_y - yF_x),$$

so that the scalar components of $\boldsymbol{M}$ become $M_x = yF_z - zF_y$, $M_y = zF_x - xF_z$, $M_z = xF_y - yF_x$.

In Fig. B6 two parallel forces $\boldsymbol{F}_1$ and $\boldsymbol{F}_2$ with equal magnitude F are acting at points whose position vectors from some origin O are $\boldsymbol{r}_1$ and $\boldsymbol{r}_2$. The sum of the moments about O is $\boldsymbol{M} = \boldsymbol{r}_1 \times \boldsymbol{F}_1 + \boldsymbol{r}_2 \times \boldsymbol{F}_2$. Substitution of $\boldsymbol{F}_2 = -\boldsymbol{F}_1$ gives $\boldsymbol{M} = \boldsymbol{r}_1 \times \boldsymbol{F}_1 - \boldsymbol{r}_2 \times \boldsymbol{F}_1$, and the

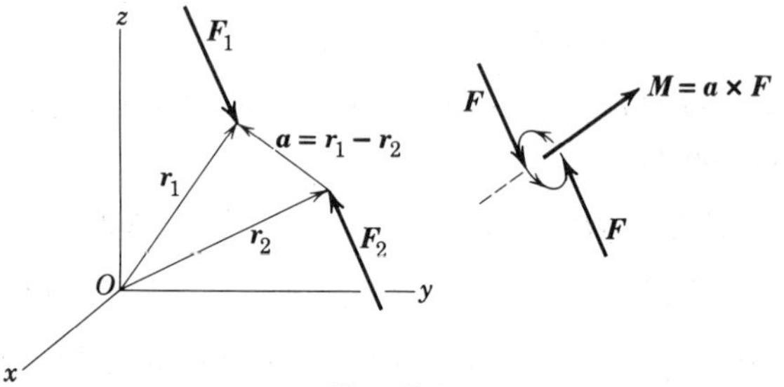

FIG. B6

distributive law permits writing $\boldsymbol{M} = (\boldsymbol{r}_1 - \boldsymbol{r}_2) \times \boldsymbol{F}_1$. Substitution of $\boldsymbol{a} = \boldsymbol{r}_1 - \boldsymbol{r}_2$, permits the moment to be written as

$$\boldsymbol{M} = \boldsymbol{a} \times \boldsymbol{F} \tag{B6}$$

which is independent of any reference to the point O. Thus the moment of two equal and opposite forces which are parallel but not collinear is the same for all moment centers. This moment is called a *couple*, and its sense is always specified by the right-hand rule for the rotation which the two forces tend to produce as shown in the sketch at the right side of Fig. B6. The magnitude of $\boldsymbol{a} \times \boldsymbol{F}$ equals the product of F and the perpendicular distance between the forces.

B6. Additional Relations. Two additional relations of vector algebra will be stated without proof, although their validity is not difficult to show geometrically.

The *triple scalar product* is the dot product of two vectors where one of them is specified as a cross product of two additional vectors. This product is a scalar and is given by any one of the equivalent expressions

$$(\boldsymbol{P} \times \boldsymbol{Q}) \cdot \boldsymbol{R} = \boldsymbol{R} \cdot (\boldsymbol{P} \times \boldsymbol{Q}) = -\boldsymbol{R} \cdot (\boldsymbol{Q} \times \boldsymbol{P}).$$

Actually the parentheses are not needed since it would be meaningless to write $\boldsymbol{P} \times (\boldsymbol{Q} \cdot \boldsymbol{R})$. It may be shown that

$$\boldsymbol{P} \times \boldsymbol{Q} \cdot \boldsymbol{R} = \boldsymbol{P} \cdot \boldsymbol{Q} \times \boldsymbol{R} \tag{B7}$$

which establishes the rule that the dot and the cross may be interchanged without changing the value of the triple scalar product. Further it may be seen upon expansion that

$$\boldsymbol{P} \times \boldsymbol{Q} \cdot \boldsymbol{R} = \begin{vmatrix} P_x & P_y & P_z \\ Q_x & Q_y & Q_z \\ R_x & R_y & R_z \end{vmatrix} . \tag{B8}$$

The *triple vector product* is the cross product of two vectors where one of them is specified as a cross product of two additional vectors. This product is a vector and is given by any one of the equivalent expressions

$$(\boldsymbol{P} \times \boldsymbol{Q}) \times \boldsymbol{R} = -\boldsymbol{R} \times (\boldsymbol{P} \times \boldsymbol{Q}) = \boldsymbol{R} \times (\boldsymbol{Q} \times \boldsymbol{P}).$$

Here the parentheses must be used since an expression $\boldsymbol{P} \times \boldsymbol{Q} \times \boldsymbol{R}$ would be ambiguous because it would not identify the vector to be crossed. It may be shown that the triple vector product is equivalent to

$$(\boldsymbol{P} \times \boldsymbol{Q}) \times \boldsymbol{R} = \boldsymbol{R} \cdot \boldsymbol{P} \boldsymbol{Q} - \boldsymbol{R} \cdot \boldsymbol{Q} \boldsymbol{P}$$

or

$$\boldsymbol{P} \times (\boldsymbol{Q} \times \boldsymbol{R}) = \boldsymbol{P} \cdot \boldsymbol{R} \boldsymbol{Q} - \boldsymbol{P} \cdot \boldsymbol{Q} \boldsymbol{R}. \tag{B9}$$

The first term in the first expression, for example, is the dot product $\boldsymbol{R} \cdot \boldsymbol{P}$, a scalar, multiplied by the vector $\boldsymbol{Q}$. The validity of Eqs. B7 and B9 may be checked easily by carrying out the indicated operations with three arbitrary vectors with numerical coefficients.

SAMPLE PROBLEMS

B1. A constant force $\boldsymbol{F} = 3\boldsymbol{i} + 4\boldsymbol{j} + 5\boldsymbol{k}$ lb. acts on a body at a point which has a displacement $\boldsymbol{s} = 2\boldsymbol{i} - 3\boldsymbol{j} - 4\boldsymbol{k}$ ft. Calculate the work done.

Solution. The dot product $U = \boldsymbol{F} \cdot \boldsymbol{s}$ represents the work done, so

$$U = F_x s_x + F_y s_y + F_z s_z$$

$$= (3)(2) + (4)(-3) + (5)(-4) = -26 \text{ ft. lb.} \qquad \textit{Ans.}$$

B2. A force $\boldsymbol{F} = 3\boldsymbol{i} + 4\boldsymbol{j} + 5\boldsymbol{k}$ lb. acts on a body at point A located as shown. Determine the moment $\boldsymbol{M}$ of $\boldsymbol{F}$ about the N-axis through O as indicated in the figure.

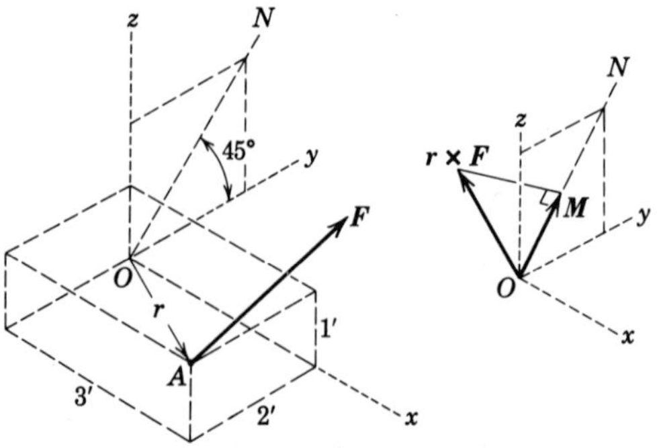

PROB. B2

Solution. Point A has the position vector $\boldsymbol{r} = 3\boldsymbol{i} - 2\boldsymbol{j} + \boldsymbol{k}$ ft. The moment of $\boldsymbol{F}$ about an axis through O normal to the plane of $\boldsymbol{F}$ and $\boldsymbol{r}$ is given by $\boldsymbol{M}_1 = \boldsymbol{r} \times \boldsymbol{F}$. The component of $\boldsymbol{M}_1$ along the N-axis has the magnitude $\boldsymbol{M}_1 \cdot \boldsymbol{n}$ where $\boldsymbol{n}$ is a unit vector along the N-axis. Thus the magnitude of the required moment is

$$M = \boldsymbol{r} \times \boldsymbol{F} \cdot \boldsymbol{n}$$

which is a triple scalar product. This product may be evaluated directly from Eq. B8. The unit vector $\boldsymbol{n}$ must first be expressed as $\boldsymbol{n} = \boldsymbol{j}/\sqrt{2} + \boldsymbol{k}/\sqrt{2}$. The determinant gives

$$M = \begin{vmatrix} 3 & -2 & 1 \\ 3 & 4 & 5 \\ 0 & \frac{1}{\sqrt{2}} & \frac{1}{\sqrt{2}} \end{vmatrix} = 3\sqrt{2} \text{ lb. ft.}$$

In vector form $\boldsymbol{M} = 3\boldsymbol{j} + 3\boldsymbol{k}$ lb. ft. *Ans.*

APPENDIX

C

MOMENTS OF INERTIA

I. MOMENTS OF INERTIA OF AREAS

C1. Definitions. There are many problems in engineering which involve the evaluation of an integral of the form $\int y^2\, dA$ where y is the distance from an element of area dA to an axis which is either in or normal to the plane of the area. Integrals of this form appear so frequently that it is of great advantage to develop them for some of the more common areas and to tabulate the results for easy reference.

Figure C1 illustrates the physical origin of these integrals. In the *a*-part of the figure the surface area $ABCD$ is subjected to a distributed pressure p whose intensity is proportional to the distance y from the axis AB. This situation was encountered in Art. 43, "Pressure on Submerged Surfaces," and is characteristic of the action of liquid pressure on a plane surface. The moment about AB due to the pressure on the element of area dA is $py\, dA = ky^2\, dA$. Thus the integral in question appears when the total moment $M = k\int y^2\, dA$ is evaluated. In the *b*-part of Fig. C1 is shown the distribution of stress acting on a transverse section of a simple elastic beam bent by equal and opposite couples applied to its ends. At any section of the beam a linear distribution of force intensity or stress, given by $\sigma = ky$, is present. The elemental moment about the axis O–O is $dM = \sigma y\, dA = ky^2\, dA$. Thus the same integral appears when the total moment $M = k\int y^2\, dA$ is evaluated. A third example is given in the c-part of Fig. C1 which shows a circular shaft subjected to a twist or torsional moment. Within the elastic limits of the material this moment is resisted at each cross section of the shaft by a distribution of tangential or shear stress τ which is proportional to the radial distance r from the center. Thus $\tau = kr$, and the total moment about the central axis is $M = \int \tau r \, dA = k \int r^2 \, dA$. Here the integral differs from the preceding two examples in that the area is normal instead of parallel to the moment axis and that r is a radial coordinate instead of a rectangular one.

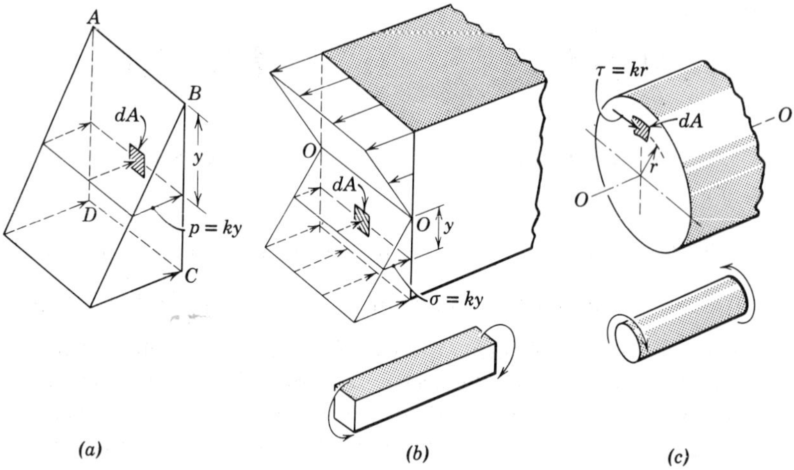

Fig. C1

The integral just illustrated is generally called the *moment of inertia* of the area about the axis in question. A more fitting term is the *second moment of area* since the first moment $y \, dA$ is multiplied again by the moment arm y to obtain the result for the element dA. The word *inertia* appears in the terminology by reason of the similarity between the mathematical form of the integrals for second moments of areas and those for the resultant moments of the so-called inertia forces in the case of rotating bodies. The moment of inertia of an area is a purely mathematical property of the area and in itself has no physical significance.

Consider the area A in the x–y plane, Fig. C2. The moments of inertia of the element dA about the x- and y-axes are, by definition, $dI_x = y^2 \, dA$ and $dI_y = x^2 \, dA$, respectively. Therefore the moments of inertia of A about the same axes are

$$I_x = \int y^2\, dA,$$
$$I_y = \int x^2\, dA, \tag{C1}$$

where the integration covers the entire area. The moment of inertia of dA about the pole O (z-axis) is, by similar definition, $dJ_z = r^2\, dA$, and the moment of inertia of the entire area about O is

$$J_z = \int r^2\, dA. \tag{C2}$$

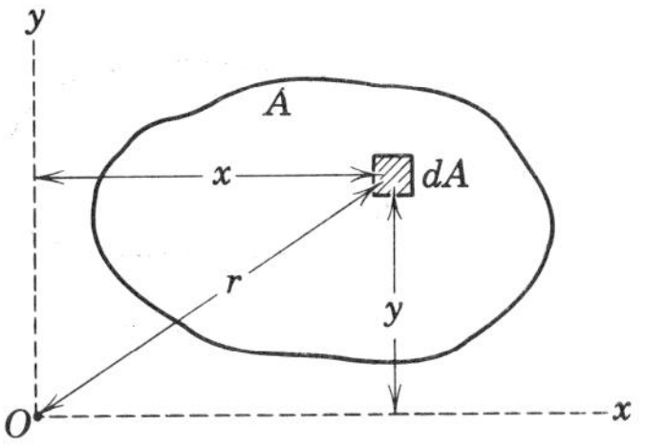

FIG. C2

The expressions defined by Eqs. C1 are known as *rectangular* moments of inertia, whereas the expression of Eq. C2 is known as the *polar* moment of inertia. Since $x^2 + y^2 = r^2$, it is clear that

$$J_z = I_x + I_y. \tag{C3}$$

A polar moment of inertia for an area whose boundaries are more simply described in rectangular coordinates than in polar coordinates is easily calculated with the aid of Eq. C3.

It should be noted that the moment of inertia of an element involves the square of the distance from the inertia axis to the element. An element whose coordinate is negative contributes as much to the moment of inertia as does an element with a positive coordinate of the same magnitude. Consequently the moment of inertia of an area about any axis is always a positive quantity. In contrast, the first moment of the area, which was involved in the computations of centroids, could be either positive or negative.

The dimensions of moments of inertia of areas are clearly L^4, where L stands for the dimension of length. Thus the units for area moments of inertia are expressed as quartic inches (in.^{4}) or quartic feet (ft.^{4}).

The choice of the coordinates to use for the calculation of moments of inertia is important. Rectangular coordinates should be used for shapes whose boundaries are most easily expressed in these coordinates. Polar coordinates will usually simplify problems involving boundaries which are easily described in r and θ. The choice of an element of area which simplifies the integration as much as possible is also important. These considerations are quite analogous to those discussed and illustrated in Chapter 5 in the calculation of centroids.

C2. Radius of Gyration. The moment of inertia of an area is a measure of the distribution of the area from the axis in question. Assume all the area A, Fig. C3, to be concentrated into a strip of negligible thickness at a distance k_x from the x-axis so that the product $k_x{}^2A$ equals the moment of inertia about the axis. The distance k_x,

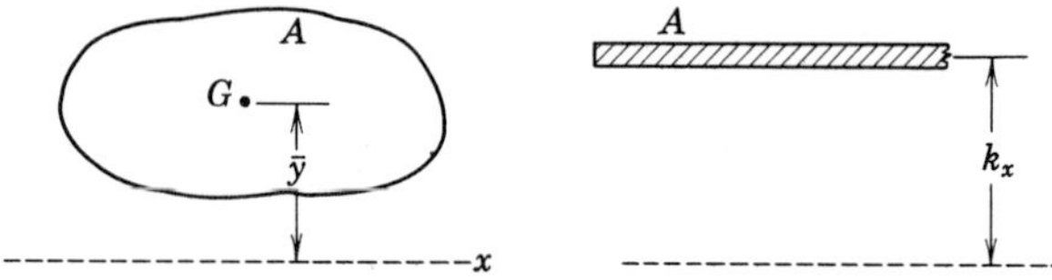

FIG. C3

called the *radius of gyration*, is then a measure of the distribution of area from the inertia axis. By definition, then, for any axis

$$I = k^2A \qquad \text{or} \qquad k = \sqrt{\frac{I}{A}}. \tag{C4}$$

When this definition is substituted in each of the three terms in Eq. C3, there results

$$k_z{}^2 = k_x{}^2 + k_y{}^2. \tag{C5}$$

Thus the square of the radius of gyration about a polar axis equals the sum of the squares of the radii of gyration about the two corresponding rectangular axes.

It is imperative that there be no confusion between the coordinate $\bar{y}$ to the centroid of the area and the radius of gyration k. The square of the centroidal distance, Fig. C3, is $\bar{y}^2$ and is the square of the mean value of the distances y from the elements dA to the axis. The quantity $k_x{}^2$, on the other hand, is the mean of the squares of these distances. The moment of inertia is *not* equal to $A\bar{y}^2$ since the square of the mean is not equal to the mean of the squares.

C3. Transfer of Axes. The moment of inertia of an area about a noncentroidal axis may be easily expressed in terms of the moment of inertia about a parallel centroidal axis. In Fig. C4 the x_o–y_o axes pass through the centroid G of the area. Let it be desired to determine the moments of inertia of the area about the parallel x–y axes.

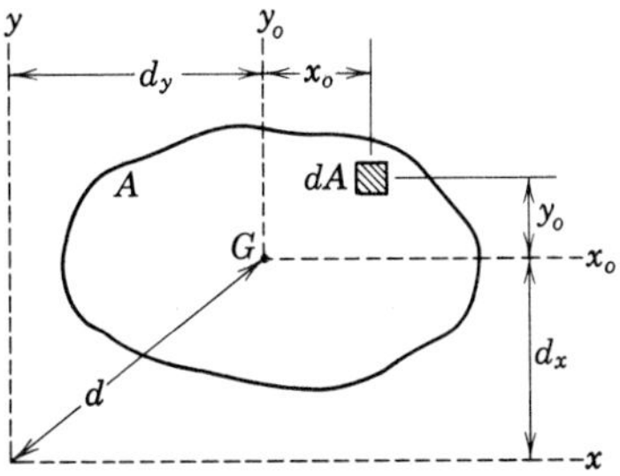

FIG. C4

By definition the moment of inertia of the element dA about the x-axis is

$$dI_x = (y_o + d_x)^2 \, dA.$$

Expanding and integrating give

$$I_x = \int y_o^2 \, dA + 2d_x \int y_o \, dA + d_x^2 \int dA.$$

The first integral is the moment of inertia $\bar{I}_x$ about the centroidal x_o-axis. The second integral is zero since $A\bar{y}_o = \int y_o \, dA$ and $\bar{y}_o$ is automatically zero. The third integral is simply Ad_x^2. Thus the expression for I_x and the similar expression for I_y become

$$\begin{aligned} I_x &= \bar{I}_x + Ad_x^2, \\ I_y &= \bar{I}_y + Ad_y^2. \end{aligned} \tag{C6}$$

By Eq. C3 the sum of these two equations gives

$$J_z = \bar{J}_z + Ad^2. \tag{C6a}$$

Equations C6 and C6*a* are the so-called *parallel-axis theorems.* Two points in particular should be noted. First, the axes between which the transfer is made must be parallel, and, second, one of the axes must pass through the centroid of the area.

If a transfer is desired between two parallel axes neither one of which passes through the centroid, it is first necessary to transfer from one axis to the parallel centroidal axis and then to transfer from the centroidal axis to the second axis.

The parallel-axis theorems also hold for radii of gyration. With substitution of the definition of k into Eqs. C6, the transfer relation becomes

$$k^2 = \bar{k}^2 + d^2, \tag{C6b}$$

where $\bar{k}$ is the radius of gyration about a centroidal axis parallel to the axis about which k applies and d is the distance between the two axes. The axes may be either in the plane or normal to the plane of the area.

A summary of the moment of inertia relations for some of the common plane figures is given in Table D5, Appendix D.

SAMPLE PROBLEMS

C1. Determine the moments of inertia of the rectangular area about the centroidal x_o–y_o axes, the centroidal polar axis G, the x-axis, and the polar axis O.

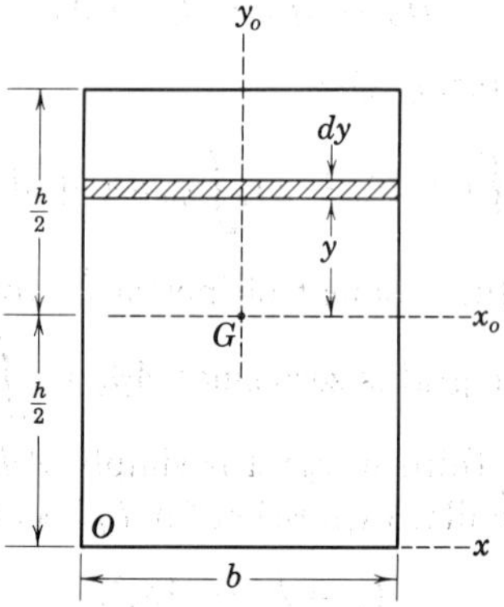

PROB. C1

Solution. For the calculation of the moment of inertia $\bar{I}_x$ about the x_o-axis a horizontal strip of area $b\,dy$ is chosen so that all elements of the strip have the same y-coordinate. Thus

$$\left[I_x = \int y^2\,dA\right] \qquad \bar{I}_x = \int_{-h/2}^{h/2} y^2 b\,dy = \tfrac{1}{12}bh^3. \qquad \textit{Ans.}$$

By interchanging symbols the moment of inertia about the centroidal y_o-axis is

$$\bar{I}_y = \tfrac{1}{12}hb^3. \qquad \textit{Ans.}$$

The centroidal polar moment of inertia is

$$[J_z = I_x + I_y] \qquad \bar{J}_z = \tfrac{1}{12}(bh^3 + hb^3) = \tfrac{1}{12}A(b^2+h^2). \qquad \textit{Ans.}$$

By the parallel-axis theorem the moment of inertia about the x-axis is

$$[I_x = \bar{I}_x + Ad_x^2] \qquad I_x = \tfrac{1}{12}bh^3 + bh\left(\frac{h}{2}\right)^2 = \tfrac{1}{3}bh^3 = \tfrac{1}{3}Ah^2. \qquad \textit{Ans.}$$

The polar moment of inertia about O may also be obtained by the parallel-axis theorem. Thus

$$[J_z = \bar{J}_z + Ad^2] \qquad J_z = \tfrac{1}{12}A(b^2 + h^2) + A\left[\left(\frac{b}{2}\right)^2 + \left(\frac{h}{2}\right)^2\right],$$

$$J_z = \tfrac{1}{3}A(b^2 + h^2). \qquad \textit{Ans.}$$

C2. Calculate the moments of inertia of the area of the circle about a diametral axis and about the polar axis through the center. Specify the radii of gyration.

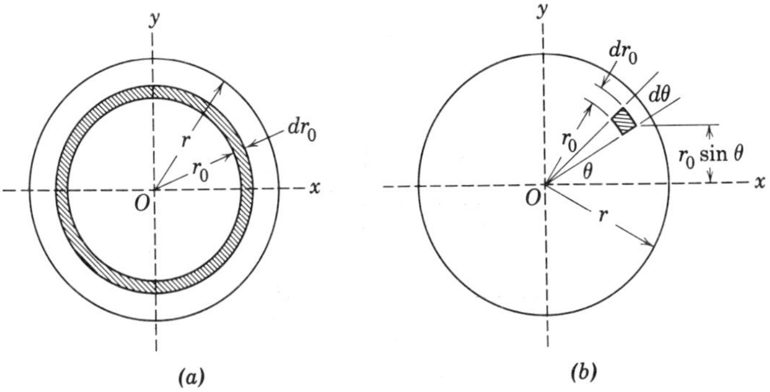

PROB. C2

Solution. An element of area in the form of a circular ring, shown in the a-part of the figure, may be used for the calculation of the moment of inertia about the polar z-axis through O since all elements of the ring are equidistant from O. The elemental area is $dA = 2\pi r_o\, dr_o$, and thus

$$\left[J_z = \int r^2\, dA\right] \qquad J_z = \int_0^r r_o^2(2\pi r_o\, dr_o) = \frac{\pi r^4}{2} = \tfrac{1}{2}Ar^2. \qquad \textit{Ans.}$$

The polar radius of gyration is

$$\left[k = \sqrt{\frac{J}{A}}\right] \qquad k_z = \frac{r}{\sqrt{2}}. \qquad \textit{Ans.}$$

By symmetry $I_x = I_y$, so that from Eq. C3

$$[J_z = I_x + I_y] \qquad I_x = \tfrac{1}{2}J_z = \frac{\pi r^4}{4} = \tfrac{1}{4}Ar^2. \qquad \textit{Ans.}$$

The radius of gyration about the diametral axis is

$$\left[k = \sqrt{\frac{I}{A}}\right] \qquad k_x = \frac{r}{2}. \qquad \textit{Ans.}$$

The foregoing determination of I_x is the simplest possible. The result may also be obtained by direct integration, using the element of area $dA = r_o\, dr_o\, d\theta$

shown in the b-part of the figure. By definition

$$\left[I_x = \int y^2\, dA\right] \qquad I_x = \int_0^{2\pi}\int_0^{r} (r_o \sin\theta)^2 r_o\, dr_o\, d\theta,$$

$$= \int_0^{2\pi} \frac{r^4 \sin^2\theta}{4}\, d\theta = \frac{r^4}{4}\frac{1}{2}\left[\theta - \frac{\sin 2\theta}{2}\right]_0^{2\pi} = \frac{\pi r^4}{4}. \qquad Ans.$$

C3. Determine the moments of inertia of the triangular area about its base and about parallel axes through its centroid and vertex.

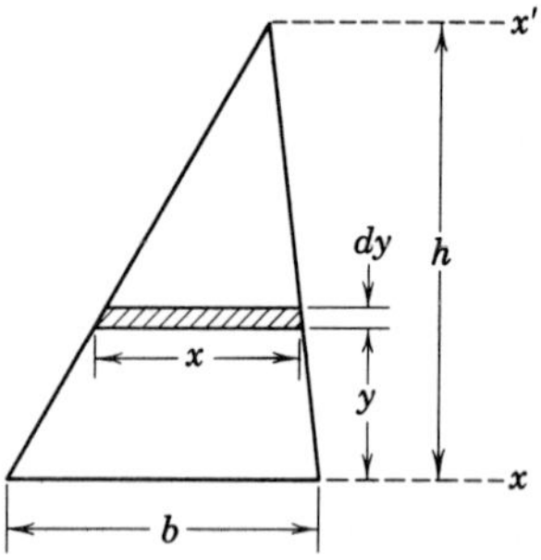

PROB. C3

Solution. A strip of area parallel to the base is selected as shown in the figure and it has the area $dA = x\, dy = [(h - y)b/h]\, dy$. By definition

$$\left[I_x = \int y^2\, dA\right] \qquad I_x = \int_0^{h} y^2 \frac{h-y}{h} b\, dy = b\left[\frac{y^3}{3} - \frac{y^4}{4h}\right]_0^h = \frac{bh^3}{12}. \qquad Ans.$$

By the parallel-axis theorem the moment of inertia $\bar{I}$ about an axis through the centroid, a distance $h/3$ above the x-axis, is

$$[\bar{I} = I - Ad^2] \qquad \bar{I} = \frac{bh^3}{12} - \left(\frac{bh}{2}\right)\left(\frac{h}{3}\right)^2 = \frac{bh^3}{36}. \qquad Ans.$$

A transfer from the centroidal axis to the x'-axis through the vertex gives

$$[I = \bar{I} + Ad^2] \qquad I_{x'} = \frac{bh^3}{36} + \left(\frac{bh}{2}\right)\left(\frac{2h}{3}\right)^2 = \frac{bh^3}{4}. \qquad Ans.$$

C4. Determine the moment of inertia about the x-axis of the semicircular area shown.

Solution. The moment of inertia of the semicircular area about the x'-axis is one half of that for a complete circle about the same axis. Thus from the results of Prob. C2

$$I_{x'} = \frac{1}{2}\frac{\pi r^4}{4} = \frac{2^4\pi}{8} = 2\pi \text{ in.}^4$$

The moment of inertia $\bar{I}$ about the parallel centroidal axis x_o is obtained next.

Transfer is made through the distance $\bar{r} = 4r/3\pi = (4 \times 2)/3\pi = 8/3\pi$ in. by the parallel-axis theorem. Hence

$$[\bar{I} = I - Ad^2] \qquad \bar{I} = 2\pi - \left(\frac{2^2\pi}{2}\right)\left(\frac{8}{3\pi}\right)^2 = 1.755 \text{ in.}^4$$

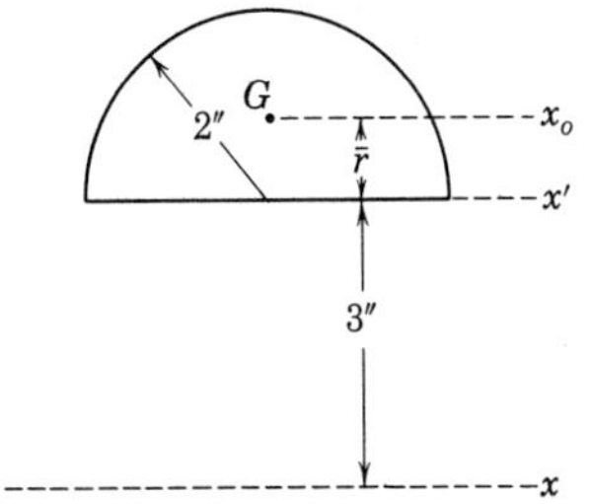

Prob. C4

Finally, transfer is made from the centroidal x_o-axis to the x-axis, which gives

$$[I = \bar{I} + Ad^2] \qquad I_x = 1.755 + \left(\frac{2^2\pi}{2}\right)\left(3 + \frac{8}{3\pi}\right)^2,$$

$$= 1.755 + 93.1 = 94.9 \text{ in.}^4 \qquad \textit{Ans.}$$

PROBLEMS

C5. Find the moments of inertia of the area of the quarter circle shown about the diametral x-axis and the polar axis through O. *Ans.* $I_x = \dfrac{\pi r^4}{16}$, $J_z = \dfrac{\pi r^4}{8}$

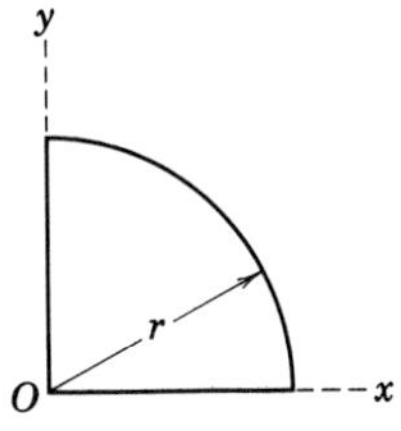

Prob. C5

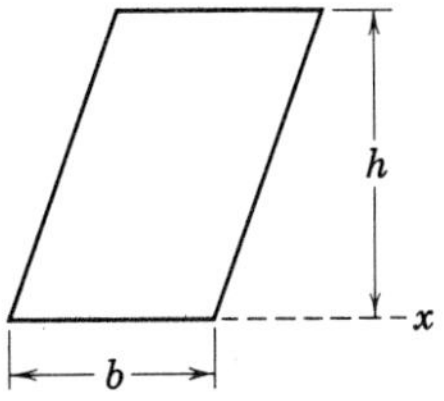

Prob. C6

C6. Find the moments of inertia of the area of the parallelogram about the base (x-axis) and about a parallel centroidal axis. (Compare with Sample Prob. C1.)

C7. Approximate the result for the moment of inertia of a circular area about a diameter by dividing the circle into strips parallel to the inertia axis and of width $r/5$. Treat the moment of inertia of each strip as its area times the square of the distance from its center to the axis.

C8. Find the radius of gyration k of a square of side b about one diagonal.

Ans. $k = \dfrac{b}{2\sqrt{3}}$

C9. Find the moment of inertia of the shaded area about the x-axis by taking a horizontal strip of area dA. *Ans.* $I_x = \frac{4}{15}ab^3$

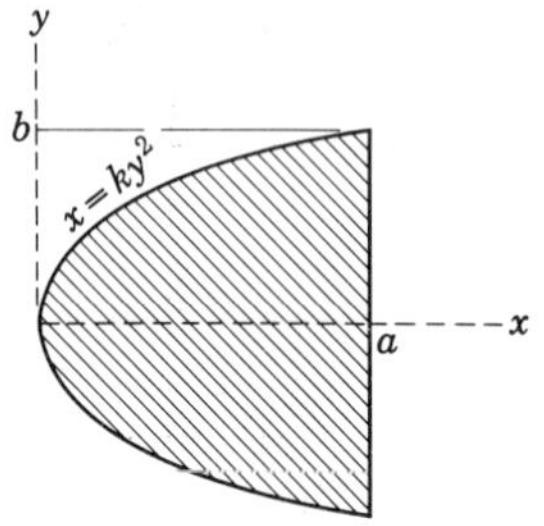

PROB. C9

C10. Solve Prob. C9 by choosing a vertical strip of area dA and applying the results of Sample Prob. C1 to this element.

C11. Find the moment of inertia of the figure in Prob. C9 about the y-axis. *Ans.* $I_y = \frac{4}{7}a^3b$

C12. Calculate the moments of inertia of the elliptical area about the major axes and the central polar axis.

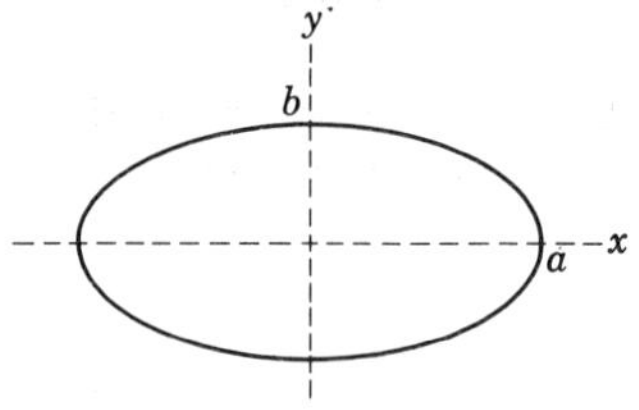

PROB. C12

C13. The x- and x'-axes are located from the centroid G of the irregular area as shown. If the moments of inertia about these axes are $I_x = 1800$ in.^{4} and $I_{x'} = 2200$ in.^{4}, determine the area A of the figure. *Ans.* $A = 20$ in.^{2}

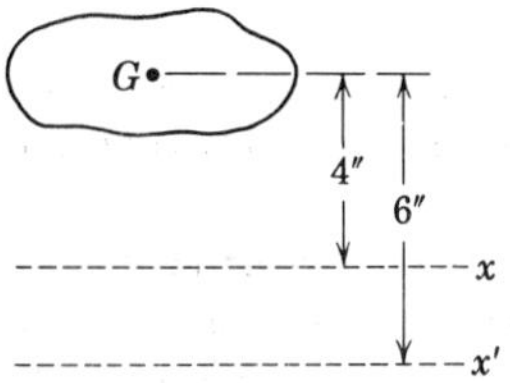

PROB. C13

C14. Use the results of Probs. C9 and C11 to find the polar moment of inertia J of the figure in Prob. C9 about the point $(a, 0)$. (The centroid is a distance $3a/5$ from the origin, and the area of the figure is $4ab/3$.)

C15. Determine the moments of inertia of the area of the circular sector about the x- and y-axes.

Ans. $I_x = \frac{r^4}{4}\left(\alpha - \frac{\sin 2\alpha}{2}\right),\ I_y = \frac{r^4}{4}\left(\alpha + \frac{\sin 2\alpha}{2}\right)$

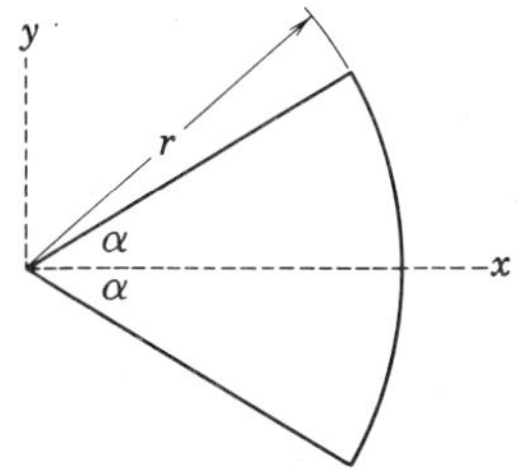

PROB. C15

C16. The area of a circular ring of inside radius r and outside radius $r + \Delta r$ is approximately equal to the circumference at the mean radius times the thickness Δr. The polar moment of inertia of the ring may be approximated by multiplying this area by the square of the mean radius. What per cent error is involved if $\Delta r = r/10$? *Ans.* Error = 0.226%

C4. Composite Areas. The moment of inertia of a composite area about a particular axis is the algebraic sum of the moments of inertia of the various parts about the same axis. The results of the problems in Art. C3 and the tabulation of results in Table D5, Appendix D, may be used to determine the moments of inertia for component parts of the shapes given. It is often convenient to regard a composite area as composed of positive and negative parts. The moment of inertia of a negative area is a minus quantity.

When the section is composed of a large number of parts, it is convenient to tabulate the results for the parts in terms of the area A, centroidal moment of inertia $\bar{I}$, distance d from the centroidal axis to the axis about which the moment of inertia of the entire section is being computed, and the product Ad^2. For any one of the parts the desired moment of inertia is $\bar{I} + Ad^2$, and thus for the entire section the desired moment of inertia may be expressed as $I = \Sigma\bar{I} + \Sigma Ad^2$.

SAMPLE PROBLEM

C17. Compute the moment of inertia and radius of gyration about the x-axis for the cross section shown.

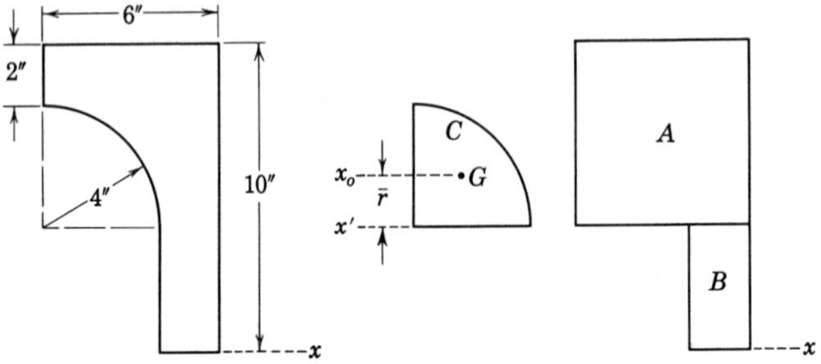

PROB. C17

Solution. The composite area may be considered as composed of the two rectangles A and B and the negative quarter circular area C. For the rectangle A the moment of inertia about the x-axis is

$[I = \bar{I} + Ad^2]$ $$I_x = \tfrac{1}{12} \times 6 \times 6^3 + 6^2 \times 7^2 = 1872 \text{ in.}^4$$

The moment of inertia of B about the x-axis is

$$I_x = \tfrac{1}{3} \times 2 \times 4^3 = 42.67 \text{ in.}^4$$

The moment of inertia of the negative quarter circle C about its horizontal diameter is

$$I_{x'} = -\tfrac{1}{4} \times \tfrac{1}{4}\pi \times 4^4 = -50.27 \text{ in.}^4$$

Transfer of this result through the distance $\bar{r} = 4r/3\pi = (4 \times 4)/3\pi = 1.697$ in. gives for the centroidal moment of inertia of C

$[\bar{I} = I - Ad^2]$ $$I = -50.27 - \left(-\frac{\pi}{4} \times 4^2\right)(1.697)^2 = -14.07 \text{ in.}^4$$

The moment of inertia of C may now be found with respect to the x-axis, and the transfer from the centroidal axis gives

$[I = \bar{I} + Ad^2]$ $$I_x = -14.07 + \left(-\frac{\pi}{4} \times 4^2\right)(4 + 1.697)^2 = -422 \text{ in.}^4$$

The moment of inertia of the net section about the x-axis is the sum of moments of inertia of its component parts. Thus

$$I_x = 1872 + 42.7 - 422 = 1493 \text{ in.}^4, \qquad \textit{Ans.}$$

and

$$k_x = \sqrt{\frac{I_x}{A}} = \sqrt{\frac{1493}{31.43}} = 6.89 \text{ in.} \qquad \textit{Ans.}$$

PROBLEMS

C18. Determine the polar moment of inertia J for the section about point O.

Ans. $J = 138.9 \text{ in.}^4$

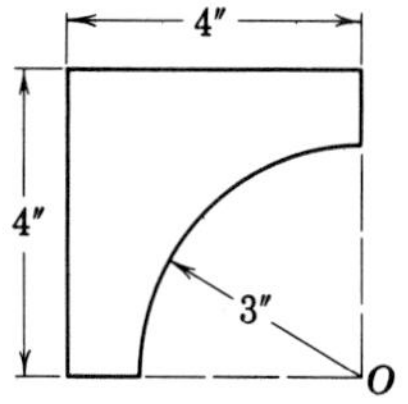

PROB. C18

C19. Find the polar moment of inertia J about point O for the cross section bounded by the two squares.

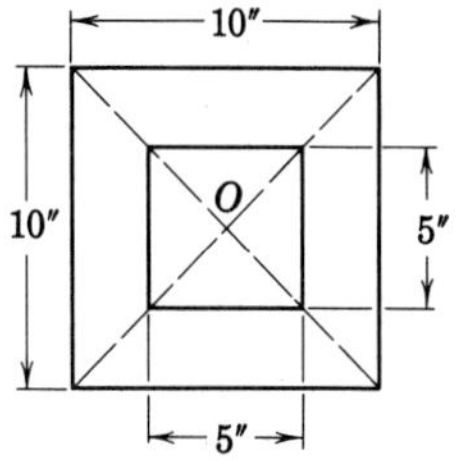

PROB. C19

C20. Find the polar moment of inertia of the net area about O.

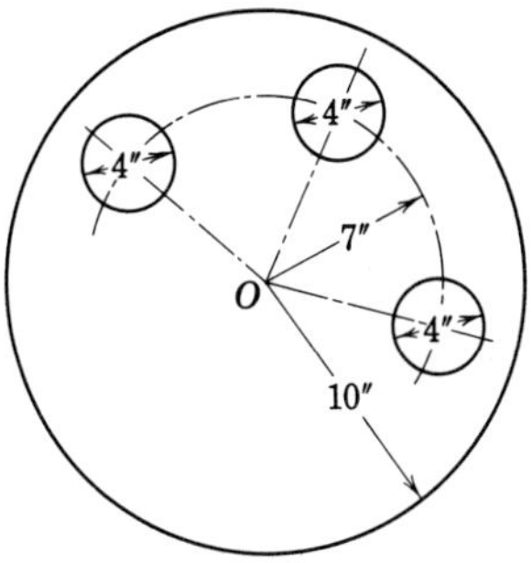

PROB. C20

C21. Determine the moment of inertia of the area of a rectangle of sides a and b about a diagonal.

Ans. $I = \dfrac{a^3b^3}{6(a^2 + b^2)}$

C22. Find the moment of inertia about the x-axis of the area between the curves $x = y^2$ and $x = y$ from $x = 0$ to $x = 1$, where x and y are in inches.

C23. Determine the moments of inertia of the *Z*-section about the centroidal x_o- and y_o-axes.

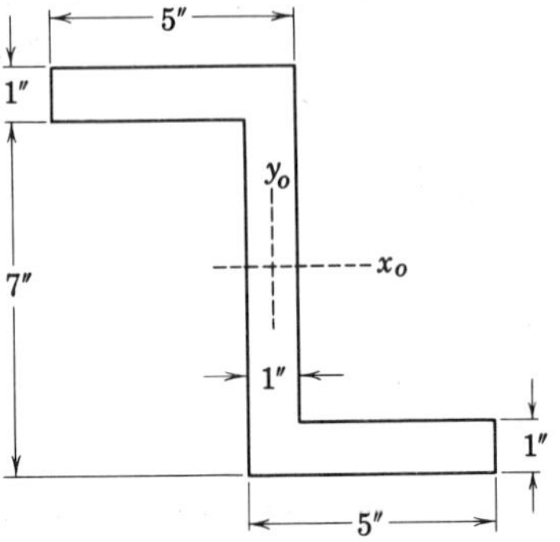

PROB. C23

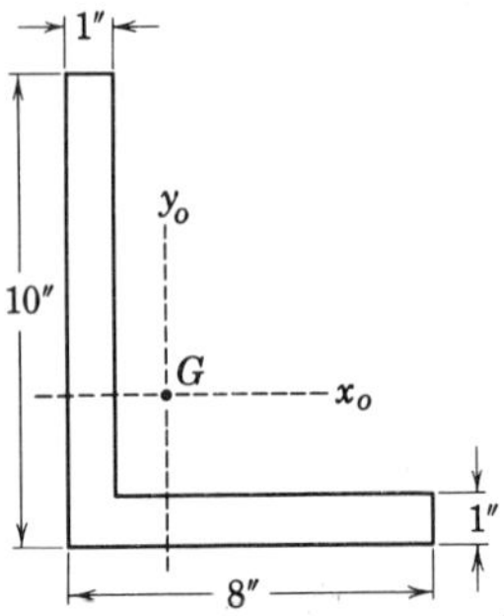

PROB. C24

C24. Determine the moment of inertia of the angle section about its horizontal centroidal axis x_o.

Ans. $\bar{I}_x = 167.3 \text{ in.}^4$

C25. Determine the moment of inertia of the area of the hexagon of side b about the x-axis.

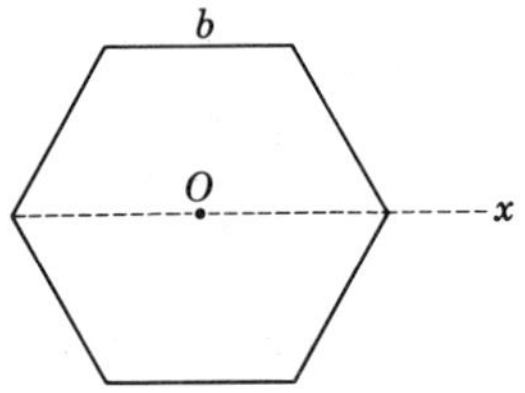

PROB. C25

C26. Determine the polar moment of inertia J of the hexagonal area of Prob. C25 about O.

Ans. $J = \dfrac{5\sqrt{3}}{8} b^4$

C27. Determine the radius of gyration of the section about the 45 deg. axis of symmetry. (*Hint:* Use the results of Prob. C15.)

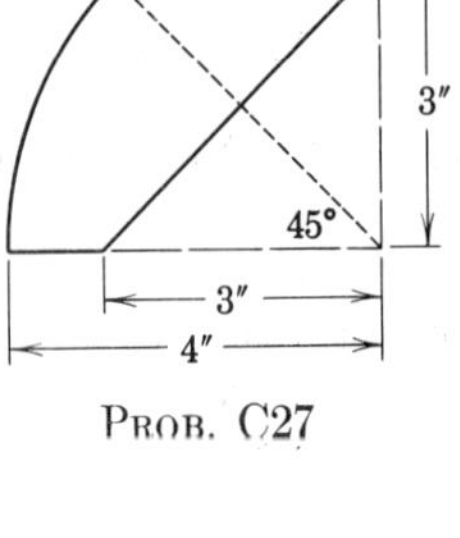

PROB. C27

C28. In the calculation of the stability of a ship's hull it is necessary to know the moment of inertia about the longitudinal center line of the area of the horizontal cross section of the hull at the waterline. Estimate this moment of inertia for the waterline shape reproduced here by dividing the area into a number of approximating strips. *Ans.* $I \cong 53{,}000$ ft.^{4}

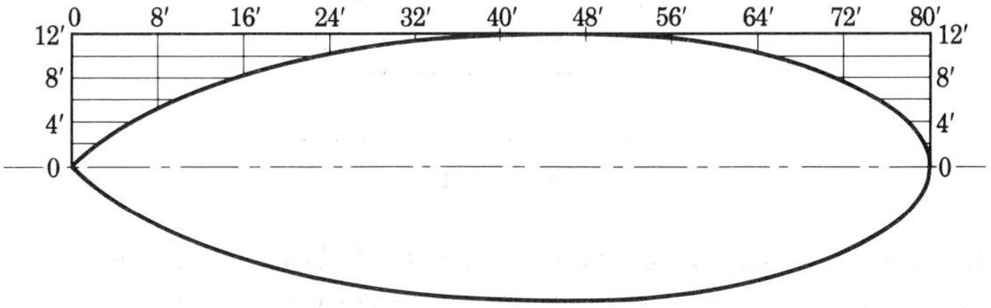

PROB. C28

C29. Determine the moment of inertia of the built-up structural section about its centroidal x_o-axis.

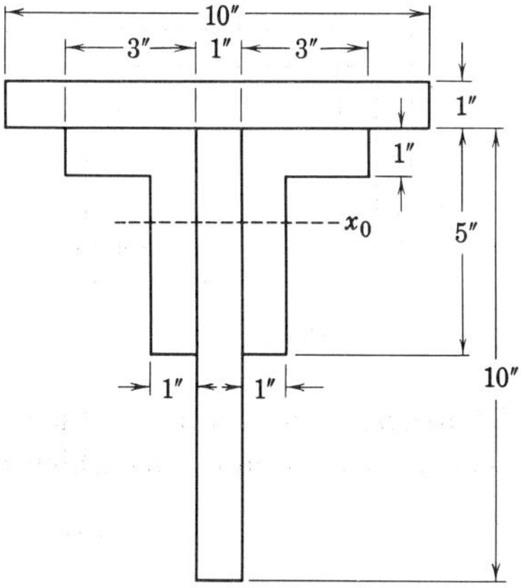

PROB. C29

C30. Calculate the moment of inertia of the standard 12 × 4 in. channel section about the centroidal x_o-axis. Neglect the fillets and radii and compare with the handbook value of $\bar{I}_x = 16.0$ in.^{4}

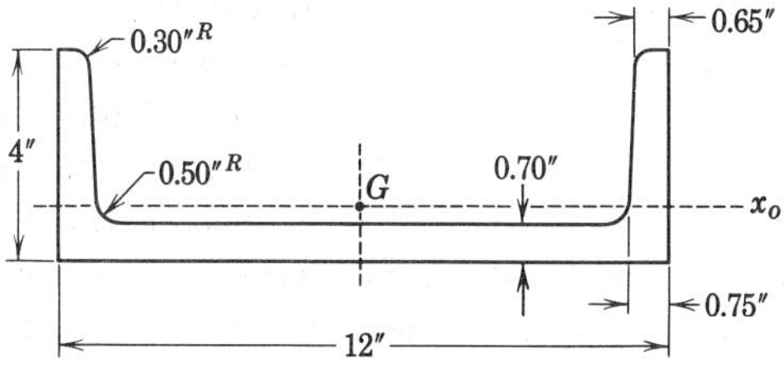

PROB. C30

C31. Determine the moment of inertia about the x-axis of the cross section shown. *Ans.* $I_x = 1611$ in.^{4}

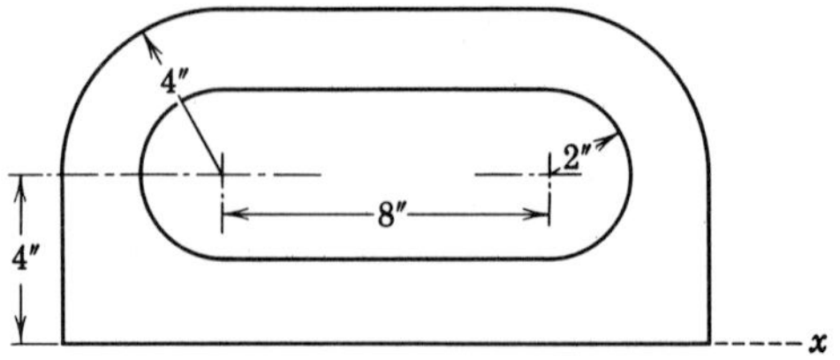

Prob. C31

C32. Determine the flange width b for the H-beam section so that the moments of inertia about the central x- and y-axes will be equal. *Ans.* $b = 16.1$ in.

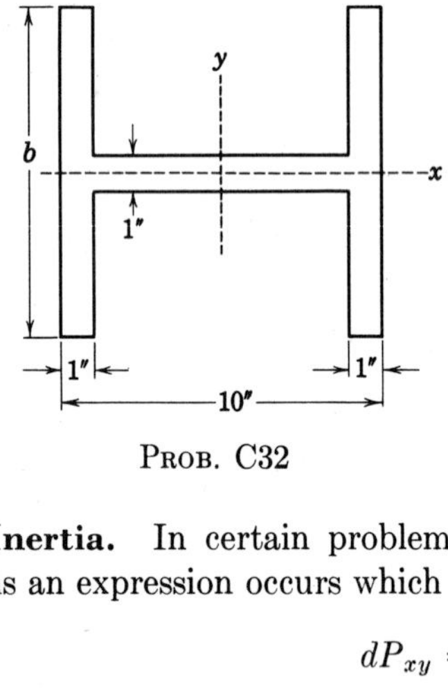

Prob. C32

C5. Product of Inertia. In certain problems involving unsymmetrical cross sections an expression occurs which has the form

$$dP_{xy} = xy\,dA,$$
$$P_{xy} = \int xy\,dA, \tag{C7}$$

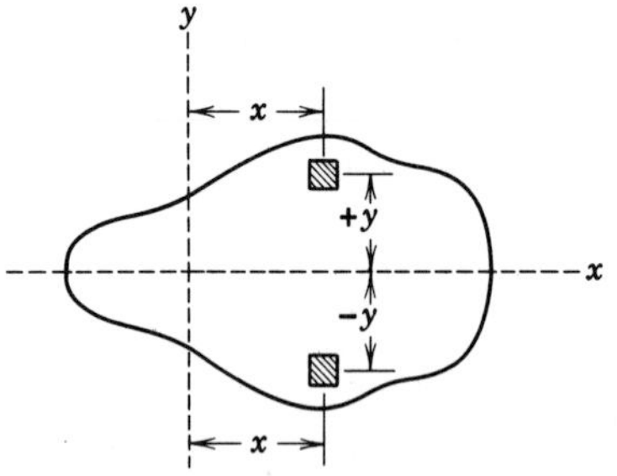

Fig. C5

where x and y are the coordinates of the element of area dA. The quantity P_{xy} is called the *product of inertia* of the area A about the x–y axes. Unlike moments of inertia, the product of inertia can be positive or negative.

By reference to Fig. C5 it can be seen for an axis of symmetry, such as the x-axis, that the sum of the terms $x(-y)\,dA$ and $x(+y)\,dA$ due to symmetrically placed elements vanishes. Since the entire area may be considered as composed of pairs of such elements, it follows that the product of inertia vanishes.

A transfer-of-axis theorem exists for products of inertia which is similar to that for moments of inertia. By definition the product of inertia of the area A in Fig. C4 about the x- and y-axes in terms of the coordinates x_o, y_o to the centroidal axes is

$$P_{xy} = \int (x_o + d_y)(y_o + d_x)\, dA,$$

$$= \int x_o y_o\, dA + d_x \int x_o\, dA + d_y \int y_o\, dA + d_x d_y \int dA,$$

$$P_{xy} = \overline{P}_{xy} + d_x d_y A, \tag{C8}$$

where $\overline{P}_{xy}$ is the product of inertia with respect to the centroidal x_o–y_o axes which are parallel to the x–y axes.

C6. Inclined Axes. It is often necessary to calculate the moment of inertia of an area about inclined axes. This consideration leads directly to the important problem of determining the axes about which the moment of inertia is a maximum and a minimum.

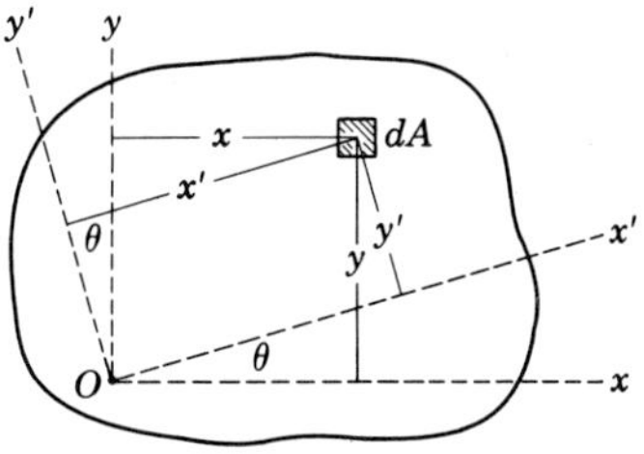

FIG. C6

In Fig. C6 the moments of inertia of the area about the x'- and y'-axes are

$$I_{x'} = \int y'^2\, dA = \int (y \cos\theta - x \sin\theta)^2\, dA,$$

$$I_{y'} = \int x'^2\, dA = \int (y \sin\theta + x \cos\theta)^2\, dA.$$

Expanding and substituting the trigonometric identities,

$$\sin^2\theta = \frac{1 - \cos 2\theta}{2}, \qquad \cos^2\theta = \frac{1 + \cos 2\theta}{2},$$

and the defining relations for I_x, I_y, P_{xy} give

$$I_{x'} = \frac{I_x + I_y}{2} + \frac{I_x - I_y}{2} \cos 2\theta - P_{xy} \sin 2\theta,$$
$$I_{y'} = \frac{I_x + I_y}{2} - \frac{I_x - I_y}{2} \cos 2\theta + P_{xy} \sin 2\theta. \qquad \text{(C9)}$$

In a similar manner

$$P_{x'y'} = \int x'y'\,dA = \frac{I_x - I_y}{2} \sin 2\theta + P_{xy} \cos 2\theta. \qquad \text{(C9}a\text{)}$$

Adding Eqs. C9 gives $I_{x'} + I_{y'} = I_x + I_y = J_z$, the polar moment of inertia about O, which checks the result of Eq. C3.

The angle which makes $I_{x'}$ and $I_{y'}$ a maximum or a minimum may be determined by setting the derivative of either $I_{x'}$ or $I_{y'}$ with respect to θ equal to zero. Thus

$$\frac{dI_{x'}}{d\theta} = (I_y - I_x) \sin 2\theta - 2P_{xy} \cos 2\theta = 0.$$

Denoting this critical angle by α gives

$$\tan 2\alpha = \frac{2P_{xy}}{I_y - I_x}. \qquad \text{(C10)}$$

Equation C10 gives two values for 2α which differ by π since $\tan 2\alpha = \tan (2\alpha + \pi)$. Consequently the two solutions for α will differ by $\pi/2$. One value defines the axis of maximum moment of inertia, and the other value defines the axis of minimum moment of inertia.

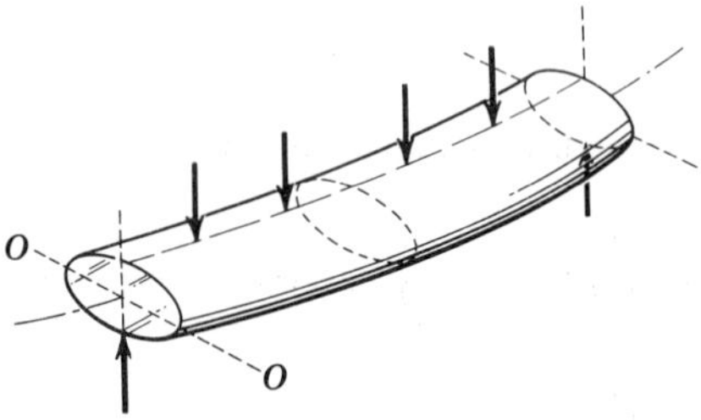

Fig. C7

These two rectangular axes are known as the *principal axes of inertia*. Substitution of Eq. C10 in Eq. C9*a* shows that the product of inertia is zero for principal axes of inertia. A beam of oval cross section loaded transversely, Fig. C7, if free to rotate about its longitudinal axis, will turn until the horizontal axis of its cross section is the minimum axis of inertia O–O.

The relations in Eqs. C9, C9a, and C10 may be represented graphically by a diagram known as Mohr's circle. For given values of I_x, I_y, and P_{xy} the corresponding values of $I_{x'}$, $I_{y'}$, and $P_{x'y'}$ may be determined from the diagram for any desired angle θ. A horizontal axis for the measurement of moments of inertia and a vertical axis for the measurement of products of inertia are first selected, Fig. C8. Next,

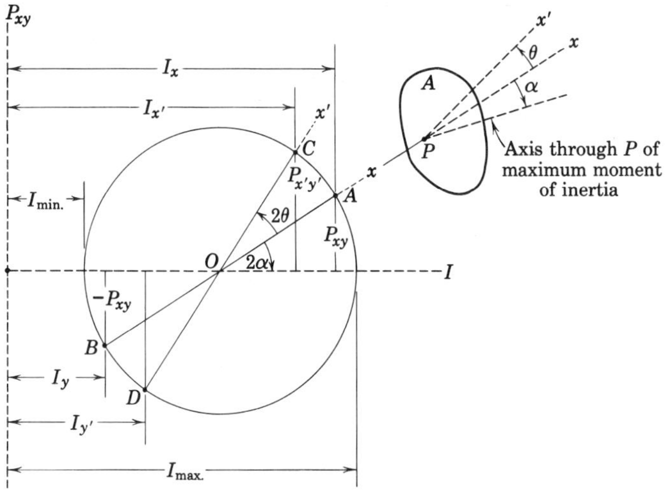

FIG. C8

point A, which has the coordinates (I_x, P_{xy}), and point B, which has the coordinates (I_y, $-P_{xy}$), are located. A circle is drawn with these two points as the extremities of a diameter. The angle from the radius OA to the horizontal axis is 2α or twice the angle from the x-axis of the area in question to the axis of maximum moment of inertia. Both the angle on the diagram and the angle on the area are measured in the same sense as shown. The coordinates of any point C are ($I_{x'}$, $P_{x'y'}$), and those of the corresponding point D are ($I_{y'}$, $-P_{x'y'}$). Also the angle between OA and OC is 2θ or twice the angle from the x-axis to the x'-axis. Again both angles are measured in the same sense as shown. It may be verified from the trigonometry of the circle that Eqs. C9, C9a, and C10 agree with the statements made.

SAMPLE PROBLEMS

C33. Determine the product of inertia for the area under the parabola shown.

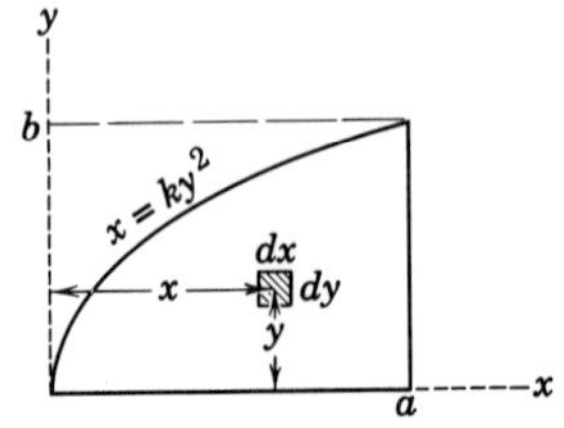

Prob. C33

Solution. The equation of the curve becomes $x = ay^2/b^2$. The product of inertia for the element $dA = dx\,dy$ is $dP_{xy} = xy\,dx\,dy$ and for the entire area is

$$P_{xy} = \int_0^b \int_{ay^2/b^2}^{a} xy\,dx\,dy = \int_0^b \frac{1}{2}\left(a^2 - \frac{a^2y^4}{b^4}\right) y\,dy = \tfrac{1}{6}a^2b^2. \qquad Ans.$$

C34. Locate the principal centroidal axes of inertia with their corresponding maximum and minimum moments of inertia for the angle section.

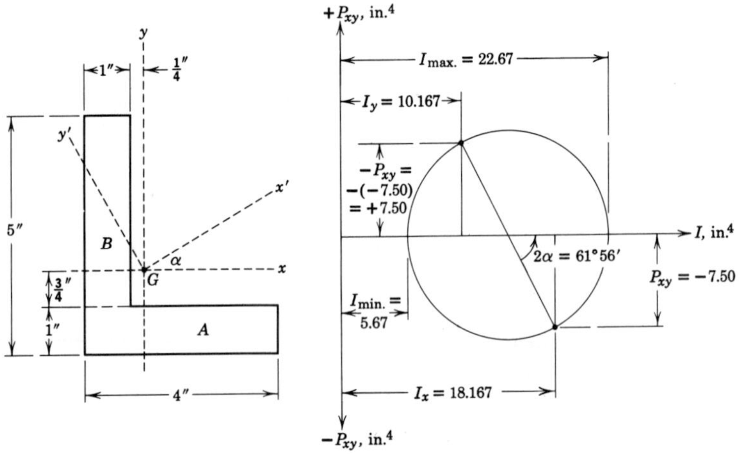

Prob. C34

Solution. The centroid G is easily located as shown. The product of inertia for each rectangle about its own centroidal axes parallel to the x- and y-axes is zero by symmetry. Thus the product of inertia for part A is

$[P_{xy} = \bar{P}_{xy} + d_x d_y A]$ $\qquad P_{xy} = 0 + (-\tfrac{5}{4})(+\tfrac{3}{4})(4) = -3.75 \text{ in.}^4$

Likewise for B,

$[P_{xy} = \bar{P}_{xy} + d_x d_y A]$ $\qquad P_{xy} = 0 + (\tfrac{5}{4})(-\tfrac{3}{4})(4) = -3.75 \text{ in.}^4$

For the complete angle

$$P_{xy} = -3.75 - 3.75 = -7.50 \text{ in.}^4$$

The moments of inertia for part A are

$$[I = \bar{I} + Ad^2] \qquad I_x = \tfrac{1}{12} \times 4 \times 1^3 + (\tfrac{5}{4})^2 \times 4 = 6.583 \text{ in.}^4,$$

$$I_y = \tfrac{1}{12} \times 1 \times 4^3 + (\tfrac{3}{4})^2 \times 4 = 7.583 \text{ in.}^4$$

In similar manner the moments of inertia for part B are $I_x = 11.583$ in.^{4}, $I_y = 2.583$ in.^{4} Thus for the entire section

$$I_x = 6.583 + 11.583 = 18.167 \text{ in.}^4,$$

$$I_y = 7.583 + 2.583 = 10.167 \text{ in.}^4$$

The inclination of the principal axes of inertia is given by Eq. C10. Therefore

$$\left[\tan 2\alpha = \frac{2P_{xy}}{I_y - I_x}\right] \qquad \tan 2\alpha = \frac{-2 \times 7.50}{10.167 - 18.167} = 1.875,$$

$$2\alpha = 61° \, 56', \qquad \alpha = 30° \, 58'. \qquad \textit{Ans.}$$

From Eqs. C9 the principal moments of inertia are

$$I_{max.} = I_{x'} = \frac{18.167 + 10.167}{2} + \frac{18.167 - 10.167}{2} \times 0.4705 + 7.50 \times 0.8824$$

$$= 22.67 \text{ in.}^4; \qquad \textit{Ans.}$$

$$I_{min.} = I_{y'} = \frac{18.167 + 10.167}{2} - \frac{18.167 - 10.167}{2} \times 0.4705 - 7.50 \times 0.8824$$

$$= 5.67 \text{ in.}^4 \qquad \textit{Ans.}$$

These results may also be obtained graphically by construction of the Mohr circle as shown to the right of the angle in the figure.

PROBLEMS

C35. Determine the product of inertia P_{xy} of the area of a rectangle about x- and y-axes coinciding with two adjacent sides of lengths a and b. The rectangle lies in the first quadrant.

C36. Obtain the product of inertia for the area of the quarter circle shown with Prob. C5 about the x- and y-axes by direct integration. *Ans.* $P_{xy} = \dfrac{r^4}{8}$

C37. Solve Prob. C21 for the moment of inertia about a diagonal of the rectangle of sides a and b by the method of this article.

C38. The moments of inertia of an area with respect to the principal axes of inertia x, y through a point P are $I_x = 32.0$ in.^{4} and $I_y = 12.0$ in.^{4} With the aid of Mohr's circle determine the moment of inertia $I_{x'}$ and the product of inertia $P_{x'y'}$ for the area about axes x', y' through P and rotated 15 deg. clockwise from the axes x, y. *Ans.* $I_{x'} = 30.66$ in.^{4}, $P_{x'y'} = -5$ in.^{4}

C39. The moments of inertia of an area about axes x, y through a point P are $I_x = 62.8$ in.^{4} and $I_y = 148.2$ in.^{4} The product of inertia P_{xy} is negative, and the minimum moment of inertia about the axis through P is 42.8 in.^{4} Determine with the aid of Mohr's circle the maximum moment of inertia and the angle α measured positive counterclockwise from the x-axis to the axis of maximum moment of inertia.

C40. Determine the maximum and minimum moments of inertia about centroidal axes for the Z-section of Prob. C23 and indicate the counterclockwise angle α made by the axis of maximum moment of inertia with the x_o-axis.
Ans. $\bar{I}_{max.} = 181.9$ in.^{4}, $\bar{I}_{min.} = 20.7$ in.^{4}, $\alpha = 30° \, 8'$

C41. Determine the maximum and minimum moments of inertia about centroidal axes for the angle section of Prob. C24 and indicate the counterclockwise angle α made by the axis of maximum moment of inertia with the x_o-axis.

II. MOMENTS OF INERTIA OF MASS

C7. Definitions. The mass moment of inertia of a body is a measure of the inertial resistance to rotational acceleration. In Fig. C9 the body of mass m is caused to rotate about the axis O–O with an angular acceleration α. An element of mass dm has a component of acceleration tangent to its circular path equal to $r\alpha$, and the resultant tangential force on this element equals the force $r\alpha \, dm$. The moment of this force about the axis O–O is $r^2\alpha \, dm$. The sum of the moments of these forces for all elements is $\int r^2\alpha \, dm$. For a rigid body α is the same for all radial lines in the body and may be taken outside the integral sign. The remaining integral is known as the moment of inertia I of the mass m and is

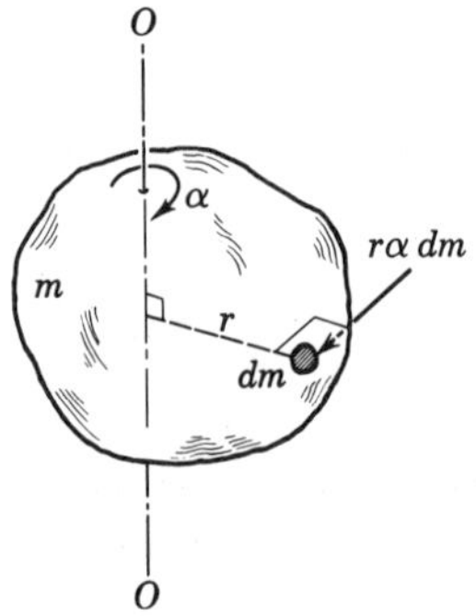

FIG. C9

$$I = \int r^2 \, dm. \tag{C11}$$

This integral represents an important property of a body and is involved in the force analysis of any body which has rotational acceleration. Just as the mass m of a body is a measure of the resistance to translational acceleration, the moment of inertia is a measure of resistance to rotational acceleration due to the mass or inertia of the body.

If the mass density ρ is constant throughout the body, the moment of inertia becomes

$$I = \rho \int r^2 \, dV,$$

where dV is the element of volume. In this case the integral by itself defines a purely geometrical property of the body. When the mass density is not constant but is expressed as a function of the coordinates of the body, it must be left within the integral sign and its effect accounted for in the integration process.

If the body is a wire or slender rod of length L and mass ρ per unit length, the moment of inertia about an axis becomes $I = \int r^2 \rho \, dL$, where r is the perpendicular distance from the element dL to the axis in question. If the body is a thin flat plate of area A and mass ρ per unit area, the moment of inertia is $I = \int r^2 \rho \, dA$. When ρ is constant over the plate, the expression becomes $I = \rho \int r^2 \, dA$. Thus the moment of inertia of the plate equals the mass per unit area times the *area* moment of inertia, described in Part I of this appendix for axes in or normal to the plane of the area.

In general the coordinates which best fit the boundaries of the body should be used in the integration. It is particularly important to make a good choice of the element of volume dV. An element of lowest possible order should be chosen, and the correct expression for the moment of inertia of the element about the axis involved should be used. For example, in finding the moment of inertia of a right circular cone about its central axis, a cylindrical element in the form of a circular slice of infinitesimal thickness should be used. The differential moment of inertia for this element is the correct expression for the moment of inertia of a circular cylinder of infinitesimal thickness about its central axis.

The dimensions of mass moments of inertia are (mass) $\times$ (distance)^2 and are usually expressed in the units *lb. ft. sec.*^{2} Frequently the units *ft.*^{2} *slugs* are used, where the slug is taken as the unit of mass.

C8. Radius of Gyration. The radius of gyration k of a mass m about an axis for which the moment of inertia is I is

$$k = \sqrt{\frac{I}{m}} \qquad \text{or} \qquad I = k^2 m. \tag{C12}$$

Thus k is a measure of the distribution of mass of a given body about the axis in question, and its definition is analogous to the definition for the radius of gyration for second moments of area. If all the mass m could be concentrated at a distance k from the axis, the correct moment of inertia would be k^2m. The moment of inertia of a body about a particular axis is frequently indicated by specifying the radius of gyration of the body about the axis and the weight of the body. The moment of inertia is then calculated from Eq. C12.

C9. Transfer of Axes. If the moment of inertia of a body is known about a centroidal axis, it may be determined easily about any parallel axis. To prove this statement consider the two parallel axes in Fig.

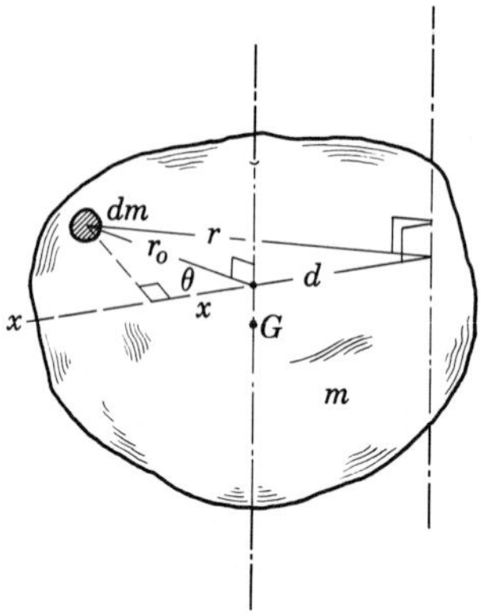

FIG. C10

C10, one of which is a centroidal axis through the center of gravity G. The radial distances from the two axes to any element of mass dm are r_o and r, and the separation of the axes is d. Substituting the law of cosines $r^2 = r_o^2 + d^2 + 2r_od \cos\theta$ into the definition for the moment of inertia about the noncentroidal axis gives

$$I = \int r^2\,dm = \int (r_o^2 + d^2 + 2r_od\cos\theta)\,dm,$$

$$= \int r_o^2\,dm + d^2\int dm + 2d\int x\,dm.$$

The first integral is the moment of inertia $\bar{I}$ about the centroidal axis, the second integral is md^2, and the third integral equals zero since the x-coordinate of the center of gravity with respect to an origin at G is zero. Thus the parallel-axis theorem is

$$I = \bar{I} + md^2. \tag{C13}$$

It must be remembered that the transfer cannot be made unless one axis passes through the center of gravity and unless the axes are parallel. When the expressions for the radii of gyration are substituted in Eq. C13, there results

$$k^2 = \bar{k}^2 + d^2, \tag{C13a}$$

which is the parallel-axis theorem for obtaining the radius of gyration k about an axis a distance d from a parallel centroidal axis for which the radius of gyration is $\bar{k}$.

C10. Product of Inertia. In a few problems of advanced mechanics the integrals

$$I_{xy} = \int xy\,dm, \qquad I_{yz} = \int yz\,dm, \qquad I_{xz} = \int xz\,dm$$

are useful. These integrals are called the products of inertia of the mass m. They may be either positive or negative. In general, a three-dimensional body has three moments of inertia about the three mutually perpendicular coordinate axes and three products of inertia about the three coordinate planes. For an unsymmetrical body of any shape it is found that for a given origin of coordinates there is one orientation of axes for which the products of inertia vanish. These axes are called the *principal axes of inertia*. The corresponding moments of inertia about these axes are known as the *principal moments of inertia* and include the maximum possible value, the minimum possible value, and an intermediate value for any orientation of axes about the given origin.

C11. Moment of Inertia with Respect to a Plane. The moment of inertia of a body with respect to a plane is useful in some problems primarily as an aid to the calculation of the moment of inertia with respect to a line. The moment of inertia with respect to the y–z plane is defined as $\int x^2\,dm$ and that with respect to the x–z plane is $\int y^2\,dm$. Since $x^2 + y^2 = r^2$, where r is the distance from dm to the z-axis, the moment of inertia I_z about the z-axis is

$$I_z = \int r^2\,dm = \int x^2\,dm + \int y^2\,dm.$$

Similar expressions may be written for the two other axes.

A summary of some of the more useful formulas for mass moments of inertia is given in Table D6, Appendix D.

SAMPLE PROBLEMS

C42. Determine the moment of inertia and radius of gyration of a homogeneous right circular cylinder of mass m and radius r about its central axis O–O.

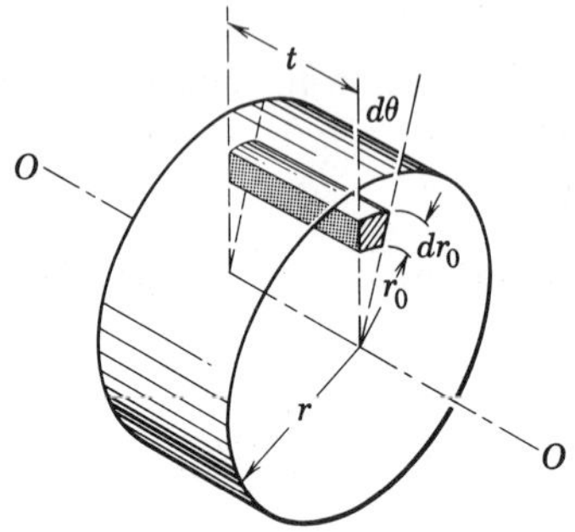

PROB. C42

Solution. An element of mass in cylindrical coordinates is $dm = \rho\, dV = \rho t r_o\, dr_o\, d\theta$. The moment of inertia about the axis of the cylinder is

$$I = \int r_o^2\, dm = \rho t \int_0^{2\pi} \int_0^r r_o^3\, dr_o\, d\theta = \rho t \frac{\pi r^4}{2} = \tfrac{1}{2} m r^2. \qquad \textit{Ans.}$$

The radius of gyration is

$$k = \sqrt{\frac{I}{m}} = \frac{r}{\sqrt{2}}. \qquad \textit{Ans.}$$

The result $I = \frac{1}{2}mr^2$ applies *only* to a solid homogeneous circular cylinder and cannot be used for any other wheel of circular periphery.

C43. Determine the moment of inertia and radius of gyration of a homogeneous solid sphere of mass m and radius r about a diameter.

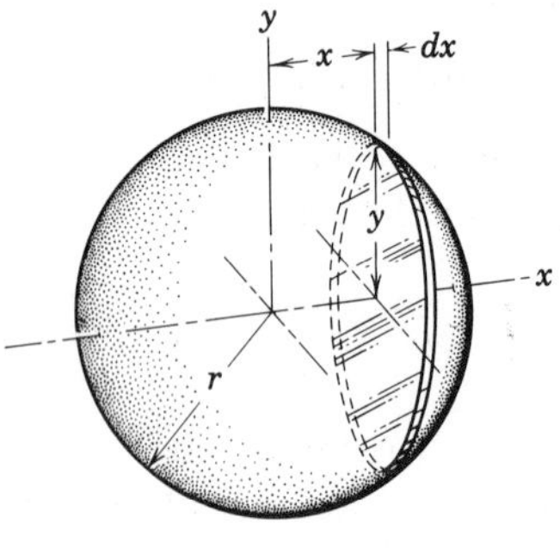

PROB. C43

Solution. A circular slice of radius y and thickness dx is chosen as the volume element. From the results of Prob. C42 the moment of inertia about the x-axis of the elemental cylinder is

$$dI_x = \tfrac{1}{2}(dm)y^2 = \tfrac{1}{2}(\pi\rho y^2\, dx)y^2 = \frac{\pi\rho}{2}(r^2 - x^2)^2\, dx,$$

where ρ is the constant mass density of the sphere. The total moment of inertia about the x-axis is

$$I_x = \frac{\pi\rho}{2}\int_{-r}^{r}(r^2 - x^2)^2\, dx = \tfrac{8}{15}\pi\rho r^5 = \tfrac{2}{5}mr^2. \qquad \textit{Ans.}$$

The radius of gyration is

$$k = \sqrt{\frac{I}{m}} = \sqrt{\frac{2}{5}}\,r. \qquad \textit{Ans.}$$

C44. Determine the moments of inertia of the homogeneous rectangular parallelepiped of mass m about the centroidal x_o- and z-axes and about the x-axis through one end.

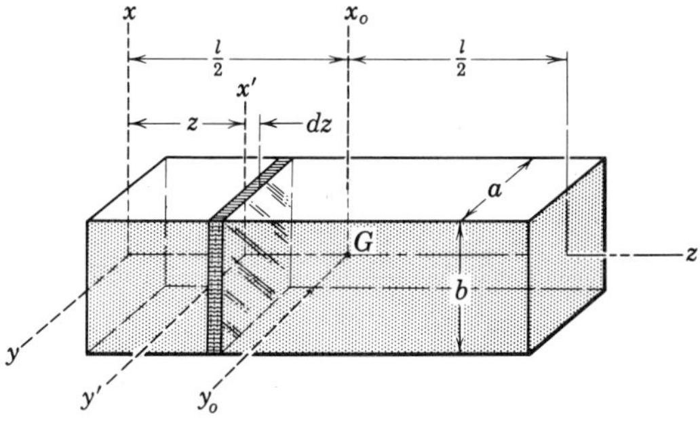

PROB. C44

Solution. A transverse slice of thickness dz is selected as the element of volume. The moment of inertia of this slice of infinitesimal thickness equals the moment of inertia of the area of the section times the mass per unit area $\rho\, dz$. Thus the moment of inertia of the transverse slice about the y'-axis is

$$dI_{y'} = (\rho\, dz)(\tfrac{1}{12}ab^3),$$

and that about the x'-axis is

$$dI_{x'} = (\rho\, dz)(\tfrac{1}{12}a^3b).$$

As long as the element is a plate of differential thickness, the principle of Eq. C3 may be applied to give

$$dI_z = dI_{x'} + dI_{y'} = (\rho\, dz)\frac{ab}{12}(a^2 + b^2).$$

These expressions may now be integrated to obtain the desired results.

The moment of inertia about the z-axis is

$$I_z = \int dI_z = \frac{\rho ab}{12}(a^2 + b^2)\int_0^l dz = \tfrac{1}{12}m(a^2 + b^2), \qquad \textit{Ans.}$$

where m is the mass of the block. By interchanging symbols the moment of inertia about the x_o-axis is

$$I_{x_o} = \tfrac{1}{12}m(a^2 + l^2). \qquad \textit{Ans.}$$

The moment of inertia about the x-axis may be found by the parallel-axis theorem, Eq. C13. Thus

$$I_x = I_{x_o} + m\left(\frac{l}{2}\right)^2 = \tfrac{1}{12}m(a^2 + 4l^2). \qquad \textit{Ans.}$$

This last result may be obtained by expressing the moment of inertia of the elemental slice about the x-axis and integrating the expression over the length of the bar. Again by the parallel-axis theorem

$$dI_x = dI_{x'} + z^2\,dm = (\rho\,dz)(\tfrac{1}{12}a^3b) + z^2\rho ab\,dz,$$

$$= \rho ab\left(\frac{a^2}{12} + z^2\right)dz.$$

Integrating gives the result obtained previously,

$$I_x = \rho ab\int_0^l\left(\frac{a^2}{12} + z^2\right)dz = \frac{\rho abl}{3}\left(l^2 + \frac{a^2}{4}\right) = \tfrac{1}{12}m(a^2 + 4l^2).$$

The expression for I_x may be simplified for a long prismatical bar or slender rod whose transverse dimensions are small compared with the length. In this case a^2 may be neglected compared with $4l^2$, and the moment of inertia of such a slender bar about an axis through one end normal to the bar becomes $I = \frac{1}{3}ml^2$. By the same approximation the moment of inertia about a centroidal axis normal to the bar is $I = \frac{1}{12}ml^2$.

PROBLEMS

C45. A bar 10 in. long has a square cross section 1 in. on a side. Determine the percentage error e in using the approximate formula $I = \frac{1}{3}ml^2$ for the moment of inertia about an axis normal to the bar and through the center of one end parallel to an edge. (See Prob. C44.) *Ans.* $e = 0.249\%$

C46. The moment of inertia of a solid homogeneous cylinder of radius r about an axis parallel to the central axis of the cylinder may be obtained approximately by multiplying the mass of the cylinder by the square of the distance d between the two axes. What per cent error e results if (a) $d = 10r$, (b) $d = 2r$?

C47. From the results of Prob. C43 state without computation the moments of inertia of the solid homogeneous hemisphere of mass m about the x- and z-axes.

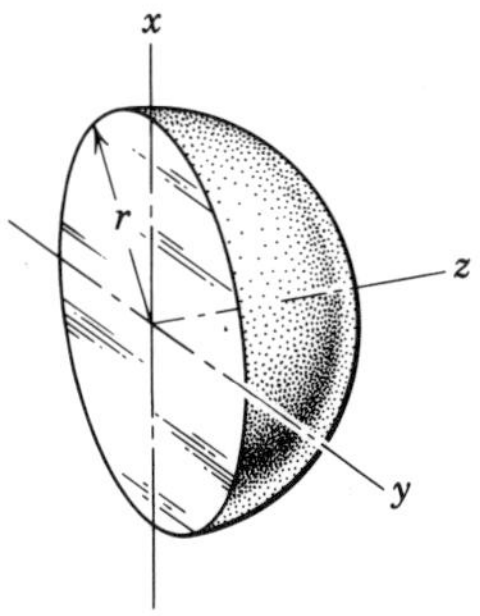

PROB. C47

C48. Determine the moment of inertia of a circular ring of mass m and inside and outside radii r_1 and r_2, respectively, about its central polar axis.

Ans. $I = \frac{1}{2}m(r_2^2 + r_1^2)$

C49. Calculate the moment of inertia of a homogeneous right circular cone of mass m and base radius r about the cone axis. *Ans.* $I = \frac{3}{10}mr^2$

C50. Without integrating determine from the results of Probs. C43 and C49 the moments of inertia about the z-axis for (*a*) the spherical wedge and (*b*) the conical wedge. Each wedge has a mass m.

Ans. (*a*) $I_z = \frac{2}{5}ma^2$, (*b*) $I_z = \frac{3}{10}mr^2$

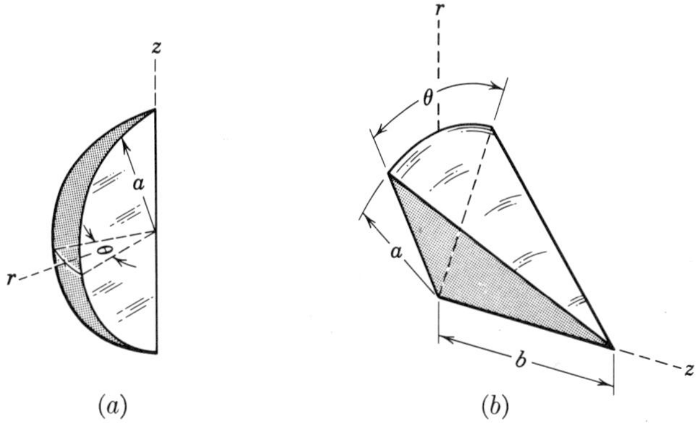

PROB. C50

C51. Find the moment of inertia of the slender rod of mass m about the x-axis.

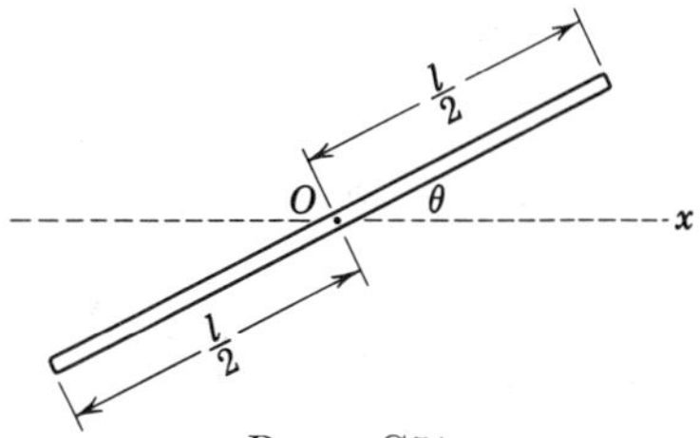

PROB. C51

C52. The moment of inertia of a body with respect to the x–y plane is 0.202 lb. ft. sec.^{2}, and that with respect to the y–z plane is 0.440 lb. ft. sec.^{2} The radius of gyration about the y-axis is 1.20 ft. Find the weight W of the body.

C53. Determine the moment of inertia of the elliptical cylinder of mass m about the cylinder axis O–O. *Ans.* $I = \frac{1}{4}m(a^2 + b^2)$

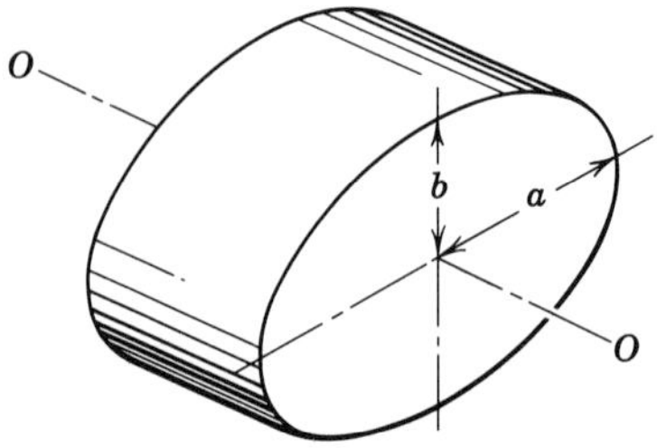

PROB. C53

C54. Determine the moment of inertia about the z-axis of the homogeneous solid paraboloid of revolution of mass m.

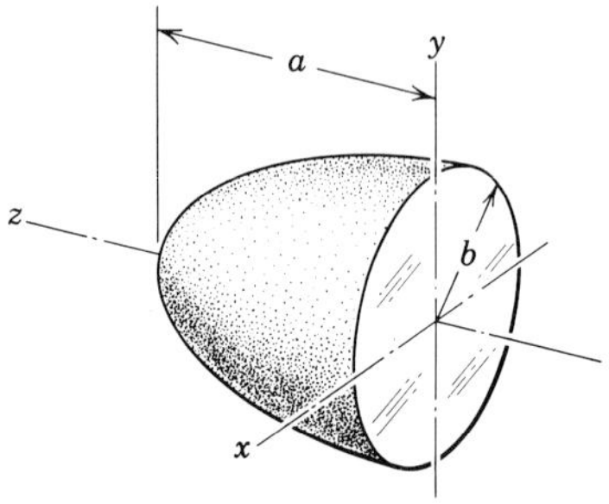

PROB. C54

C55. Find the moment of inertia of the tetrahedron of mass m about the z-axis.

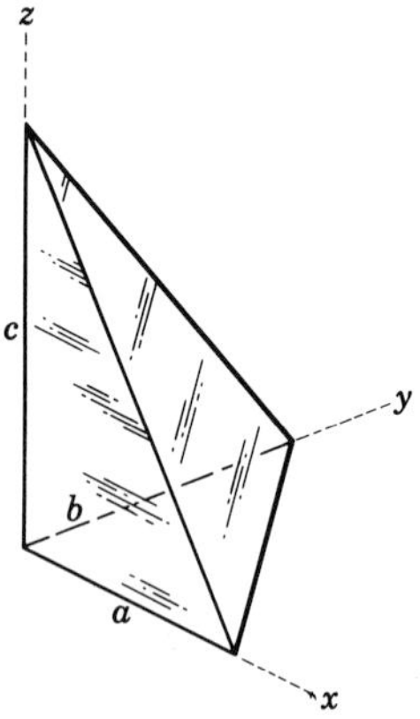

PROB. C55

C56. The homogeneous bar of square cross section has a mass m. Determine the moment of inertia of the bar about the centroidal x-axis shown which is a diagonal of the square section. *Ans.* $I_x = \frac{1}{12}m(a^2 + l^2)$

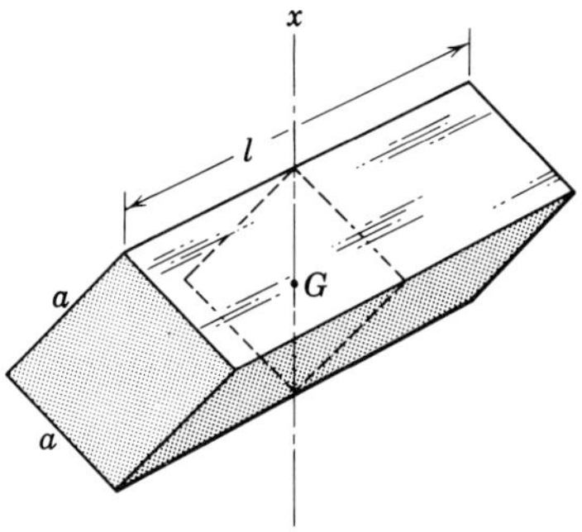

PROB. C56

C57. Determine the moments of inertia of the homogeneous right circular cylinder of mass m about the x_o-, x-, and y'-axes shown.

Ans. $I_{x_o} = \frac{1}{12}m(3r^2 + l^2)$, $I_x = \frac{1}{12}m(3r^2 + 4l^2)$, $I_{y'} = \frac{3}{2}mr^2$

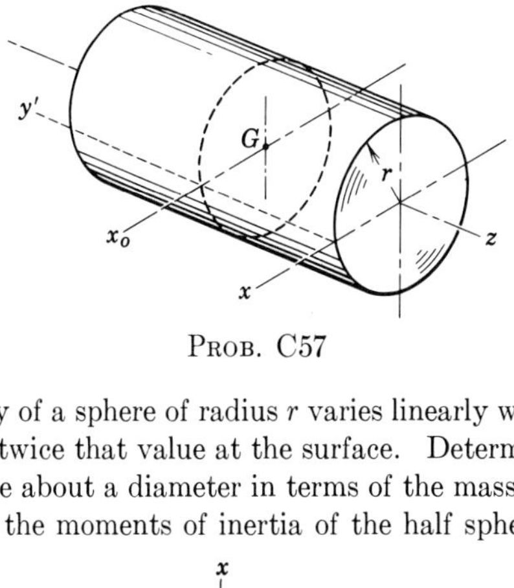

PROB. C57

C58. The density of a sphere of radius r varies linearly with the radius from ρ_o at the center to twice that value at the surface. Determine the moment of inertia of the sphere about a diameter in terms of the mass m of the sphere.

C59. Determine the moments of inertia of the half spherical shell with re-

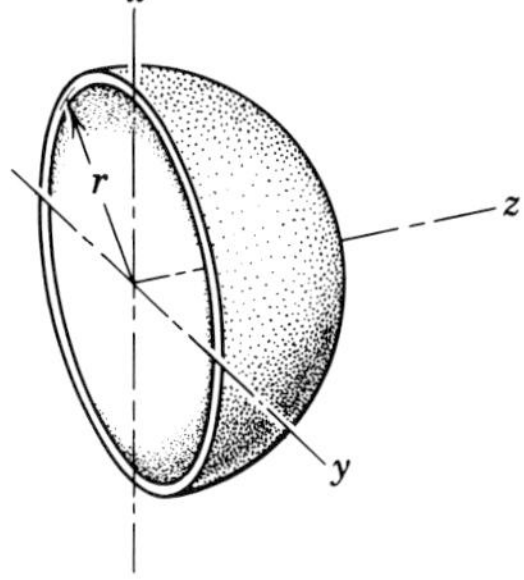

PROB. C59

spect to the x- and z-axes. The mass of the shell is m, and its thickness is negligible compared with the radius r. *Ans.* $I_x = I_z = \frac{2}{3}mr^2$

C60. Determine the moment of inertia of the conical shell of mass m about the axis of rotation. Wall thickness is negligible. *Ans.* $I_z = \frac{1}{2}mr^2$

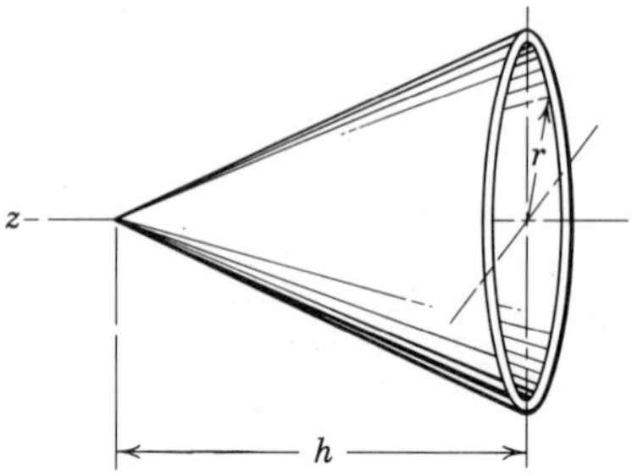

Prob. C60

* **C61.** Determine the moment of inertia about the z-axis of the bell-shaped shell of uniform small thickness if the mass is m. *Ans.* $I_z = \dfrac{15\pi - 44}{6(\pi - 2)} ma^2$

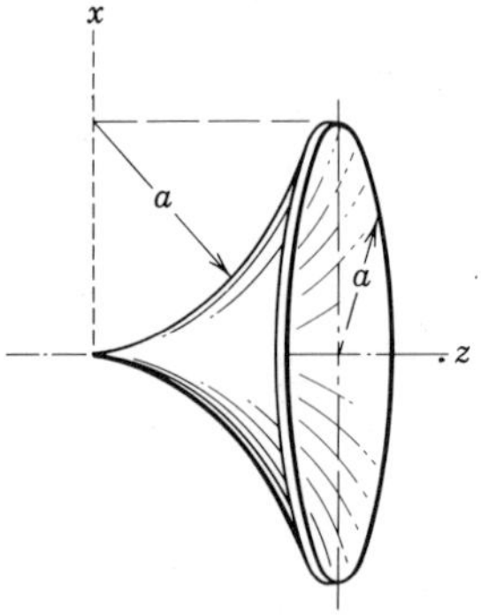

Prob. C61

* **C62.** Determine the moment of inertia about the generating axis of a complete ring of circular section (torus) with the dimensions shown in the sectional view. *Ans.* $I = m(R^2 + \frac{3}{4}a^2)$

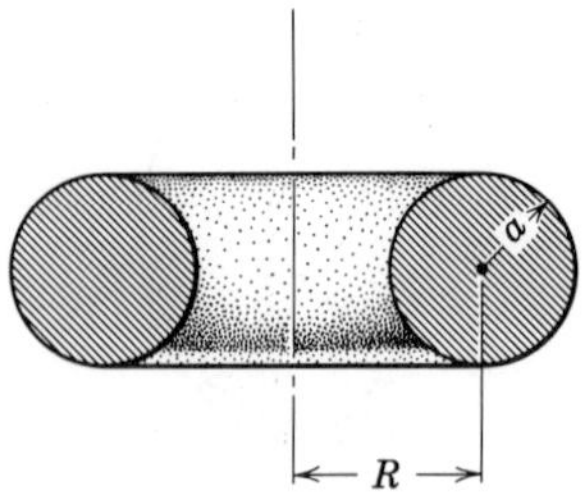

Prob. C62

C12. Composite Bodies. The defining integral, Eq. C11, involves the square of the distance from the axis to the element and so is always positive. Thus, as in the case of area moments of inertia, the mass moment of inertia of a composite body is the sum of the moments of inertia of the individual parts about the same axis. It is often convenient to consider a composite body as defined by positive volumes and negative volumes. The moment of inertia of a negative element, such as a hole, must be considered a minus quantity.

PROBLEMS

C63. Calculate the moment of inertia about the z-axis of the cylinder with the hemispherical cavity if the net mass is m. *Ans.* $I_z = \frac{7}{10}ma^2$

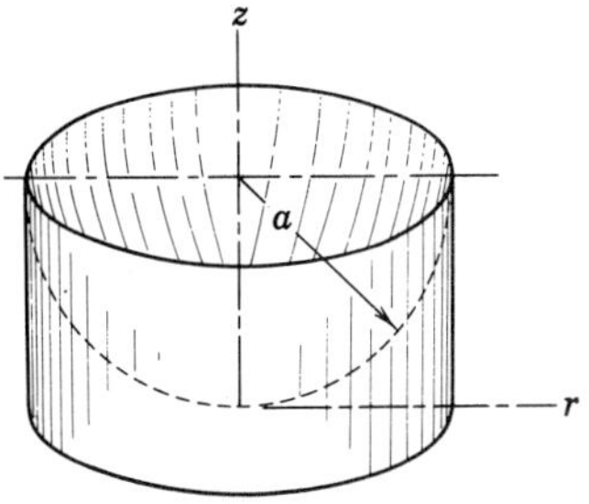

Prob. C63

C64. Calculate the moment of inertia about the central axis of the aluminum rotor shown in section.

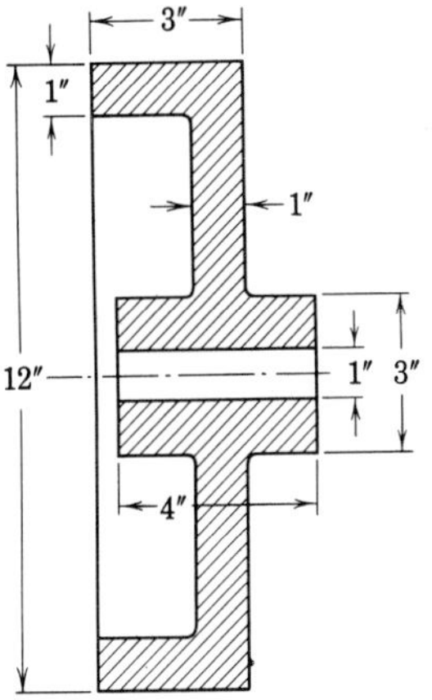

Prob. C64

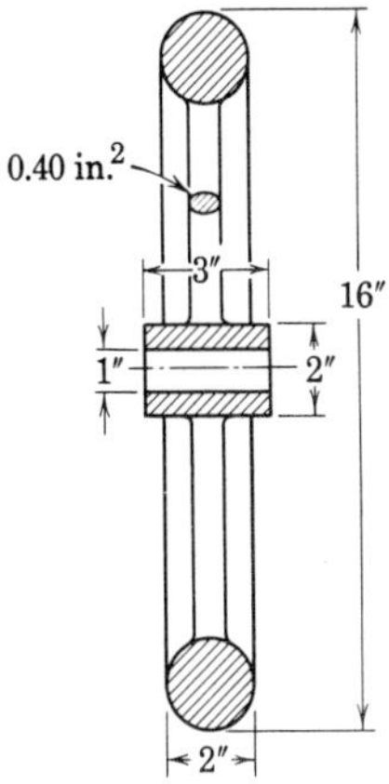

Prob. C65

C65. Calculate the moment of inertia of the steel handwheel about its axis.

There are six spokes, each of which has a uniform cross-sectional area of 0.40 in.^{2} *Ans.* $I = 0.431$ lb. ft. sec.^{2}

C66. Determine the radius of gyration of the homogeneous rotor, shown in section, about its central axis. *Ans.* $k = 2.43$ in.

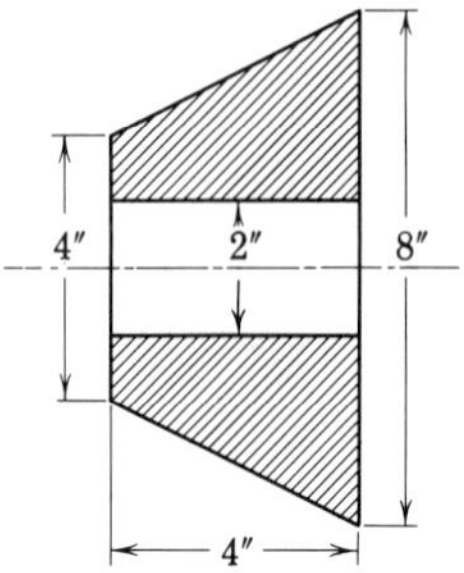

PROB. C66

C67. The slender rod bent into the shape shown weighs 0.52 lb./ft. Determine the moment of inertia of the rod about the x-axis.

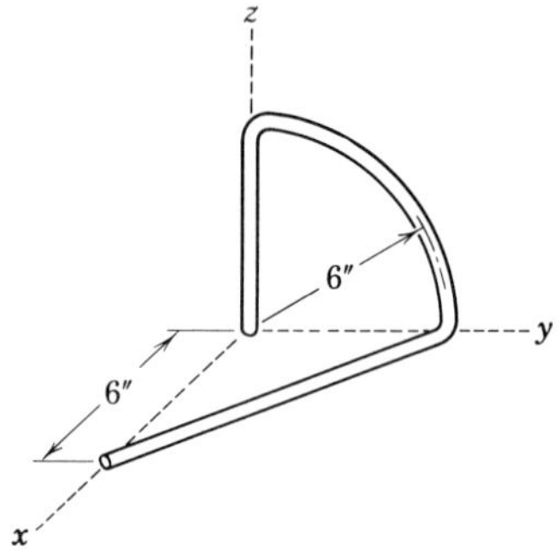

PROB. C67

C68. Determine the moment of inertia of the mallet with respect to the axis O–O. The head is made from hardwood weighing 65 lb./ft.^{3}, and the handle is made from steel weighing 0.283 lb./in.^{3} *Ans.* $I_O = 0.1896$ lb. ft. sec.^{2}

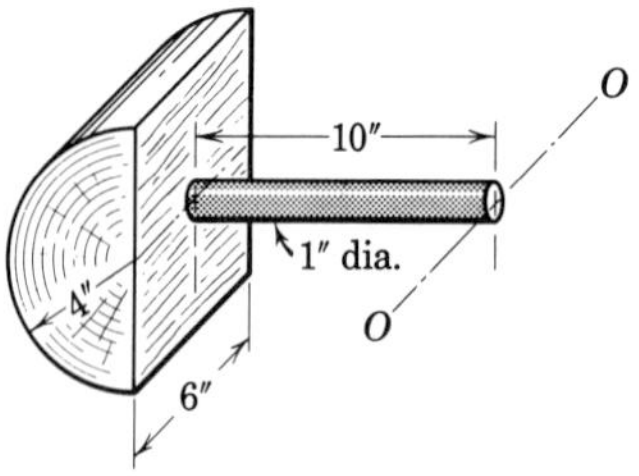

PROB. C68

C69. The part shown weighs 3.22 lb. Determine its moment of inertia about the axis *O–O*.

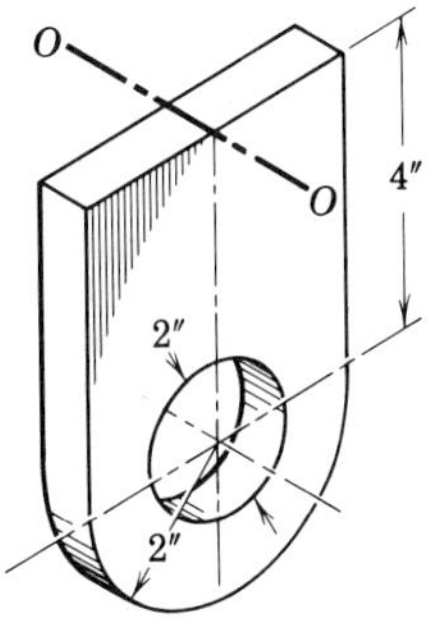

PROB. C69

* **C70.** Determine the moments of inertia of the steel body shown about axes *A* and *B*. *Ans.* $I_A = 0.1446$ lb. ft. sec.^{2}, $I_B = 0.302$ lb. ft. sec.^{2}

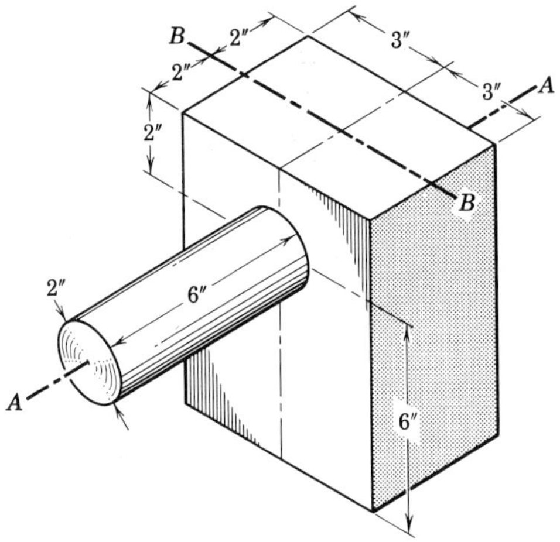

PROB. C70

* **C71.** Determine the radius of gyration of the symmetrical steel link about the axis O–O. *Ans.* $k = 4.36$ in.

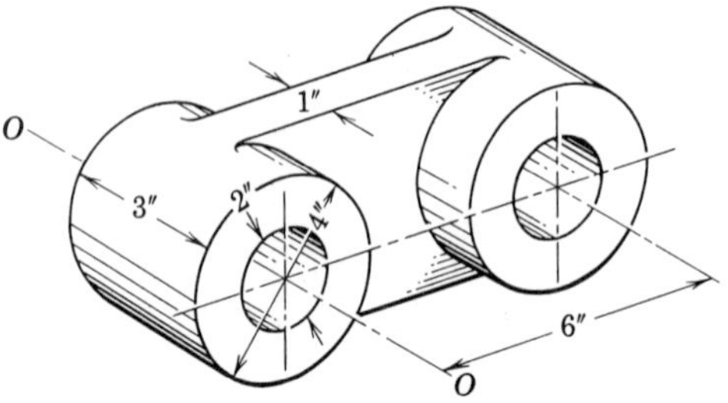

PROB. C71

* **C72.** The desired moment of inertia of the steel rocker about the O–O axis is 0.204 lb. ft. sec.^{2} Determine the necessary thickness t. *Ans.* $t = 3.17$ in.

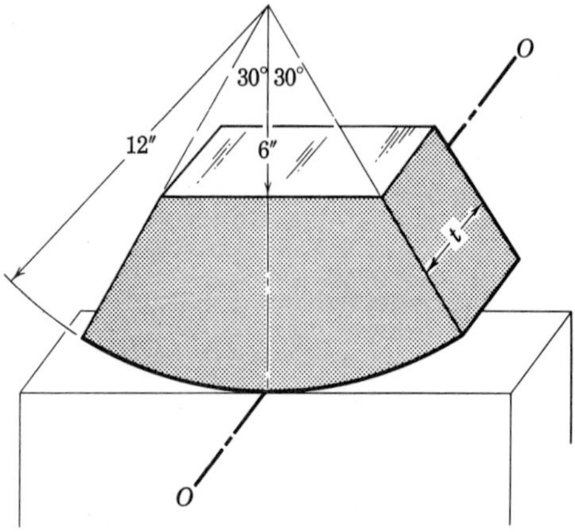

PROB. C72

APPENDIX D

USEFUL TABLES

TABLE D1. DENSITIES, lb./ft.^{3}

Aluminum	168	Mercury	847
Concrete (av.)	150	Oil (av.)	56
Copper	556	Steel	489
Earth (wet, av.)	110	Water (fresh)	62.4
(dry, av.)	80	(salt)	64
Ice	56	Wood (soft, pine)	30
Iron (cast)	450	(hard, oak)	50
Lead	710		

TABLE D2. COEFFICIENTS OF FRICTION

The coefficients in the following table represent typical values only. Actual coefficients for a given situation will depend on the exact nature of the contacting surfaces. A variation of the order of 25 to 100 per cent from these values could be expected in an actual problem, depending on prevailing conditions of cleanliness, roughness, pressure, lubrication, and velocity.

TABLE D2. COEFFICIENTS OF FRICTION—*Continued*

Contacting Surfaces	Coefficient of Static Friction	Coefficient of Kinetic Friction
Metal on metal (dry)	0.2	0.1
Metal on metal (greasy)	0.1	0.05
Rubber or leather on wood or metal (dry)	0.4	0.3
Hardwood on metal (dry)	0.6	0.4
Hardwood on metal (greasy)	0.2	0.1
Hemp on metal (dry)	0.3	0.2
Wire rope on iron pulley (dry)	0.2	0.15
Rubber tires on smooth pavement (dry)	0.9	0.8
Asbestos brake lining on cast iron	0.4	0.3
Metal on ice	. . .	0.02
Steel on wet grindstone	. . .	0.7
Cast-iron brake shoes on steel railway tires		
(10 m.p.h.)	. . .	0.3
(30 m.p.h.)	. . .	0.2
(60 m.p.h.)	. . .	0.05

	Coefficient of Rolling Friction, f_r
Pneumatic tires on smooth pavement	0.02
Steel tires on steel rails	0.006

TABLE D3. USEFUL MATHEMATICAL RELATIONS

A. Series (expression in bracket following series indicates range of convergence)

$$(1 \pm x)^n = 1 \pm nx + \frac{n(n-1)}{2!}x^2 \pm \frac{n(n-1)(n-2)}{3!}x^3 + \cdots \quad [x^2 < 1]$$

$$\sin x = x - \frac{x^3}{3!} + \frac{x^5}{5!} - \frac{x^7}{7!} + \cdots \quad [x^2 < \infty]$$

$$\cos x = 1 - \frac{x^2}{2!} + \frac{x^4}{4!} - \frac{x^6}{6!} + \cdots \quad [x^2 < \infty]$$

$$\sinh x = \frac{e^x - e^{-x}}{2} = x + \frac{x^3}{3!} + \frac{x^5}{5!} + \frac{x^7}{7!} + \cdots \quad [x^2 < \infty]$$

$$\cosh x = \frac{e^x + e^{-x}}{2} = 1 + \frac{x^2}{2!} + \frac{x^4}{4!} + \frac{x^6}{6!} + \cdots \quad [x^2 < \infty]$$

TABLE D3. USEFUL MATHEMATICAL RELATIONS—*Continued*

B. Differentials

$$\frac{dx^n}{dx} = nx^{n-1}, \qquad \frac{d(uv)}{dx} = u\frac{dv}{dx} + v\frac{du}{dx}, \qquad \frac{d\left(\frac{u}{v}\right)}{dx} = \frac{v\frac{du}{dx} - u\frac{dv}{dx}}{v^2}$$

$$\lim_{\Delta x \to 0} \sin \Delta x = \sin dx = \tan dx = dx$$

$$\lim_{\Delta x \to 0} \cos \Delta x = \cos dx = 1$$

$$\frac{d \sin x}{dx} = \cos x, \qquad \frac{d \cos x}{dx} = -\sin x, \qquad \frac{d \tan x}{dx} = \sec^2 x$$

$$\frac{d \sinh x}{dx} = \cosh x, \qquad \frac{d \cosh x}{dx} = \sinh x, \qquad \frac{d \tanh x}{dx} = \operatorname{sech}^2 x$$

C. Integrals

$$\int x^n\, dx = \frac{x^{n+1}}{n+1}$$

$$\int \frac{dx}{x} = \log x$$

$$\int \sqrt{a + bx}\, dx = \frac{2}{3b}\sqrt{(a+bx)^3}$$

$$\int \frac{dx}{\sqrt{a+bx}} = \frac{2\sqrt{a+bx}}{b}$$

$$\int \frac{x\, dx}{a+bx} = \frac{1}{b^2}[a + bx - a \log (a + bx)]$$

$$\int \frac{dx}{a+bx^2} = \frac{1}{\sqrt{ab}} \tan^{-1} \frac{x\sqrt{ab}}{a} \quad \text{or} \quad \frac{1}{\sqrt{-ab}} \tanh^{-1} \frac{x\sqrt{-ab}}{a}$$

$$\int \sqrt{x^2 \pm a^2}\, dx = \tfrac{1}{2}[x\sqrt{x^2 \pm a^2} \pm a^2 \log (x + \sqrt{x^2 \pm a^2})]$$

$$\int \sqrt{a^2 - x^2}\, dx = \tfrac{1}{2}\left(x\sqrt{a^2 - x^2} + a^2 \sin^{-1} \frac{x}{a}\right)$$

$$\int x\sqrt{a^2 - x^2}\, dx = -\tfrac{1}{3}\sqrt{(a^2 - x^2)^3}$$

$$\int x^2\sqrt{a^2 - x^2}\, dx = -\frac{x}{4}\sqrt{(a^2 - x^2)^3} + \frac{a^2}{8}\left(x\sqrt{a^2 - x^2} + a^2 \sin^{-1} \frac{x}{a}\right)$$

$$\int x^3\sqrt{a^2 - x^2}\, dx = -\tfrac{1}{5}(x^2 + \tfrac{2}{3}a^2)\sqrt{(a^2 - x^2)^3}$$

TABLE D3. USEFUL MATHEMATICAL RELATIONS—*Continued*

$$\int \frac{dx}{\sqrt{x^2 \pm a^2}} = \log (x + \sqrt{x^2 \pm a^2})$$

$$\int \frac{dx}{\sqrt{a^2 - x^2}} = \sin^{-1} \frac{x}{a}$$

$$\int x\sqrt{x^2 \pm a^2}\, dx = \tfrac{1}{3}\sqrt{(x^2 \pm a^2)^3}$$

$$\int x^2\sqrt{x^2 \pm a^2}\, dx = \frac{x}{4}\sqrt{(x^2 \pm a^2)^3} \mp \frac{a^2}{8} x\sqrt{x^2 \pm a^2} - \frac{a^4}{8} \log (x + \sqrt{x^2 \pm a^2})$$

$$\int \frac{x\, dx}{\sqrt{x^2 - a^2}} = \sqrt{x^2 - a^2}$$

$$\int \frac{x\, dx}{\sqrt{a^2 \pm x^2}} = \pm\sqrt{a^2 \pm x^2}$$

$$\int \sin x\, dx = -\cos x$$

$$\int \cos x\, dx = \sin x$$

$$\int \sec x\, dx = \frac{1}{2} \log \frac{1 + \sin x}{1 - \sin x}$$

$$\int \sin^2 x\, dx = \frac{x}{2} - \frac{\sin 2x}{4}$$

$$\int \cos^2 x\, dx = \frac{x}{2} + \frac{\sin 2x}{4}$$

$$\int \sin^3 x\, dx = -\frac{\cos x}{3} (2 + \sin^2 x)$$

$$\int \cos^3 x\, dx = \frac{\sin x}{3} (2 + \cos^2 x)$$

$$\int x \sin x\, dx = \sin x - x \cos x$$

$$\int x \cos x\, dx = \cos x + x \sin x$$

$$\int \sinh x\, dx = \cosh x$$

$$\int \cosh x\, dx = \sinh x$$

$$\int \tanh x\, dx = \log \cosh x$$

$$\int e^{ax} \sin px\, dx = \frac{e^{ax}(a \sin px - p \cos px)}{a^2 + p^2}$$

$$\int e^{ax} \cos px\, dx = \frac{e^{ax}(a \cos px + p \sin px)}{a^2 + p^2}$$

$$\int \log x\, dx = x \log x - x$$

$$\int xe^{ax}\, dx = \frac{e^{ax}}{a^2} (ax - 1)$$

TABLE D4. CENTROIDS

Arc Segment

$$\bar{r} = \frac{r \sin \alpha}{\alpha}$$

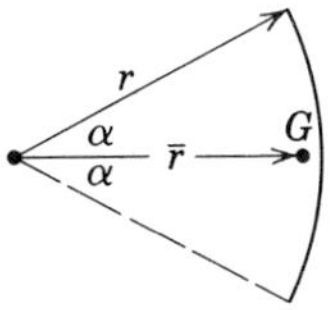

Quarter and Semicircular Arcs

$$\bar{y} = \frac{2r}{\pi}$$

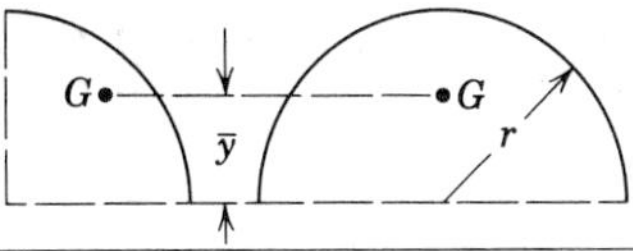

Triangular Area

$$\bar{y} = \frac{h}{3}$$

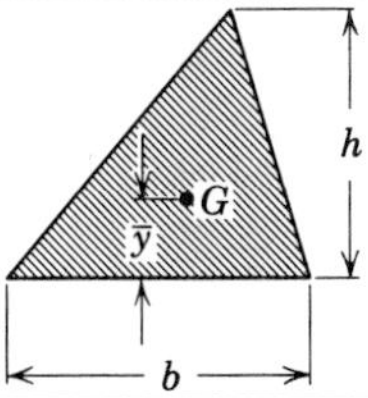

Trapezoidal Area

$$\bar{y} = \frac{1}{3} \frac{2a_1 + a_2}{a_1 + a_2} h$$

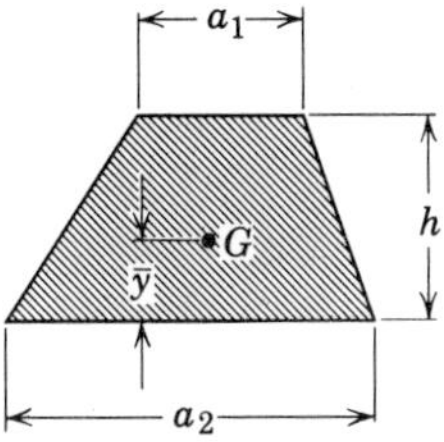

Area of Circular Sector

$$\bar{r} = \frac{2}{3} \frac{r \sin \alpha}{\alpha}$$

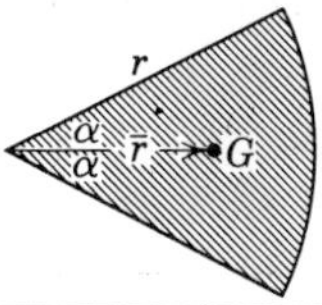

Quarter and Semicircular Areas

$$\bar{y} = \frac{4r}{3\pi}$$

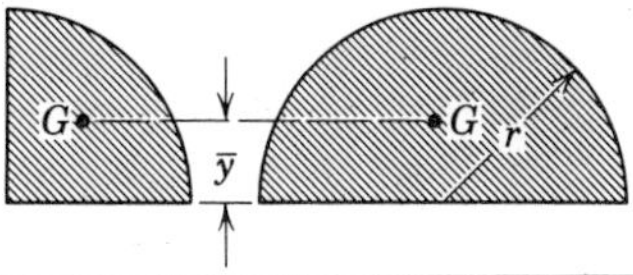

Area of Elliptical Quadrant

$$\bar{x} = \frac{4a}{3\pi}$$

$$\bar{y} = \frac{4b}{3\pi}$$

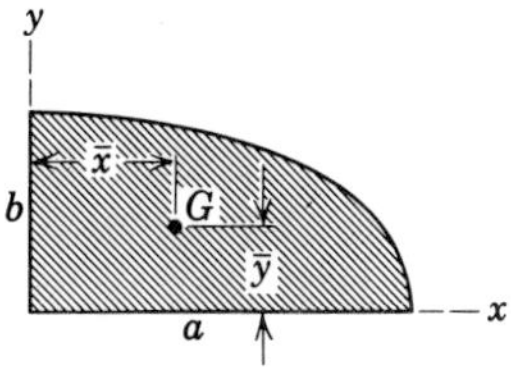

TABLE D4. CENTROIDS—*Continued*

Lateral Area of Cone or Pyramid

$$\bar{y} = \frac{h}{3}$$

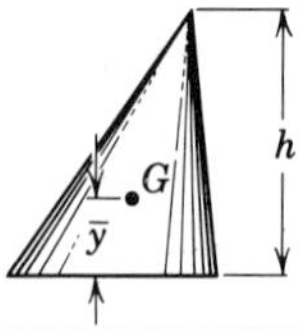

Area of Hemisphere, or Hemispherical Shell

$$\bar{r} = \frac{r}{2}$$

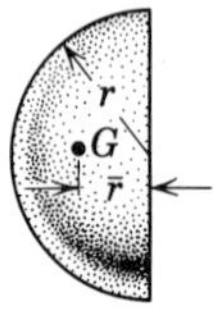

Volume of Cone or Pyramid

$$\bar{y} = \frac{h}{4}$$

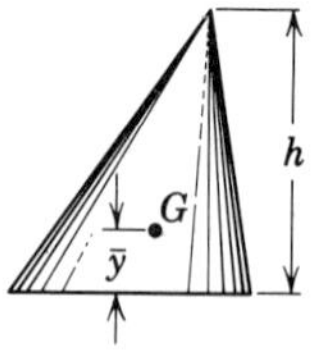

Hemispherical Volume

$$\bar{r} = \frac{3r}{8}$$

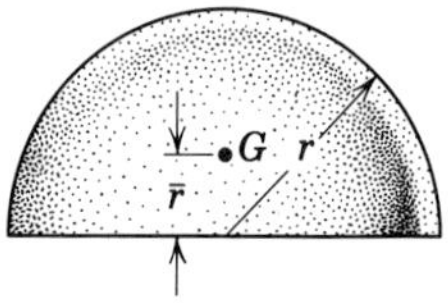

Volume of Paraboloid of Revolution

$$\bar{x} = \frac{a}{3}$$

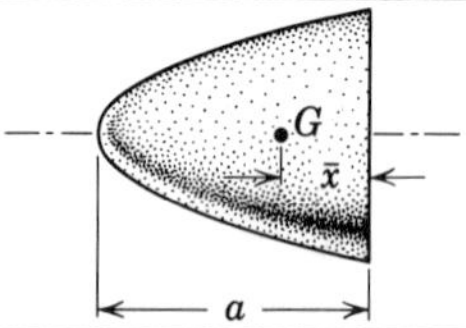

Volume of Half Ellipsoid of Revolution

$$\bar{x} = \frac{3a}{8}$$

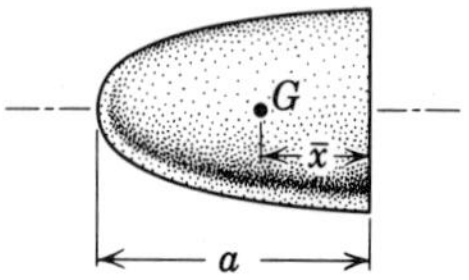

TABLE D5. MOMENTS OF INERTIA OF AREAS

Rectangle

$$\bar{I}_x = \frac{bh^3}{12}$$

$$I_x = \frac{bh^3}{3}$$

$$\bar{J} = \frac{bh}{12}(b^2 + h^2)$$

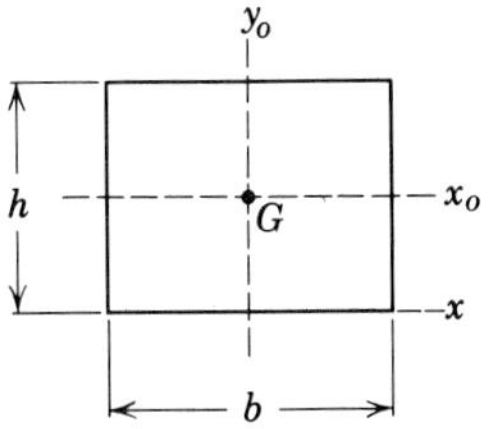

Triangle

$$\bar{I}_x = \frac{bh^3}{36}$$

$$I_x = \frac{bh^3}{12}$$

$$I_{x'} = \frac{bh^3}{4}$$

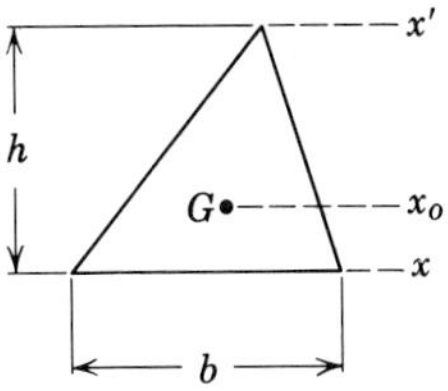

Circle

$$\bar{I}_x = \bar{I}_y = \frac{\pi r^4}{4}$$

$$\bar{J} = \frac{\pi r^4}{2}$$

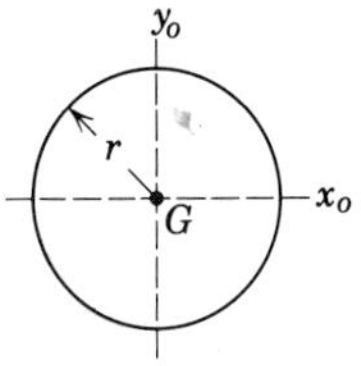

Ellipse

$$\bar{I}_x = \frac{\pi a b^3}{4}$$

$$\bar{I}_y = \frac{\pi a^3 b}{4}$$

$$\bar{J} = \frac{\pi ab}{4}(a^2 + b^2)$$

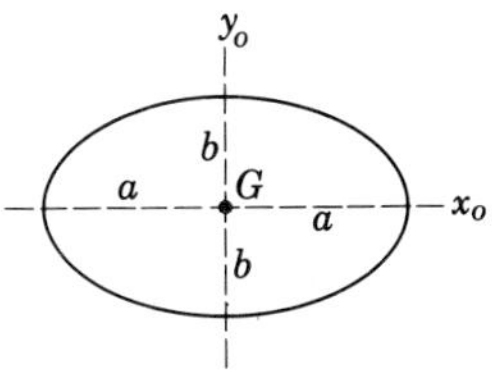

Table D6. Moments of Inertia of Mass

(m = mass of homogeneous solid shown)

Circular Cylindrical Shell

$$I_z = mr^2$$

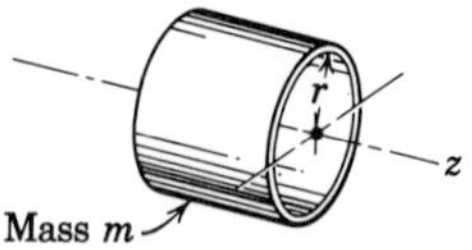

Right Circular Cylinder

$$I_z = \tfrac{1}{2}mr^2$$

$$I_x = \tfrac{1}{12}m(3r^2 + 4l^2)$$

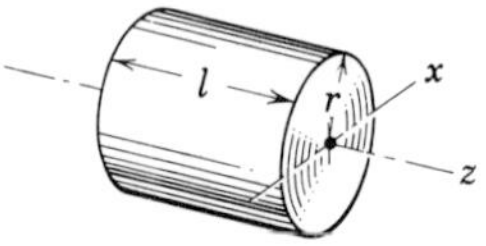

Sphere

$$I_z = \tfrac{2}{5}mr^2$$

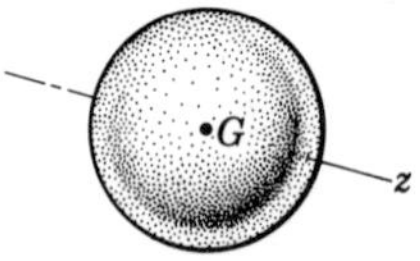

Semicylinder

$$I_z = \tfrac{1}{2}(\tfrac{1}{2} \times 2mr^2)$$

$$= \tfrac{1}{2}mr^2$$

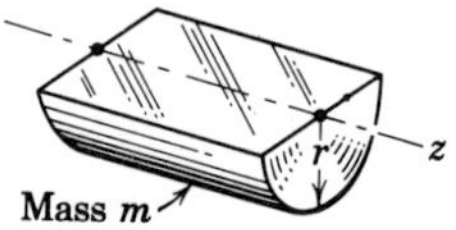

Hemisphere

$$I_x = I_z = \tfrac{1}{2}(\tfrac{2}{5} \times 2mr^2)$$

$$= \tfrac{2}{5}mr^2$$

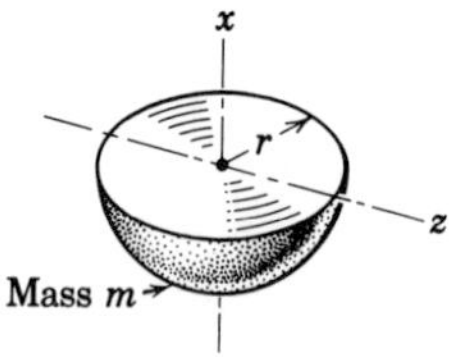

Rectangular Parallelepiped

$$I_z = \tfrac{1}{12}m(a^2 + b^2)$$

$$I_x = \tfrac{1}{12}m(4l^2 + a^2)$$

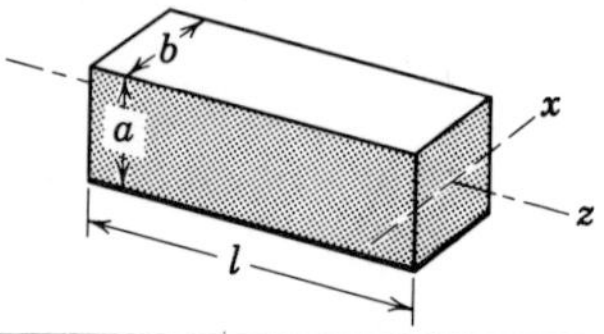

Uniform Slender Rod

$$I_x = \tfrac{1}{3}ml^2$$

$$I_{x_0} = \tfrac{1}{12}ml^2$$

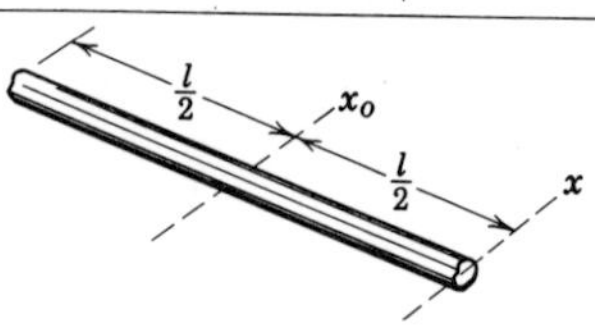

TABLE D6. MOMENTS OF INERTIA OF MASS—*Continued*

(m = mass of homogeneous solid shown)

Right Circular Cone

$I_z = \frac{3}{10}mr^2$

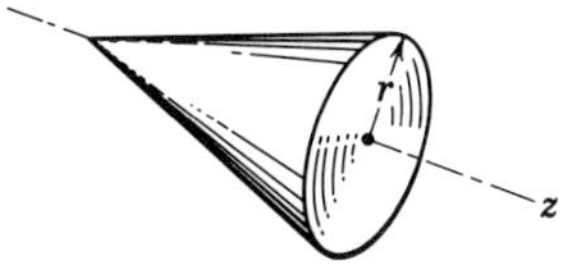

Elliptical Cylinder

$I_z = \frac{1}{4}m(a^2 + b^2)$

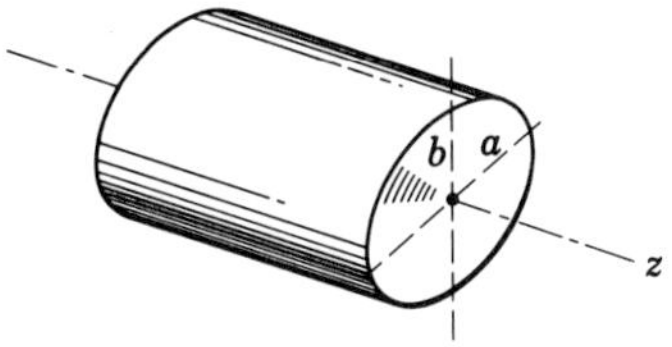

Hemispherical Shell

$I_x = I_z = \frac{2}{3}mr^2$

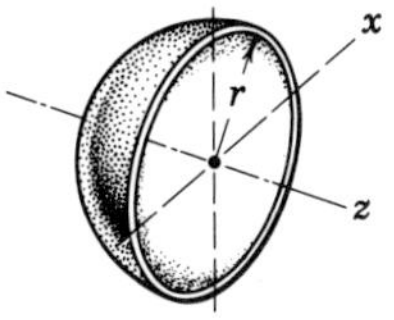

Torus (complete)

$I_z = m(R^2 + \frac{3}{4}a^2)$

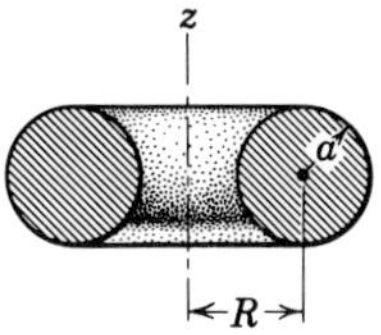

INDEX